.0180

SM99007072
05/00
£95.00 SPK
(Pow)

D1588725

POWYS COUNTY LIBRARY
LLYFRGELL SIR POWYS
LLANGATTOCK

1872328229

Criminal Law
and
Forensic Psychiatry

Criminal Law & Forensic Psychiatry

D.J. Power
TD,MB,MRCPsych,DPM,DMJ

co-authors

Patrick Curran
QC,MA(Oxon)

J.M. Hughes
TD,OStJ,BSc,MB,FRCP(Ed),FRCPsych

Barry Rose Publishers Ltd
Little London, Chichester,
West Sussex

ISBN 1 872328 22 9
© 1996, Barry Rose Law Publishers and authors
All rights reserved. No part of this book work may be reproduced in any form
whether electronic, photocopying, or any other form of recording without the
prior written permission of Barry Rose Law Publishers Ltd or on licence from
the Copyright Licensing Agency Ltd.

Published by
Barry Rose Law Publishers Ltd
Chichester, England

Printed in Great Britain by Antony Rowe Ltd, Chippenham, Wiltshire

Criminal Law and Forensic Psychiatry
by
D.J. Power
T.D. M.B. M.R.C.Psych. D.P.M. D.M.J.

Former Senior Medical Officer, HM Prison Service;
Hon Consultant Psychiatrist, University Hospital of Wales;
Lecturer in Forensic Psychiatry, Morgannwg Hospital, Bridgend;
Member of the Welsh Office Working Party for the Establishment of Secure
Psychiatric Units;
Ex-member of the Forensic Specialist Section, Executive Committee of the Royal
College of Psychiatrists;
Fellow of the Royal Society of Medicine;
Member of the British Academy of Forensic Science;
Contributor to Lord Woolf's Inquiry into Prison Disturbances;
Registered as Expert Witness

Patrick Curran Q.C., M.A. (Oxon)

J.M. Hughes
T.D. O.St.J. B.Sc. M.B. F.R.C.P. F.R.C. (Psych)

Current Appointment: Consultant Psychiatrist in Substance Abuse, Gwent
Community Health Trust
Former Appointments: Physician Supt and Consultant Psychiatrist, St. Cadoc's
Hospital, Caerleon
Former Consultant Psychiatrist to Health Advisory Service
Manager Gwent Mental Health Unit
Formerly: Chairman Gwent Div BMA
Chairman Welsh Division R. Coll. of Psychiatrists

Contents

Foreword

by

The Rt. Hon. Sir Frederick Lawton

When I started in practice at the Bar in 1935, mental hospitals were still referred to as lunatic asylums. The official in the Royal Courts of Justice who had the function of managing the property of those who, through mental illness, were unable to do so themselves was known as the Master in Lunacy. Psychiatric evidence was only heard in court when there was an issue of fitness to plead, or a defence of insanity was raised to a charge of murder. I have no recollection of hearing the word "psychiatry" until the early years of the Second World War when I learned that the RAMC had officers called psychiatrists, who were useful in getting unsuitable soldiers discharged. Other lawyers in the armed services came to appreciate their value too.

After 1945, demobilized lawyers began to use the services of psychiatrists on behalf of clients charged with criminal offences. If mental instability was a good reason for discharging a soldier, it might be one for not imprisoning an offender. Judges and magistrates were slow to accept the value of psychiatric evidence; a few never did. Much of the blame for this was due to extravagant claims which were made by some doctors as to what they could do by way of treatment for their patients. Claims were made, for example, that homosexuality could be "cured". As the years went by, all concerned with the administration of criminal justice came to appreciate the value of psychiatric evidence, not only in relation to the issues of guilt and innocence, but also to sentencing. By the time I retired from the Court of Appeal, which was in 1986, there were psychiatric reports in about a quarter of all appeal papers, and in nearly all those relating to young offenders who had been given custodial sentences.

Both as a barrister and as a Judge, I had to learn the significance and value of psychiatric evidence on a case-to-case basis. The psychiatrists and neurologists with whom I had consultations when I was at the Bar did their best to instruct me. I learned a lot about amnesia when I was defending *Podola* and about traumatic neurosis from my practice in personal injury cases, but inevitably, there were gaps in my knowledge. Often there were no psychiatric witnesses to help and it was impractical for financial reasons to get any. As a barrister, I had read a few books and

ix

written for the general public on such topics as homosexuality and other sexual deviations. Forensically they were not helpful. As a Judge I had to rely on what I was told by witnesses and read in reports. Often I would have liked more information.

I retired from the Bench too soon. How I would have welcomed this remarkable book, entitled *Criminal Law and Forensic Psychiatry*. When sitting in the Criminal Division of the Court of Appeal I would always have had it beside me, alongside *Archbold's Criminal Pleading and Practice*. I regard it as an essential working tool for all who professionally have to deal with offenders.

The reason is that it deals comprehensively with every aspect of crime: motivation, performance and disposal, whether by treatment or punishment. Every type of crime, from murder to bestiality, is discussed in relation to the mental factors which may have motivated the offender. The author does not seek to suggest that all offenders are suffering from some form of mental imbalance. He accepts, for example, that greed motivates many shoplifters; but he goes on to discuss other factors which may have been operating. Any lawyer who is instructed to defend an alleged shoplifter will be guided by this book towards making the appropriate inquiries and calling the most helpful witnesses. The lawyer reader is not encouraged to be his own psychiatric expert, but he is provided with case histories which will enable him to understand how psychiatric factors operate. The medical reader is also provided for; he has available an extensive bibliography with which he can check all the author's statements and theories.

I found reading this book a chastening experience. I was reminded time and time again of the mistakes which I had made when appearing in or trying cases because I had not appreciated the psychiatric significance of some pieces of evidence. I am sure that ownership and knowledge of this book will make for better justice, both for those who are suffering from mental abnormalities and also for those who dishonestly claim to be.

Preface

The object of this book is to convey some fundamental principles of forensic psychiatry to those whose interest is so inclined. The work is based on 17 years' experience acquired in local prisons of Her Majesty's Prison Service in England and Wales, which involved extensive court experience.

The views expressed do not necessarily represent those of the Home Office. It is, in my opinion, not generally recognized that the medical care of inmates in Her Majesty's prisons is second to none and satisfactory liaison with the National Health Service is essential.

The chapters are designed to have wide appeal not only to members of the medical and nursing professions but also the judiciary, police, criminologists, probation officers, social workers and psychologists.

I wish to state that I have personal knowledge of the case histories described in this book. Names of accused persons, dates and relevant courts are omitted on the instructions of the Home Office so as to conform with the Official Secrets Act and relevant communications from the Home Office in this context are in possession of the publisher. These cases are included with the object of describing the backgrounds of persons charged with various types of crime and to illustrate the nature of written and oral psychiatric evidence submitted to courts. Verdicts and disposal decisions by the courts are also described. It was not the intention to follow any of these cases to the Court of Appeal (Criminal Division). Furthermore, as a general principle, I do not consider it appropriate that I should make comments (critical or otherwise) on decisions reached by courts, although in some instances I have made observations where appropriate.

Some of the selected case histories described in this work were compiled when the 1959 Mental Health Act was operative and consequently they are described in conformity with definitions and terminology used in the 1959 Act upon which court decisions were based and references to the Criminal Justice Act 1948 are retained in the histories for the same reason. However, the histories would, to a large extent, be relevant to the Mental Health Act 1983, but there are exceptions particularly in relation to psychiatric disposal of psychopathically disordered offenders owing to removal of age restrictions and the confusion caused by the inclusion of part of the definition of psychopathic disorder in the definitions of mental and severe mental impairment and appropriate comments have been made in the text. The remainder of the book is written in the general context of the Mental Health Act 1983, with some references to the Powers of the Criminal Courts Act 1973, which has been replaced by the Criminal Justice Act 1991.

In view of the growing public concern, I have included a chapter on the psychiatric assessment of mentally disordered persons who are an immediate and serious danger to the public or a potential danger.

Reference is also made to the Government's proposals for the reorganisation of the Probation Service.

I have quoted from *some* authors who wrote books and articles a considerable number of years ago. I see no reason for dismissing such works as "dated" provided they are clinically accurate, relevant to the text, interesting and have not been repeated.

Acknowledgements

My grateful thanks are due to the following:

J.S. Christie, psychological tester, and G. McLoughlin, B.A., senior psychologist, for their valuable assistance in the sections on intelligence testing Chapter XI, Mental Impairment and Crime.

Dr D.J. Berry Ph.D., L.R.I.C., Principal Biochemist, Poisons Unit, New Cross Hospital, London, whose excellent contribution on testing for drugs is a most important addition to Chapter VII.

S. Pragnell of the Northampton and West Juvenile Liaison Bureau, Personal Communication (1991).

W. Campling of the St Charles Youth Treatment Centre, Brentwood, Essex.

D. Farrell, Secretary and Director, Dyfrig House, Alcoholic Rehabilitation Unit, Cardiff. Dyfrig House is an integral part of the South Glamorgan Council on Alcoholism.

Dr C.Smith, Medical Director, Central Mental Hospital, Dublin.

Professor R.J. Daly, M.A., M.D., F.R.C.P., F.R.C.Psych., Department of Psychiatry, University College Cork and Cork Regional Hospital.

A. Littler, R.M.N., F.E.T.C., C.M.S., Development Officer, South Glamorgan Health Authority and based at Whitchurch Hospital, Cardiff.

D.A. Jones, B.A., S.R.N., R.M.N., F.E.T.C., M.R.S.H., Cert.Ed., Senior Nurse Manager, Inservice Training: Education, South Glamorgan Health Authority and based at Whitchurch Hospital.

Drs K. Norton, M.A., M.D., M.R.C.Psych. and B. Dolan Ph. D., of the Henderson Clinic, Belmont for their help with the section on the treatment of psychopaths.

Dr D. O'Connor, B.Sc., M.Ed., Ph.D., Dip. Educ., School of Education, University of Newcastle upon Tyne for his contributions on solvent abuse.

I would also like to express my gratitude to J.M. Newnham and C.J. Parry of the South Glamorgan Social Services for their invaluable contribution.

Grateful thanks for work on the legal sections of the book are offered to the following:

David Wynn Morgan, B.A. (Oxon), of Gray's Inn and the Wales and Chester Circuit Barrister, for the table of sentencing powers and provisions.

Bernard Powell, Ph.D., Barrister, for assistance in researching the cases on diminished responsibility.

Judge Martin Stephens, Q.C. for kind advice and encouragement throughout.
Bruce Houlder, Q.C., Christopher Pitchford Q.C. and Elizabeth McGahey, B.A., Barrister for reading the manuscript of Chapters 1 and 2 and for offering many helpful suggestions for improvement.

I would like to thank the Prison Department of the Home Office for providing the facilities which made this work possible.

Table of Statutes

Table of Cases Cited

CHAPTER I

Crime and Punishment

BY PATRICK CURRAN

The law itself provides no specific definition of crime. In everyday practice the two most obvious characteristics of a criminal offence are: first, that it is wilful[1] conduct of a kind which is subject to legal prohibition; and secondly, that the consequence of, and remedy for, such conduct is prosecution and punishment at the instance of the state. It is the element of liability to punishment, or a penalty, which is the fundamental characteristic of crime.[2]

Thus a criminal offence is committed when a person of sufficient age[3] and of sound mind[4] is responsible for conduct which is prohibited as criminal (either at common law or by the provisions of a penal statute)[5]. The trial and disposal of such offences is the responsibility of representatives of the state.

The mundane reality of criminal practice is that most of the criminal offences tried daily by the courts are essentially regulatory in nature. For example, minor road traffic offences, minor transgressions of licensing laws, failure to pay television licence fees, and a huge variety of summary offences contrary to legislation as varied as the Trade Descriptions Act 1968, the Fraudulent Mediums Act 1951 and the Salmon Act 1986.

1. In the sense of "non-accidental", although grossly negligent acts may satisfy this test, in the case, for example, of manslaughter.
2. Lord Atkin discussed the point in a characteristically lucid paragraph in his speech in *Proprietary Articles Trade Association v. Attorney-General for Canada* [1931] A.C. 310, at 324:
   "... the criminal quality of an act cannot ... be discovered by reference to any standard but one: is the act prohibited with penal consequences? Morality and criminality are far from co-extensive, nor is the sphere of criminality necessarily part of a more extensive field covered by morality, unless the moral code necessarily disapproves of all acts prohibited by the state, in which case the argument moves in a circle."
3. See *post*, p. 34 *et seq.*
4. See *post*, p. 35 *et seq..*
5. Definitions of crime might be said, however, to vary with the ever-increasing categories of interested social and political observers: see, for example, the perceptive discussion by Coleman and Bottomley, "Police Conceptions of Crime and 'No Crime'" [1976] Crim. L.R. 344.

Statistics published in March 1991 showed that in 1989 1.9 million people were prosecuted in the courts: of these, 449,000 people were prosecuted for indictable offences, 586,000 for non-motoring summary offences, and 847,000 for summary motoring offences. A total of 6.3 million fixed-penalty notices were issued.[6] Many (if not most) of these offences are known as offences of "strict liability" or "strict responsibility". This means that the offender is guilty if the prosecution can show simply that he or she did some prohibited act, whether deliberately or not. Thus if a bishop inadvertently drove his car at 32 m.p.h. in a built-up area, he would be as much guilty of the offence of exceeding the speed limit as the car thief who deliberately drove at over 100 m.p.h. to escape from the police. In this example, both have committed the same strict liability offence (exceeding the speed limit), but the car thief *may* additionally have committed some more serious offence, such as dangerous driving, which is not an offence of strict liability. In that case, the mere fact that the prosecution can show that he drove at over 100 m.p.h. is not necessarily sufficient to found criminal liability; the prosecution must go further and prove the appropriate degree of criminal intent to commit the offence.[7]

Whilst psychiatrists are frequently called upon to treat persons who have committed very minor offences, it is with the more serious[8] kinds of criminal conduct, particularly homicide, that lawyers' difficulties in relation to psychiatric questions are at their greatest, and there may well be a corresponding obscurity in the legal conundrums which the psychiatrist is called upon to help solve.[9]

It is with such offences and the procedures for their prosecution and

6. Criminal Statistics, England and Wales (HMSO)
7. See s.1, Road Traffic Act 1991, and the new s.2A of the Road Traffic Act 1988.
8. Experience has shown that even the most trivial charges, such as parking offences, can, in the eyes of the accused, be so serious as to lead to genuine distress. Any allegation which involves an accusation of dishonesty (e.g. fraudulent use of a vehicle excise licence, or bilking a taxi fare) against a person of good character, is bound to be regarded as "serious". But it is necessary, for practical purposes, to limit the scope of this chapter to a discussion of indictable offences. Moreover, consideration of questions of fitness to plead (*R. v. Metropolitan Stipendiary Magistrate Tower Bridge, ex p. Anifowosi* (1985) 149 J.P. 748), and insanity defences, cannot be undertaken by magistrates' courts: but see Stephen White: "Insanity Defences and Magistrates Courts" [1991] Crim. L.R. 501.
9. This is hardly surprising when diminished responsibility, for example, is a purely legal device, imported by English law from Scotland, with no scientific basis and no recognized medical definition: see *post* p.51 *et seq.*

disposal that this chapter is concerned. The reader who is concerned with summary offences and offences of strict liability should consult some of the standard works upon summary offences for a more detailed treatment of the principles and practice by which liability is established.[10]

Criminal Procedure

Before the Second World War magistrates' courts were often referred to as "police courts", a term which may derive from the series of statutes passed from 1792 onwards by which Metropolitan Stipendiary[11] Magistrates and the Metropolitan Police Force were established.[12] Under these Acts of Parliament the rudiments of a modern penal system were introduced. The basic structure of the system remains as it was in the nineteenth century, and may be represented as follows.

Table I

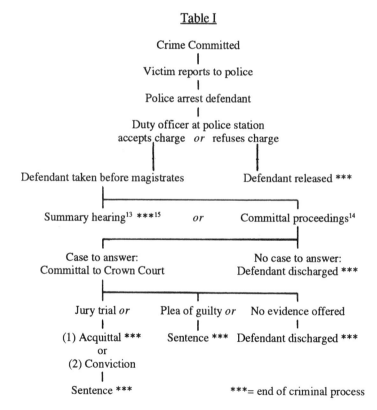

Crime Committed
|
Victim reports to police
|
Police arrest defendant
|
Duty officer at police station
accepts charge *or* refuses charge

Defendant taken before magistrates | Defendant released ***

Summary hearing[13] ***[15] *or* Committal proceedings[14]

Case to answer: Committal to Crown Court | No case to answer: Defendant discharged ***

Jury trial *or* Plea of guilty *or* No evidence offered

(1) Acquittal *** | Sentence *** | Defendant discharged ***
or
(2) Conviction
|
Sentence *** ***= end of criminal process

Criminal process is commonly undertaken by the state, under the authority of the Crown Prosecution Service, although private individuals retain certain rights of prosecution. For practical purposes the Prosecution of Offences Act 1985 (under which the Crown Prosecution Service was created) replaces all previous legislation upon the subject. By s.4 of the Act the right of private individuals to bring prosecutions is expressly preserved, but the Director of Public Prosecutions has the power to take over any such prosecution. If, having done so, no evidence is offered, and a verdict of not guilty is recorded by direction, the defendant cannot be charged or tried again for the same offence.

Determination of criminal proceedings involves either trial by the magistracy for offences capable of summary trial, or trial by jury for indictable offences not tried summarily.[16] Punishment of crime is exclusively reserved for the magistracy and judiciary.

10. See, e.g., *Stone's Justices' Manual*. Whilst some indictable offences are strict liability offences (e.g. many bankruptcy offences under the Insolvency Act 1986) it will be seldom, if ever, that such offences are likely to present the forensic psychiatrist with any significant problem.

11. i.e. "paid". The Metropolitan magistrates were the first professionally trained and salaried magistrates.

12. This system was in fact to provide greater opportunities for injustices to be corrected. Under the Metropolitan Police Courts Act 1839, for example, a right of appeal against sentence was provided where the sentence exceeded a fine of £3 or one month's imprisonment. Until 1925 no such right existed outside the Metropolitan police courts. The right of appeal given by the Summary Jurisdiction Act 1879 gave a right of appeal to Quarter Sessions only where there had been a determination of guilt, not on a plea of guilty. The history is set out in the judgments of Lord Goddard, C.J. and Byrne J. in *R. v. London Quarter Sessions, ex parte Borg* [1958] 1 Q.B.43.

13. For purely summary (most minor offences) or "either way" offences.

14. Where offence alleged is indictable only, e.g. murder or rape, or where offence is "either-way" offence, e.g. theft or assault, and (a) defendant elects trial or (b) magistrates determine more suitable for trial on indictment.Committal proceedings are abolished by s.44(1) of the Criminal Justice and Public Order Act 1994 (see Addendum p.541 *et seq.*). They are replaced by a 'transfer for trial' procedure.

15. A defendant may be committed to the Crown Court for sentence following summary trial.

16. A comprehensive review of the relevant criteria was given in the Mode of Trial Practice Note of 26th October, 1990(1991) 92 Cr. App. R. 142.

17. The juvenile court was replaced by the youth court under the provisions of the Criminal Justice Act 1991. It has extensive, although not exclusive, powers to deal with persons under 18.

The Structure of the System of Criminal Courts

The basic structure of the system of courts with criminal jurisdiction may be represented in pyramid form as follows:

Table II

House of Lords
(Final court of appeal)
|
Court of Appeal (Criminal Division)
(All appeals against conviction and sentence from Crown Courts in England and Wales)
|
Crown Court (Jury Trials or Judge Alone*)
(Jurisdiction includes (a) trial of persons committed for trial by magistrates, and (b) appeals against conviction and/or sentence by magistrates' courts)
|
Magistrates' Courts

*Sentence cases (Guilty pleas or sentence following conviction by jury)

The Coroner's Court is not a court of criminal jurisdiction and its former power to commit a person for trial by coroner's "inquisition" has been abolished.

In practice, all criminal process begins in the magistrates' court. The youth court[17] is a magistrates' court, with jurisdiction to deal with the cases of children and young persons aged 10 to 17 inclusive.

Classification of Offences

The classification of criminal offences is occasionally the cause of some confusion. The basic division, in the case of an adult[18] is between minor transgressions of the law, known as "summary offences" which are dealt with only by the magistrates' court, and the most serious kinds of crime which can be tried only on indictment in the Crown Court. Thus there are purely summary offences (e.g. minor road traffic offences such as driving without due care and attention) and purely indictable offences (e.g. murder, or rape).

There are, however, offences which can be dealt with either in the magistrates' court or in the Crown Court, known simply as "either-way"

18. The position of juvenile offenders is not dealt with here. Detailed explanation of the law relating to the prosecution and trial of children and young persons is to be found, for example, in *Stone's Justices' Manual.*

offences. Such offences vary greatly according to the circumstances in which they are committed: one offence of theft, for example, may involve a tin of baked beans worth less than 50p, whilst another may concern gold bullion worth £50 million. In such circumstances the magistrates determine the mode of trial, and are likely to send ("commit") [19] a serious "either-way" offence for trial to the Crown Court. Whilst the prosecution are entitled to make submissions upon the appropriate forum, the magistrates have a complete discretion, subject to the right of a defendant to elect trial by jury.

Any defendant is entitled to ask for trial by jury of any indictable offence. Thus, for example, in the case of the alleged theft of the tin of baked beans, the person accused may be of good character, to whom the accusation is of the utmost gravity, who will settle for nothing less than trial (and anticipated acquittal) by the jury.[20]

In certain circumstances a defendant may be committed to the Crown Court for sentence, after a trial and conviction by the magistrates, if, having heard evidence of the defendant's character and antecedents, the magistrates are of the view that greater powers of punishment than are available to them are required to deal with the defendant's case.

Trial on indictment

A criminal trial begins with arraignment, i.e. with the indictment being put to the accused, with the requirement that he pleads guilty or not guilty. It is at this very first stage that one of the most fundamental medico-legal issues may be raised.

Fitness to Plead

The rules governing the resolution of the question of fitness to plead give illustrations of the problems which can arise when the law attempts to

19 Will be 'transfer' – see footnote 14.
20 There is nothing new in this. Shakespeare's Duke of Norfolk declined the king's offer of an easy disposal of an allegation of treason by saying:

> "My life thou shalt command, but not my shame,
> The one my duty owes, but my fair name...
> To dark dishonour's use thou shalt not have...
> My dear, dear lord,
> The purest treasure mortal times afford
> Is spotless reputation: ...
> Mine honour is my life, both grow in one,
> Take honour from me and my life is done:
> Then dear my liege, mine honour let me try:
> In that I live, and for that I will die."
> Richard II, Act I, Scene 1.

provide for the future regulation of cases involving every imaginable variety of mental condition.

Ascertaining whether or not an individual is "fit to plead" is a basic requirement of any civilized system of justice. The quaintness of the terminology should not disguise the reality of the question which is posed.

Criminal process is a serious business: it directly affects the life or liberty of the individual charged. If the individual charged is not capable of understanding the charge, or the evidence, or capable of giving instructions to his advocate, then the process becomes worse than a mockery of justice, since it ignores the disability of the principal participant in the events into which the trial is supposed to be making a serious enquiry. Recent changes in the law have been made by the Criminal Procedure (Insanity and Unfitness to Plead) Act 1991.[21]

This Act, which came into force on January 1st, 1992, was the result of Parliament's decision to make reforms in three main areas:

(1) By amending the law relating to (a) the special verdict of not guilty by reason of insanity, and (b) the question of fitness to plead;

(2) by widening and increasing the powers of the courts in the event of defendants being found to be insane or unfit to plead; and

(3) by providing for a "trial of the facts" in the cases of defendants found to be unfit to plead.

The term "fitness to plead" is a broad one: it concerns *any* disability which prevents the accused from communicating with his legal advisers, from understanding the charge against him, or from following the proceedings.[22] Until very recently, however, the consequences of being found unfit to plead (even if quite innocent of the conduct alleged by the prosecution) were virtually identical to those in the following quite different circumstances:

21. The interesting background to this statute is described in an article in the *Criminal Law Review* by Stephen White ([1992] Crim. L.R. 4) which provides a thorough examination and analysis of the scope of the provisions, the contrast with the previous legislation and the consequences of the Act both generally and in terms of the disposal of the cases of persons affected by it.

22. In *Pritchard* (1836) 7 C. & P. 303, Alderson B. directed the jury to consider the case of a defendant who appeared to be deaf, dumb and not of sane mind upon each of the following questions: (i) was the defendant "mute of malice" or "mute by the visitation of God"?; (ii) was he able to plead?; (iii) was he sane or not?

(i)   to those following acquittal by the special verdict of not guilty by reason of insanity, or

(ii) (astonishingly) to those following *conviction* of the offence charged, on the basis of full criminal responsibility, where the court was satisfied that the defendant was suffering from a mental disorder requiring the making of a hospital order (i.e. detention in a special and secure hospital) without limit of time.

Under the Trial of Lunatics Act 1883 (s.2(1)) where the jury found that a defendant was "insane", but had committed the physical acts which otherwise amounted to the crime alleged, they were to return a special verdict of "guilty but insane". By the Criminal Procedure (Insanity) Act 1964 ("the 1964 Act") (s.1) this special verdict was replaced by that of "not guilty by reason of insanity".

The practical effect of such a verdict in most cases, however, was that the defendant had to be committed to a mental hospital indefinitely, and his or her fate was hardly distinguishable from that of a person who was convicted of a serious offence but who (whilst *fit* to plead) nevertheless deserved to be sentenced to be detained under a hospital order with a restriction order made without limit of time.[23]

It was, therefore, hardly surprising that the experience of the courts was that persons whose mental condition was such that they might have been expected to avoid a trial by claiming unfitness to plead, would more often than not plead guilty, even to a very serious offence, in order to avoid the consequences of the provisions of the 1964 Act, as the requirement of restriction without limit of time might not inevitably follow in such a case.

By s.1(1) of the 1991 Act it is provided that a jury shall not return a special verdict under s.2 of the Trial of Lunatics Act 1883 as amended by the Criminal Procedure (Insanity) Act 1964 (s.1), except on the written or oral evidence of two or more medical practitioners, at least one of

---

23. Theoretically, under the 1964 Act, a person convicted of manslaughter (on the ground of diminished responsibility) for an appallingly savage killing, where the diagnosis was paranoid schizophrenia, and the prognosis poor, *might* receive the same "disposal" as an otherwise quite harmless individual accused of shoplifting in a sweet shop, if that individual was deaf and dumb, unable to read or write, and unable to communicate with his legal advisers or to understand the nature of the proceedings, and thus unfit to plead (as in, e.g. *R. v. Governor of Stafford Prison, ex parte Emery* [1909] 2 K.B. 81). Thus any device to avoid a finding of not guilty by reason of insanity was likely to be employed by an accused's legal advisers, even where the charge was one of murder or manslaughter.

whom is duly approved by the Secretary of State for the purposes of s.12 of the Mental Health Act 1983 as having special experience in the treatment of mental disorder.[24]

The new procedure which is to be followed in all such cases is set out in s.2 of the 1991 Act. The fundamental matters are as follows:

1. Where, on the trial of any person, the question arises (at the instance of the defence or otherwise) whether the defendant is under any disability which (apart from the provisions of the Act itself) would constitute a bar to his or her being tried, the provisions of s.4(1) of the Criminal Procedure (Insanity) Act 1964,[25] apply.[26]

2. If the court considers it expedient to do so, *and* is of the opinion that it is in the interests of the accused, consideration of the question of fitness to be tried may be postponed until any time up to the opening of the case for the defence.[27]

3. If, before the question of fitness to be tried is deliberated upon,[28] the jury acquit[29] on the merits generally,[30] the question shall not be determined.[31]

4. Where, however, the question of fitness to plead is to be

24. A practitioner approved for the purposes of s.12 is also eligible to act in cases governed by the evidence provisions contained in s.54 of the Mental Health Act 1983. Approval by the Secretary of State may be sought on application by the practitioner, who is likely to be required to give details of medical qualifications, posts held since qualifying, courses attended on the diagnosis of mental treatment and disorder and details of special experience in the diagnosis or treatment of mental disorder.

25. As substituted by the provisions of s.2 of the Criminal Procedure (Insanity and Unfitness to Plead) Act 1991.

26. S.4(1).

27. S.4(2).

28. "falls to be determined" is the phrase used by the draftsman.

29. In most circumstances this is likely to be upon the direction of the Judge, following a successful submission of "no case", but a jury retains the right to say that they wish to hear no more and to acquit at any stage after the close of the prosecution case.

30. Upon each count in respect of which fitness to be tried may be in issue.

31. S.4(3).

32. See s.4(5) as amended. The wording of the Act makes it clear that the issue is not one which it is possible for prosecution and defence to resolve by agreement, with or without the sanction of the Judge. Moreover, by subs.(6) it is expressly provided that the jury may only make a determination of the issue on the written or oral evidence of two or more registered medical practitioners, at least one of whom is duly approved.

33. i.e. when the indictment is first put.

       determined, it must be determined by a jury.[32]

5.   If the issue is to be determined on arraignment[33] and "the trial proceeds", the accused shall be tried by a jury "other than that" which determined the issue of fitness to plead.[34]

6.   Where the question is to be determined after arraignment, the court may direct whether the same or a different jury shall determine the matter.[35]

7.   Medical evidence is essential for the jury's determination.[36]

8.   A "trial of the facts"[37] must be held where the accused has been found to be under a disability in order to determine whether or not the accused "did the act or made the omission"[38] which constitutes the conduct relied upon by the prosecution in each count: i.e. the conduct which, if accompanied by the appropriate *mens rea,* would amount to the criminal offence charged.[39]

9.   If the jury are satisfied in the trial of facts that the accused did the relevant act or made the relevant omission, they must make a finding to that effect. If, however, they are not satisfied, they must acquit, as if on the merits in the trial proper.[40]

10.   Provision is made for a different jury to hear the trial of the facts after arraignment.[41]

11.   A new s.5 is substituted for the old s.5 in the 1964 Act, in respect of the court's powers to deal with persons who either (a) have been found not guilty by reason of insanity on a special verdict; or (b) have been found to be unfit to plead and, in the trial of facts, have been found to have done the act or made the omission

---

34. Subs.(5)(a).
35. Subs.(5)(b).
36. Subs.(6): see note [23] *ante.*
37. This term is to be found in the short title of the Act, and is a convenient one to use, although it is not specifically used elsewhere in the Act.
38. This is a phrase which White (*ante*) has observed "has a long pedigree, from the Trial of Lunatics Act of 1883 to s.37(3) of the current Mental Health Act." [1991] Crim. L.R. 4, at 9.
39. Subs.4A.
40. S.4A(3) and (4).
41. S.4A(5).
42. S.5(2)(a) and sch.1: effectively an order for the detention of the accused in a hospital specified by the Secretary of State, with *or without* an order restricting discharge: see sch.2, para.2.
43. S.5(2)(b) and sch.1.

alleged against them. The court now has the power to make either an "admission order", [42] or a "guardianship order"[43] under the Mental Health Act 1983; a "supervision and treatment order",[44] or an absolute discharge.[45]

12. Where the charge involved is murder, however, the alternatives to an admission order are not available, and the admission order itself must have a restriction direction without limit of time.[46]

In respect of appeals there are, in particular, provisions amending the Criminal Appeal Act 1968 in respect of the consequences of findings made on a trial of the facts.

Proceedings After Plea

Functions of Judge and Jury
Where a case is tried on indictment, the functions of Judge and jury are quite separate and distinct: the Judge's task is to supervise the conduct of the trial, (including ruling upon matters of law raised during it by either side), to give directions to the jury on the relevant law, to summarize the important features of the evidence, and, if the verdict is one of guilty, to impose the appropriate sentence.

By contrast, the facts – i.e. the resolution of the issues of fact upon the evidence given in the case – are entirely for the jury. They, and not the Judge, decide where the truth lies. If, having heard all the evidence, the jury is sure of guilt, they are duty-bound to convict, that is, to find the defendant guilty. If they are not sure of guilt, they must acquit, and find the defendant not guilty. A defendant who has been acquitted by the jury is entitled to be discharged forthwith.

The Burden and Standard of Proof
A person is presumed innocent until the contrary is proved by the prosecution. For all practical purposes, the burden of proof of primary criminal liability rests upon the prosecution from beginning to end of the case. Thus, unless and until the prosecution have called the necessary minimum evidence to establish both that the offence charged was committed, and that the defendant committed it, an acquittal is inevitable,

44. S.5(2)(b)(ii) and sch.2.
45. S.5(2)(b)(iii).
46. S.5(3) and sch.1, para.2(2).
47. *Galbraith* [1981] 145 J.P. 406.

and a verdict of not guilty will be directed by the Judge at the close of the prosecution case.[47]

The standard which is required of the prosecution is the highest possible: a jury may not convict unless they are satisfied so as to be sure of guilt. This means exactly the same thing as the formerly more common (and arguably more authoritative) formula "proof beyond reasonable doubt".[48]

Where the primary facts are admitted (for example, that the defendant was responsible for causing fatal injuries to a person whom he is alleged to have murdered) but some special defence is raised in answer (for example, diminished responsibility) then the burden of proving particular matters *in relation to that defence* may shift to the defendant. If so, the standard of proof is not the same as that required of the prosecution: the defendant need only show that he has established these matters on the balance of probabilities to be entitled to succeed.

Evidence: The Rule Against Hearsay
It is unnecessary to consider the law of evidence here in any detail. One aspect of it, however, does require some brief treatment, as there is occasionally disagreement between prosecution and defence over the admissibility of what the defendant told a psychiatrist in the course of an interview. As some part, at least, of a psychiatrist's opinion is bound to depend upon his or her acceptance of the truth of the facts related by the defendant, a few guidelines may be of some assistance.

The rule against hearsay is designed to prevent the occurrence of a fundamental fallacy in the process of proof. The purpose of taking oral testimony is that witnesses can be seen and assessed in giving evidence to the jury of what they themselves observed. The jury have to decide whether or not the witness is reliable and accurate. To assist them,

48. See *Smith* "Developments in the Law of Evidence 1954-63" {1964} Crim. L.R. 434 at 437.
49. A source of much confusion, even to the experienced. Suppose a witness in chief is describing a robbery. No admission or concession as to any material fact has been made. For Prosecuting Counsel to ask the witness, "Did you then see the defendant point a gun at the bank clerk?" would be a grossly leading question. It is for the witness to volunteer information, not Counsel. In the example given, Counsel has simply told the witness the answer he wants (i.e. the accused then pointed a gun at the bank clerk) and has asked him if he agrees with it. It would *not* have been a leading question to have asked "What happened then?"

Counsel examining the witness in chief is required to take care not to ask leading questions,[49] and the witness is then exposed to the probing of opposing Counsel in cross-examination. The jury then decide, as the tribunal of fact, if they accept the account or not.

If a witness were permitted to say "I know X, the defendant, robbed the bank, because my neighbour, Z, was there and she told me she saw him do it", the witness would have replaced the jury in the function of assessing the reliability of Z and, having come to a conclusion about it, would then be passing it on to the jury for acceptance without their having any means of testing Z's reliability. It is Z who should be in the witness box, not someone who heard Z give an unsworn account.

Hearsay is a concept which has caused much difficulty to generations of law students. But contrary to much popular belief (even amongst some practitioners) the rule does not in all circumstances forbid a witness from telling the court what someone else told him. Such evidence is admissible if the fact to be proved is what was said. A conversation is just as much a fact, which can be witnessed, as a road accident is. But evidence of a conversation is *not* admissible to prove *the truth* of what was said. This is sometimes explained by saying that hearsay may not be admitted "testimonially".

In the medico-legal context, it might be that a psychiatrist would be permitted to say on oath that the defendant told him, for example, that he saw flashing lights before his eyes[50] before his mind went blank, and the next conscious memory he has is of the deceased lying dead at his feet. The fact that that is what the defendant said may be of significance in considering any psychiatric opinion based upon the interview with the defendant (particularly, the prosecution would say, if no mention of flashing lights has been made to the police or to any other doctor). But the question of whether the defendant *did* see flashing lights, and the question of whether his mind went blank, is one which can only be answered by the jury on direct oral testimony from the defendant, if he chooses to give it.

Objectionable hearsay is not cured by any of the following devices:

1. By announcing that the maker of the statement will be called;
2. By repeating what was said by another to a defendant, and asking

---

50. A phenomenon which seems, at critical moments, to afflict a remarkable proportion of persons charged with homicide.

him if he agrees with it; (if he does not agree, the evidence of both question and answer is inadmissible; but even if he does agree with it, to be admissible the evidence of such agreement can only be based upon his independent knowledge of the truth of the facts stated;[51]

3. By asserting that the defendant was present when the remark in question was made: if the truth of the contents of the remark is in question, the fact that it was said once or a hundred times in the presence of the defendant does not make it admissible as evidence of the truth of the facts stated.[52]

Medical Evidence Generally

It is important to recognize the boundaries within which the courts have permitted expert evidence from psychiatrists and clinical psychologists to be given.

In *Byrne*[53] the appellant was charged with the murder of a young girl, whom he had strangled and mutilated. He admitted the facts, but pleaded diminished responsibility. The Judge directed the jury to the effect that if the appellant killed the girl under an abnormal sexual impulse which was so strong that he found it difficult or impossible to resist, but that he was otherwise normal, the section would not apply. He was convicted of murder and appealed on the ground of a misdirection of law in relation to s.2 of the Homicide Act 1957.

The Court of Appeal held that the phrase "abnormality of mind" in s.2 of the Act (which had to be contrasted with the time-honoured expression in the *M'Naghten* Rules, "defect of reason") meant a state of mind so different from that of ordinary human beings that the reasonable man would term it abnormal. It covered the mind's activities in all its aspects: perception, judgment of right and wrong, and the ability to exercise willpower to control physical acts in accordance with that rational judgment.

---

51. A device which was sometimes used in interviews was for a police officer to say "But your wife has told us that ..." and to proceed to set out a hearsay account of events, in the hope that the defendant would admit the truth of the account.

52. It may be otherwise if the *reaction* of the defendant to the words used is in fact the evidence which the prosecution rely upon, in the way that Hamlet relied upon Claudius' reaction to the play and his own narrative of its plot in *Hamlet*, Act III, scene ii, 269-289.

53. [1960] 2 Q.B. 396.

Whether or not an accused was suffering from any abnormality of mind was a question for the jury. Upon this question medical evidence was no doubt of importance, but the jury were entitled to take into account all the evidence, including the acts or statements of the accused and his demeanour. They were not bound to accept the medical evidence if there was other material before them which in their judgment outweighed it.[54]

The aetiology of the abnormality of mind, however, *was* a matter to be determined on expert evidence.

"Assuming that the jury are satisifed on the balance of probabilities that the accused was suffering from 'abnormality of mind' the crucial question nevertheless arises: was the abnormality such as substantially impaired his mental responsibility for his acts in doing or being a party to the killing? This is a question of degree, and essentially one for the jury. Medical evidence is, of course, relevant, but the question involves a decision not merely as to whether there was some impairment of the mental responsibility of the accused for his acts but whether such impairment can properly be called 'substantial', a matter upon which juries may quite legitimately differ from doctors.

Furthermore, in a case where the abnormality of mind is one which affects the accused's self-control, the step between 'he did not resist his impulse' and 'he could not resist his impulse' is, as the evidence in this case shows, one which is incapable of scientific proof. *A fortiori* there is no scientific measurement of the degree of difficulty which an abnormal person finds in controlling his impulses. These problems which in the present state of medical knowledge are scientifically insoluble, the jury can only approach in a broad, common-sense way." *per* Lord Parker C.J. at 400.

The court held that the trial Judge's direction amounted to a direction that difficulty or even inability to exercise willpower on the part of an accused to control his physical acts could not amount to such abnormality of mind as substantially impaired his mental responsibility. That was a misconstruction of the statute.

In *Weightman*[55] it was held that psychiatric evidence was not admissible to show the truth or otherwise of a confession purportedly made by a

---

54. See also *R. v. Lanfear* (1968) 132 J.P. 193; 52 Cr.App. R.S. 176(CA). Note also observation of Watkins L.J. in *R. v. Sanders* 93 Cr. App. R. 245 at 247.
55. (1990) 92 Cr. App. R. 291,

defendant with an"abnormal personality", who did not suffer from any mental illness.

In the case of *Rivett*[56] the defence claimed that the defendant was insane at the time of the killing. The facts were that the defendant had been associating with a schoolgirl, to her parents' disapproval. One evening she went with the defendant to the school she attended, where he had sexual intercourse with her in a bicycle shed. The defendant then strangled her. He was seen later that evening walking alone and acting apparently normally.[57] Three medical experts gave evidence to support an insanity defence. The jury rejected this evidence and found him guilty of murder.[58] On appeal it was held that it was for the jury to determine the issue of insanity on the basis of all the evidence, after proper direction by the Judge, and not for medical men, however eminent, to do so. The jury having heard all the evidence were satisfied that the defendant was responsible for his actions and it was not for the Court of Appeal to say that he was not.

In *Attorney-General for South Australia v. Brown*[59] it was held that psychiatric evidence is not essential in order to prove insanity: evidence of the words and conduct of the defendant before and at the time of the offence alleged may be adequate to show insanity. But where, by contrast, there is no suggestion of any mental abnormality, medical evidence is not admissible on the question of intent: the intention of a normal individual is entirely a matter for the jury.[60]

The question of the admissibility of psychiatric evidence in respect of credibility is one which has frequently been the cause of practical problems. In *Turner*[61] the appellant confessed to killing his girlfriend by battering her to the head and face with a hammer after she had told him that she had affairs with other men and that he was not the father of her expected child. The appellant relied on the defence of provocation at trial. The Judge refused to allow the defence to call a psychiatrist to give his opinion that the appellant was not violent by nature but that his personality was such that he could have been provoked in the circumstances and that

56. (1951) 34 Cr.App. R. 87.
57. Although, still later in the evening, he was seen with a shotgun and cartridges, and he told a friend that he was going to take his own life. He was arrested and, following a calm and emotionless confession to the police, he went to sleep in his cell with ease.
58 This was a case of capital murder, decided almost a decade before diminished responsibility (see *post*) became available as a defence.
59. [1960] A.C. 432,
60. *Chard* (1971) Cr. App. R. 268 (a case of murder).

he was likely to be telling the truth. This opinion was based on the psychiatrist's own observations and upon hearsay information from medical records, from the appellant (who did not give evidence) and his family and friends. The decision to exclude the evidence, on the basis that it was hearsay character evidence,[62] and was irrelevant and inadmissible, formed the basis of an appeal.

The Court of Appeal dismissed the appeal, holding that (1) since the question whether the appellant was suffering from mental illness as defined by the Mental Health Act 1959 was not in issue, the psychiatric evidence that the appellant was not suffering from mental illness, although otherwise admissible, was irrelevant and had rightly been excluded; (2) opinion evidence, if relevant and not based on hearsay, might be admissible to prove that the appellant was likely to be telling the truth, since the appellant's veracity and the possibility of his having been provoked were matters within the competence and experience of a jury, but the appellant must (first) prove the facts upon which the opinion is based by admissible evidence.

The judgment of the Court of Appeal concludes with these words:

"... we are firmly of the opinion that psychiatry has not yet become a satisfactory substitute for the common sense of juries or magistrates with their experience of life."

The appellant had sought to rely on the decision in *Lowery* (*post*) but it was held that this case was decided on its own facts: the issues were unusual and special to that case and it was not authority for the proposition that in all cases psychologists and psychiatrists can be called to prove the probability of the accused's veracity.

In *Lowery*,[63] co-defendants, L and K, were accused of murdering a girl in a sadistically cruel manner. L gave evidence of his good character and said that, although present at the scene, he had been unable to prevent the murder because of his fear of K. K was allowed to call a psychologist to give evidence that an investigation of the personalities of K and L showed that L had a strong aggressive drive, a basic callousness and found some

61. (1975) 139 J.P. 136.
62. At one point the psychiatrist had said that "by all accounts" the appellant was a placid, rather quiet and passive person, ... even-tempered and in no way aggressive: in fact, in the two years preceding the killing he had been convicted of possession of an offensive weapon and assault with intent to rob.
63. [1974] A.C. 85; [1973] 3 W.L.R. 235.

sadistic pleasure in observing the suffering in others. K showed some similar tendencies, but less markedly so with no indication of sadism. They were both convicted of murder. L appealed against the admissibility of the evidence. It was held, dismissing the appeal, that while evidence of criminal tendencies was not admissible, evidence which could help the jury in considering the probabilities of L and K respectively telling the truth as to what took place when the girl was killed was relevant and admissible as a result of L's assertions against K.

In a case where a man killed his cohabitee in pursuance of what he alleged was a suicide pact, the Court of Appeal held that the trial Judge had correctly refused to admit the evidence of a psychiatrist which the defendant had sought to adduce to prove the partial defence available under s.4 of the Homicide Act 1957: *Wood* [1990] Crim. L.R. 264.

Psychiatric Evidence Concerning Reliability of Confessions

There have been a number of important developments within this area in recent years.

In the case of *Ward*[64] the appellant was said, by two experts called to give evidence in the appeal proceedings, to have suffered from "a personality disorder so severe as to be properly categorised as mental disorder." She had been charged with ten counts of murder and three charges of causing explosions. The charges arose out of terrorist incidents which were thought to have been the work of the IRA. The appellant was arrested after the last explosion and was interviewed by the police. At the trial the prosecution relied upon evidence of admissions and confessions made to the police and upon scientific evidence[65] linking the defendant with the offences. The Court of Appeal, reconsidering the case on a second reference by the Home Secretary, reviewed the law concerning the admissibility of evidence of psychiatrists and psychologists as to an accused's reliability in making admissions.

In *Toohey v. Metropolitan Police Commissioner*[66] the House of Lords had allowed the appeals of defendants who had been refused leave at the trial to call evidence of a police surgeon that the complainant was more prone to hysteria than a normal person and that the hysteria might be exacerbated by alcohol. The Court of Appeal had upheld the trial judge, applying its own decision in the case of *Gunewardene*[67].

64. (1993) 96 Cr. App. R. 1.
65. (which was subsequently discredited)
66. [1965] 129 J.P.181 a case of assault with intent to rob.
67. (1951) 115 J.P.415.

The leading speech in the House of Lords in *Toohey* was given by Lord Pearce[68]. In the course of it he said,

"Human evidence shares the frailties of those who give it. It is subject to many cross-currents such as partiality, prejudice, self-interest and above all, imagination and inaccuracy. Those are matters with which the jury, helped by cross-examination and common sense, must do their best. But when a witness through physical (in which I include mental) disease or abnormality is not capable of giving a true or reliable account to the jury, it must surely be allowable for medical science to reveal this vital hidden fact to them...So, too must it be allowable to call medical evidence of mental illness which makes a witness incapable of giving reliable evidence, whether through the existence of delusions or otherwise."[69]

It was held in *Toohey* that *Gunewardene's* case had been wrongly decided: medical evidence was admissible to show that a witness suffered from some disease or defect or abnormality of mind which affected the reliability of their evidence. Moreover, such evidence was not merely confined to a general opinion of the unreliability of the witness, but might also deal with all the matters necessary to show, not only the foundation of and reasons for the diagnosis, but also the extent to which the credibility of the witness was affected.

In *Ward* Glidewell L.J., giving the judgment of the court, referred to *Lowery* and to *Turner*, and to a decision of the Court of Appeal in which *Turner* was followed, *Javed Masih*[70]. He then dealt with the important case of *Everett*[71]. In that case the defendant pleaded guilty to indecent assault after the trial Judge ruled that evidence of admissions made to the police should not be excluded. The defendant was aged 42 but tests before his trial revealed a mental age of 8. He appealed against conviction on the ground that the evidence of the admissions was wrongly admitted. The Court of Appeal held, quashing the conviction, that the Judge had been in error in deciding the question of admissibility by reference only to the tapes of the interview, and in not taking into account medical evidence of the mental condition of the defendant.

It was held that when considering the circumstances which existed at the time of the confession the test which was to be applied was an

68. All other members agreed.
69. See page 162.
70. [1986] Crim. L.R. 395.
71. [1988] Crim. L.R. 826.

objective one. What was material was not what the officers thought about the defendant's mental condition, if they gave it any consideration at all, but, as was subsequently ascertained from the doctors, what the mental condition of the defendant actually was. Had the evidence of the doctors been taken into account, it was inevitable that the defendant would have been regarded as a person in respect of whom the relevant Code of Practice, made under the Police and Criminal Evidence Act 1984, should have been obeyed by the police officers, who should have ensured the presence of an independent mature person.

Watkins L.J., giving the judgment of the court, said,

> "What the Judge in fact did was to rule in effect that he did not have to take account of the medical evidence of the mental condition of the appellant. On the contrary, he listened to the tape recording and expressed himself ... to be satisfied that the appellant had understood the questions and made rational answers to them. That is not the function of a Judge in such a situation as this. He must ... have regard to the whole circumstances and take account of the medical evidence ... Having done so, he may decide, ... whether the prosecution have discharged the burden upon it. Here it most certainly had not."

In *Raghip*[72] the Court of Appeal were also reconsidering an appeal for a second time, following a reference by the Home Secretary. Farquharson L.J. and Alliott and Cresswell JJ. held that a differently-constituted division of the court had been wrong to conclude that psychological evidence as to Raghip's intelligence and suggestibility would not have assisted the jury in determining the reliability of an alleged confession made by him. Raghip and others had been convicted of the murder of P.C. Blakelock on the Broadwater Farm estate in Tottenham. Raghip had an IQ of 74. He was aged 19 years and 7 months at the date of trial, but had the mental age of a child of 9 years and 9 months, and a reading age of a child of $6^{1}/_{2}$.

A psychologist and a consultant psychiatrist who had given evidence at the trial had since indicated that their original assessments of Raghip were mistaken. For the purposes of the appeal, they agreed with another expert instructed after the trial, that the defendant was abnormally suggestible. It was said in the course of the judgment that by December 1988 it had become the regular practice of Judges to admit psychiatric or psychosocial evidence when considering submissions under sections 76

72. Reported as *Silcott, Braithwaite and Raghip, The Times*, December 9, 1991.

and 77 of the Police and Criminal Evidence Act 1984 as to the admissibility of confessions. It was unfortunate that *Everett* had not been cited to the Court of Appeal at the original hearing, but it had not "found its way into any law report[73]."

Everett, the court held, was clear authority that the circumstances which were to be considered by the trial Judge under section 76(2)(b) included the mental condition of the defendant at the time of interview and that that decision was to be taken on the medical evidence rather than the trial Judge's own assessment of the defendant's performance in interview.

It was true, the court observed, that Everett's IQ was only 61, which placed him in the mental defective range, whilst Raghip's IQ of 74 placed him on the borderline, but the judicial approach should not be governed, in considering submissions under this provision of section 76, upon which side of an arbitrary line drawn at 69/70 (or elsewhere) the IQ fell. By section 77(3) of the Police and Criminal Evidence Act 1984 "mentally handicapped" included "significant impairment of intelligence and social functioning."

The Court of Appeal held that the psychological evidence before them would have been admissible before the trial Judge in support of a submission under section 76(2)(b) that the confessions were inadmissible, and the trial Judge would have been likely to have acceded to such a submission. If, contrary to their view, the Judge had rejected the submission, he would have been bound to have given the warning required by section 77(1) of the 1984 Act.[74]

The court then turned to consider the question of whether the same psychological evidence would have been admissible *before the jury*. The court distinguished between psychiatric or psychological evidence going to a defendant's *mens rea* and such evidence going to the reliability of any confession he might have made. It appeared that it was common practice for juries to hear the same expert evidence in the trial which the Judge had heard on the *voir dire*.

In the course of the previous application for leave to appeal, Lord Lane C.J. said the jury were in as good a position, if not better, than the psychologist to judge how amenable Raghip was to suggestions. That approach[75], it had been held in *Everett,* was the wrong approach for the

---

73. The original hearing in the case in the Court of Appeal was on December 19, 1988: the case of *Everett* was in fact reported in the December 1988 issue of the *Criminal Law Review.*

74. See now *Campbell* [1995] Crim. L.R. 157,C.A., and *Bailey, The Times,* January 26, 1995.

Judge. Raghip's mental age was such that he could not be regarded as normal, but that could not have been divined by the layman simply observing him in the witness box. Psychological evidence was required to assist the jury and would have been admissible at his trial. His conviction was held to be unsafe and unsatisfactory.

In *McKenzie*[76] the defendant had been a patient at Rampton special hospital since 1987. It was contended at the defendant's trial for two offences of murder and two offences of arson that he suffered from a degree of mental incapacity which rendered his confessions so unreliable that they should be excluded. Medical evidence was given that the defendant was determined to stay at Rampton and might say whatever would achieve that result. The trial Judge held that the confessions would not be excluded under the Police and Criminal Evidence Act 1984, since no pressure had been put upon the defendant by the police, and the jury would have expert medical evidence to help evaluate the defendant's reliability.

The Court of Appeal held that where the prosecution case against a defendant, who suffers from a significant degree of mental handicap, depends wholly upon uncorroborated confessions, which are unconvincing in that they lack incriminating details, or are inconsistent with other evidence, or are inherently improbable, the Judge should, in the interests of justice, take the initiative and withdraw the case from the jury.

Sentence

On 1st October, 1992, the provisions of the Criminal Justice Act 1991 came into effect. These provisions made radical alterations to the courts' powers of sentence, and to the procedures by which those powers are exercised.They are set out as amended by the Criminal Justice Act 1993 ("CJA 1993").

Pre-sentence Reports

In particular, by s.3(1), in determining whether a custodial sentence is appropriate, and in determining the length of that sentence, the court must[77] obtain and consider a "pre-sentence report" upon the offender. (This provision has an exception which is set out in s.3(2) in which the court is allowed to exercise its discretion not to call for a pre-sentence report, if the offender has been convicted of an offence triable only on indictment (e.g. rape or robbery) and the court thinks it is unnecessary to obtain one.)

75. "... the 'judge for yourself' approach ..."

76. *The Independent*, July 28, 1992.

77. By s.168(1) of the Criminal Justice and Public Order Act 1994, the court may now dispense with a pre-sentence report if the defendant is over 18.

Mentally Disordered Offenders: Medical Reports

Under s.4 of the Act there are a number of additional requirements which are provided for in the case of mentally disordered offenders, before the court can impose a custodial sentence (other than a sentence which is fixed by law.[78])

Under s.4(1) the court must obtain and consider a "medical report"[79] subject to the exception in s.4(2) where the court considers it unnecessary.

Before a custodial sentence is passed upon an offender who is or appears to be mentally disordered, the court must consider any information which is before it relating to his medical condition and the likely effect of a custodial sentence upon that condition, and on any treatment which may be available. The section does not, however, prohibit a court from passing a custodial sentence in the case of an offender who is or appears to be mentally disordered if, for example, no appropriate hospital place is available.[80]

Table III sets out the courts' main powers of sentence.

Table III [81]
Conditional Discharge

1. Act and Section	P.C.C.A. 1973 s. 1(A) as amended by C.J.A. 1991 s. 8 and sch. 1, and by C.J.P.O.A. 1994, s. 168 and sch. 9
2. Appropriate Offences	Any offence for which punishment is not fixed by law.
3. Age limits	None.
4. Limits on the Courts	None.
5. Pre-sentence report needed	No, unless defendant under 18.
6. Condition of Order	Commits no further offences during period of order.
7. Duration	Up to 3 years.

78. e.g. murder (in the case of a person convicted of murder, the only sentence which the law at present allows to be passed is one of life imprisonment).

79. Defined by s.4(5) as a report (oral or written) by a duly approved registered medical practitioner. "Duly approved" refers to approval under s.12 of the Mental Health Act 1983.

80. Thus preserving by statute one of the most striking examples of injustice to the mentally disordered: i.e. the way in which the criminal-justice system, despite loud protests from Judges themselves, has frequently caused mentally disordered offenders convicted of serious offences to be sent to prison for the safety of the public (when it is accepted on all sides that hospital treatment is needed), simply because there is no hospital place available.

81. [Note] Table III compiled by David Wynn Morgan, M.A., (Oxon), Barrister.

Suspended Sentence

1. Act and Section	P.C.C.A. 1973 s. 22 as amended. C.J.A. 1991 s. 5.
2. Appropriate Offences	Any offence punishable by imprisonment.
3. Age limits	Over 21.
4. Limits on the Courts	The sentence of imprisonment must be no more than 2 years. The case must be one for which a sentence of imprisonment would have been appropriate even without the power to suspend and the power can be justified by exceptional circumstances.
5. Pre-sentence report needed	Yes (see note 77).
6. Condition of Order	Commits no other offence punishable with imprisonment during the period specified in the order.
7. Duration	1-2 years.

Combination Order
(Community Service and Probation)

1. Act and Section	C.J.A. 1991 s. 11.
2. Appropriate Offences	Any offence for which Probation or Community Service is appropriate.
3. Age limits	Over 16.
4. Limits on the Courts	The offence or the combination of the offence and any offence associated with it must be serious enough to warrant a Community Service or Probation Order.
5. Pre-sentence report needed	Yes (see note 77).
6. Condition of Order	(a) To perform unpaid work for the Community as directed. (b) To be under the supervision of a Probation Officer.
7. Duration	Community Service: 40-100 hrs. Probation 12 months-3 years.

Community Service Order

1. Act and Section	P.C.C.A. 1973 s. 14 as amended by C.J.A. 1991 s. 10 and CJA 1993 s. 66.
2. Appropriate Offences	Offences punishable with imprisonment or a fine.
3. Age limits	Over 16.
4. Limits on the Courts	The offence, or the combination of the offence and any offence associated with it must be serious enough to warrant such an order.
5. Pre-sentence report needed	Yes (see note 77).
6. Condition of Order	Perform unpaid work for the Community as directed
7. Duration	40-120 hours in 12 months.

Probation Order

1. Act and Section	P.C.C.A. 1973 s. 2 as amended by C.J.A. 1991 s. 8 and CJA 1993 s.66.
2. Appropriate Offences	Any offence.
3. Age limits	Over 16.
4. Limits on the Courts	The offence, or the combination of any offence and other offences associated with it must be serious enough to warrant such an order.
5. Pre-sentence report needed	Yes (see note 77).
6. Condition of Order	Such as the court considers necessary including requirements as to: (i) Residence; (ii) Activities; (iii) Attendance at Probation Centre; (iv) (For sexual offenders) treatment for medical condition; (v) Treatment for drugs/alcohol dependency.
7. Duration	Six months to 3 years.

Immediate Imprisonment

1. Act and Section	P.C.C.A. 1973 ss. 20, 21. C.J.A. 1991 ss. 1-4 and CJA 1993 s.66.
2. Appropriate Offences	Any offence punishable with imprisonment.
3. Age limits	Over 21.
4. Limits on the Courts	(i) The offence, or the combination of the offence and one or more offences associated with it, is so serious that only such a sentence would be justified; or (ii) When the offence is violent or sexual, that only such a sentence would be adequate to protect the public from serious harm.
5. Pre-sentence report needed	Yes, unless offence is indictable only.
6. Condition of Order	[Remain in prison.]
7. Duration	Subject to revision and/or parole.

Hospital Order

1. Act and Section	M.H.A. 1983 s. 37.
2. Appropriate Offences	Any offence punishable with imprisonment, other than one for which sentence is fixed by law.
3. Age limits	None.
4. Limits on the Courts	(i) Evidence from two medical practitioners, one of whom must be approved under the M.H.A. 1973, that offender is suffering from mental illness, psychopathic disorder, severe mental impairment or mental impairment. (ii) That mental disorder is of a nature and degree which makes it appropriate for him to be detained in hospital for medical treatment. (iii) If the disorder is psychopathic disorder or mental impairment the treatment is likely to alleviate or prevent a deterioration of the offender's condition. (iv) Having regard to all circumstances including the offence, the offender's character and antecedents and to other available disposals, a

hospital order must be the most suitable.

(v) That arrangements have been made for hospital admission within 28 days of the order being made.

5. Pre-sentence report needed	Yes (see note 77).
6. Condition of Order	To remain in hospital as directed.
7. Duration	Until discharge order by Hospital Managers or Mental Health Review Tribunal.

N.B. May be made in conjunction with a Restriction Order under s. 54 M.H.A. 1983 if court considers it necessary for the protection of the public from serious harm from the offender. The restriction order may be for a specific period or without limit of time.

CHAPTER II

The Mental Element in Crime
BY PATRICK CURRAN

Conduct and Intent

It is a basic principle of the criminal law that no crime can be committed without criminal intent in some form. The Latin maxim *"actus non facit reus, nisi mens sit rea"* is the foundation for the supposed elementary principle that a crime consists in the doing of some act (*actus reus*) accompanied by a guilty mind (*mens rea*). The full maxim might be translated as "conduct does not amount to a crime without criminal intent."[82]

Lord Diplock suggested that it might be better to avoid bad Latin and to speak about "the conduct of the accused and his state of mind at the time of that conduct" instead of *actus reus* and *mens rea*. The maxim had many years previously attracted the disapproval of the doyen of Victorian common-law Judges, Stephen J., in *Tolson*[83].

What constitutes criminal intent may vary according to the offence charged. An illustration of this may be seen in the case of the offences of murder and manslaughter. Both offences involve the unlawful killing of another. The defendant in either case must be proved to have been responsible for that act of killing. In murder the prosecution must then prove that he intended either to kill or to cause grievous bodily harm, but manslaughter involves no such intent. The *mens rea* of manslaughter might well be simply gross negligence or recklessness. It is certainly not necessary to prove that the defendant had feelings of guilt.[84]

---

82. In a discussion of this most basic of maxims in the case of *Miller* [1983] 1 All E.R. 973, HL, Lord Diplock said:

   "The question" [certified by the Court of Appeal to be one of general public importance] "speaks of *actus reus*. This expression is derived from Coke ... by converting incorrectly into an adjective the word *reus* which was there used correctly in the accusative case as a noun ... the use of the expression *actus reus* ... is liable to mislead, since it suggests that some positive act on the part of the accused is needed to make him guilty of a crime and that a failure or omission to act is insufficient to give rise to criminal liability unless some express provision in the statute that creates the offence so provides."

83 (1889) 23 Q.B.D. 168, at 185-187.

Duress and Coercion

The conduct or omission alleged to be criminal must, however, be the product of the individual's free will. Thus if D is held by X by force, and X uses D's hand, against D's will, to push V over a cliff to her death, X may be guilty of V's murder, but D is obviously innocent, and entitled to be acquitted, even though it was his hand which was the physical instrument which was used as the direct cause of V's death. On the other hand, if X *threatens* to kill D unless D pushes V over the cliff, using physical violence upon D until he eventually succumbs to the coercion and throws V to her death, D is certainly liable to be convicted of manslaughter, at least: D retained the theoretical choice of refusing to bow to the threats. Duress is never a defence to murder or attempted murder.[85]

Intoxication

Intoxication, whether by drink or drugs, if self-induced, is in general no defence to a basic charge of crime. Where the crime is one of "specific intent" (such as murder, where the specific intent to be proved is an intent to cause death or really serious injury) the jury are entitled to take evidence of intoxication into account in deciding the extent to which the prosecution have proved specific intent, but "a drunken intent is still an intent". See, generally, the leading case of *Majewski*.[86] This subject is considered in greater detail in respect of diminished responsibility below.

Necessity

"Necessity", as such, is no defence, save in the case of self-defence. The main authority in this area is the grisly case of *Dudley and Stephens*,[87] in which the defendants were charged at Devon Assizes with the murder of a boy of 17. The defendants and the boy were members of the crew of the yacht *Mignonette* which was lost in a storm on a voyage to Sydney, New South Wales. The defendants and the boy, and a fourth man, were cast adrift in an open boat a thousand miles from land: their only food consisted of two tins of turnips. After 18 days, and seven days without food, Dudley, with the assent of Stephens, killed the boy so that they

---

84. See, generally, Smith "The Guilty Mind in the Criminal Law" (1960) 76 L.Q.R. 78 and Ashworth, "Reason, Logic and Criminal Liability" (1975) 91 L.Q.R. 102.
85. *Howe* (1987) 151 J.P. 265; [1987] A.C. 417
86. (1976) 140 J.P. 315.
87. (1884) 14 Q.B.D. 273. See the meticulously researched account of the story of this case in *Cannibalism and the Common Law* by Prof. A. W. Brian Simpson (Penguin Books, 1986).

might eat his body. At the time the boy was killed, there was no reasonable prospect of relief, and there was every probability that unless they ate the boy, or one other of their number, they would have died of starvation. The defendants were held to be guilty of murder, and their plea of necessity was held to be no defence. Lord Coleridge, C.J., said:

> "It must not be supposed that in refusing to admit temptation to be an excuse for crime it is forgotten how terrible the temptation was; how awful the suffering; how hard in such trials to keep the judgment straight and the conduct pure. We are often compelled to set up standards we cannot reach ourselves, and to lay down rules which we could not ourselves satisfy. But a man has no right to declare temptation to be an excuse, though he himself have yielded to it, nor allow compassion for the criminal to change or weaken in any manner the legal definition of the crime."

Accident

Purely accidental conduct, if not so negligent as to be conceived criminal, is a defence. It is otherwise, however, if the accident occurs in the course of intentionally criminal conduct: for example, if D intends to shoot X, but accidentally kills Y, then accident is no defence. If his intention was to kill X he is guilty of the murder of Y under the principle of "transferred malice". If in the course of committing a bank robbery, D, in his haste to make customers lie on the floor, knocks over an elderly person, Z, who suffers a fractured skull and dies, D may well be guilty of manslaughter, as the death was caused by an unlawful and dangerous act – even if it was accidental in the sense of being unintentional.

By s.8 of the Criminal Justice Act 1967 it is provided that:

> "8.   A court or jury, in determining whether a person has committed an offence:
>
> (a)   shall not be bound in law to infer that he intended or foresaw a result of his actions by reason only of its being a natural and probable result of those actions; but
>
> (b)   shall decide whether he did intend or foresee that result by reference to all the evidence drawing such inferences from the evidence as appears proper in the circumstances."

This section is an example of legislation which is passed to remedy a development in case law that is widely regarded as undesirable. In this case it was the notorious case of *DPP v. Smith.*[88]

Essentially s.8 says that no assumptions are to be made as to what an accused intends or foresees as the result of his actions. A thousand people might regard driving at high speed with a policeman attempting to hang on to the exterior of the car as conduct which was likely to cause serious injury to the officer, and that the driver of the car therefore intended to cause such injury, by continuing to drive with the officer hanging on, even though he may not specifically have desired to cause injury to the officer, but simply wished to escape. What the thousand think or foresee in such circumstances is irrelevant: the question is entirely subjective – what did *this* defendant (Smith) think or foresee?[89]

Provocation

Provocation is a partial defence, but only to a charge of murder. The offence of murder is committed where a person unlawfully kills another, with intent to kill, or intending to cause grievous bodily harm. There are many qualifications to the definition to cater for exceptional circumstances[90] but it is unnecessary to consider these here.

The important qualifications for present purposes are that conduct which admittedly falls within this definition may be reduced by operation of law from murder to manslaughter if (a) the defendant's responsibility was diminished by reason of abnormality of mind,[91] or (b) there was provocation of a particular kind,[92] or (c) if the defendant was party to a suicide pact.[93]

---

88. (1960) 124 J.P. 473; (1960) 44 Cr. App. R. 261.
89. Smith was convicted of the capital murder of a policeman, and was sentenced to death. His appeal to the Court of Appeal was allowed, and a verdict of manslaughter was substituted. The prosecution appealed to the House of Lords, who restored the conviction for capital murder. It is not difficult to see why Parliament was driven to intervene: Smith and a friend had simply stolen some scaffolding clips. The unfortunate and courageous police officer, P.C. Meehan, knew Smith and was attempting to look into the car when Smith suddenly drove off. Smith later said "I knew the man: I wouldn't do it for the world... I didn't mean to kill him, but I didn't want him to find the gear."
90. For example, it must be shown that the deceased died from the injury relied upon by the prosecution within a year and a day of the attack: if after this, the law presumes that the death was by some other cause. The Law Commission has recommended abolition of this rule: Law Com. No. 230, HMSO.
91. Homicide Act 1957, s.2.
92. Homicide Act 1957, s.3.
93. Homicide Act 1957, s.4.

Diminished responsibility is, in practice, the single most important area of common concern for lawyers and psychiatrists, as is demonstrated, to some extent, by the figures from the *Criminal Statistics* showing the various defences in homicide cases below.[94] The subject is considered in detail at p.51 *et seq.*

Provocation is specifically a matter for the jury. The section is in the following terms:

> "3. Where on a charge of murder there is evidence on which the jury can find that the person charged was provoked (whether by things done or by things said or by both together) to lose his self-control, the question whether the provocation was enough to make a reasonable man do as he did shall be left to be determined by the jury; and in determining that question the jury shall take into account everything both done and said, according to the effect which, in their opinion, it would have on a reasonable man."

It will be noted that, if the jury consider (on a subjective basis) that there is evidence that the defendant was *actually* provoked, then the test of the degree of provocation is objective. The leading authority is *Camplin*[95]. The judge should explain to the jury that "the reasonable man" referred to is a person having the power of self-control to be expected of an ordinary person of the sex and age of the accused, but in other respects sharing such of the accused's characteristics as they think would affect the gravity of the provocation to him, and that the question is not merely whether such a person would, in like circumstances be provoked to lose his self-control, but would also react to the provocation as the accused did. Medical evidence may be admissible: see the New Zealand cases of *Takka*[96] and *Leilua*[97]. In *Ahluwalia*[98] a new trial was ordered in a case of murder, where there was a long history of domestic violence by the deceased towards his wife (the accused.) No medical evidence was called at the trial to show that the accused suffered from "battered woman syndrome" or post-traumatic stress disorder, but material before the Court of Appeal suggested there might be a *diminished*

94. At p. 35.
95. (1978)142 J.P. 320; [1978] A.C. 705.
96. [1978] 2 N.Z.L.R. 198 ("obsessively compulsive personality").
97. [1982] N.Z. Recent Law 118 (post-traumatic stress disorder).
98. 96 Cr App. R. 133.

responsibility defence, which had not been put before the jury.[99] In effect, however, the Court of Appeal left open the possibility that either of these conditions[100] *might* be relevant characteristics for the purposes of provocation.

The burden of proof to exclude provocation is upon the prosecution.

Forgetfulness

"Absentmindedness", simple inattention, or preoccupation, are not usually considered to be states of mind which can be the subject of criminal charges, since conscious criminal intent is absent. It may be otherwise, however, in the case of manslaughter charged upon the basis of gross negligence or in the case of any criminal offence which it is alleged was committed recklessly.

In *Clarke*[101] it was held that a momentary failure to concentrate was not within the *M'Naghten* Rules (see *post* at p. 36). The appellant was charged with theft from a shop; her defence was that she had put the goods into her bag without realizing what she was doing through absentmindedness during a period of depression.

Loss of memory after the commission of a criminal offence is never a defence in itself, if the defendant was conscious at the time: *Russell v. H.M. Advocate*[102] and *Podola*.[103]

Mistake

The case of *Morgan* (1975) 61 Cr. App. R. 136, H.L., was a case of rape. The principal defendant, M, had invited a number of other men to have intercourse with his wife, falsely telling them that she would put up a show of resistance, but would in fact be consenting. The trial Judge directed the jury that a defendant was not entitled to be acquitted on the grounds that he may have believed that the woman was consenting, unless the belief would also have been reasonable. A majority of the House of Lords held that this was wrong. Although the speeches of the majority differ from each other in certain aspects of their reasoning, the case is authority for the proposition that if the belief (in consent) was honestly

99. Cf. *Straw* [1995] 1 All E.R. 187 C.A. (Defendant at trial expressly refused to rely on defence of diminished responsibility; could *not* attempt to raise defence on appeal).
100. "battered woman syndrome" or post-traumatic stress disorder.
101. (1972) 136 J.P. 184; (1972) 56 Cr. App. R. 225.
102. 1946 S.C. (J) 37.
103. [1960] 1 Q.B. 325.

held it did not matter that it was not based upon reasonable grounds. If the defendant was or may have been labouring under a mistaken view of the facts, he must be judged according to his mistaken (but honest) view of the facts.

Infancy

Children under 10 cannot, in law, commit any criminal offence: s.50 of the Children and Young Persons Act 1933[104] provides that it shall be conclusively presumed that no child under the age of 10 can be guilty of any offence.

At common law a child under the age of 14 was formerly presumed to be incapable of doing wrong,[105] but this rebuttable presumption was recently held by the Divisional Court no longer to exist in English law.[106]

In the recent case of *A v. DPP* [1992] Crim. L.R. 34, the appellant was aged 11. He had been found guilty[107] of an offence contrary to s.5 of the Public Order Act 1986. He had been one of a gang of youths standing together in a street when a police vehicle passed. He was seen to throw a half brick and a quarter brick at the vehicle. He and others in the gang then ran away. The Justices found that the appellant was of normal size and development for his age. They also held that his action in running away enabled them to draw the inference that he was seeking to conceal himself and to avoid apprehension.

The appellant appealed against the finding of guilt on the ground that the prosecution had not rebutted the presumption of *doli incapax*. The prosecution relied upon the finding of the Justices with respect to his running away. The appeal was allowed and the finding of guilt was quashed on the following grounds:

(1)   The Justices were not entitled to conclude merely from the appellant's appearance that he was normal in the respects necessary in investigating his criminal responsibility.

(2)   The test was not knowledge of unlawfulness but whether the child knew what he was doing was so seriously wrong that it went beyond mere naughtiness or childish mischief.

(3)   The appellant's running away was not by itself sufficient to enable the Justices to find that the presumption in law had been

104. As amended by s.16(1) of the Children and Young Persons Act 1963.
105. Or *"doli incapax"*.
106. *C. (a minor) v. D.P.P.* (1994) 158 J.P. 389; [1994] 3 W.L.R. 888.
107. The term "finding of guilt" is used instead of "conviction" in the case of a juvenile.

rebutted: a naughty child would run away even if he was only guilty of non-criminal misconduct. In the absence of other evidence, for example of his upbringing, or of his reaction when seen by the police, the Justices could not justifiably have based their decision on that fact alone.

A boy under 14 was formerly conclusively presumed to be incapable of committing the offence of rape.[108] This presumption no longer exists by virtue of ss. 1 and 2 of the Criminal Justice Act 1993.

Once children have attained the age of 14 they are presumed by law to be capable of knowing right from wrong. Whilst they are subject to special treatment in terms of the criminal process, and are usually (although not exclusively) tried and sentenced in youth courts,[109] they may be, and frequently are, tried with adults in the magistrates' court, and may in certain circumstances be tried in the Crown Court. Special powers of sentence are provided for in the case of persons under the age of 21.

Sanity and Insanity

It is a presumption of law, in the absence of proof to the contrary, that every person is mentally sane.[110] "Mental" is derived from the Latin *mens* – "the mind" and "sane" is from *sanus*– "sound" or "healthy".[111]

The statistical significance of insanity as a "defence" to criminal charges generally may to some extent be gauged from the figures for suspects indicted for homicide by outcome of proceedings 1979-1989 in the *Criminal Statistics for England and Wales* (HMSO): in that period there were some 5,234 persons charged with murder, manslaughter or infanticide, of these 10 were found not guilty by reason of insanity, 19 were found unfit to plead, whereas 889 were found guilty of manslaughter on the ground of diminished responsibility.

Under the Mental Health Act 1983 "mental disorder" is defined and classified in four categories:

108. Despite the fact that since early Victorian times cases have occurred in which there has been evidence of post-pubertal 14-year-olds – see, for example, *Jordan* (1839) 9 C. & P. 118.
109. Formerly juvenile courts.
110. *R. v. Layton* 4 Cox C.C. 149, *M'Naghten's Case* (1843) 10 Cl. & Fin. 200, [1843-1860] All E.R. Reprint 229.
111. Thus, for example, Juvenal's *"Orandum est ut sit mens sana in corpore sano."* (Pray to have a sound mind in a sound body.) Satires, X, 356.
      The term *"mens sana"* may perhaps usefully be compared with the state of mind described above as being of primary relevance to the criminal law – *"mens rea"*.

(1)   mental illness;
(2)   arrested or incomplete development of mind;
(3)   psychopathic disorder
(4)   any other disorder or disability of mind.[112]

"Severe mental impairment", "mental impairment" and "psychopathic disorder" are also each defined in the Act,[113] but it is specifically provided that,"Nothing in subs. (2) [of s.1] shall be construed as implying that a person may be dealt with under this Act as suffering from mental disorder ... by reason only of promiscuity or other immoral conduct, sexual deviancy, or dependence upon alcohol or drugs."[114]

The terms "mental illness"[115] and "insanity", however, are *not* defined by the Act, and can only be interpreted in the context of the criminal law by reference to authorities such as *W v. L*[116] and *M'Naghten's Case.*[117]

The lawyer or the psychiatrist approaching the question of the state of mind of any person accused of crime, therefore, must continually bear in mind that the terminology of the criminal law in these matters is in many respects *sui generis* and not necessarily capable of direct importation into any other context, whether medical or legal.

The M'Naghten Rules

These rules derive from *M'Naghten's Case* (1843) 10 Cl. & Fin. 200, [1843-1860] All E.R. Reprint 229.[118]

Daniel M'Naghten was a native of Glasgow. For many years he had suffered from paranoid feelings – particularly against the Tory Party – which he considered to be conspiring with agents of the Catholic Church to persecute him. As a result, he eventually decided to kill the Tory leader

112. Mental Health Act 1983, s. 1(2).
113. *Ibid.*
114. Section 1(3).
115. But see *W. v. L. (mental health patient)* [1974] Q.B. 711, [1973] 3 All E.R. 884, during the course of the hearing of which the Court of Appeal were invited to consider the *Report of the Royal Commission on the Law Relating to Mental Illness and Mental Deficiency* (1957) Cmnd. 169. Lawton L.J. commented that the absence of any recommendation for a definition of "mental disorder' in the Mental Health Act 1959 "which would meet the requirements of doctors", seemed to have been an oversight on the part of the Commission.
116. *Ante.*
117. *Below.*
118. *Sub nom. M'Naghten's Case.* See also 4 State Trials (N.S.) 847; 1 Town St. Tr. 314; 1 Carr. & Kir. 130. n.; *sub nom. Insane Criminals* 8 Scott, N.R. 595, H.L.; 14 Digest (Repl.) 61.

and Prime Minister, Sir Robert Peel. He made careful preparations for the attack, but mistook Peel's secretary, Edward Drummond, for the Prime Minister, and shot him dead by mistake. He was tried for Drummond's murder, and acquitted on the ground of insanity.

The verdict caused debates to take place in the House of Lords, and it was decided to take the opinion of the Judges as to the nature and extent of the unsoundness of mind which would excuse the commission of a crime of this kind.[119]

The opinion of the Judges[120] was given by Lord Tindal, C.J.:

> "The first question proposed by your Lordships is this: What is the law respecting alleged crimes committed by persons afflicted with insane delusion in respect of one or more particular subjects or persons: as, for instance, where at the time of the commission of the alleged crime the accused knew he was acting contrary to law, but did the act complained of with a view, under the influence of insane delusion, of redressing or revenging some supposed grievance or injury, or of producing some supposed public benefit?
>
> In answer to which question,... [in respect of] those persons who labour under such partial delusions only, and are not in other respects insane, we are of opinion that, notwithstanding the party accused did the act complained of with [the view described in the question] he is nevertheless punishable according to the nature of the crime committed, if he knew at the time of committing such crime that he was acting contrary to law ...
>
> Your Lordships are pleased to inquire of us, secondly, 'What are the proper questions to be submitted to the jury where a person alleged to be afflicted with insane delusion respecting one or more particular subjects or persons is charged with the commission of a crime (murder, for example), and insanity is set up as a defence?' And, thirdly, 'In what terms ought the question to be left to the jury as to the prisoner's state of mind at the time when the act was committed?' And as these two questions appear to us to be more

119. In the circumstances, the rules themselves do not derive from a *judicial* decision of the House of Lords. In that sense, according to the strict doctrine of precedent in English law, the Rules are not binding authority. However, they have been recognized in many subsequent judicial decisions as correctly representing the law – as recently as *Burgess* [infra] [1991] 2WLR 1206.

120. Except that of Maule, J.

conveniently answered together, we have to submit our opinion to be, that the jurors ought to be told in all cases that every man is presumed to be sane, and to possess a sufficient degree of reason to be responsible for his crimes, until the contrary be proved to their satisfaction; and that to establish a defence on the ground of insanity, it must be clearly proved that, at the time of committing the act, the party accused was labouring under such a defect of reason, from disease of the mind, as not to know the nature and quality of the act he was doing; or if he did know it, that he did not know that what he was doing was wrong ... If the accused was conscious that the act was one which he ought not to do, and if that act was at the same time contrary to the law of the land, he is punishable; and the usual course therefore has been to leave the question to the jury, whether the party accused has a sufficient degree of reason to know that he was doing an act that was wrong: and this course we think is correct, accompanied with such observations and explanations as the circumstances of each particular case may require.

The fourth question ... is this: 'If a person under an insane delusion as to existing facts, commits an offence in consequence thereof, is he excused?' To which question the answer must depend on the nature of the delusion: ... [if] he labours under partial delusion only, and is not in other respects insane, we think he must be considered in the same situation as to responsibility as if the facts with respect to which the delusion exists were real. For example, if under the influence of delusion he supposes another man to be in the act of attempting to take away his life, and he kills that man, as he supposes, in self-defence, he would be exempt from punishment. If his delusion was that the deceased had inflicted a serious injury to his character and fortune, and he killed him in revenge for such supposed injury, he would be liable to punishment.

The [last] question ... is: 'Can a medical man conversant with the disease of insanity, who never saw the prisoner previously to the trial but who was present during the whole trial ..., be asked his opinion as to the state of the prisoner's mind at the time of the commission of the alleged crime, or his opinion whether the prisoner was conscious at the time of doing the act that he was acting contrary to law, or whether he was labouring under any, and what delusion at the time?' In answer thereto, we state to your Lordships that we think the medical man under the circumstances supposed, cannot in strictness be asked his opinion in the terms above stated, because each of those questions involves the determination of the truth of the facts deposed to, which it is for the jury to decide, and the questions are not mere questions upon a matter of science, in which case such evidence is admissible. But where the facts are admitted or not disputed, and the question becomes substantially one of science only, it may be convenient to allow the question to be put in that general form, though the same cannot be insisted upon as a matter of right."

The most recently reported judicial consideration of the *M'Naghten* Rules is to be found in the case of *Burgess*[121]. It deals so comprehensively with both the legal and medical issues involved in *M'Naghten* insanity and in "insane automatism" that it is necessary to give an extensive citation from the judgment of the Court of Appeal. The defendant was tried on a count of wounding with intent. His defence was that he lacked the necessary intent, in that, during undisputed violence to the victim, he was sleep-walking and suffering from non-insane automatism.

The background to the incident was that the complainant occupied the flat immediately above that of the defendant. They were on friendly terms. They were in the habit of watching video films together in her flat. She realised that the defendant was probably fond of her. She did not wish to allow their relationship to develop beyond mere friendship. The defendant was then 32 years of age. He was sexually inexperienced and of a somewhat solitary disposition. He always behaved impeccably towards her and had made no physical advances. He had hopes that her friendship towards him might develop into something deeper.

On the evening in question the defendant came up to her flat with some video tapes. They had one glass of Martini each. There was no suggestion of any intoxication. Having watched one video tape, she fell asleep on the sofa. The next thing she knew was that something hard had hit her on the head. She woke up, dazed, to find herself surrounded by glass from a broken bottle and confronted by the defendant who was holding the video recorder up high, clearly intending to bring it down on her head, which he did. He was speaking loudly. He seemed vicious and angry, which was quite out of character. She fell to the floor, whereupon he put a hand round her throat. She said that she loved him, whereupon he appeared to come to his senses and to show great anxiety for what he had done. He later

121. [1991] 2 W.L.R. 1206.

telephoned for an ambulance.

He gave evidence at the trial. He said he was not conscious of bottling up or repressing his feelings for the complainant. He, like her, had fallen asleep. He remembered waking up, coming into focus and feeling confused. It then dawned on him that he was holding the complainant down on the floor. He had no memory of hitting her at all, either with the bottle or with the video recorder. He had run away after the incident and had driven round the countryside. During that period he wrote three letters to her, stating that he did not know what he was doing when he attacked her. He must have had a black-out. He did not wish to continue living.

Expert medical evidence was called by the prosecution and the defence. The Judge, on the assumption that the defendant was unconscious at the time of his acts, ruled that the medical evidence adduced concerning automatism amounted to evidence of insanity within the *M'Naghten* Rules and was not merely evidence of non-insane automatism. The jury found the defendant not guilty by reason of insanity. The defendant appealed.

It was held, dismissing the appeal, that on a defence of automatism the Judge had to decide, first, whether a proper evidential foundation had been laid for the defence and, secondly, whether the evidence showed the case to be one of insane automatism within the *M'Naghten* Rules, or one of non-insane automatism. The Judge had undertaken that task and, in the light of the medical evidence, had been right to conclude that the defendant's state was an abnormality or disorder which, albeit transitory and unlikely to recur in the form of serious violence, was due to an internal factor which, whether functional or organic, had manifested itself in violence and might recur. It therefore amounted to a "disease of the mind;" and the Judge's ruling had been correct.

The court added that a danger of recurrence of a mental disorder manifesting itself in violence may be an added reason for categorising the condition as a disease of the mind but the absence of such danger was not a reason for saying that it could not be a disease of the mind and that there was an apparent incongruity in labelling such a disability as insanity.

The reason for the finding of not guilty in these circumstances was the absence of the intent which must be proved to accompany the defendant's actions before guilt can be established. What the law regards as insanity for the purpose of these enactments may be far removed from what would be regarded as insanity by a psychiatrist.

There could be no doubt but that the defendant, on the basis of the jury's verdict, was labouring under such a defect of reason as not to know what he was doing when he wounded the complainant. The question was whether that was from "disease of the mind."

The first point which had to be understood was that the phrase was "disease of the mind" and not "disease of the brain." Devlin J. said in *Kemp*[122]:

"The law is not concerned with the brain but with the mind in the sense that 'mind' is ordinarily used, the mental faculties of reason, memory and understanding. If one read for 'disease of the mind' 'disease of the brain,' it would follow that in many cases pleas of insanity would not be established because it could not be proved that the brain had been affected in any way, either by degeneration of the cells or in any other way. In my judgment the condition of the brain is irrelevant and so is the question of whether the condition of the mind is curable or incurable, transitory or permanent. There is no warranty for introducing those considerations into the definition in the *M'Naghten* Rules. Temporary insanity is sufficient to satisfy them. It does not matter whether it is incurable and permanent or not."

The defendant plainly suffered from a defect of reason from some sort of failure (for lack of a better term) of the mind causing him to act as he did without conscious motivation. His mind was to some extent controlling his actions which were purposive rather than the result simply of muscular spasm, but without his being consciously aware of what he was doing.

On this aspect of the case the Court of Appeal approved what was said by Martin J. and approved by a majority in the Supreme Court of Canada in *Rabey v. The Queen*[123] (where the facts bore a similarity to those in the instant case although the diagnosis was different):

"Any malfunctioning of the mind or mental disorder having its source primarily in some subjective condition or weakness internal to the accused (whether fully understood or not) may be a 'disease of the mind' if it prevents the accused from knowing what he is doing, but transient disturbances of consciousness due to certain specific external

122. [1957] 1 Q.B. 399, 407.
123. [1980] 2 S.C.R. 513, 519, 520.

factors do not fall within the concept of disease of the mind ... In my view, the ordinary stresses and disappointments of life which are the common lot of mankind do not constitute an external cause constituting an explanation for a malfunctioning of the mind which takes it out of the category of a 'disease of the mind.' To hold otherwise would deprive the concept of an external factor of any real meaning."

The distinction between "internal" and "external" factors appeared in the speech of Lord Diplock in *Sullivan*, where he said, at p.172:[124]

"I agree with what was said by Devlin J. in *Kemp*[125], that 'mind' in the *M'Naghten* Rules is used in the ordinary sense of the mental faculties of reason, memory and understanding. If the effect of a disease is to impair these faculties so severely as to have either of the consequences referred to in the latter part of the rules, it matters not whether the aetiology of the impairment is organic, as in epilepsy, or functional, or whether the impairment itself is permanent or is transient and intermittent, provided that it subsisted at the time of commission of the act. The purpose of the legislation relating to the defence of insanity, ever since its origin in 1800, has been to protect society against recurrence of the dangerous conduct. The duration of a temporary suspension of the mental faculties of reason, memory and understanding, particularly if, as in Mr. Sullivan's case, it is recurrent, cannot on any rational ground be relevant to the application by the courts of the *M'Naghten* Rules, though it may be relevant to the course adopted by the Secretary of State, to whom the responsibility for how the defendant is to be dealt with passes after the return of the special verdict of 'not guilty by reason of insanity.'

Lord Denning in *Bratty v. Attorney-General for Northern Ireland*[126] said:

"Upon the other point discussed by Devlin J., namely, what is a 'disease of the mind' within the *M'Naghten* Rules, I would agree with him that this is a question for the judge. The major mental diseases, which the doctors call psychoses, such as schizophrenia, are clearly

124. (1984) 148 J.P. 207.
125. [1957] 1 Q.B. 399, 407.
126. [1963] A.C. 386, 412.
127. (1955) 119 J.P. 283.

diseases of the mind. But in *Charlson's* case[127], Barry J. seems to have assumed that other diseases such as epilepsy or cerebral tumour are not diseases of the mind, even when they are such as to manifest themselves in violence. I do not agree with this. It seems to me that any mental disorder which has manifested itself in violence and is prone to recur is a disease of the mind. At any rate it is the sort of disease for which a person should be detained in hospital rather than be given an unqualified acquittal."

If there were a danger of recurrence that might be an added reason for categorizing the condition as a disease of the mind. On the other hand, the absence of the danger of recurrence would not be a reason for saying that it could not be a disease of the mind. Subject to that possible qualification, Lord Denning's suggested definition was adopted in *Burgess.*

Sleep was a normal condition, but the evidence indicated that sleep-walking, and particularly violence in sleep, was not normal. On the evidence[128], the Judge was right to conclude that this was an abnormality or disorder, albeit transitory, due to an internal factor, whether functional or organic, which had manifested itself in violence. It was a disorder or abnormality which might recur, though the possibility of it recurring in the form of serious violence was unlikely. Therefore since this was a legal problem to be decided on legal principles, on those principles the answer

128. The evidence of two medical experts called by the defence was that Mr. Burgess's actions had occurred during the course of "a sleep disorder."

The first was asked,

"Assuming this is a sleep associated automatism, is it an internal or external factor?" Answer: "In this particular case, I think that one would have to see it as an internal factor."

Then in cross-examination:

Question: "Would you go so far as to say that it was liable to recur?" Answer: "It is possible for it to recur, yes."

Finally, in answer to a question from the judge, namely, "Is this a case of automatism associated with a pathological condition or not?" Answer: "I think the answer would have to be yes, because it is an abnormality of the brain function, so it would be regarded as a pathological condition."

The second expert agreed with the first as to the internal rather than the external factor. He accepted that there is a liability to recurrence of sleep walking. He could not go so far as to say that there is no liability of recurrence of serious violence but he agreed with the other medical witnesses that there is no recorded case of violence of this sort recurring.

was as the Judge found it to be. It does however go further than that. One of the psychiatrists stated that the condition would be regarded as pathological. Pathology was the science of diseases. It seemed therefore that in this respect at least there is some similarity between the law and medicine.

The Judge was alive to the apparent incongruity of labelling this aspect of disability as insanity. He drew attention to a passage in the speech of Lord Diplock in *Sullivan*, a case which is considered in detail immediately below:

"... it is natural to feel reluctant to attach the label of insanity to a sufferer from psychomotor epilepsy of the kind to which Mr. Sullivan was subject, even though the expression in the context of a special verdict of 'not guilty by reason of insanity' is a technical one which includes a purely temporary and intermittent suspension of the mental faculties of reason, memory and understanding resulting from the occurrence of an epileptic fit. But the label is contained in the current statute, it has appeared in this statute's predecessors ever since 1800. It does not lie within the power of the courts to alter it. Only Parliament can do that. It has done so twice; it could do so once again."

Epilepsy

The law as to epilepsy was explained in the decision of the House of Lords

The prosecution's expert said that this was not a sleep walking episode at all. If it was a case where the appellant was unconscious of what he was doing, the most likely explanation was that he was in what is described as an hysterical dissociative state. That is a state in which, for psychological reasons, such as being overwhelmed by his emotions, the person's brain works in a different way. He carries out acts of which he has no knowledge and for which he has no memory. It is quite different from sleep walking. He then went on to describe features of sleep walking. He said:

"Firstly, violent acts in sleep walking are very common. In just an exposure of one day to a sleep walking clinic, you will hear of how people are kicked in bed, hit in bed, partially strangled – it is usually just arms round the neck, in bed, which is very common. Serious violence fortunately is rare. Serious violence does recur, or certainly the propensity for it to recur is there, although there are very few cases in the literature – in fact I know of none – in which somebody has come to court twice for a sleep walking offence. This does not mean that sleep walking violence does not recur; what it does mean is that those who are associated with the sleeper take the necessary precautions. Finally, should a person be detained in hospital? The answer to that is: Yes, because sleep walking is treatable. Violent night terrors are treatable. There is a lot which can be done for the sleep walker, so sending them to hospital after a violent act to have their sleep walking sorted out, makes good sense."

in *Sullivan* (1984) 148 J.P. 207. The facts of that case were that the defendant, who was "a man of blameless reputation",[129] was a life-long epileptic. Pharmacological therapy had reduced the severity of his attacks to *petit mal*, or psychomotor epilepsy, but he continued to suffer one or two attacks each week. On a day in May 1981 he visited an old lady "for whom he was accustomed to perform regular acts of kindness"[130] and was talking to her and to another friend, a man of 80, when he had an epileptic fit. In the course of this fit he attacked the old man by kicking him about the head and body, causing injuries which required treatment at hospital.

The defendant was charged with causing grievous bodily harm with intent, and alternatively with unlawfully inflicting grievous bodily harm. The defendant gave evidence. He described his history of epilepsy, and said that he had no memory of any of the material events. He did not dispute the evidence for the prosecution (which came from the old lady), and the prosecution did not cross-examine the defendant: his evidence was accepted as true.

The medical evidence in the case on behalf of the defendant was given by two specialists from the neuropsychiatry epilepsy unit at the Maudsley Hospital. Their undisputed evidence was that the appellant's acts in kicking the old man had all the characteristics of epileptic automatism at the third, or post-ictal, stage of *petit mal*, and that, in view of his history of psychomotor epilepsy and the hospital records of his behaviour during previous seizures, the strong probability was that the appellant's acts of violence towards the victim took place while he was going through that stage.

The evidence given of the pathology of a seizure due to psychomotor epilepsy was that after the first stage, the prodram, which preceded the fit itself, there was a second stage, the ictus, lasting a few seconds, during which electrical discharges into the temporal lobes of the brain occurred. The effect of these discharges would have caused the sufferer in the post-ictal stage to make movements of which he was not conscious, including, (and this was a characteristic of previous seizures which the appellant had suffered) automatic movements of resistance to anyone trying to come to his aid. These movements of resistance might, very rarely, involve violence.

---

129. Per Lord Diplock, who gave the leading speech.
130. *Ibid.*

At the conclusion of the evidence, the Judge was asked to rule whether the jury should be directed that if they accepted this evidence it would not be open to them to bring a verdict of not guilty, but they would be bound in law to return a special verdict of not guilty by reason of insanity. The Judge ruled that the jury should be so directed.

After this ruling the appellant, on the advice of his counsel, changed his plea to guilty to assault occasioning actual bodily harm (a plea which was accepted by the prosecution). The jury, on the direction of the Judge, brought in a verdict of guilty of the offence for which the Judge sentenced him to three years' probation, subject to the condition that during that period he submitted to treatment at the Maudsley Hospital.

The Court of Appeal upheld the Judge's ruling. It dismissed the appeal but certified that a point of law of general public importance was involved in the decision, namely:

> "Whether a person who is proved to have occasioned, contrary to s.47 of the Offences Against the Person Act 1861, actual bodily harm to another, whilst recovering from a seizure due to psychomotor epilepsy, and who did not know what he was doing when he caused such harm, and has no memory of what he did, should be found not guilty by reason of insanity."

In the course of the leading speech in the House of Lords, Lord Diplock, after referring to *M'Naghten's Case*,[131] went on to deal with the case of *Bratty*.[132] In that case the appellant was convicted of the murder of a girl by strangulation. He claimed to have been unconscious of what he was doing at the time, and put forward alternative defences of "non-insane automatism" and insanity. The only evidence to support either defence was medical evidence that he might be suffering from psychomotor epilepsy. No other pathological explanation was given to show that his actions might have been carried out by him when acting (as claimed) as an automaton. The trial Judge first put the defence of insanity to the jury. They rejected it, refusing to bring in the special verdict. The Judge then refused to put the alternative defence of automatism. His decision was upheld by the Court of Criminal Appeal for Northern Ireland and the House of Lords, upon the basis that the jury having rejected the explanation that Bratty might have been acting unconsciously whilst undergoing an

131. (1843) 10 Cl. & Fin. 200, *supra*.
132. *Bratty v. A-G for Northern Ireland* [1963] A.C. 386; [1961] 3 W.L.R. 965; [1961] 3 All E.R. 523, H.L.

attack of psychomotor epilepsy, there was no evidence to support the suggestion that he was acting unconsciously from any other cause.

In *Bratty*'s case the doctors all agreed that psychomotor epilepsy was a "disease of the mind". In *Sullivan*'s case, 20 years later, the effect of all the medical evidence was said to be that epilepsy was not a disease of the mind. The House of Lords considered that the question of whether the aetiology of the impairment undoubtedly caused by epilepsy was organic or functional was unimportant; the purpose of the defence of insanity was to protect society against the recurrence of dangerous conduct. Therefore, if the consequence of an epileptic fit was that the sufferer's mental faculties of reason, memory and understanding were temporarily suspended, during the course of which time an offence was committed, the appropriate verdict was not guilty by reason of insanity.[133]

Automatism Generally

Whilst this condition is often divided by lawyers into two categories: "insane automatism" and "non-insane automatism" separate consideration here need only be given to the latter category. If insanity is the cause of the automatic act, the case falls to be dealt with under the law relating to insanity generally.[134] In *Kemp*[135] the accused was charged with causing grievous bodily harm to his wife. It was common ground that he hit her over the head with a hammer without any apparent motive, and that at the time he was unaware of the nature and quality of his act. There was evidence that the accused was suffering from arteriosclerosis which interfered with the flow of blood to his brain. The sole issue was whether the accused was suffering from a disease of the mind, in which case the proper verdict would (then) have been "guilty but insane" or whether the disease was not a disease of the mind in which case the verdict should be not guilty. In the course of his summing-up Devlin, J., said:

"The hardening of the arteries is a disease which is shown on the evidence to be capable of affecting the mind in such a way as to cause a defect, temproarily or permanently, of its reasoning and understanding, and is thus a disease of the mind within the meaning of the rule [in *M'Naghten's Case*]."

133. See also *Smith* (1922) 5 Cr. App. R. 10; *True* (1922) 16 Cr. App. R. 164; *Windle* (1952) 116 J.P. 365.
134 see *Burgess* [supra p. 39 *et seq*].
135. [1956] 3 All E.R. 249.

The defendant was found guilty but insane.

In *Clarke*[136] it was held that a momentary failure to concentrate was not within the *M'Naghten* Rules (appellant charged with theft from a shop; her defence was that she had put the goods into her bag without realizing what she was doing through absentmindedness during a period of depression).

In *Smith*[137] the defendant was charged with the murder of a man who had entered his bedroom whilst the defendant was asleep. At trial his defence was that he had attacked the deceased whilst "asleep", i.e. when not conscious of doing so. Psychiatrists who saw the defendant in prison on remand reported that his responsibility for the killing was substantially impaired, but the defendant pleaded neither insanity nor diminished responsibility. The prosecution obtained leave to cross-examine the defendant upon certain statements which he had made to the psychiatrists, which the prosecution said were inconsistent with the "sleepwalking" defence.

The Judge also allowed the prosecution to call psychiatrists in rebuttal of what the defendant was saying (i.e. that he had killed the deceased while asleep); the psychiatrists said that the defendant's account was not physically possible. The defendant applied for leave to appeal, contending, *inter alia*, that the psychiatrists' evidence should not have been admitted, because the issue of whether the killing was done in a state of automatism was for the jury to decide in the light of their own experience, without medical assistance and the psychiatrists' evidence was irrelevant to that issue.

Dismissing the application on this and other grounds, the Court of Appeal held that automatism was an abnormal medical condition, which was not within an ordinary juryman's experience, and a jury was therefore entitled to expert help when automatism was pleaded. It followed that the jury was entitled to the benefit of the psychiatrists' evidence in deciding whether the applicant had committed the killing in a state of automatism.

In *Budd*[138] the appellant was convicted of dangerous driving. When he was stopped it was evident both that he had been drinking and had been involved in a road accident. His defence was that at the time of the dangerous driving he was in a state of automatism as a result of

136. *Op. cit.* n. 101.
137. [1979] 1 W.L.R. 1445; [1979] 3 All E.R. 605.
138. [1962] Crim. L.R. 49.

concussion suffered in the road accident. His appeal against conviction was allowed, the Judge having directed the jury that it was for the appellant to show on the balance of probabilities that he was driving "in this automatic state". The Court of Criminal Appeal held that *Bratty* had established that no burden of proof rested upon the defence to establish automatism. Further, the court accepted that "a proper foundation"[139] had been laid for consideration of the defence, so that the conviction of dangerous driving should be quashed.

A thorough review of the subject of non-insane automatism, and a detailed treatment of many important Commonwealth authorities, is to be found in an article by R. D. Mackay "Non-Organic Automatism – Some Recent Developments" at [1980] Crim. L.R. 350.

Diabetes

In the case of *Bingham* [1991] Crim. L.R. 433, B, a diabetic, was arrested for shop-lifting. He had taken a can of coca-cola and a packet of sandwiches, together worth £1.16, at a time when he had £90 in his pocket. He had paid for one can of coke, and was stopped on leaving the store. He replied to questions by saying "no comment". His defence was automatism, based on the claim that, at the time, he was suffering from hypoglycaemia (low blood sugar) and was unaware of his actions. The Judge refused to leave the defence to the jury.

On appeal it was held, allowing the appeal, that the arguments submitted to the Judge failed to distinguish between hyperglycaemia and hypoglycaemia, the former being too much sugar in the blood, and the latter too little. On the evidence, it was conceivable that hyperglycaemia might raise difficult problems in respect of the *M'Naghten* Rules, and might result in verdicts of not guilty by reason of insanity. Hypoglycaemia was not caused by the initial disease of diabetes, but by the treatment in the form of too much insulin, or by insufficient quality or quantity of food to counter-balance the insulin. Generally speaking, that would not give rise to a verdict of not guilty by reason of insanity but would, if it was established and showed that the necessary intent was or might be lacking, provide a satisfactory defence to an alleged crime, such as theft, due to lack of *mens rea*. "Those simple facts would be plain to anyone who

139. There is a nice distinction between the laying of a foundation for a defence and the burden of proving a defence. It may be that a foundation is laid if the defence put forward a sufficiently adequate suggestion of a defence as to amount to more than a fanciful doubt: compare the raising of the issue of self-defence in an assault case.

troubled to read *Quick*[140] and *Hennessy*[141]. In the present case, the problem was hypoglycaemia and the Judge had to decide whether, on the evidence, there was a *prima facie* case for the jury to decide whether B was suffering from its effects and, if so, whether the Crown had shown that he had the necessary intent under the Theft Act.

It was not doubted that B was a diabetic and there was evidence that he might have been suffering from the effects of a low blood-sugar level at the relevant time.[142] There was therefore some evidence to support his defence, although the jury might well have dismissed it as insufficient. It was not for the Court of Appeal to decide whether the jury would have thought the evidence to be impressive. It should have been left to them and the failure so to do was a material irregularity.[143]

See also *Bailey*,[144] *Martin*,[145] *Bentley*,[146] and *Watmore v. Jenkins*.[147]

---

140. (1973) 147 J.P. 763.
141. [1989] 1 W.L.R. 287.
142. (1) A witness had observed that "his eyes were not behaving normally", (which she had attributed to the fact that he was shop-lifting as shop-lifters tended to look around before stealing). (2) His behaviour in answering "no comment" was strange. Further, when it was suggested to him that if he gave his name and address the police would not be called and he, presumably, would escape with a caution, he did not take advantage of the offer which, in a perfectly intelligent man, seemed a very strange thing. Against that was his failure to tell the police doctor that he was suffering from a hypoglycaemic attack, which he explained at the trial on the basis that he feared it would prolong his arrest.
143. The commentary which follows the report of *Bingham* [supra] in the *Criminal Law Review* is by Professor Smith. His observation is that if a person was in a state of automatism at the time of the alleged offence, he cannot be guilty of the offence. The only question is whether he is to be found simply not guilty or not guilty by reason of insanity. The outcome depends on how the automatism was caused. If it was caused by an "external factor", the verdict will simply be not guilty, if by an "internal factor", not guilty by reason of insanity. Diabetes is obviously an internal factor; so if the diabetes results in hyperglycaemia which causes automatism the defendant is "insane" within the meaning of the M'Naghten Rules. The administration of insulin is an external factor and, if it results in hypoglycaemia which causes automatism, the defendant is simply not guilty. It is as if the automatism had been caused by an accidental blow on the head.
144. (1983) 147 J.P. 558.
145. *The Times*, 25th October, 1957.
146. [1960] Crim. L.R. 777.
147. (1962) 126 J.P. 432.

Diminished Responsibility

Background

The defence of diminished responsibility was introduced into the law of England and Wales by the Homicide Act 1957. Whilst this statute abolished the death penalty for certain types of murder, it specifically provided for capital punishment in five specific sets of circumstances (e.g. murder by shooting)[148]. The Act was passed some seven years before the Murder (Abolition of Death Penalty) Act 1965 effectively did away with the death penalty for murder altogether.[149]

Diminished responsibility was a concept which had developed in Scottish case-law, and was described by the Royal Commission on Capital Punishment in their report in 1953[150] as being similar to provocation in that,

"... it is a device to enable the courts to take account of a special category of mitigating circumstances in cases of murder and to avoid passing sentence of death in cases where such circumstances exist.[151]"

It is of importance to remember, when considering the authorities set out below, that in those cases decided between 1957 and 1965 the life of the appellant, and the lives of other persons charged with capital murder in similar circumstances, might depend upon the result of the court's construction of the statutory words.[152]

It may very well be that the legal and medical difficulties which have bedevilled the interpretation of the concept of diminished responsibility from the outset can be largely explained by the perceptive description of it by the Royal Commission as "a device". But it is to be noted that Major

148. By s. 5 it was provided that the following were capital murders:
   (a) any murder done in the course or furtherance of theft;
   (b) any murder done by shooting or causing an explosion;
   (c) any murder done in resisting or preventing arrest or in escaping from custody;
   (d) murder of a police officer doing his duty, or anyone assisting him;
   (e) murder of a prison officer by a prisoner.
149. The Murder (Abolition of Death Penalty) Act 1965 provided for the suspension of the death penalty from 1965 to 1970 when abolition was confirmed.
150. Report of the Royal Commission on Capital Punishment 1953.
151. *Ibid.*, p.144.
152. In *Matheson* [1958] 1 W.L.R. 474 *Walden* [1959] 1 W.L.R. 1008, *Spriggs* [1958] 1 Q.B. 270; [1958] 2 W.L.R. 162; 1 All E.R. 300 and *Dunbar* [1958] 1 Q.B. 1; [1957] 3 W.L.R. 330; 2 All E.R. 737, for example, the defendants were each sentenced to death. Matheson and Dunbar succeeded in appealing against conviction (and therefore sentence); Walden and Spriggs did not.

Lloyd George, in speaking for the Government in the Commons upon the Bill, said that the provisions were not intended,

> "to provide a defence to persons who are merely hot-tempered, or who, otherwise normal, commit murder in a sudden excess of rage or jealousy."[153]

The Statutory Provisions

By s. 2(1) of the Homicide Act 1957 it is provided that:

> "Where a person kills ... he shall not be convicted of murder if he was suffering from such abnormality of mind (whether arising from a condition of arrested or retarded development of mind or any inherent causes or induced by disease or injury) as substantially impaired his mental responsibility for his acts and omissions in doing or being a party to the killing."

Sub-section (2) provides that:

> "On a charge of murder, it shall be for the defence to prove that the person charged is by virtue of this section not liable to be convicted of murder."

Fundamental Questions

There are two basic questions which must be answered if the defence of diminished responsibility is to be raised.

(1) Is there evidence of the existence of abnormality of mind at the time of the killing which can be shown to have arisen from (i) a condition of arrested or retarded development; *or* (ii) through any inherent causes; *or* (iii) by having been induced by disease or injury? If so, then, (2) Did that abnormality of mind substantially impair the defendant's responsibility for (his or her part in) the killing?

Before embarking upon more detailed consideration of these ingredients by reference to cases in which the section has been judicially considered, it is important to note that in England and Wales diminished responsibility is a defence which can only be raised in cases where the defendant is charged with murder.[154] Even if it is raised successfully, its effect can only be to render the defendant not guilty of murder but guilty of manslaughter.

153. *Hansard*, H.C. Debates, Vol. 560 Col. 1154.
154. Homicide Act 1957, s. 2(3). It cannot, for example, be raised as a defence to attempted murder.

Secondly, it is clear that although the two may in many cases coincide in fact, in law there is little significant relationship between the concepts of insanity and diminished responsibility: see, for example, *Rose v. R.*[155] and *Seers*.[156]

Burden and Standard of Proof

The first reported decision upon diminished responsibility under the 1957 Act was a capital case, *Dunbar*.[157] It turned solely upon the question of the burden and standard of proof where diminished responsibility was alleged. In summing up to the jury the Judge had said:

"Something has been said about the balance of probabilities and about the burden of proof and about doubt, and so on. I prefer to leave you with the simple words of the Act of Parliament, '... it shall be for the defence to prove... ; and if it does not, the defence goes'."[158]

The Court of Criminal Appeal held that the Judge had failed to make it clear to the jury that in discharging the burden of proof upon the defence in respect of this single issue, a lower standard was required than that demanded of the prosecution throughout a criminal trial: i.e. the defence need only show diminished responsibility on the balance of probabilities, not beyond reasonable doubt.[159] See also *Grant*.[160]

Abnormality of Mind at the Time of The Killing

It would hardly be controversial to suggest that the state of mind of any person who kills another (otherwise than inadvertently and accidentally) is likely to be abnormal at the time of the killing. However, the section

---

155. (1962) Cr. App. R. 105.
156. [1985] Crim. L.R. 315. Note the commentary upon the report of this case by Professor Smith at p. 316.
157. [1958] 1 Q.B. 1; [1957] 3 W.L.R. 330; 2 All E.R. 737.
158. At [1957] 3 W.L.R. 334.
159. The Solicitor-General, when clause 2 of the Homicide Bill was being debated in the House of Commons, had said that sub-section (2) (which makes no express reference to the standard of proof) was appropriately worded, as it was not the Government's intention to impose any more than proof upon the balance of probabilities. There was "the plainest possible authority" (*Carr-Briant* [1943] K.B. 607) that the word "prove" in relation to "a defence onus" meant no more than that: see *Hansard*, H.C. Debates, Vol. 561, Cols. 456-457.
160. [1960] Crim. L.R. 424.

requires proof by the defence that the abnormal state of mind which is relied upon as constituting a state of diminished responsibility, arises from one of the particular causes specified in the Act; nothing else will do.

Those particular causes are: (i) arrested or retarded development; *or* (ii) any "inherent causes"; *or* (iii) induction by disease *or* injury.

It is clear that the defence will not be permitted to suggest to the jury that anything may be assumed or inferred from the circumstances alone. If diminished responsibility is to be considered, the jury must be satisfied by evidence given on behalf of the defence.

No Obligation to Give Evidence Upon Defendant Personally

In *Bathurst*[161] the defendant did not himself give evidence, although medical evidence was called on his behalf in support of the assertion of diminished responsibility. He was an intelligent man who had become infatuated with a young woman "half his age" and had lived with her for over three years. When she left him for another man, he bought a knife, went to the other man's house, asked to speak to her alone, and stabbed her in the heart. He was found in great distress kneeling at the side of the dying girl. He called two psychiatrists who gave evidence that he was suffering from reactive depression, which they said was a mental illness which substantially impaired his responsibility. The prosecution called two psychiatrists who said that in their view the depression was not of such a degree as to be described as a mental illness. The defendant was unanimously convicted of murder by the jury after a retirement of only 25 minutes.

Leave to appeal was granted only because of the "strong comment" of the Judge (Melford Stevenson J.) upon the defendant's failure to give evidence "even in relation to a matter where there is a burden of proof on him." Allowing the appeal, the Court of Appeal held that although there might be cases of diminished responsibility in which a defendant "ought" to go into the witness box, the cases in which comment upon his failure to do so might be made would be very rare.

Indeed, Lord Parker C.J. said:

"... almost in every case counsel defending a prisoner raising this defence would prevent him, if he could, from going into the witness box; and I think that the experience of all practising barristers would

161. [1968] 1 All E.R. 1175.

be the same. The accused may be suffering from delusions, he may be on the border of insanity; it would be the last thing that any counsel would do to allow his client into the witness box, and in those cases ... any comment upon his failure to do so would be clearly unfair."[162]

There was, the court held, no real challenge to the truthfulness of the defendant in giving information to the medical experts, and the Judge's comments were unfair. Substituting a conviction for manslaughter, the court observed that where comment was justified in such a case, it might properly take the form that if a defendant fails to go into the witness box to discharge the burden upon him (i.e. presumably where his truthfulness to the doctors *is* challenged) and thus fails to prove facts to support a medical opinion, he runs the risk of not being able to show diminished responsibility.

Medical Evidence
In *Bailey*[163] the 17 year-old defendant, having met a girl for the first time, for no apparent reason brutally battered her to death with an iron bar. Three doctors gave evidence to support his defence of diminished responsibility. They agreed that the defendant was suffering from an abnormality of mind at the time of the offence induced by epilepsy, and that this caused his mental responsibility to be significantly impaired. In summing up, the Judge reminded the jury of the importance of the medical evidence but also pointed out that the opinions of the doctors were not binding on them. The jury unexpectedly returned a verdict of guilty of murder.

On appeal the court held that the jury had acted unreasonably in returning a verdict which could not be supported by the evidence. There was no evidence to negate the doctors' opinion, and therefore the jury should not have disregarded it. A verdict of manslaughter was substituted for that of murder.

In *Jennion*, [164] the appellant, who had a history of emotional instability, killed her aunt in a fit of temper, striking her on the head with an ashtray and strangling her with a cord. At trial she claimed diminished responsibility. Two doctors supported this defence, whilst a consultant psychiatrist called by the Crown gave evidence in rebuttal. This witness

162. At p. 1178 B-C, but see now ss. 34–38 C.J.P.O.A. 1994 (Addendum).
163. (1978) 66 Cr. App. R. 31.
164. [1962] 1 W.L.R. 317.

expressed the opinion that whilst the appellant suffered from an abnormality of mind and was a mildly psychopathic personality, the condition was not such as to have substantially impaired her mental responsibility. She appealed against her conviction of murder.

It was held that where medical experts differ as to the effect of abnormality of mind, it is for the jury, after proper direction by the Judge, to resolve the issue.

In *Vinagre*[165] the appellant killed his wife out of jealousy. He was charged with murder. Psychiatric reports provided by the Crown suggested that he may have been suffering from what was described as the "Othello Syndrome" (defined as "morbid jealousy for which there was no cause".[166]) The trial Judge accepted his plea of diminished responsibility and sentenced him to life imprisonment for manslaughter. He appealed against sentence.

The appeal was allowed and the sentence varied to seven years' imprisonment. Lawton, L.J., took the opportunity to comment that the concept of the "Othello Syndrome" was "not one which appeals to this Court" and that pleas to manslaughter on the grounds of diminished responsibility should only be accepted when there is clear evidence of mental imbalance.[167]

In *Dix*,[168] during a trial for murder, defence counsel raised the issue of diminished responsibility, relying only on the defendant's evidence to support the defence. The Judge ruled that the defendant needed to provide an evidential basis for placing the defence before the jury including the calling of medical evidence to abnormality of mind.

Dismissing the appeal, the Court of Appeal held that whilst s. 2(1) did not require that medical evidence be adduced to support the defence, it made it a practical necessity if the defence was to begin to run at all.

---

165. (1979) 69 Cr. App. R. 104.
166. An inappropriate allusion to Shakespeare's tragic hero: Othello's jealousy was deliberately and carefully fomented by Iago's suggestions, deceptions and subterfuges.
167. The opinion in the single report before the Court of Appeal appears to have been equivocal on the issue of morbid jealousy. Lawton, L.J., indicated that, for justice to be done, an attempt should have been made to establish whether the wife's affair was imagined (in which case morbid jealousy applied) or real (in which case jealousy simpliciter applied). See, however, the case of *Cox* [1968] 1 W.L.R. 308: plea to manslaughter on ground of diminished responsibility may be accepted where the evidence is plain.
168. (1981) 74 Cr. App. 306., C.A.

However, in *Bradshaw*[169] the court explained that whilst "as a concession to the defence" in some cases of diminished responsibility doctors are sometimes allowed to base their opinions on what the defendant has told them (i.e. hearsay), without those matters being proved by first-hand admissible evidence, a doctor might not state what a patient told him about past symptoms *as evidence of those symptoms*, since that would be a breach of the rule against hearsay, but could give evidence of what the patient told him in order to explain the grounds *upon which he came to a conclusion* in respect of the patient's condition. If, however, the doctor's opinion was wholly based upon hearsay, unsupported by any direct, admissible evidence, the Judge would be justified in telling the jury that the defendant's case was based upon a flimsy or non-existent foundation and that they should reach their conclusion bearing that in mind.[170]

In *Campbell (Colin)*,[171] the defendant killed and mutilated the body of a female hitch-hiker. He was charged with murder. At trial he raised the defence of provocation. Diminished responsibility was not formally raised as a defence, but a psychiatrist who had been called by the defence to support provocation gave evidence which suggested abnormality of mind in the form of epilepsy. The Judge directed the jury that there was no evidence to substantiate diminished responsibility. The appellant appealed on the basis that the Judge should have left this issue to the jury.

It was held that it was for the defence to raise the issue and to prove it on a balance of probabilities. The psychiatrist called by the defence had referred in evidence to "abnormality of mind", but had not been asked to consider whether this was sufficient substantially to impair mental responsibility. Accordingly there was no *prima facie* evidence before the jury of diminished responsibility, and the Judge's direction on this point was correct.

In *Sanders*[172] the appellant developed diabetes and other afflictions some time after his common-law wife left him. He became depressed. He later became jealous when she started seeing another man. When she visited him one day he clubbed her to death with a hammer. There was evidence to suggest that this was premeditated. Two psychiatrists gave unequivocal and uncontradicted evidence that he suffered abnormality of mind due to reactive depression at the material time. The jury did not

169. (1986) 82 Cr. App. R. 79.
170. See the observations set out above at p.12-14, Chapter I, on the Rule against Hearsay.
171. (1986) 84 Cr. App. R. 255.
172. (1991) Cr. App. R. 245.

accept his plea of diminished responsibility and convicted him of murder.

On appeal it was held that where the medical evidence is unequivocal and uncontradicted, the trial Judge should direct the jury to accept it if there are no other circumstances to consider. Where, however, such other circumstances exist, the medical evidence should be assessed in the light of those other circumstances. The jury had borne other matters in mind when assessing the whole evidence and their verdict was not unreasonable.

In *Walton*[173] the defence psychiatrist said that the defendant was suffering from diminished responsibility; although not directly contradicted by other medical witnesses, that evidence was not supported by those witnesses, and the defendant's conviction for murder was upheld.

In *Spriggs*[174] the Judge in summing up simply handed the jury a copy of the relevant part of the Homicide Act 1957, without further explanation. The Court of Criminal Appeal declined to interfere.[175] But the need for care by the Judge in reminding the jury of the medical evidence in summing up is illustrated by the case of *Terry*.[176]

One writer has taken the extreme position that the jury are entitled to reject the medical evidence in total even if it is (1) unanimous; (2) unchallenged and (3) there is no other material in the case.[177]

"Arrested or Retarded Development"

See *Atkinson*[178] and *Egan*[179] where the respective juries were directed to consider whether such factors gave rise to the defence whilst ignoring the effects of alcohol. Both juries found that the defence was not raised on the evidence.

---

173. (1978) 142 J.P. 151.
174. [1958] 1 Q.B 270; [1958] 2 W.L.R. 162; 1 All E.R. 300N.
175. It is inconceivable that such a practice would be condoned by the Court of Appeal today.
176. (1961) 45 Cr. App. R. 180: bad practice simply to give the jury a copy of the transcript of the medical evidence, when they needed assistance to undersand and appreciate the effect of the evidence. See also *Walden* [1959] 1 W.L.R. 1008; 3 All E.R. 203.
177. Cohen, M.J. (1981) N.L.J. 667.
178. [1985] Crim. L.R. 314.
179. [1992] 4 All E.R. 470

Inherent Causes

(a) Sexual Psychopathy

In *Matheson*[180], the facts were that the appellant, "a confirmed practising sodomite", killed a boy, cut the body in half, disembowelled it, packing the intestines in a suitcase, hid the remains, sent anonymous postcards to the boy's mother indicative of a desire to torture, and then gave himself up to the police. His defence of diminished responsibility at trial was supported by unchallenged evidence of three doctors that he suffered from abnormality of mind due to arrested or retarded development as substantially impaired his mental responsibility. He was convicted of murder.

On appeal it was held that the jury's decision was unreasonable in view of the unchallenged medical evidence and a manslaughter verdict was substituted for that of murder. Although there was evidence of premeditation, an abnormal mind is as capable as a normal mind of forming an intention and a desire to kill.

(b) Irresistible Impulse

The leading case is that of *Byrne*.[181] The facts of that case and the Court of Appeal's ruling are summarized at p.14 supra (Chapter I).

In *King*,[182] the appellant, a Ugandan,[183] was convicted of the murder of his son, mother-in-law and two sisters-in-law. He denied killing his son but admitted killing the others. His defence on these three counts was provocation for one count and diminished responsibility due to irresistible impulse for the other two. He claimed that his loss of control was due to impaired mental responsibility at the time of the offences and was normal for "a person of his racial type [*sic*]." The Judge directed the jury that irresistible impulse was no defence to a murder charge and that in deciding whether there was any mental abnormality at the material time they must consider whether the mental condition of the defendant was peculiar to him alone or of a kind to be expected from his racial type, in which case it was not an abnormality at all.

The Court of Criminal Appeal held that this was a proper direction.

---

180. [1958] 1 W.L.R. 474.
181. [1960] 2 Q.B. 396.
182. [1965] 1 Q.B. 443; [1964] 3 W.L.R. 980; (1965) 129 J.P. 276.
183. But described in many reports of the case as "an African".
184. [1936] 2 All E.R. 1138;

See also *Smith (Sandie)(post)* and *Sodeman*[184], *Flavell*[185]and *Kopsch*[186]

(c) Reactive Depression

In *Seers*[187] the appellant stabbed and killed his wife outside the hostel in which she had been staying. He was charged with murder. At trial he claimed that he had been provoked, and also invoked the defence of diminished responsibility, on the ground of chronic reactive depression. The medical evidence given both by the prosecution and the defence psychiatrists[188] was to the effect that the appellant was indeed suffering from chronic reactive depression. Both expert witnesses agreed that a reactive depressive illness *could* amount to an abnormality of mind within the meaning of s.2, but they differed as to whether, on the facts, it had in fact done so in the instant case.

The Judge directed the jury that the test to be applied to determine whether the appellant's responsibility was diminished was whether he could be described in popular language as "partially insane" or "on the borderline of insanity". Both doctors had been asked whether this description could be applied to the appellant, and both agreed that it could not.

On appeal, it was held that there had been a substantial misdirection on the issue of diminished responsibility.

Byrne[189] should not be read as laying down that in every case where diminished responsibility is raised the jury must necessarily be directed that the test is always to be partial or borderline insanity. There may be cases where the abnormality of mind may not be readily relatable to any of the generally recognized types of insanity in the broad popular sense. There is no single safe formula for directing the jury; the direction must always be related to the particular evidence in the case *(Rose, ante)*. In a case of this sort dealing with a depressive illness, it was not appropriate to direct a jury solely in terms of partial or borderline insanity as the test of diminished responsibility. *Byrne*'s case could be distinguished as a case where the evidence of doctors justified inviting the jury to determine the degree of impairment of mental responsibility by such a test.

See also *Bathurst ante.*

185. (1926) 19 Cr. App. R. 141;
186. (1925) 19 Cr. App. R. 50 at 51-2
187. [1985] Crim. L.R. 315; (1985) 149 J.P. 124.
188. Curiously, the defence called the prison medical officer, whilst the prosecution relied upon an independent consultant psychiatrist.
189. *Ante* p. 14.

(d) Morbid Jealousy

In the case of *Ahmed Din*[190] the defendant brutally killed a fellow Pakistani by stabbing him seven times with a sharpened hacksaw blade, nearly severing the head and after death cutting off the penis. The deceased had been a lodger with the defendant, his wife and children and was suspected of having an affair with the wife. Two doctors gave evidence to support his defence of diminished responsibility at trial, both saying that the defendant suffered from abnormality of the mind due to paranoia, substantially impairing his mental responsibility. The prosecution apparently accepted diminished responsibility and only cross-examined the doctors to eliminate insanity.

When questioned by the Judge both doctors intimated that if the defendant had grounds for believing in his wife's infidelity there would not have been a paranoid state and he would have been sane.

The doctors had previously spoken to the defendant and the daughter, but not the wife, to establish whether there had been an affair and formed the view that the defendant suffered from delusions. No evidence was adduced at trial to establish that the defendant was suffering delusions about his wife's infidelity and thus the doctor's opinion was based entirely on hearsay. The jury returned a verdict of guilty of murder.

On appeal the court held that in this case the defence of diminished responsibility depended on a question of fact, whether the accused had solid grounds for believing in his wife's infidelity. The defence failed to prove this fact and had only relied on hearsay evidence of the doctors. In the circumstances it was not unreasonable for the jury to decline to accept the medical evidence and the appeal was dismissed.

See also *Asher*[191]

(e) Hysterical Dissociation

See *Eeles* (1972) *The Times*, November 22nd.

(f) Pre-Menstrual Tension Syndrome

The question of whether pre-menstrual tension syndrome ("PMTS") might afford grounds for a claim of diminished responsibility was considered by the Court of Appeal in the case of *Craddock*.[192]

---

190. (1962) 2 All E.R. 123.
191. (1981) *The Times*, June 9th.
192. This decision was considered in Brahams: "Rejection of the pre-menstrual syndrome as a defence in English Law" 1982 *Lancet* i 1134-1135, but see also, by the same author, "Pre-menstrual syndrome: a disease of the mind?" 1981 *Lancet* ii: 1238-1240.

The defendant, who had a long history of uncontrolled disruptive behaviour, including attempts at suicide, killed a fellow barmaid. Her behaviour was described by an expert witness as having been caused by PMTS.

However, in *Smith (Sandie)*[193] the appellant alleged that her behaviour of making threats to kill and possessing an offensive weapon was due to PMTS. This condition was being controlled by injections of progesterone but at the time of the offences her doctor had reduced the dosage. The Judge directed the jury that automatism was not a defence which was capable of consideration by them, and that there was no defence in law of irresistible impulse. This direction was appealed.

The Court of Appeal held that the defence of automatism was not available to the appellant and that there was no authority for a defence of irresistible impulse due to a temporary medical condition (i.e. PMTS).

"Induced by Disease or Injury"
(a) Drink; drugs generally

One of the earliest cases in which an attempt appears to have been made to bring the effects of alcohol into question as a possible cause of "injury" was *Di Ducca*[194], where the defendant alleged, *inter alia*, diminished responsibility resulting from the toxic effect of a drink which he had consumed. On appeal it was held that it was unnecessary to decide whether or not the transient effect of alcohol could amount to an injury within the meaning of s. 2(1), as there was no evidence whatever of "abnormality" – the defendant's behaviour was at most evidence of the "bravado" induced by alcohol.

More recently the law was explained in even more definite terms: self-induced intoxication can neither be the cause of, nor can it contribute to, injury, for the purposes of s. 2: see *Fenton*.[195]

In that case the appellant was a man who had led a turbulent life, with incidents of instability and violent temper. On a day when his behaviour was described as "odd" he drank a considerable quantity of whisky and of gin, and then drove a car. The car was followed into a *cul-de-sac* by a police car. The appellant pulled out a revolver and shot and killed the driver of the police car. He later drove to a nightclub where he shot and killed a further three people. No less than five psychiatrists gave evidence

193. (1982) Crim. L.R. 531.
194. (1959) 43 Cr. App. R. 167.
195. (1975) 61 Cr. App. R. 261.

in support of the defence of diminished responsibility. The appellant was described as an aggressive psychopath with marked paranoid traits, who had a history of reactive depression, and that the excessive quantity of alcohol which he had consumed resulted in a state of disinhibition and possible confusion. The car chase had created a sensation of being trapped. These factors contributed to his abnormality of mind at the time of the killings, and it was likely that in the absence of any one of them the killings would not have taken place.

The Judge directed the jury, *inter alia*, that they should convict of murder if satisfied that the combined effect of the factors *other than alcohol* was insufficient to amount to a substantial impairment in the mental responsibility of the appellant. The Court of Appeal held that whilst a craving for drinks or drugs can produce an abnormality of mind, self-induced intoxication cannot of itself produce an abnormality of mind due to inherent causes. The Judge had been right to leave to the jury the issue of whether or not the defence was established in view of the other factors which contributed to the abnormality of mind.

(b) Alcoholism

In the case of *Tandy*[196] the defendant was a woman who was described as an alcoholic. She consumed the greatest part of a bottle of vodka and then strangled her 11-year-old daughter. She was tried for murder and claimed diminished responsibility by reason of her alcoholism. In evidence she said that she was able to exercise some control over her drinking even after taking her first drink of the day. This was contradicted by the medical expert witness called on her behalf. The Judge directed the jury that if they found that she had voluntarily taken the first drink of the day, she could not claim that any resultant abnormality of mind was "induced by disease". The jury convicted her of murder. She appealed upon the ground that the direction had wrongly withdrawn from the jury the issue of whether she had proved such a craving for drink as in itself to produce an abnormality of mind.

Dismissing the appeal, the Court of Appeal held that the appellant had to show (1) that she was suffering from an abnormality of mind at the time of the act of strangulation; (2) that that abnormality was induced by "the disease of alcoholism"; and that (3) the abnormality of mind substantially impaired the appellant's mental responsibility for the act of strangling her daughter.

196. [1988] Crim. L.R. 308; (1988) 152 J.P. 453.

The court observed that,

"The appellant would not establish the second element of the defence unless the evidence showed that the abnormality of mind at the time of the killing was due to the fact that she was a chronic alcoholic. If the alcoholism had reached the level at which her brain had been injured by the repeated insult from intoxicants so that there was gross impairment of her judgment and emotional responses, then the defence of diminished responsibility was available to her, provided that she satisfied the jury of the third element of the defence. Further, if the appellant were able to establish that the alcoholism had reached the level where although the brain had not been damaged to the extent just stated, the appellant's drinking had become involuntary, that is to say she was no longer able to resist the impulse to drink, then the defence of diminished responsibility was available to her, subject to her establishing the first and third elements, because if her drinking was involuntary, then her abnormality of mind at the time of the act of strangulation was induced by her condition of alcoholism.

On the other hand, if the appellant had simply not resisted an impulse to drink and it was the drink taken on the [day in question] which brought about the impairment of judgment and emotional response, then the defence of diminished responsibility was not available to the appellant."

It was held that the evidence suggested that it was indeed the drink taken on the day in question which brought about the impairment of judgment. There was accordingly no material misdirection, and the appeal was dismissed.

The matter has most recently been considered in the cases of *Egan*[197] and *Inseal*.[198] In *Egan* the defendant killed a 79-year-old widow, having entered her house in a state of intoxication. Medical evidence was given to the effect that the defendant suffered from (a) abnormality of mind by reason of arrested or retarded development; and (b) intellectual impairment with possibly some psychopathic disorder. The jury were directed to disregard the effect of alcohol, and to look solely at the evidence bearing on the abnormality of mind due to the other factors to decide whether the defendant came within s. 2(1). The jury convicted the defendant of

197. [1992] 4 All E.R. 470.
198. [1992] Crim. L.R. 35 C.A.

murder. The Court of Appeal upheld the Judge's directions, which they said were in accordance with *Gittens*[199] and *Atkinson*[200], two cases which were to be regarded as leading authorities on the subject of diminished responsibility where drink was a factor. Where it was maintained that alcoholism alone could establish the defence, *Tandy*[201] applied. Guidance as to the meaning of "substantial" should be explicitly provided for the jury by the Judge following the dicta in *Lloyd*.[202]

"Substantial" Impairment

In *Simcox*[203] the defendant, who had previous conviction for murder, shot and killed one person, shot and wounded two others, and then shot himself. The medical evidence was that the defendant was suffering from abnormality of mind due to paranoid personality, but the medical expert witnesses would not go so far as to say that the impairment was "substantial". In dealing with the defence of diminished responsibility the Judge indicated that there was no scientific test of "substantial" impairment, and told them to use a common-sense approach. On appeal against his conviction for murder, it was held that the Judge's direction had been correct: not only was there no scientific test, there was no statutory one either. The jury had to look at all the circumstances in a common-sense way. The appeal was dismissed.

In *Lloyd*[204] it was held that "substantial" did not mean "more than minimal", as the defence had submitted. In *Egan* (*supra*) it was said, *obiter*, that guidance to juries should be explicitly provided by the Judge in summing up by using "one or other of the two meanings" of "substantial" given in *Lloyd*: i.e. (1) The jury should approach the word in a common-sense way, or (2) the word meant "more than some trivial degree of impairment which does not make an appreciable difference to a person's ability to control himself, but it means less than total impairment."

A person may be quite "sane", may fully intend to kill another, and may quite consciously carry out the killing, but may nevertheless be able to invoke the defence of diminished responsibility successfully: in the case of *Rose*,[205] an appeal from the West Indies, medical evidence was given

199. (1988) Cr. App. R. 45.
200. [1984] 3 W.L.R. 327.
201. [1967] 1 Q.B. 175. See also p. 63.
202. [1985] Crim. L.R. 314.
203. [1964] Crim. L.R. 402.
204. [1967] 1 Q.B. 175.
205. (1961) 45 Cr. App. R. 496.

that the appellant, who had killed a prison overseer, suffered from "punch-drunk syndrome" as a result of previous head injuries. This, the expert said, caused the appellant to suffer "periods of insanity [*sic*] and completely absent moral responsibility".

The Judge directed the jury to apply the "borderline of insanity" test in considering the defence of diminished responsibility, and relied upon the M'Naghten Rules to direct the jury as to insanity, saying, *inter alia*, that if they thought that the appellant knew exactly what he was doing, and intended to do it, he was guilty of murder. The Privy Council held that this was a misdirection, as a man might know exactly what he was doing, and intend to do it, yet might still suffer from such abnormality of mind as substantially impaired his mental responsibility. They approved the direction given by the Court of Criminal Appeal in *Byrne*.

In *Gomez*[206] the Judge's summing up was held to be defective by reason of the implication that any abnormality of mind, to fall within the terms of s.2, must have existed from birth.

206. (1964) 48 Cr. App. R. 310.

CHAPTER III

Preparation of Psychiatric Evidence in Relation to Persons Remanded in Custody

Reports dealing with the services of mentally disordered offenders were published late 1991. They were based on investigations undertaken jointly by the Home Office and the Department of Health. Recommendations were made to the effect that defendants should not be remanded to the hospitals of penal institutions for psychiatric reports. Obviously those who represent an immediate and serious danger to the public would need to be remanded to adequately secure psychiatric facilities which would preferably exist in the relevant court area. However, the following sections deal with the responsibility of prison medical officers to furnish medical reports to courts. Such reports concern those remanded in custody and may be called for in the following circumstances:

(a)   By the court when considering making a probation order requiring treatment for a medical condition, a hospital order or a guardianship order or otherwise for the purpose of determining the most suitable method of dealing with an offender; or by a magistrates' court which may remand a defendant for medical examination or commit a defendant for trial on bail with a requirement for such examination.

(b)   By a court before sentencing any offender to undergo a custodial sentence.

(c)   By a court in a case in which the defendant has been convicted of murder, manslaughter or arson.

(d)   By the court, prosecution or defence in any case in which the accused's mental condition is an issue, e.g. where fitness to plead, insanity, diminished responsibility or incapacity to form the intent required to commit the offence charged are in contention.

These matters are referred to later in this chapter and dealt with in more detail in Chapter Two.

Courts are concerned with five aspects of a medical report:

(i)   Fitness to plead. The final decision on this issue can only be made in the Crown Court by a jury after hearing two medical practitioners who must be recognized under s.12(2) of the Mental Health Act 1983, as having special experience in the diagnosis or treatment of mental disorder.

(ii)   Recommendations under s.37 of the Mental Health Act 1983 which are submitted if the accused is suffering from a mental disorder within the meaning of the Act. If the recommendations are acceptable, the court will make a Hospital Order authorizing the admission of the defendant to and his detention in an ordinary mental hospital, in a secure unit or a special hospital if considered a serious danger to the public. The two doctors who sign recommendations under s.37 of the Act, must be recognized under s.12(2). The Hospital Order is a legal authority. The recommendation in the report is not. An individual accepted for treatment on the basis of a Hospital Order must be admitted to hospital immediately from court or within 28 days of the date of issue of the order, and in the latter instance he would usually await transfer in a prison hospital. Section 37 of the Act cannot be implemented unless a hospital, which may be an ordinary mental hospital, a special hospital or secure unit, is specifically named in the order. An order under s.41 of the Mental Health Act restricting discharge with or without limit of time is usually applied if the accused is sent to a special hospital and *may* also be applied if he or she is admitted to a secure psychiatric unit or to an ordinary mental hospital. To obtain such an order the accused must be committed to a Crown Court which must hear oral evidence from at least one of the doctors who signed the recommendations under s.37. Section 37 of the Act cannot be implemented by the Crown Court unless the accused pleads guilty or is found guilty by a court. However, where magistrates would have power on conviction to implement the section, they may do so without convicting the offender.

(iii)   Recommendations under s.37 of the Act in relation to a person convicted of an offence punishable with a custodial sentence who has reached the age of 16 may, if the nature or degree of mental disorder warrants it, include a recommendation for the offender's reception into guardianship. The court may place the offender under the guardianship of a local-services authority or a person approved by the authority, provided the authority or that person is willing to act.

(iv) Medical reports from one or two doctors may indicate that the accused should have residential psychiatric treatment as a condition of *probation*. Provided arrangements for reception and treatment have been made, and if the court is in agreement, the patient must be transferred to hospital on the day of his appearance in court. Out-patient psychiatric treatment by a psychiatrist or general medical practitioner may be implemented as a condition of probation. The criteria are based on the accused person's *mental condition* and forms of mental disorder need not be specified. Psychiatric treatment as a condition of probation is implemented on the basis of s.3 of the Powers of the Criminal Courts Act 1973. The doctor recommending treatment as a condition of probation must be recognized under s.12(2) of the Mental Health Act 1983.

(v) An account of the physical health of the accused is an essential part of a report to court.

Psychiatric evidence is submitted in the form of written reports which may or may not be supported by oral evidence. Medical reports on behalf of remand inmates are submitted by prison medical officers at the request of magistrates' and Crown courts and a consultant psychiatrist is asked for a second opinion if there is reason to suspect mental disorder. Courts are sometimes criticized for over-referral of offenders for reports which deal with the mental and physical health of offenders. These reports may be requested because of the severity of the crime, persistent anti-social behaviour, simulation of mental disorder and/or bizarre behaviour in court due to the effects of alcohol and/or drug abuse. I believe that such criticisms are not justified even if these individuals are subsequently psychiatrically assessed as not suffering from mental disorders requiring treatment. The courts have the ultimate responsibility of disposal. Furthermore, such repeated requests may be justified because serious mental illnesses such as paranoid psychosis or psychotic depression may be "masked" by anti-social behaviour or a defendant may rarely, and for a temporary period, simulate sanity in order to avoid psychiatric treatment or imprisonment. Evidence of a serious mental illness may only become evident during a prolonged remand period or imprisonment. Even if a court does not request a medical report, a prison medical officer should make a voluntary report if there is a reason to suspect that an inmate is mentally disordered within the meaning of the Mental Health Act 1983 or is suffering from a lesser degree of mental abnormality, especially if dangerous to the public. Solicitors are at liberty to ask one or more psychiatrists to examine any inmate on remand and facilities must be provided by the prison authorities.

The following are examples of how a medical report may influence the manner in which a court deals with an offender:

(i)   it helps the court to assess degrees of culpability and responsibility for lawbreaking:

(ii)   it helps the court to decide on a means of disposal designed to prevent further lawbreaking (the implementation of s.37 of the Mental Health Act 1983 may achieve this end); and

(iii) a court may recommend psychiatric investigation with a view to treatment during the course of a prison sentence or youth custody, or as a condition of a probation order. This recommendation is readily implemented at such establishments as Grendon Underwood and Feltham Youth Custody Centre.

Those remanded for psychiatric reports and/or suspected of mental disorder are admitted to the prison hospital immediately. *Those charged with homicide are automatically admitted to prison hospital even if a mental disorder is not suspected.* A detailed history is essential and three or four interviews are necessary for the average report to court, which includes the accused person's account of the offence with which he is charged, with particular reference to allegations of amnesia. There may be inconsistencies in the original account of the crime indicating possible attempts to deceive, and examination may reveal evidence of mental disorder, alcoholism and/or drug dependency and the influence of these conditions on the current charge. Family history, type of childhood, progress at school and employment record are noted. Marital and sexual difficulties are recorded. The examiner tries to assess possible motivation for simulation by considering whether the alleged crime would warrant a long or a short sentence if mental disorder were excluded. Entries in occurrence books by members of the prison hospital staff provide information as to general behaviour, appearance, manner of speech, contact with reality, appetite and type of sleep. The preparation of a psychiatric report for a court also involves study of information from the following sources:

(i)   Information from the clerk of the court, depositions and forensic pathology reports in cases of homicide.

(ii)   Information from general medical practitioners and from psychiatric and general hospitals. A history of residential or out-patient psychiatric treatment is always significant when one is considering the possibility of current mental disorder.

(iii) Intelligence quotient and personality tests. A history of attendance at a special hospital would suggest mental impairment.

(iv)   Police reports of the number and nature of previous offences, with particular reference to convictions for violence, sexual offences and arson, indicate potential danger to the public and the possibility of admission to a special hospital if the accused is also mentally disordered within the meaning of the Mental Health Act 1983. The police also provide information concerning the circumstances of current charges. An unprovoked attack upon a person where excessive force was used and little or no attempt made to evade detection may indicate mental disorder.

(v)   Social inquiry reports from probation officers provide information about home background, school and work records, ability to adapt to community life and attitudes to help offered. Good liaison between prison doctors and probation officers is essential for the preparation of accurate reports. I recall the case of a middle-aged man who was accused of the attempted murder of his teenage daughter by cutting her throat with an open razor. The probation officer revealed that the victim had acquired a boyfriend a few weeks before the attack. The accused had badly beaten another daughter about two years previously under similar circumstances. Consequently, under certain circumstances he tended to indulge in a particular pattern of violent behaviour in regard to his daughters. The future welfare of three younger daughters had to be considered. He was sentenced to life imprisonment.

(vi)   Information from near relatives, close friends and religious advisers concerning the personality of the accused with particular reference to type of behaviour induced by different environmental situations.

In the case of an individual charged with *murder*, the prison medical officer supplies three reports. First, a pre-trial report is sent to the Director of the Prison Medical Service when the inmate is committed from the magistrates' court to the Crown Court. The date of committal and names of the courts are specified. The report should refer to the nature of the charge and surrounding circumstances, and the current mental condition of the accused is described. An opinion must be expressed as to the necessity of having the accused examined by an *independent* psychiatrist selected by the Home Office from a list of approved psychiatrists. Secondly, a further report is made to the Director of Public Prosecutions which is discussed in more detail below. Thirdly, a post-trial report is sent to the Under Secretary of State and the Director of the Prison Medical Service when an individual found guilty of murder or manslaughter is sentenced to life imprisonment, but only to the Director in the event of acquittal or a sentence less than life imprisonment. The post-trial report gives an account of the nature of all medical evidence at the trial, the verdict of the court and relevant remarks by the Judge. Copies of psychiatric reports are sent with post-trial reports. When the charge is murder, the prison medical officer has a *statutory duty* to submit a medical report to the Director of Public Prosecutions at least seven days before the trial. If the prison medical officer considers that mental disorder is apparent or suspect, an independent psychiatrist will also be asked to submit a report to the Director of Public Prosecutions, the adjective "independent" being applied to this psychiatrist in order to avoid prejudice during the trial and in the event of an appeal. The Director of Public Prosecutions distributes copies of all relevant reports to the Crown Court, the prosecution and the defence. The defence is at liberty to have its client examined by any number of psychiatrists that they choose to instruct, and may or may not produce their findings in evidence. The report to the Director of Public Prosecutions may be considered under five headings: (1) an introductory paragraph; (2) the accused person's condition on reception into custody; (3) previous medical and social history; (4) developments during the period in custody; and (5) conclusions reached. Clinical assessment involves consideration of the nature of the crime, previous medical history and the current mental and physical health of the accused person.

(1) *The introductory paragraph* deals with information from the sources already mentioned. It should be specifically stated that the depositions have been studied. The prison medical officer should state the number of interviews he has had with the accused and he is expected to have had at least six before reporting. A study of the forensic pathology report gives information about the mode of death and degree of force used. Use of firearm or instrument to kill adds to the gravity of the offence in the eyes of the law. The pathology report and other relevant medical reports indicate whether the deceased suffered from an illness which could have caused death from *natural* causes.

(2) *The condition of the accused at the time of reception into custody* is described. The prison medical officer should carry out his examination *on the day of reception into custody* as the accused may have been arrested on the day of the crime and the doctor will then be in a position to express an opinion as to the mental state of the accused on that particular day. This evidence would be relevant if the defence was based on the mental condition of the accused. A thorough physical examination is necessary and careful note is made of any injuries and the accused's explanation of how these injuries were acquired. All cuts, bruises and abrasions must be measured, and colour, consistency and presence or absence of tenderness noted. Bony injuries are carefully described. The accused may have been taking some form of medication which could accelerate or delay healing and this information would be particularly relevant in the event of a plea of manslaughter on the grounds of provocation.

(3) *Previous medical and social history* is taken in detail. General medical practitioners and near relatives supply valuable information and it is especially important for reporting doctors to interview relatives of individuals charged with murder. Social inquiry reports are also helpful. Depositions and police reports give information about the crime and the accused is requested to give a detailed account of the immediate circumstances of the homicide, the statements made by the accused to the medical examiner being compared with those made to the police in order to detect inconsistencies. The forensic pathologist's reports which indicate the manner in which the deceased was killed are studied. The apparent motive for the crime must be considered in close association with the character of the accused and his total life history. Previous medical history is important in deciding the applicability of diminished responsibility. Mental or physical illness may have caused an alteration

in personality before the homicide, and relevant information may be obtained from relatives, family doctors, teachers, employers, religious advisers, police, probation officers and friends as indicated. One should endeavour to trace a point in time after which acquaintances may have said of the accused "he has changed", "he is not as he used to be", or "he is now odd and peculiar". A history of psychiatric treatment, especially on a residential basis, would help to allay suspicion of feigning mental disorder. One endeavours to decide if the accused is a truthful person by a study of his personality aided by information from the sources mentioned. Inquiry is made concerning previous convictions especially for offences of a sexual or violent nature. His mode of behaviour whilst serving sentences in prison, in youth custody or detention centres, may help in assessing character and personality. Attention is given to childhood influences and school record, and if the accused attended a special school for the intellectually backward, one would assume that his intelligence was below average, although this would not necessarily mean mental impairment within the meaning of the Mental Health Act 1983. Cruelty, lack of parental care and sexual assaults during childhood, would tend to warp personality development. A genuine mental disorder would prevent an individual from following his occupation or would at least reduce his working efficiency, and an unduly suspicious attitude towards a marital partner would lead one to consider paranoid psychosis, if the suspicions were unjustified. Sexual perversions may be symptomatic of mental disorder or may indicate defective morality, and may also have some connection with motivation for homicide. Excessive indulgence in alcohol, drugs or gambling could be relevant to the circumstances of an alleged homicide but not necessarily from the point of view of mitigation. Valuable information may be gained by interviewing near relatives and studying letters written by the accused.

(4) *Developments during the period in custody* would include an account of behaviour and demeanour as observed by the medical officer and members of the prison hospital staff. Reference is made to the degree of contact with reality, personal appearance, hygiene, mood variation, sleep pattern and appetite. Any abnormal loss of consciousness is noted. Routine investigations carried out on every individual charged with murder include: (i) tests for venereal disease, including HIV infection; (ii) psychometric tests including the intelligence quotient (Wechsler Adult Intelligence Scale), the Raven's Progressive Matrices Tests and

personality tests as indicated; (iii) electroencephalograms which may be activated by ingestion of alcohol if the accused is alleged to have been under the influence of alcohol at the material time of the homicide; (iv) X-rays of chest and skull; (v) electrocardiogram; (vi) chromosomal studies may be undertaken but an abnormal sex chromosome pattern *per se* would fail as the basis of a plea of diminished responsibility; and (vii) blood urea estimations, fasting blood-sugar assessments and glucose-tolerance tests may be necessary if the homicide took place when the accused was allegedly suffering from clouding of consciousness. The polygraph (Haward, 1990) measures physiological responses such as pulse, blood pressure, respiration and skin conductance in the form of graphic tracings, in response to questioning with the object of detecting lies and deception. This test is also called electrodermometry because skin conductance is the most sensitive element in the test. The skill of the operator in carrying out the test and interpreting the results is most important. Popularly known as the lie-detection test, it is admitted as evidence in criminal courts by two-thirds of the states in the United States of America and Lykken (1974) found the test reliable in 20,000 instances. However, British courts will not admit polygraph evidence, despite the proven unreliability of the testimony of some eyewitnesses whose evidence was originally admitted. Consequently, this test is not undertaken for our courts.

(5) *Conclusions* The report is completed by giving conclusions as to the mental and physical state of the accused. An opinion is first given as to whether the accused is fit to plead. The prosecution may accept evidence to the effect that the accused is unfit to plead but the final decision is for the jury.

The Criminal Procedure (Insanity and Unfitness to Plead) Act 1991 has been dealt with in Chapter I. The following remarks concern the prison medical officer's duty when the Act has been implemented.

When an individual is found not guilty by reason of insanity or unfit to plead, transfer to a National Health Service hospital is implemented if he or she has been returned to the prison hospital from court and when the charge is murder, the accused may be admitted to a special hospital. The following documents are sent to the **Under Secretary of State** to implement the admission:

(i) a form giving particulars of the offences and the court's decision;

(ii) copies of relevant medical reports;
(iii) a form giving the history of the accused;
(iv) a list of previous convictions;
(v) a copy of the court order;
(vi) a social inquiry report, and
(vii) a covering letter specifying the name of the hospital willing to receive the accused.

A memorandum is sent to the **Director of the Prison Medical Services** on transfer to hospital, which must take place within two months of the court's decision.

One next considers whether **diminished responsibility** is applicable to the accused. This subject is considered in detail in Chapter Two and consequently I here refer to medical aspects of the plea. If a plea of diminished responsibility is successful, the charge is reduced from murder to manslaughter and as the penalty for the latter offence is not fixed by law, s.37 of the Mental Health Act 1983 could then be implemented by the issuing of a hospital order if the accused is mentally disordered within the meaning of the Act and a restriction order with or without limit of time under s.41 of the Act would usually be added. It is important provisionally to arrange for a vacancy in an adequately secure mental hospital or unit before the trial date and the Judge will expect this arrangement to have been made so that he may, at his discretion, implement s.37 of the Act at the conclusion of the trial. This vacancy is arranged by sending a detailed letter, giving all relevant psychiatric information about the accused, to the *Special Hospital Service Authority* or to the relevant regional hospital authority depending on the type of hospital most appropriate to the patient's needs, at least 14 days before the trial date.

Doctors submitting psychiatric reports recommending implementation of s.37 of the Mental Health Act 1983 must be recognized under s.12(2) of the same Act and statements to this effect should be made at the end of their reports. A doctor may issue a psychiatric report indicating that, in his opinion, diminished responsibility is applicable to the accused and in this circumstance the specific form of mental disorder should be described and the words "such abnormality of mind as to substantially impair his mental responsibility for his acts and omissions in doing the killing" should be written in full. An opinion as to the applicability of diminished responsibility should not be based exclusively on the psychiatric state of the accused during the remand period. Psychiatrists sometimes give the impression that they are presenting opinions as facts when giving evidence in court.

There follows a list of *defects (aberrations) of personality* which vary in degree and are distinct from psychotic and neurotic illness and psychopathic disorder. However, the latter conditions may eventually affect a minority of persons with personality defects depending on type and severity. Personality defects may be put forward as a defence in the context of diminished responsibility and include deeply ingrained maladaptive patterns of behaviour generally recognizable by the time of adolescence or earlier and continuing throughout most of adult life, although often becoming less obvious in middle or old age. The personality is not average either in the balance of its components, their quality and expression, or in its total aspect. As a result, the patient suffers or others have to suffer and there is adverse effect upon the individual and society.

Psychopathic personality is characterized by disregard for social obligation, lack of feeling for others, and impetuous violence or callous unconcern. There is a gross disparity between behaviour and the prevailing social norms. Behaviour is not readily modifiable by experience, including punishment. People with this personality disorder are affectively cold and may be abnormally aggressive and/or irresponsible. Their tolerance to frustration is low. They blame others or offer plausible rationalizations for the behaviour that brings them into conflict with society.

Explosive personality disorder is characterized by instability of mood with liability to intemperate outbursts of anger, hate, violence, or affection. Aggression may be expressed in words or as physical violence. The outbursts cannot readily be controlled by the affected persons.

Epileptic personality often shows itself before the sufferer has any fits. Selfishness and egocentricity are marked, and although they profess an interest in others, their interest is almost completely centred in themselves. Untruthfulness, deceit and vanity are common traits and attempts are frequently made to get other people into trouble. They often adopt a martyred attitude, tend to be irritable and childish and at times are liable to outbursts of violence. The memory is often impaired and fabrications may occur as a result.

Hysterical personality includes a personality disorder characterized by shallow, labile affectivity, dependence on others, craving for appreciation and attention, suggestibility, and theatricality. There is often sexual immaturity such as frigidity or over-responsiveness to stimuli.

Paranoid personality is characterized by excessive sensitivity to setbacks or what are taken to be humiliations and rebuffs, a tendency to distort experience by miscontruing the neutral or friendly actions of others as hostile or contemptuous, and a combative and tenacious sense of personal rights. The patient may be prone to jealousy or excessive self-importance. Some such persons may feel helplessly humiliated and put upon. Others, likewise excessively sensitive, are aggressive and insistent. In all cases, there is excessive self-reference and sometimes fanaticism.

Affective personality is characterized by a lifelong predominance of a pronounced mood, which may be persistently depressed, persistently elated, or alternately elated and depressed. During periods of elation there is unshakable optimism and an enhanced zest for life and activity, whereas periods of depression are marked by worry, pessimism, low output of energy, and a sense of futility.

Asthenic personality is characterized by passive compliance with the wishes of elders and others, and a weak, inadequate response to the demands of daily life. Lack of vigour may show itself in the intellectual or emotional spheres. There is little capacity for enjoyment.

Schizoid personality is characterized by withdrawal from affectional, social, and other contacts, with autistic preference for fantasy and introspective reserve. The patient's behaviour may be slightly eccentric or indicate avoidance of competitive situations. Apparent coolness and detachment may mask an incapacity to express feelings.

Anankastic personality is characterized by feelings of personal insecurity, doubt, and incompleteness leading to excessive con-scientiousness, stubbornness and caution. There may be insistent and unwelcome thoughts or impulses, which do not attain the severity of those seen in obsessive-compulsive neurosis. The patient feels a need to check repeatedly in an attempt to ensure perfection and meticulous accuracy.

The neurotic personality is characterized by disturbances of feelings, attitudes and habits enough to impair normal social functioning and efficiency. The symptoms are best understood as manifestations of anxiety or as ineffective ways of dealing with anxiety. Fear is prominent in symptomatology. The individual of neurotic personality is unduly vulnerable to stress and prone to experience fears, anxieties and inhibitions for which there is no apparent justification. Emotional and intellectual insight is retained. A plea of diminished responsibility would succeed if neurotic illness reached a degree of intensity preventing the individual from leading a normal life in the occupational, marital and social spheres, thus constituting *neurotic illness* which may take the form of anxiety, depression, hysteria or obsessionalism. Neurotic depression is usually a progressive reaction to a long period of stress.

Diminished responsibility may or may not apply to an individual who committed homicide during the course of *alleged psychotic illness*. However, the onus would be on the defence to convince the jury that the accused was suffering from abnormality of the mind so as to substantially impair his mental responsibility for his acts and omissions in doing the killing(s). Such convincing would be more difficult if the accused was apparently not psychotic during the remand period before the trial and during the same. A plea of diminished responsibility based on "abnormal personality" *per se* would probably not succeed unless the accused also suffered from some recognized form of mental disorder. The influence of psychoneurotic illness on a plea of diminished responsibility would depend on the degree of the illness and whether it could be regarded by the jury as an inherent cause as indicated in the Homicide Act, 1957. An impulsive and apparently motiveless crime with little or no attempt at concealment, would suggest that the accused may have suffered from a *psychotic illness* at the material time. A psychotic may experience a complete or partial remission of symptoms, but nevertheless diminished responsibility could apply if homicide was perpetrated during the course of such a remission. The plea could also succeed in schizo-affected psychosis where signs and symptoms of schizophrenia are evident but depressive symptoms tend to dominate the clinical picture. Schizo-affective psychosis tends to be episodic and personality deterioration is not usually evident during the periods of remission. Diminished responsibility may also be applicable to the *psychopath* who has committed homicide. Legal opinion is divided on this issue, but the plea would succeed if the psychopathy had reached such a degree of severity as to constitute abnormality of mind as to substantially impair his mental responsibility for his acts and omissions in doing the killing and/or if the accused also suffered from some other serious form of mental disorder or epilepsy. Homicide by an individual with an anti-social personality but who is not psychopathically disordered within the meaning of the Act would present medico-legal problems and a decision concerning the applicability of diminished responsibility would be made by a jury on the basis of all available information. There is no correlation between electroencephalographic findings and personality types. However, a defence of diminished responsibility may be put forward on behalf of an aggressive psychopath allegedly in such a state of rage and fury as to induce clouding of consciousness at the material time of the killing. Again, the jury would ultimately decide on the basis of all available evidence and especially past history. The success of a plea of diminished responsibility on the basis of head injury, including brain damage, would depend on the post-traumatic mental state of the accused at the time of the homicide, conforming to the definition of diminished responsibility as described in the Homicide Act, 1957. A case where a plea of diminished responsibility was put forward on behalf of a person with a history of head injury, is referred to in Chapter V. A plea of diminished responsibility based on *mental impairment* would succeed, and a similar plea would be successful in the presence of a degree of intellectual retardation short of impairment but sufficient to substantially impair a defendant's responsibility. Mental impairment as defined in the 1983 Act is not synonymous with low intellect and factors such as emotional instability, lack of sense of responsibility, inability to control actions and weakened volition must also be considered. The average range of intelligence quotient is 85 to 115 and figures below 80 are usually taken to suggest impairment. The presence of a high degree of emotional instability or epilepsy would probably ensure the success of a plea of diminished responsibility even though an intelligence quotient ranged from 70 to 85. A proportion of coloured immigrants may achieve deceptively low scores when tested by the Wechsler-Bellevue Scale and those scores may be accounted for by cultural and educational factors, which Raven's progressive matrices test (testing "Basic" intelligence) is said to eliminate, and which should be applied to all persons charged with homicide. But the Raven's test is of limited value as some ten per cent of the general population could be placed in the lowest score category (Grade E), which is equivalent to an intelligence quotient of about 80. *Epilepsy* may be symptomatic or idiopathic and a plea of diminished responsibility by an epileptic may be based on one or more of three possibilities.

(i)   The crime may have been unconnected with the ictal episode.

(ii) As indicated in Chapter Nine, a plea of "not guilty, by reason of insane epileptic automatism" under the M'Naghten Rules, 'Criminal Procedure (Insanity and Unfitness to Plead) Act 1991', would be made if the homicide was allegedly committed during a period of clouding of consciousness associated with or replacing an ictus. East (1939) expressed the opinion that epilepsy is "comparatively infrequently" associated with murder or other crime. He also found ten epileptics amongst 300 individuals admitted to Broadmoor Special Hospital for treatment after committing homicide. Definite motivation for a homicide and cunning attempts at concealment would suggest clarity of consciousness at the material time.

(iii) The accused may be suffering from some form of mental disorder in addition to epilepsy.

Epilepsy secondary to organic cerebral pathology such as brain injury, cerebral tumour or cerebral arteriosclerosis, is referred to as idiopathic and not infrequently influenced by heredity. Cerebral pathology due to the above causes may or may not be associated with epilepsy. A plea of diminished responsibility on the grounds of organic cerebral pathology would succeed if a jury agreed that it was a disease causing abnormality of mind, as defined in the Homicide Act, 1957.

I shall now refer to court decisions on three individuals who pleaded diminished responsibility with the object of having their charges reduced from murder to manslaughter. I have had personal knowledge of these cases.

Case 1: A middle-aged man was charged with the murder of his wife. He pleaded not guilty to murder but guilty to manslaughter on the grounds of diminished responsibility. Two psychiatrists gave evidence to the effect that this plea was not applicable and a third psychiatrist stated that the plea did not apply to the accused. The defence alleged that the defendant had developed an obsession about his late wife and suffered from a paranoid complex concerning her alleged infidelity. This paranoid state was also said to be of such severity as to substantially impair his responsiblities for his actions in doing the killing. The defence psychiatrist alleged that the presence of the paranoid complex could be established if evidence was available to the effect that the defendant's late wife had not been unfaithful to him, and his son gave evidence to this effect. The plea of diminished responsibility was successful and the charge reduced to manslaughter. A sentence of ten years' imprisonment was imposed. One may conclude that a defence of diminished responsibility may succeed on the basis of alleged psychopathology such as paranoid personality and other abnormal attitudes which cannot be proved to exist but may be accepted by the jury as influencing an accused person. The psychiatric evidence against the plea of diminished responsibility in this case was based upon the following criteria:

(i)   no evidence whatsoever of mental disorder during the remand period of four months;

(ii)   no history of previous mental disorder: the accused had had no treatment for any psychiatric condition, even on an out-patient basis;

(iii) lack of any evidence of social incompetence prior to the homicide: the accused had in fact been working regularly up to the material time of the crime;

(iv)   there was no history of epilepsy, cerebral injury or organic disease which could have caused him to behave in an anti-social manner.

Case 2: A middle -aged man was charged with murdering his wife by inflicting head injuries with a blunt instrument. During the ten years preceding the crime he had been an in-patient in a psychiatric hospital on five occasions and had been diagnosed as a simple schizophrenic and inadequate psychopath. There was no evidence of psychosis or epilepsy during the remand period. The charge was reduced to manslaughter when the prosecution decided not to contest the plea of diminished responsibility. The accused expressed paranoid ideas about society in general.

Case 3: A man was charged with the murder of his two young children by suffocation. He subsequently attempted to dispose of their bodies by incineration and flushing down a toilet. A psychiatrist gave evidence that at the material time, the accused was suffering from reactive depression which was not of sufficient severity to justify a plea of diminished responsibility. There was no history of epilepsy or psychosis. Defence counsel suggested that the crimes were abnormal because of the manner of commission and mode of attempted disposal of the bodies and the psychiatrist was influenced in the witness box to alter his opinion and agree that diminished responsibility was applicable to the accused on the grounds that an abnormal crime indicated serious impairment of judgment which in turn indicated mental abnormality which substantially impaired his mental responsibility in doing the killings. This circular argument about an alleged abnormal crime would not necessarily imply serious impairment of judgment at the material time *unless the accused gave illogical reasons for his criminal behaviour*. In this instance he did not give any reason and had managed his affairs quite well before and after the crimes. The accused was convicted of murder on both counts when the plea was rejected by the jury. He was sentenced to life imprisonment. The Criminal Division of the Court of Appeal later substituted a conviction of manslaughter on the grounds of diminished responsibility.

Case 4: The Peter Sutcliffe case, however, had shown up difficulties about diminished responsibility and mental condition generally. Though doctors on both sides agreed that the Yorkshire Ripper was a paranoid schizophrenic, the jury found that diminished responsibility was not made out and he was convicted of 13 murders and seven attempted murders on August 22nd, 1981. He was sentenced to life imprisonment with a recommendation that he should serve at least 30 years . The jury was, of course, the final arbitrator, although Crown Prosecution, Defence Counsel and the then Attorney General had apparently agreed that Sutcliffe was suffering from paranoid schizophrenia even before he was arraigned. It is reasonable to assume the jury regarded him as a sexual sadist *per se*. Sutcliffe was sent to Broadmoor Special Hospital in March 1984 on the basis of a transfer direction under s.47 of the Mental Health Act 1983. The diagnosis was *paranoid schizophrenia*. A restriction order without limit of time, under s.49 of the Act, was added.

Comment: If Sutcliffe was mentally disordered for some six years immediately prior to his trial, the diagnosis was probably paranoia (as recognized by the World Health Organisation), as opposed to paranoid schizophrenia. His paranoid delusions and defective judgment obviously involved an obsessional and pathological hatred of women. However, he was capable of working regularly and planned his crimes with much cunning and even tried to "cover his tracks". He deceived the forces of law and order for a considerable time because the personality disintegration of schizophrenia was not, as yet, evident. Schizophrenia implies personality disintegration with anomalies of thought processes which are also incongruous with emotion and behaviour. Loss of empathy, thought-blocking, primary delusions, ideas of reference and control by outside influences, serious defects of judgment, autism, poverty of emotional responses, disturbances of perception, hallucinations, psychomotor retardation or excitation are also characteristic of schizophrenia. All of these symptoms would not necessarily be present at any particular time, but such an individual would not be capable of constructive planning or regular work in the community. In time, paranoia may, of course, degenerate further into paranoid schizophrenia. I had experience of an individual who pleaded diminished responsibility on the grounds of alleged schizophrenia. The plea was unsuccessful, and the psychiatric evidence was somewhat conflicting. During the course of the trial a psychiatrist was asked whether he would have diagnosed schizophrenia if the accused had not been charged with murder, a hypothetical question which cannot be satisfactorily answered by confining one's attention to the circumstances of the homicide. Consideration must also be given to any available psychiatric history, symptomatology and evidence of inability to cope with responsibility before the homicide.

A personal study of 50 unselected people convicted of murder gave the following results:

(a) the average age of the group was 34 years;
(b) 19 had very unhappy and insecure childhoods;
(c) the family histories of ten suggested psychopathic tendencies in one or both parents who apparently did not suffer from other forms of mental disorder;
(d) 32 suffered from varying degrees of psychopathy;
(e) 26 had previous convictions other than murder;
(f) 46 expressed relief of tension after the homicides;
(g) 34 had a life-long desire to escape anonymity;
(h) only eight expressed guilt feelings and all but 8 resented authority.

Comment: The majority did not have unhappy childhoods and

furthermore their future behaviour could not have been predicted on the basis of heredity. The majority expressed relief of tension after the killings, desire to escape anonymity, had no guilt feelings and all but eight resented authority. These are features which could be compatible with the psychopathy found in 32 of the study group. The absence of psychosis was incompatible with the fact that 979 people successfully pleaded diminished responsibility during the years 1979 to 1989 (inclusive) and 384 hospital orders under the Mental Health Acts of 1959 and 1983 were issued in respect of this group. Hospital orders are usually issued in respect of persons suffering from various forms of psychosis and mental impairment. The overall age was somewhat higher than expected.

References

East, W.N. (1939) *Psychological Treatment of Crime,* Home Office Report, 9, HMSO, London.

Haward, L.R.C. (1990) *Polygraph: A Dictionary of Forensic Psychology*, [pp. 103-104 Medilaw/Barry Rose, Chichester.]

Lykken, D.T. (1974) "Psychology and the Lie-Detector Industry", *American Psychology*, 2: 725.

CHAPTER IV

Some Social Factors in Crime

The neo-Freudian theory of crime postulates that the individual starts life as a self-centred organism intent on satisfying his own desires at all costs, and with no concern for the rights and convenience of others. He is aggressive and conscience is non-existent. As he develops, he gradually and painfully learns to live in harmony with others by taking into himself the values and standards of the society in which he lives. The process of social indoctrination requires the ritualistic repetition of generally accepted values, beliefs and standards.

The individual is frequently subjugated to the group in our society and always in totalitarian societies.

People tend to be subjected to pressures from groups, but the division of labour in our society is accompanied by a growth of individualism, with the result that traditional pressures of the group on the individual have become weaker, and to succeed each individual must be an achiever in a competitive world. These considerations may explain why crime tends to be low in traditional peasant societies and high in free, advanced industrial societies. Our society wishes people to conform but at the same time expects them to compete. We teach the child that he must respect the rights of others yet, later in life, when he ventures out into the world of business, he must expect to push himself and others to the limit of endurance in order to succeed in his particular enterprise. Such words as "aggressive" are used of salesmen as well as of offenders. If an individual is inadequately socialized and has not learned to live with others, he may come into conflict with the rest of society, a theory which the histories of many offenders supports. These views are also supported by Messner (1988) who indicated a relationship between violent crime and socio-economic factors such as hardships and deprivations. He also referred to the cultural theory to the effect that criminal violence could be the outcome of the normal processes of social learning and that certain social groups allegedly endorse values that are supportive of violent behaviour. These theories would obviously refer to a minority of persons.

Kolvin *et al* (1988) studied the relationship between deprivation and criminality across several generations, by follow-up studies of the families who took part in the Newcastle Thousand Family Survey. The relevant data including criminal records, had been preserved. The results indicated that children who grew up in deprived as opposed to non-deprived families, were definitely more at risk of offending during later childhood and beyond.

To illuminate the role of criminal activity among the homeless, particularly the homeless mentally ill, Fischer (1988) compared 634 arrests of homeless persons with 50,524 arrests in the general housed population that were made in Baltimore, USA. Significant differences were found in the demographic characteristics of the two groups of arrested persons and in the types of offences prompting the arrests. Among the homeless, those arrested tended to be male, white, and over the age of 45 and to have committed trivial, victimless crimes and the minority who committed more serious crimes such as assault and burglary tended to be primarily motivated by a desire to maintain subsistence in the absence of housing.

Penrose (1945) indicated that a country's prison population varies inversely with its mental hospital population. The law is broadly true for Western Europe and follows from statistical analyses of the two populations indicating the existence of a large overlap between the two, as much as 85 per cent (Guze, 1976) and also demonstrating the sociological importance of the concept of the mentally abnormal offender. A large proportion of prisoners display psychiatric signs and symptoms, and a large proportion of psychiatric inpatients have behaved in a criminal manner. Penrose's Law is believed to reflect the effects of social labelling, the same group moving from one type of institution to the other as social attitudes change or political expediency dictates. In my experience this law is generally true today but for the less serious criminal offences committed by males. The extension of community psychiatric care could make Penrose's Law obsolete.

Bowlby (1957) advanced the theory that deprivation, or the poor quality of mother love during childhood could lead to normal intellectual development but warped emotional development. One may reasonably assume that Bowlby's theories have social significance beyond the immediate effects of maternal deprivation, and consequently there might be some justification for limiting the employment of mothers, who probably constitute the majority of the 36 per cent of married women employed in our economy. On the other hand, the children of working mothers may do better at school because they have had the benefit of attending nursery schools.

Hood (1966) showed that long periods of institutionalization, including time in children's homes, are correlated with social failure by the criterion of subsequent reconviction of those who underwent Borstal training, although time spent in children's homes cannot specifically be held responsible for subsequent lawbreaking.

In modern society the need of the majority for law and order conflicts with society's demand that the individual exercises individual judgment and autonomy.

Crime may be regarded as having a function, in that it allows society to restate its norms by dealing with offenders through the criminal courts. Merton (1957) described the conflict between the goals that were supposed to be important for everyone and the differential availability of the means of attaining them. As everyone cannot get to the top by honest means, some people will utilize crime to gain advancement when no other avenue is open to them. In the context of the Merton theory, it is easy to understand why "big time" criminals frequently invest their ill-gotten gains in legitimate business.

The lawbreaking gang is a social unit at variance with society in general. Gangs are essentially metropolitan and recruit from the under-privileged, slum-dwellers, coloured people, children of broken homes and the unemployed. The gang acts as a cohesive force in the lives of certain young people whose motto appears to be that "if life is not lived today, it may not be livable tomorrow" (Morris, 1957). The gang tends to diminish the frequent psychic traumata generated by personal and family disorganization. The forces of society are seen as hostile, whether they be teachers, policemen, social workers, employers, or the judiciary, and the greater the pressure imposed by society the greater the role of the gang in maintaining its own identity, fear of the loss of which tends to arouse intense resentment possibly leading to further and more serious lawbreaking.

Miller (1962) lists six focal concerns of social classes four and five:

(i)   *Trouble.* For males usually means trouble with the law, but for females it usually means sexual involvement with disadvantageous consequences. Trouble can be a status symbol for some but for others it is a source of negative status.

(ii) **Toughness,** which is a combination of physical strength and strong volition.

(iii) **Excitement** is sought because life is rather boring and getting into trouble, such as rioting and looting, means getting into exciting situations.

(iv) **Consciousness of fate.** The average unskilled worker, however hard he works, will never significantly alter his situation, which explains the popularity of gambling in our society.

(v) **Astuteness of mind.** Working-class culture is also concerned with a particular astuteness of mind expressed by the ability to make money by card playing and backing horses. This astuteness is also expressed by quickness of wit and exemplified by the continual joking that takes place at work. Such astuteness draws admiration from members of their own group.

(vi) **Autonomy** which is expressed by a desire for independence and a rejection of old values.

The degree of severity of crimes involving theft, violence, sex or destruction of property will depend individually and collectively upon personality type and chance environmental happenings. People with serious personality defects tend to break the law more frequently than those who have well-integrated personalities. Tatum (1988) studied 60 individuals who had life-long histories of eccentricity and social isolation. They were predominantly young males and the majority were of average intelligence. Lack of social confidence, inability or unwillingness to live independently, evanescent sexual relationships and poor work records characterized all or the great majority of the study group. Some 50 per cent of the group indulged in antisocial behaviour and nearly 25 per cent committed offences including criminal damage, indecent exposure, arson, attempted rape and other forms of violence usually directed against their mothers. Some 48 per cent suffered from secondary psychiatric disorders such as anxiety and obsessional states, neurotic depression and paranoid, manic-depressive, organic and schizophrenic psychoses. The psychoses accounted for 11.7 per cent of the total group. Horror videos and pornography whether "soft" or "hard" and however presented will precipitate violence in a small but not negligible, minority of persons who are so *predisposed.* Alcohol and/or illicit drugs will further increase these tendencies.

The spread of crime

Wilkins (1960) studied individuals found guilty of indictable offences during 1946-57 with special emphasis on those born during 1925-6 and 1948-9. He found that people who lived through their fifth year during the 1939-45 war, had the greatest tendency to indulge in subsequent lawbreaking. The inference is that disruptive social conditions such as the breakup of families, living in a strange environment, undue danger to near relatives, relative poverty, homelessness and general insecurity, may have most damaging psychological effects on children during the fifth year of their lives. These particular groups were referred to as delinquent generations.

There is an increase in the amount of material property available to be stolen. But there has been a spread of crime across class boundaries since the end of the 1939-45 war, which is more difficult to explain. There is an increase in the number of juvenile delinquents coming from the families of skilled and white-collar groups. One of the most common offences is the taking and driving away of motor vehicles without the owner's consent. Car thieves do not necessarily come from broken or unsatisfactory homes. Car stealing is an expression of group delinquency and this type of offence may be regarded as a need to express masculinity.

Youth culture is essentially classless and so consequently juvenile delinquency is not confined to any particular class of persons. Crime is influenced by the age factor and one notes that middle-aged persons rarely indulge in taking and driving away cars.

Organized professional crime is important here because of its tendency to spread. The volume of highly planned crime has increased during the past 20 years and detection has not been possible in many instances. Crime is now organized with a fair degree of sophistication. Large-scale organized gambling is legal in Britain and the police are well aware that such gambling is associated with crime. Violence is sometimes practised by certain criminal types because gambling debts are not recoverable in law.

Patterns of Crime

Criminologists now tend to concentrate their studies on particular patterns of crime. It is of little value, for example, to study violent crime solely in terms of the psychopathology of the offender. We must know the circumstances under which certain individuals resort to violence. It is more important to appreciate that a husband may kill his wife because of morbid jealousy rather than because he had an unhappy childhood.

Miller (1962) postulates three inter-related factors in the genesis of crime:

(i)   the psychological factors, meaning the individuals who are intelligent, domineering and emotionally labile by nature;

(ii)   the family factors, meaning various frustrations at home such as sibling rivalry and lack of rapport with parents;

(iii) the social factor, indicating an attempt to become the centre of attraction in an anti-social group in order to compensate for feelings of neglect and rejection by the immediate family.

Personality development is the result of two processes, the first being the individual's response to the living and non-living environment in which he lives, and the second, the expression of inner capacitites that lead the individual to explore and attempt to change the world about him. Young people may be active politically and yet feel frustrated at their apparent inability to change things. There is the problem of the delinquent who actively rebels against the existing social order.

The provisions for social security, while preventing material hardship, may not compensate for the humiliation of idleness.

Both sex and drugs are themes that stimulate social excitement, leading some adults to take up an unduly inhibited position, and others to go to the opposite extreme.

The following remarks do not refer to sexual deviation secondary to mental disorder. Heredity and environmental factors are concerned in the aetiology of sexual deviation but environmental ones are the most important. In the matter of sex education, children and adolescents may be taught the "wrong lesson" leading to fear of members of the opposite sex, or undue affection for members of the same sex. They may learn the right lesson too well, and consequently, fail to develop normal inhibitions in sexual matters. Offences such as rape and indecent assault may result. Yet again, they may not be taught any lesson at all and this ignorance of sexual matters may lead to bisexual activities.

Violent Crime

Criminal statistics may be crude or refined and are usually incomplete. Crimes which are not reported to the police are referred to satistically as "dark figures" and cause concern because of implications of threats, intimidation and blackmail.

The total number of notified offences recorded by the police for England and Wales for the period July 1991 to June 1992 (inclusive), was 5,459,4000, as compared with 4,928,700 recorded between July 1990 and June 1991.

During the period July 1991 and June 1992, some 95 per cent of crimes were against property and violent offences accounted for only 5 per cent. The following table gives the distribution of violent crime.

Table IV
*Notifiable offences recorded by the police by offence

England and Wales	Number of offences (thousands) and percentages			
Offence group	12 months ending		Change	
	June 1991	June 1992	Number	Percentage
Violence against the person	186.4	199.5	13.1	6.6
Sexual offences	29.3	29.7	0.4	1.4
Robbery	39.8	49.5	9.7	19.6
Burglary	1,113.8	1,286.7	172.9	13.4
Total theft & handling stolen goods	2,583.3	2,825.9	242.6	8.6
Vehicle crime	1,405.8	1,503.0	97.2	6.5
Fraud and forgery	164.2	174.6	10.4	6.0
Criminal damage	779.0	856.0	77.0	9.0
Other notifiable offence	32.8	37.5	4.7	12.5
Total all offences	6334.4	6962.4	628.0	9.0

The totals of above offences for 1993 and 1994 were 5526.3 and 5251.1 respectively.

The average annual increase in all notifiable offences over the last decade was 6 per cent.

About 3 times more cases of crime against the person are solved as opposed to crime against property and this general trend is evident from year to year. This relatively high detection rate reflects to some extent the greater police attention given to dealing with crimes against the person because of the public anxiety caused when violent and sexual offenders remain at large in the community, but it also reflects the fact that many such offenders are known to the victims who can therefore usually give

*   Notifiable offences for England and Wales, July 1991 to June 1992, Home Office Statistical Bulletin, July 1992, Research and Statistics Dept., 50 Queen Annes Gate, London.

fairly accurate information to the police and consequently no great problem of detection arises.

About 30 per cent of all crimes remain unsolved.

"Mugging" has become prominent in recent years and may be defined as the infliction of physical violence in an urban or "street" setting, in the furtherance of theft. The violence may be of minor or severe degree. The definition of mugging does not include injuries caused by motor vehicles.

The offenders may or may not be under the influence of alcohol and/or drugs and the great majority are not mentally disordered, but "emotional" problems are often pleaded by defence Counsels. It is obvious that the victims tend to suffer from post-traumatic emotional disturbances.

Norris *et al.* (1990) stressed the value of mental health services for the victims of this type of crime and 392 such victims were studied. Those who had recovered most rapidly had received early treatment from these services.

Flint *et al.* (1992) stressed the importance of education programmes for critical-care surgeons, specialists who treat trauma victims who do not need critical care and those in charge of urban hospitals which care for the poor and needy in New Orleans. Some progress has been made with the object of resolving conflicts involving these care systems in the context of treating the victims of urban violence. It is not clear if psychiatric care facilities were included in this study.

Whaley (1992) indicated that interpersonal violence is a major problem for black youths living in poor urban areas. Divers lines of research suggest that interpersonal violence involving inner-city black youth may be the result of environmental stresses, racial identity problems and mental and physical ill-health. The author indicates the importance of a culturally sensitive approach resulting in more attention to the prevention of interpersonal violence among black youth.

Only about 10 per cent of the police service are detectives and comparitively few of the remainder will become involved with any frequency in the detection of violent offenders, although of course the police give investigation of crimes of violence relatively high priority.

Unemployment and Crime

I would like to make some reference to the implications of unemployment.

Three phases of unemployment were described by Eisenberg (1938).

1.   Feeling of shock and disbelief followed by optimism and

appreciation of a well-deserved holiday, especially when adequate payments are made.

2. Increasing worry and despondency when the individual realizes the seriousness of the problem. Discouragement, loss of confidence and self-esteem and discord within the family follow serious but unsuccessful attempts to find work. Neurotic disorders, depression and hostility may occur.

3. The third phase is characterized by "non-occupational" identity. He or she experiences feelings of helplessness and submissiveness and work is not sought regularly, as the person is convinced there is little hope of success. Conscientious people will also be emotionally disturbed by the realization that they are a burden on the state.

All unemployed people do not necessarily experience all the above phases. Unemployment is more worrying for married people with families. Other stresses tend to have cumulative effects when people are out of work. Brenner (1973) indicates that suicide and homicide rates and admissions to mental hospitals are influenced by lack of employment. Crime rates, including inner-city rioting and football hooliganism are likely to be increased by idleness. The fact that people are unemployed does not necessarily mean that they cannot obtain money to attend "away" games.

Idleness results in a fall in income and financial worries. Those who are unemployed or have little work to do, tend to live in a restricted environment because they meet fewer people and lack money to socialize. The quality of interpersonal contacts is also reduced, leading to decline in social position. Most people find their work interesting and stimulating, and consequently initiative and the development of new skills are encouraged. Unemployment deprives people of these experiences. Indecisiveness may also be a product of unemployment because decision-making is encouraged and becomes habitual in the work situation. The great majority of people who are out of work feel threatened, humiliated and anxious about the future. Fear of becoming unemployable and loss of self-respect are also experienced. Idleness also causes increased family tensions and divorce rates. Warr (1989) also indicated that unemployment, especially when prolonged, is associated with a higher incidence of impairment of mental health, suicide and suicidal attempts than in the employed population. Idleness also causes excessive cigarette smoking but alcohol tends to be taken to excess only by heavy drinkers. Smith (1991) agrees with the investigations of Eales (1988) to the effect that 14 per cent of a group of 80 unemployed men, suffered from depression and anxiety.

Professor Linford Rees (1981) made four recommendations. First, full-scale prospective longitudinal studies should be started to define the psychological and physical hazards of unemployment more precisely and find ways of obviating them and to identify high-risk groups. Secondly, counselling and services should be provided for the unemployed and those due to be made redundant, to help them to use their time more effectively and maintain their morale. Thirdly, adequate programmes of job creation and training are needed for all grades of work. Finally, doctors and social workers should be alert to the adverse effects of unemployment both on the unemployed person and on the family, and general practitioners in particular should be on the lookout for anxiety and depressive states.

Racism

In the context of racism, the opinion is generally held by coloured people that the acting out of prejudices against them is much more harmful than the prejudices themselves. For example, will coloured people be accepted in a housing area predominantly occupied by white people? The Faulkner housing estate in Liverpool was built by the City Council as part of its slum-clearance programme and a high proportion of black families were allocated houses. It is alleged that in August 1971, white vigilante squads began a series of attacks on blacks in protest at the council's policy. Other issues are whether coloured children will be accepted in a school in which the majority of pupils are white; whether positions of shared responsibility are denied to coloured people; whether coloured people are permitted to participate freely and fairly in business enterprises.

The police have been criticized for their attitudes to coloured people, but the fact that insufficient numbers of coloured people join the police force does not in itself mean that the police are racist.

Coloured people who believe that they are under privileged and who may lead a ghetto-type existence may also believe that the society in which they live is optionless as far as they are concerned, and such beliefs may generate violence. Polarization of resentments could occur if coloured police officers were made responsible for law and order only in areas inhabited predominantly by coloured people and *vice versa*.

Liverpool's ethnic minorities, 40,000 strong, make up between 8 and ten per cent of the city's population. The area profile group issued a report in 1983 which indicated that only three black trainee nurses out of a total of 306 were employed by the Liverpool Area Health Authority. Furthermore, the City Council allegedly employed fewer than 300 black staff out of 31,000. It is also alleged that only 15 per cent of 739 places on work-experience programmes run by Liverpool Manpower Services Commission in 1982 were occupied by black people.

Rioting

It is reasonable to assume a relationship exists between racism, unemployment and inner-city rioting. Geoffrey Dear, Chief Constable, West Midlands, made some relevant comments to the Handsworth riots which occurred in Birmingham in September 1985. He voiced the opinion that the rioting was deliberately started by drug dealers in retaliation for police raids. He was working on the assumption that those who control organized crime will make use of discontented young people for their own purposes. He also stated that leaflets giving instructions on how to make petrol bombs were distributed on the second day of the rioting.

Chief Constable Dear and Lord Scarman share the belief that the use of plastic bullets is justified in order to re-establish law and order when a riot reaches such a degree of intensity that lives are threatened. It is much preferable for the police to control a riot rather than have recourse to army intervention. There is no incompatibility between using vigorous means, including plastic bullets, to suppress a serious large-scale riot where lives are put at risk, and police officers attempting to establish good relationships with ethnic minorities in the same inner-city areas. Lord Scarman also indicated that social justice must be established by understanding the social conditions which cause inner-city riots. Failure of a person from an ethnic minority to assimilate successfully into the host society leads to feelings of isolation, alienation, frustration, bitterness and hostility. Such assimilation may fail because of the resentment generated when an ethnic minority justifiably refuses to adopt the customs of the host society. Poor rapport between the police and ethnic minorities has also been alleged as a cause of rioting. There is another proposal to give employment to young black people by providing government funds to rebuild inner-city areas. Local authorities and the Department of Health and Social Security would also co-operate in this venture.

A report sponsored by the West Midlands County Council entitled "A Different Reality" (1986) was in the form of a non-judicial independent inquiry into the Handsworth riots. This report rather strongly disagreed with Chief Constable Dear's views and it alleges that the black community of Handsworth is subjected to social deprivation, racial disadvantage, harsh policing and day-to-day oppression which leads to violent resistance. The report recommended that blacks be given a say in decision-making by public sector agencies and local authorities and also advocates greater investment in black areas and stronger laws to stamp out racial discrimination. The report also indicates that of 6,650 police officers in the West Midlands force, only 95 are from ethnic minorities. It could be that members of such minorities do not apply to join the police force in sufficient numbers because of apprehension that they could be scorned by their own ethnic group as a result of joining the forces of law and order. The report also indicates that black people will accept nothing less than equal treatment, justice and control of their own destiny.

The Bradford riots by young Muslims in June 1995 were caused by a strong sense of alienation based on rejection of the immoral aspects of British culture such as prostitution, sexual perversion and drug abuse. Other sources of discontent included unemployment (allegedly 30 per cent among Muslims in Bradford) and the alleged unfriendly police who blame widening of the generation gap between young Muslims and their law-abiding leaders. Leaders of the Asian community were unable to prevent the riots.

Interrogation:

The Chief Superintendent of Hendon Police College (1991) indicates that the purpose of interrogation should be to gather information and that interrogators should adopt a kindly manner and be aware of the ethics and psychology of correct questioning and use of conversational skills. Accurate recording of data using written and audiovisual media is also essential.

> "Confessions are the primary aims of police interrogations and 80 per cent of all crimes are said to be solved by this method, and convictions would fall by more than 70 per cent without them." (Brandon, 1973.) "Confessions not only shorten police time considerably, but once made, often precede other statements which lead to the arrest of accessories, recovery of stolen property, or ***corroborative***

incriminating real evidence, such as the murder weapon."
(Gudjonsonn, 1983.) "False confessions, which contributed to the
development of the European witch hunts of the 16th and 17th
century, today still cause social concern. Miscarriages of justice
continue to occur from false confessions, such as that for Timothy
Evans, pardoned seven years after his execution for murder." (Haward,
1990.) "Confession is the most attractive way of solving crimes.
Getting one should be recognized as a genuine temptation." (Mr.
Justice Barry, 1963.)

Four methods have been used to test the validity of confessions:

(a) Formal structure analysis, a method of attributing a level of
     confidence by correlating statements made by any witness, the
     accused and the policeman recording the "confession" (Trankell,
     1982);
(b) Reading facility index used to match the confession with other
     statements by the accused;
(c) Stylometry, is the linguistic analysis of origin of statements. This
     is the preferred method and its validity was first established half
     a century ago. The method has developed with computer
     analysis into one of highly sophisticated refinement.
(d) The electrostatic detection apparatus.

The questioning and treatment of persons by the police are now
controlled by the Police and Criminal Evidence Act 1984 and the
accompanying "Code of Practice". Section 76 of the Act provides that
statements obtained by pressure, or in consequence of anything said or
done which was likely in the circumstances existing at the time to render
unreliable any confession, should be excluded by the court.

MacKeith *et al.* (1990) studied 200 false confessions and found that
autosuggestion and undue compliance are important contributory factors.
Adverse family history, miserable childhood and adolescence and
abnormal mental state may increase the likelihood of an individual
making a false confession when a police officer asks ... 'do you now wish
to make any statement?'

The subject of confessions in relation to psychiatric evidence is
considered in Chapter I.

Social and environmental factors may influence illicit drug-taking

The second report of the Brain Committee on drug addiction was published in 1965. This report stressed the element of "contamination", meaning that addicts have a strong tendency to pass on their illicit drug-taking habits to susceptible individuals.

Trafficking in illicit drugs tends to spread from dock areas to adjacent city centres because every ship which docks in a port is a potential carrier of illicit drugs.

Publicity through the media concerning the effects and consequences of illicit drug-taking may well arouse curiosity and influence some immature young people to experiment by taking drugs such as cannabis, amphetamines and lysergic acid. This type of experimentation may lead to addiction or habituation.

Studies in the United States reveal that poverty *per se* is not an important causal factor in drug addiction. Drug abuse is a general problem in "free" societies and likely to become more urgent as populations increase and communications become more widespread and efficient, resulting in drugs of addiction becoming more readily available.

Drug addiction is largely a product of chemical advance and chemistry should provide a solution to the problem, having helped to create it.

Adequate information to the public as to the harmful effects of illicit drug taking is an important factor in prevention.

The drug problem in New York represents about 50 per cent of the total drug problem in the United States.

Drug "pushers" are usually addicted and the prospect of making "fast" money is invariably an overwhelming temptation.

Poor social conditions in which deprived people live form a breeding ground for illicit drug-taking and "pushing". Deprived people feel that they are denied social recognition and are regarded as second-class citizens by the establishment of the country in which they live. Deprivation is not synonymous with poverty nor is it confined to minorities – coloured or otherwise.

Young drug dependents tend to meet in cafes in cities and towns where illicit drugs are bought and exchanged.

A drug such as morphine may be administered to relieve the pain of physical illness or injury and habituation or addiction may follow.

Early signs of illicit drug-taking may be noticed in children and adolescents. The following pointers are relevant even though adolescence is characterized by inconsistent behaviour patterns.

(i)   At school – sudden loss of interest and performance in studies or sports, general evasiveness, truancy, and problems over discipline. Unaccountable depression or cheerfulness at work and play over a period should lead to suspicion.

(ii)   At home – unaccountable changes in habits and moods, loss of appetite and weight, and the sudden development of clandestine friendships, especially with older people. A personality change which persists and for which the parents can find no rational explanation should lead to suspicion of illicit drug-taking and parents should keep this possibility in mind. The unexpected discovery of tablets, capsules or peculiar-smelling cigarettes in the home should prompt parents to make further inquiries in regard to the children. Unexpected decline in personal appearance and hygiene could be significant.

(iii) At work – late time-keeping, frequent changes of occupation, problems with employers and failure to settle down.

Alcoholism

Alcoholism is a wide-ranging social problem rather than purely and simply an illness. One can only successfully deal with it by approaching it from both aspects.

The first difficulty is to define it, which the second report of the World Health Organization Sub-Committee on Alcoholism did in 1952 as follows:

> Alocholics are those excessive drinkers whose dependence upon alcohol has attained such a degree that they show a noticeable mental disturbance or an interference with their bodily, mental and spiritual health and their smooth social and economic functioning, or who show prodromal signs of such developments and they therefore require treatment.

Excessive drinking is any form of drinking which goes beyond traditional and customary dietary use or beyond the ordinary social drinking customs of a given community. Both these definitions are relative and sociological, rather than absolute.

The factors diagnostic of addictive or non-addictive types of alcoholism as described by Jellinek (1952) are first an overpowering need or desire to continue taking alcohol and to obtain it by any means, secondly a tendency to increase the dose, and finally the development of psychological and physical dependence upon it.

The addictive alcoholic has an obsessive compulsion to continue taking alcohol and in common with the non-addictive alcoholic takes alcohol to counteract anxiety, tension, despondency and fear of social isolation. This is a mental illness. Both are distinguished from the social drinker, although the boundaries may be rather indistinct when consumption exceeds approximately five pints of beer or 10 units of spirits daily.

The Report of the Health Education Advisory Committee for Wales (1987) undertook a general survey in the context of the problem caused by alcohol consumption in the U.K. and came to the following conclusions:

The cost to British industry of alcohol misuse was £1,614,000,000 in 1983 and involved 8 to 15,000,000 working days lost yearly due to alcohol-induced sickness. The cost would obviously be higher in 1995 and would not include the cost to society of family stress and the burden placed on probation and social services.

Excessive consumption is also involved in:

60 per cent of para suicide attempts;
54 per cent of fire fatalities;
50 per cent of homicides;
42 per cent of serious head injuries;
30 per cent of deaths through drowning;
30 per cent of domestic accidents;
10 per cent of deaths in persons under 25;
33 per cent of divorce petitions cite alcohol as a major factor;
20 per cent of general male hospital admissions;
30 per cent of child abuse cases.

Epidemiology
There are inherent difficulties in estimating the incidence of alcoholism and a number of alternative methods have been tried. In the first place, although the World Health Organization definition of alcoholism is generally accepted, it is open to a variety of interpretations and obviously the accuracy of estimates of incidence must depend on the accuracy of the definition of the condition and a variation of definition will produce a variation in prevalence (Clark, 1966).

A variety of alternative ways of estimating the incidence of alcoholism have been used, such as hospital admissions, road accident statistics, drunkenness arrests, and illnesses due to alcoholism, including cirrhosis of the liver.

Jellinek's formula, which relates the incidence of alcoholism to the incidence of cirrhosis of the liver, is based on the assumption that when alcohol consumption is low, deaths from cirrhosis of the liver attributable to alcoholism are correspondingly low. He compared four periods of American history to reach his conclusions. This formula gives a prevalence of 11 per thousand of the population for England and Wales or 360,000 alcoholics (Hore, 1976).

The formula is open to question for a variety of reasons and particularly the unreliability of figures of alcohol-related cirrhosis mortality, possibly because doctors either fail to identify alcoholism or refrain from including it in the death certificate out of respect for the feelings of the family. The World Health Organization has accepted a figure of 550,000 alcoholics in England and Wales. In 1977, Donnan and Haskey indicated that in England and Wales 750,000 people suffered from alcohol abuse to such an extent that their lives and health had been seriously damaged. Steel (1986) indicated that this statistic was still valid for 1984-85.

However, Alcohol Concern indicates that 9 per cent of the population of the U.K. (7 per cent males and 2 per cent females) take alcohol in amounts injurious to health, namely more than 51 units per week for males and over 36 units for females. The inference is that 9 per cent of the population of some 60,000,000 of the U.K. are alcoholic or potentially alcoholic. This is an astonishingly high figure. These are figures for 1990 and the latest available.

Alcoholism is not unknown in members of the medical profession. The General Medical Council (1973) reported that the largest category among disciplinary cases concerning psychiatric illness in doctors was those addicted to alcohol and drugs. Murray (1976) in his Scottish study found that first admission rates for alcohol dependence were 2.7 times higher in doctors than in socio-economic class 1 controls. He also showed that the death rate from liver cirrhosis among doctors in England and Wales was 3.5 times that in the general population. Most studies suggest that alcohol-dependent doctors tend to present later for treatment, often have to be treated compulsorily, are more difficult to manage in hospital and discharge themselves against medical advice.

Lloyd (1990) studied 100 doctors who suffered from alcohol and drug dependence and found that 76 achieved sustained recovery for an average of nearly 5 and a half years after attending self-help groups (at various times) for six-month periods. Some 53 doctors were referred to the Health Committee of the GMC for alcohol and/or drug abuse from 1981 and 1993.

Vaillant *et al* (1972) alleged that personalities who are unduly vulnerable emotionally are attracted to medicine. Consequently, work stress cannot be the only factor in alcohol and/or drug dependence. The obsessive compulsive personality combined with unhappiness and insecurity in childhood and adolescence tended to predispose to psychiatric disorder. Alcoholism and illicit drug-taking could be expressions of such disorder. Lloyd *et al* (1984) noted this type of personality in 20 per cent of a medical student population. Thapar (1990) indicated that it is evident that both occupational stress and personality play an important role in the genesis of psychiatric morbidity. Probably the true cause lies somewhere between, with the interpretation of both factors. Firth-Cozens (1987) estimated prevalence of emotional disturbance among junior doctors as 50 per cent.

The drinking pattern of the addictive alcoholic in the wine-producing countries where continuous wine drinking is the rule, is different. Here addicts show overt evidence of drunkenness because there is a more or less constant process of "topping up" leading to a slow rise in, and a relatively stable, blood alcohol level.

Phases of Alcoholism (from Jellinek)
An addictive alcoholic goes through three phases (i) prodromal, (ii) crucial, and (iii) chronic. Table 5 is adapted from Jellinek with some modifications.

Table V

Phases of Alcoholism (from Jellinek)

		Onset of loss of control and amnesic periods begin with increased alcoholic tolerance		Onset of prolonged intoxication	
Relies on toxic effects of alcohol to relieve tension		Onset of paranoid ideas and personality deterioration		Decrease in alcohol tolerance	
Social drinking	Non-addictive symptomatic alcoholism	Prodromal Phase (6 months- 5 years)	Crucial Phase	Chronic Phase	Personal habits deteriorate and dementia may ensue

15-20 yrs Addictive Alcoholism

(i) The prodromal phase begins with evidence of loss of control already described and is also characterized by periods of amnesia for events which occurred during a drinking bout. Such periods of memory loss are usually due to interference with cerebral metabolism but sometimes to loss of consciousness during a drinking bout. Fear of social censure soon leads to surreptitious drinking and obsessional preoccupation with alcohol. When the addictive alcoholic attends a social function his main concern is whether sufficient alcohol will be provided to satisfy his needs. The average duration of this phase is six months to five years.

(ii) In the crucial phase the alcoholic tries to rationalize his drinking behaviour. Loss of self-esteem and feelings of guilt and remorse are inevitable and he tries to compensate by grandiose and extravagant behaviour. Emotional lability is evident. He loses friends and social isolation follows. The addict also tends to project his guilt feelings on to others and this leads to paranoid attitudes and jealousy which in turn lead to occupational and marital difficulties.

He next begins to take elaborate steps to protect his supply of alcohol and the first hospital admission usually occurs during this phase. The crucial phase is characterized by a great struggle on the part of the addict against complete loss of social footing. He may be able to cope with his job but neglects his family.

(iii) The chronic phase begins with prolonged intoxication when drinking bouts become more frequent and the day's drinking begins in the early morning. Indefinable fears, ethical deterioration and impaired thinking become evident. He gradually descends the social scale, tends to associate with unsuitable companions and frequents places of low repute and may become involved with the police because of theft, assault or sexual indiscretions. Neglect of diet results in malnutrition and symptoms of vitamin deficiency. His compensatory rationalization usually fails him at this stage, he admits defeat and usually becomes accessible to treatment at this point. This phase is also characterized by diminished tolerance of alcohol and a comparatively small quantity may cause a transient psychotic episode of sudden onset. Characteristic of this episode are clouding of consciousness, senseless rage, aggression, excitation, illusions, hallucinosis and delusional ideas. He may inflict injuries on innocent people when in this condition, which lasts for a few hours to several days, and is terminated by a prolonged sleep. Subsequent amnesia is characteristic. I believe that the term "pathological drunkenness" (also called *mania a potu*) should be restricted to this condition.

Similar episodes may be caused when alcohol in small quantities is taken by epileptics, psychopaths and a proportion of those who have recovered from fairly serious head injuries.

Alcohol dementia may be regarded as the eventual outcome of the chronic phase, and affects a minority of addictive drinkers, especially in the absence of treatment.

Two clinical syndromes commonly occur during the chronic phase of addictive alcoholism but may also become manifest in the non-addictive alcoholic of some years' standing. The syndrome may be (i) of acute onset including delirium tremens, "pathological drunkenness" and acute alcoholic hallucinosis; (ii) chronic alcoholic hallucinosis, Korsakov's psychosis and the Ganser syndrome. Alcoholism is one of the causes of Korsakov's psychosis which is characterized by amnesia of varying degree for some years before the psychosis is established. A memory defect for recent events is particularly evident. Whitty and Zangwill (1966) stated that "a fixation amnesia with a facile and expansive confabulation" is a common feature. Similar neuropathological processes underly Wernicke's encephalopathy and Korsakov's psychosis.

Norvig and Nielson (1956) in a follow-up of 221 male alcoholics for periods varying from two-and-three-quarters to five-and-a-quarter years after discharge from hospital found that during this period 15 (7 per cent) committed suicide. Robins *et al* (1959) studied a series of 119 consecutive suicides and found that 31 (26 per cent) of the series had histories of alcoholism. These workers also found that 77 per cent of alcoholics who committed suicide had previously disclosed their intention.

Aetiology of Alcoholism

The more formal factors in the aetiology of alcoholism may be considered under four headings: (i) psychological, (ii) hereditary, (iii) metabolic and (iv) social.

(i) Psychological

Almost all investigators have considered that a person has to be psychologically unstable before he can become an alcoholic and there has been argument as to whether a person with a stable personality can become one. French workers, particularly of the older school, have always maintained that this can happen and their viewpoint has to be considered against the background of the national attitude towards drinking in France and the prejudices inherent in a country where a considerable part of the national economy is devoted to the production, marketing, exporting and consumption of wines and spirits. My own view is that it may happen rarely than an emotionally stable person who overdrinks for social reasons over a period of years, becomes an alcoholic, but generally speaking, the condition occurs in emotionally unstable people.

Alcohol is initially taken to control anxiety and tension, and gradually the individual becomes conditioned to depend more and more on this artificial aid to adjustment. Alcoholism may be symptomatic of many mental disorders. Some alcoholics are psychopathic personalities, but these form a minority group and the conditions are not synonymous. However, the psychopaths are important in that they need a different approach from the other patients and it is essential to recognize them because of the disruptive and morale-lowering effect which they have on other alcoholics undergoing in-patient hospital treatment or in Alcoholics Anonymous. Psychologists allege that even addictive alcoholism *per se* is not a mental illness and would respond to "conditioning" therapy.

An interesting investigation by Cade (1956) gives some insight into some psychological factors behind alcoholism in Australia where the incidence of alcoholism is ten times greater in males than in females, which is probably culturally determined, as drinking in females is frowned upon. He found that alcoholism constituted 40 per cent of the male admissions (as opposed to eight per cent of female admissions) to an acute psychiatric unit and he found that the sum of admissions for alcoholism and depression were roughly equal for the two sexes. From this he deduced that males tend to use alcohol to deal with emotional problems, whereas females who do not do so tend to fall into a depression instead. Widows of alcoholics tend to remarry alcoholics, indicating that some women may choose alcoholic husbands possibly to satisfy emotional needs in themselves.

In the United Kingdom, the incidence of alcoholism used to be six times greater in males than in females but the sex ratio is now about equal.

Williams (1968) divides alcoholics into four categories:

(1) Good - meaning the regular social drinker;
(2) Mad   - meaning the depressives and schizophrenics;
(3) Sad   - meaning the chronic inadequates;
(4) Bad   - meaning the psychopathic personalities.

The psychoanalytic theory assumes that alcoholism is a defence against anxiety and therefore a feature of a number of psychiatric states. If alcohol relieves the inhibitions of neurotic or emotionally unstable humans, such relief may act as reinforcement to further drinking and therefore to the development of alcoholism. Research has shown that health problems come with drinking over these amounts:

Table VI
Relationship between units and quantity of alcohol:

Men	Women	
21-35 units a week – risky	14-21 units a week – risky	
36 units or more a week – dangerous	22 or more units a week – dangerous	

		Units
BEERS AND LAGERS		
Ordinary strength beer or lager	1 pint	2
CIDERS		
Average cider	1 pint	3
SPIRITS		
	1 standard single measure in most of England and Wales (1/6 gill)	1
TABLE WINE (including cider wine and barley wine)	1 standard glass	1
SHERRY AND FORTIFIED WINE		
	1 standard small measure	1

These figures are approximate

Table VII
Rate of Elimination of Alcohol from the Body

On average it takes one hour for the body to get rid of
the alcohol in one unit

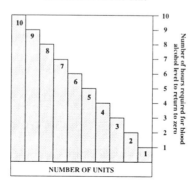

(ii) Hereditary

Heredity has been implicated in various ways but nobody has suggested that alcoholism is inherited as a primary trait. Schachter and Cotte (1950) carried out investigations which suggested that alcohol had a direct effect on the germ cells. They assessed the intelligence quotients of 234 children of alcoholics and used 336 children of non-alcoholics as controls. The intelligence quotients were within normal limits in 56 per cent of alcoholics as compared with 71 per cent of the controls. Retarded learning ability was noted in 22 per cent of the offspring of the alcoholics as compared with 12 per cent of the controls.

Amark (1951) found no excess of schizophrenia, manic-depressive psychosis, epilepsy or mental impairment in the relatives of 645 alcoholics but he found that 15 per cent of the latter were psychopathic personalities. He also assessed the risk of alcoholism in the siblings of the group as 25 per cent compared with 3-4 per cent risk in the general population.

Mardones (1946) demonstrated that rats deprived of the "B" vitamin factor increased their alcoholic consumption under conditions of self-selection, different rat strains varying in their susceptibility to this deprivation.

Bohman *et al* (1987) studied the inheritance of alcoholism in 862 men and 913 women (all adopted by non-relatives) and concluded that both male and female adoptees were at greater risk to develop alcohol abuse if their biological as opposed to their adoptive parents, were alcoholic.

Finn *et al* (1989) described studies which illustrate autonomic hyperactivity in sons of alcoholics and that this response is elicited by a wide range of stimuli which vary from the stressful to the incidental. It also occurs independently of coping strategy. This hyperactivity, which is particularly characteristic of multigenerational sons of alcoholics is significantly dampened by alcohol.

Monteiro *et al* (1988) reviewed studies of men at high risk of the future development of alcoholism. The most prominent differences between young men with and without a family history of this disorder include decreased intensity of reaction to ethanol for sons of alcoholics compared with control subjects. Decreased amplitude of the P300 wave of the event-related potential and a different pattern of background cortical electroencephalographic activity (alpha waves) for subjects at high risk of future alcoholism, were also observed.

(iii) Metabolic

The rate of metabolism of alcohol in the body rarely exceeds 100 mg. per kilogram per hour. This supplies one-eighth of the energy needs of the body per hour. Metabolic changes are obviously produced in the body by alcoholism as evinced in withdrawal symptoms. However, there is little evidence of true tolerance in the sense of increased tissue metabolism.

Williams (1951) described a genotrophic theory of the aetiology of alcoholism. A cardinal precept of this theory is that each individual's metabolism is genetically determined. He goes on to postulate that people with "genetically determined partial enzymatic defects" are handicapped because carbohydrates are less readily metabolized by their tissues. He believes that such people prefer alcohol to carbohydrates as the former more easily provides them with a source of rapidly available energy.

The following information also concerns genetic and metabolic factors in the causation. Cloniger *et al* (1987) indicated that alcoholism may be inherited in the form of a predisposed personality type but Martin *et al* (1985) gave "challenge" doses of alcohol to 200 pairs of twins and concluded that the elimination of alcohol was essentially under genetic control. Marshal *et al* (1991) indicates that alcohol is usually broken down in the liver by acetaldehyde dehydrogenase without side-effects such as tachycardia, nausea, vomiting and flushing of the skin. These investigators also found that many Oriental people have a variant of acetaldehyde dehydrongenase which is virtually inactive resulting in the side effects described above and consequently conferring protection against developing dependence on alcohol. They also conclude that different genes are concerned in the inheritence of alcoholism. Some may influence the amount of alcohol consumed and others may contribute to susceptibility to dependence on alcohol or to physical disease due to alcoholism. Strong environmental, including cultural, factors probably interact with these genetic influences. The same investigators significantly conclude that: "once the transmission of alcoholism is broken down into its component parts then the way will be much clearer for laboratory studies to identify the genes that confer susceptibility."

Smith (1949) believed that alcoholism may be due to adrenocortical insufficiency because of similarities between delirium tremens and the crisis of Addison's disease. In both conditions the serum potassium and nitrogen are raised and serum sodium, chloride and glucose are lowered. H+ion concentration and acidosis are also found in both conditions.

(iv) Social factor
Eastern countries value the contemplative and non-aggressive personality and condemn alcohol, but accept opiates and other drug addictions. In the Western world emphasis is on the outgoing personality with an aggressive attitude towards life, and alcohol is accepted and opium rejected.

Ethnic studies indicate that alcoholism is rare in people of Jewish and Chinese stock in the United States of America, but common in those of Irish and Scandinavian descent. These differences are explained on cultural, religious, sociological, psychological and climatic grounds. However, a biogenetic explanation is also possible because the four racial groups have a high intermarriage rate within their own groups.

Nutritional standards of a country may delay or prevent the physical and mental complications of alcoholism.

Kennedy (1957) believed that a social factor in the form of the "expense account" alcoholic is an increasing source of alcoholism. Factors such as loneliness, isolation in large cities, the boarding-house type of existence, and marital discord are important in causation. A deterioration in the sense of personal responsibility as a result of the concept of the Welfare State is also worthy of consideration.

Statistics on the incidence and complications of alcoholism in any particular country depend to a large extent on the general level of prosperity and the price of alcohol. Social factors such as marital state, economic resources, occupation and police record have prognostic value.

The Alcoholism Sub-Committee of the World Health Organization in 1952 classified alcoholics into non-addictive and addictive types and I have attempted to incorporate the various alcoholic syndromes in the general framework of this classification, as this has a practical application in treatment, but it does not represent rigid clinical entities, as there exists a continuous series of gradations between the occasional social drinker and the addictive alcoholic.

The social drinker takes alcohol in certain circumstances because it is the custom of the community in which he lives, taking alcohol on socially appropriate occasions, but not always in amounts suited to his capacity. This is a form of drinking accepted in most civilized societies and a minority of social drinkers become alcoholics. When an individual reaches the stage at which he depends on alcohol to alleviate the stresses of everyday life, he may then be regarded as a non-addictive alcoholic, the alcohol temporarily improving his sense of well-being and relieving his social and personal anxiety.

A minority of non-addictive alcoholics become addictive drinkers, the drinking pattern varying with culture and geographical location. In the USA, Canada and Northern Europe the addictive alcoholic tends to indulge in heavy spirit drinking which leads to a sharp rise in the blood alcohol level. This type of alcoholic not only depends on the toxic effects of alcohol to alleviate anxiety, but also loses control so that the first drink gives rise to a compulsion to take more. Such drinking bouts end in sickness or unconsciousness or both, tend to be periodic and are sometimes referred to as dipsomania.

Addictive drinkers can, however, control whether or not they will take the initial drink in a given situation. They become increasingly restless and despondent for a few days before the drinking bout and some tend to take their food in a rather ravenous manner. Some are talented people who seem to need alcohol periodically to alleviate intolerable tension. They work hard during their "good periods" and some tend to fill in their spare time with artistic pursuits which are designed to ward off anxiety and avoid introspection.

Alcoholism is a major social and public health problem and in the USA is said to be the fourth largest. Attempts made there to deal with it through curative programmes both in the community and in industry have met with some success and there have been some interesting community studies of social attitudes to alcoholism. It was found that the lower socio-economic groups showed the widest divergence in regard to understanding of the problems of the alcoholic, and that middle-aged people showed greater tolerance and understanding of the problem than younger or older age groups.

Alcohol and law-breaking

According to an investigation by Schmidt and Smart (1959) alcoholic drivers were involved in a significantly larger number of accidents per year, and in a larger number of accidents per mile driven than a control series, were more accident prone even when sober, and were more frequently arrested and suspended from driving. An interesting finding in this survey was that in each individual case, a cluster of road accidents occurred in the 12 months preceding the first treatment for alcoholism, and involvement in accidents must therefore be an important factor in causing alcoholics to seek treatment.

Alcohol may influence other illegal behaviour. A survey of 150 successive prisoners received into a prison in England was carried out by the writer with the object of investigating the influence of alcohol on criminal behaviour. The 150 prisoners were charged with a variety of indictable and non-indictable offences and the group was quite unselected. The figures indicate that alcohol has a substantial influence on crime.

Of the total group, 100 committed their crimes when under the influence of alcohol and 47 (on their own admission) would not have broken the law had they been sober. Three planned their crimes carefully and took alcohol to gain courage to carry them out. Of the total group, 90 were investigated as to their childhood circumstances and 19 stated that they had unhappy and insecure childhoods. The remaining 71 stated they had had happy and relatively secure childhoods and good parental care, and of these 25 were addictive or non-addictive alcoholics. Consequently, one may conclude that favourable childhood circumstances do not necessarily act as a shield against alcoholism in later life and this in turn implies other factors in the aetiology of alcoholism.

Washbrook (1976) described a specific group of 32 alcoholic inmates of Birmingham Prison, who were quite distinct from the average prison population. Their ages varied from 32 to 64 years. They were recidivists but no member of the group had ever been sentenced to more than six months' imprisonment, and all their offences were connected directly with excessive consumption of alcohol. They were pathetic, inadequate, unemployed and of "no fixed abode". Their pattern of life could be explained on the basis of social regression. None of the group had any realistic plans for the future and they constituted a considerable nuisance value from the social and custodial points of view.

Groups varying numerically but similar in pathological, social and alcoholic backgrounds are to be found in every local prison of the country.

Offences of drunkenness, Home Office Statistical Bulletin (1993) indicated that there has been a progressive decrease in the number found guilty of drunkenness in England and Wales since 1981 (Table VIII). However, the number of cautions for drunkenness increased from 725 in 1981 to 41,108 in 1993.

Table VIII

1983	1984	1985	1986	1987	1988	1989	1990	1993
96,241	60,507	49,176	38,413	42,313	45,261	42,910	37,838	18,799

Road Accidents, Great Britain (1991), The Casualty Report, indicates that 7,350 aged over 16 years died in Great Britain in road accidents and of these 3,300 drivers had blood alcohol estimations and 29.7 per cent had a blood alcohol above 80 mg per 100 ml. The report dealt with the years 1985 to 1989 (inclusive).

The Home Office Statistical Bulletin in 1992, indicated that 113,000 individuals were found guilty of "driving after consuming alcohol or taking drugs" by all courts in England and Wales in 1990. The corresponding figure for 1980 was 78,000 and, furthermore, some 114,700 motorists had screening breath tests because they were involved in accidents in England and Wales in 1991, 13.2 per cent proving positive. The corresponding figures for 1987 were 68,000 and 18.1 per cent.

Figures published in *"Road Accidents, Great Britain 1991: The Casualty Report"* (Department of Transport) reveal that some 391,769 drivers were involved in injury road accidents in 1991 and 109,919 were breath-tested and 8,613 failed the tests. Corresponding figures for 1981 were 390,736, 41,027 and 12,303. It may be concluded that the public has become more conscious of the serious consequences of driving after excess consumption of alcohol during the above ten-year period.

Teanby (1992) indicated that 1,706 pedestrians were killed and 58,374 were injured in road accidents in Great Britain in 1989. The influence of alcohol is not stated.

The subject of alcohol and law-breaking is also considered in Chapter II.

Treatment

It is taken for granted that the alcoholic seeks treatment when his consumption of alcohol renders him incapable of following his employment and leading a normal life, and it is axiomatic that treatment at home is seldom, if ever, successful. The role of the family doctor is to help convince the patient that his condition needs treatment and he will but rarely be approached by the alcoholic himself; it is the relatives who usually seek advice.

When the specialist sees the patient he will usually find him unco-operative or the alcoholic may feel himself "cornered" and promise faithfully to "cut it down", which he never does. The co-operation of the patient is more likely to be obtained when the alcoholism has produced a crisis such as a prosecution for a driving or other offence, or dismissal from work. When this happens the immediate need is for admission to hospital, where treatment can be carried out in a new environment and where the patient has no access to alcohol.

In practice, admission to hospital usually means to a psychiatric hospital. General hospitals tend to avoid admitting alcoholics on the grounds that they cannot deal with these potentially difficult and disturbed patients. A few special units for treatment of alcoholics are available under the National Health Service, but additional special units are urgently required and until they are provided responsibility for treatment falls mainly on the existing psychiatric hospitals. Private institutions may be inebriates' homes or active treatment centres.

Treatment falls naturally into two phases. The first is the detoxification phase and withdrawal of alcohol. The patient will usually enter hospital in an acutely intoxicated state and also suffering from dehydration and malnutrition, which is dealt with by giving copious glucose fluids and parentrovite. Alcohol should be cut off completely when the patient first enters hospital. In order to control the withdrawal symptoms, including delirium tremens, Librium in doses of 50 mg. I.M. has proved effective and may be repeated four-hourly as necessary. After the patient's general condition has improved, usually within 48-72 hours, the Librium may be continued in doses of 60 mg. daily by mouth for ten days.

It is only when the stages of detoxification and withdrawal are nearing completion that the patient's condition allows the full psychiatric assessment which is necessary to decide on methods of rehabilitation. If the alcoholism is symptomatic of an underlying psychiatric condition, the latter must be treated. The patient's relatives and associates must be interviewed as his alcoholism may be a reaction to maladjustments at home or at work. Any attempts at rehabilitation which neglect measures designed to adapt the patient to his environment are doomed to failure.

Aversion therapy, by inducing nausea and vomiting by means of apomorphine or emetine and timed to coincide with the taking of alcohol, is of only temporary value. Disulfiram, itself inert, but producing unpleasant physical symptoms when alcohol is taken within a subsequent 24-hour period, has also been used as a form of aversion therapy. After the patient has experienced the unpleasant effects of taking alcohol after Disulfiram in safe dosage, he is told to take one tablet before breakfast every morning and thus help to avoid alcohol during the day by one positive effort of will each morning. The main use of this therapy is to reinforce other treatments, and a stable home background where relatives adopt an understanding, rather than moralizing attitude is helpful.

All alcoholics need long-term support, and group methods as practised by Alcoholics Anonymous and in hostels for alcoholics are valuable in helping to prevent relapse.

Kennedy and Fish (1959) lay down the following six cardinal rules for the compulsive alcoholic after the acute stage of treatment has been completed:

1. There is no alternative to total abstinence for addictive alcoholics but strictly limited drinking or the taking of alcohol-free beers, lagers or wines may be suitable for others.

2. It must be assumed that the patient is completely unreliable where alcohol is concerned and he must understand that he will be treated on this assumption.

3. He must be told that his promises will not be accepted.

4. Group techniques and religious help are completely compatible with individual therapy.

5. Positive interests must be developed as a substitute for the alcoholic habit.

6. Aversion methods may reinforce, but cannot replace, psychotherapy.

Murray (1989) regards alcohol as probably the most popular mood-altering drug which has frightening consequences when abused. Genetic factors and sociocultural influences contribute to alcoholic behaviour. Study of endocrines, neurotransmitters, and neuropeptides may reveal biological markers to help identify those at risk from alcoholism.

Drinking patterns are often based on the expectation of alcohol's mood-altering quality. The focus of treatment has expanded to include not only drinking behaviour but also emotional, social and vocational adjustment. Controlled drinking has proved effective for some and antidepressant medication may be necessary for associated depression.

The psychotherapist must convince the alcoholic that he suffers from a genuine disease and guilt feelings are therefore unnecessary.

Alcoholism is an important health problem which, at present, is not being adequately dealt with in the United Kingdom. The present facilities for its treatment are poor. As the problem is increasing there is need of public health and educational activities to counteract this trend and to make better known the treatment facilities which exist. Alcoholism is a problem which has so many aspects that it is essential to identify the important ones before dealing with them and there is need for more research into its various aspects.

Research into patterns of alcohol usage is very important. Research into how to recognize the early stages of the process is also essential, and as the problem varies from country to country and from region to region, so local research is also necessary.

Valuable information could be obtained by investigating the social criteria which influence the admission of alcoholics to hospital or which influence them to request treatment.

About 25 per cent of alcoholics have physical complications and it is important to treat these as early as possible. The acute phase should be dealt with either in an open ward of a general hospital or in a psychiatric unit incorporated in a general hospital. Alcoholics are unduly vulnerable emotionally, experience guilt feelings and adopt defeatist attitudes when they periodically succumb to temptation. Consequently long-term support and supervision are necessary.

The main problem in treating the alcoholic is to devise an effective rehabilitation programme. Alcoholics Anonymous may be helpful, but the meetings should not be held in mental hospitals and as all classes mingle it is necessary to ensure that less educated people feel at ease. Hostels for alcoholics are referred to at the end of this chapter.

A clinic in the form of a social club would be helpful in rehabilitation. A doctor experienced in the treatment of alcoholism should attend each meeting and a receptionist interview each member on joining. The informality and friendliness would soon gain the alcoholic's confidence and family doctors could also visit periodically. The general practitioner has an important part to play in the treatment of the alcoholic. Early recognition and appropriate advice to individuals and families is of the utmost importance.

There is a general impression amongst members of the public that alcoholism is not a disease and the alcoholic tends to be regarded as an irresponsible "waster". Consequently, education of the public would lessen the stigma on the alcoholic and therefore lessen his burden. Lectures and advertising campaigns could help in this way.

There is at present no specific cure for alcoholics and the most one may hope to accomplish is to arrange the individual's life in such a way as to enable him to find compensation for his abstinence from alcohol and thus "keep the beast at bay", and the following is a description of the organization and work of a hostel for alcoholics in one area of South Wales.

Dyfrig House opened in Cardiff in 1966 under the auspices of the South Wales Council for Alcoholism, providing accommodation for 24 people. A treatment-orientated hostel with a small induction unit, it is based on group work and the "therapeutic community" principle, aiming to assist alcoholics who are sufficiently motivated towards recovery.

Alcoholics from all walks of life and of both sexes who are preferably of average intelligence are most suitable for admission and ex-offenders whose criminal activities are directly attributable to alcoholism, and who meet other requirements, are also suitable.

Treatment methods at Dyfrig House, Cardiff and Ty Palmyra Hostel, Newport

Some 282 people were referred to Dyfrig House in 1988-89 and 133 were admitted. Thirty-one were discharged and regarded as successfully rehabilitated.

The Ty Palmyra Hostel at Newport, Gwent, was opened in 1987. It is a 19-bed hostel for recovering alcoholics and similar to Dyfrig House except that it is also used for the rehabilitation of drug dependents. It is a purpose-built hostel and supported by the Gwent Council for alcoholism and drug abuse. Residents enter on a voluntary basis at least seven days after detoxification and undertake to stay for six months. Breach of rules means expulsion. The residents have group therapy sessions twice daily and individual counselling is also available. A clinical psychologist is also available for specialist advice. The alcoholics tend to come from the Newport area but drug dependents are accepted from parts of the U.K. other than Newport because those from the latter city would have too much local knowledge as to sources of illicit drugs and they would also tend to return to their former drug-taking associates. All residents receive help with family care and accommodation after leaving the hostel and may return at any time for advice and help.

A general medical practitioner is on call for each hostel, and it is hoped to establish local alcoholic reception centres in relation to hostels, where alcoholics can be assessed and placed in a hostel best suited to their needs as there are different types of alcoholics as well as different forms of alcoholism.

There is a need for a private centre, away from each hostel, where those who have a drinking problem can talk confidentially with an experienced counsellor, and country hostels are also envisaged for the future.

The management committee of each hostel consists of a chairman, secretary, warden and deputy, a medical practitioner, a probation officer and a representative of the social services. Financial support is provided by the Welsh Office for Dyfrig House. An honorary treasurer assists with the financial problems.

Rehabilitation of the alcoholic does not necessarily require psychiatric supervision, and similar hostel arrangements would be effective for the rehabilitation of drug dependents.

The prognosis for alcoholism is not particularly good as merely 12.5 per cent of alcoholics are totally abstinent after five years.

Government response to the problem of alcoholism is to some extent non-committal. Working Party reports and the Powers of Criminal Courts Act 1973 supported the setting up of medical treatment and detoxification centres. It was envisaged that pilot schemes for these centres would be implemented in 1975. These developments would further help the existing work carried out by hostels.

Referral agents are asked to submit all relevant social inquiry reports, psychiatric reports and police antecedents, when applicable, directly to the residential social worker. Referrals originate mainly from psychiatrists, prison medical officers, general medical practitioners, employers, social workers, police, Salvationists, Alcoholics Anonymous and some self-referrals. The probation and after-care services have established an alcoholic intervention unit in Cardiff which has liaison with the community alcoholic team of South Glamorgan with the object of educating the public concerning the evil effects of alcohol abuse. The team trains primary care workers and also gives direct counselling and support to alcoholics and their families and advice about "safe drinking".

There is satisfactory liaison between Dyfrig House, the probation services, the social services, mental hospitals and the local prison. Courts increasingly seek the knowledge and expertise of hostel staff, and hostels such as Dyfrig House make an important contribution to keeping petty offenders out of prison and to their rehabilitation in the community. The hostel provides a secure therapeutic environment in which alcoholics can come to terms with their drinking problem and adjust to the pressures in the community. A proportion of the residents at Dyfrig House are referred by probation and after-care officers and prison welfare officers who find the facilities offered at the hostel extremely valuable in view of the large number of alcoholics on their case-loads. Experiments are in progress to link the hostel to other forms of rehabilitation available to the probation service, such as day training centres. Weekly advisory group meetings are held at the local prison.

Ideally, an interview should be arranged between the applicant and the resident social worker. In most cases, admission is for an assessment period of two or three weeks during which time the applicant will be seen by a general medical practitioner and where applicable, by a psychiatrist, a liaison probation officer and/or a disablement resettlement officer. The final decision on admission is made by the administrator who takes into consideration the opinions of the committee and resident group.

It is emphasized that people come to Dyfrig House to prepare for leaving, and this recognition as a premise for mutual effort, is implicit in all formal and informal group discussions. No time limit is set for the achievement of the goal, as the group must be cognizant of, and sensitive to, the particular obstacles to each individual's progress.

The emphasis is, and must be, on "resident responsibiliity" in all matters pertaining to the day-to-day management of the house and in the organization of the therapeutic activities of the unit. The residents have their own front-door keys, answer the telephone, arrange the cooking of food and household chores at weekends and, with no resident staff, are under no recognizable institutional constraint. The premise on which they work is mutual trust and respect.

One general house meeting is held on one evening each week and there is a daily meeting for newcomers. The effect on the group of the behaviour of individuals and vice versa is discussed with a view to understanding, not only what is happening within the group, but what has happened to the inter-personal relationships of the residents in the past and the adjustments that each person has to make to cope successfully with the future.

The telephone service at Dyfrig House provides information and advice, and also acts as a referral agency, a service it is hoped to develop and improve through separate information and advice offices, and a community centre for alcoholics who cannot be contained within a normal hostel setting.

Alanon undertakes help for Alcoholics free of charge.

The Alcoholic helpline telephone number for the United Kingdom is 0891 500 166.

References

A Different Reality, West Midlands County Council (1986).

Alcohol Concern statistics quoted from the General Household Survey (1990) by the Office of Population Censuses and Surveys., HMSO

Amark, C. (1951) "A Study in Alcoholism: Clinical Social-Psychiatric and Genetic Investigations", *Acta Psychologica et Neurologica Scandinavica*, Supplement 70.

Barry, J. *The Times*, May 2, (1963).

Bohman, M. et al (1987) "The Genetics of Alcoholism and Related Disorders", *J. Psychiat. Research,* Vol. 21(4), 447-52.

Bowlby, J. (1957) "Maternal Care and Mental Health", *Bulletin of the World Health Organization*, Geneva, 3,355.

Brandon, R. (1973) *Wrongful Imprisonment*, Allen and Unwin.

Brenner, M. H. (1973), *Mental Illness and the Economy*, Harvard University Press, Cambridge, Mass.

Cade, J. F. J. (1956) "Alcoholism – A Community Responsibility", *Medical Journal of Australia*, 1.363.

Clark, W. (1966) "Operational Definition of Drinking Problems and Associated Prevalence Rates", *Quarterly Journal of Studies on Alcohol*, 27.648.

Cloniger, C. R. (1987) "Neurogenetic Adaptive Mechanisms in Alcoholism", *Science* 236: 410-6.

Criminal Statistics (1982) (England and Wales), Home Office, Cmnd. 9048, HMSO, London.

Donnan, S., Haskey, J. (1977) *Population Trends No. 7.* OPCS, HMSO, London.

Drug Addiction. Interdepartmental Committee on Drug Addiction (1965) Chairman, Lord Brain, HMSO, London.

Eales, M. J. (1988) "Depression and Anxiety in Unemployed Men", *Psychol. Medicine* 18: 935-45.

East, W. N. (1939) *Psychological Treatment of Crime,* Home Office Report, 9, HMSO, London.

Eisenberg, P. (1938) "The Psychological Effects of Unemployment", *Psycho. Bull.,* 35, 358-90.

Finn, P., Peterson, J., (1989) *Neuropsychopharmacol. Biol. Psychiatry,* 13 (3-4), 489-96.

Firth-Cozens, J. (1987) "Emotional Distress in Junior House Officers". *Br. Med. J.* 295: 533-6.

Fischer, P. J. (1988) "Criminal Activity Among the Homeless: A Study of Arrests in Baltimore, U.S.A.", *Hosp. Community Psychiatry,* Vol. 39(1), 46-51.

Flint, L., Carrico, C. J., (1992) "Care of Victims of Urban Violence and the Education of Trauma and Critical Care Surgeons. A Troubled Partnership", Department of Surgery, Tulane University School of Medicine, New Orleans, U.S.A., *Arch-Surg.* Vol: 127(9), pp. 1085-8.

General Medical Council (1973), Report to the Merrison Enquiry into the Regulation of the Medical Profession. *Br. Med. J.* (Suppl.) iii: 170.

Gloag, D. (1992) "Law Catches Up with Dangerous Driving", *Br. Med. J.* Vol. 305, p. 74.

Gudjonsson, G. H. (1983) " Psychological Analysis of Confession Statements", *J. For. Sci. Soc.* 23, 113.

Guze, S. B. (1976), *Criminality & Psychiatric Disorder,* Oxford Univ. Press.

Haward, L. R. C. (1990), *A Dictionary of Forensic Psychology*, Medilaw/Barry Rose, Chichester, pp. 38-39.

Hiscox, D. (1988-89), *South Glamorgan Council on Alcohol Report*.

Hood, R. J. (1966), *Homeless Borstal Boys,* G. Bell and Sons, London.

Home Office (1978), *Judges Rules*, Home Office Circular No. 89.

Hore, B. D. (1976) *Alcohol Dependence*, Butterworths, London.

Jellinek, E. M. (1952), *The Phases of Alcohol Addiction in Mental Health*. Second Report of Alcohol Subcommittee, World Health Organization, Geneva, 48.26.

Jellinek, E. M. (1960), *The Disease Concept of Alcoholism*, Hill House Press, New Haven, Conn.

Kennedy, A. (1957) "Individual Reactions to Change as seen in Senior Management in Industry", *Lancet*, 1.261.

Kennedy, A., Fish, F. G. (1959) *Alcoholism, Alcoholic Addiction and Drug Addiction in Recent Progress in Psychiatry*, Vol. 3, J. and A. Churchill, London.

Kolvin, I., Miller, F. J., Fleeting, M., Kolvin, P. A., (1988) " Social and Parenting Factors affecting Criminal-offence: Findings from the Newcastle Thousand Family Study (1947-1980)", *Brit. J. Psychiatry*, Vol. 152, 0-90.

Lewis, E. D. (1929) *An Investigation into the Incidence of Mental Deficiency*. Report of the Mental Deficiency Committee (Wood Report), HMSO, London.

Lloyd, C., Gartrell, N. K. (1984) "Psychiatric Symptoms in Medical Students". *Compr. Psychiatry* 25: 552-65.

Lloyd, G. (1990) "Alcoholic Doctors Can Recover", *Br. Med. J.* No. 6726, Vol. 300, 728-730.

Mackeith, J. A., Gudjonsson, G. H. (1990) "A Proven Case of False Confession: Psychological Aspects of the Coerced-Complaint Type", *Medicine, Science and the Law*, Vol.30, pp. 329-55.

Mackeith, J. A., Gudjonsson, G. H. (1988) "Retracted Confessions: Legal, Psychological and Psychiatric", *Medicine, Science and the Law*, Vol. 28, pp. 187-94.

Mardones, J., Segovia, N. and Onfrey, E. (1946) "Relationship between the Dose of Factor N and the Alcohol Intake of Rats under Self-selection Conditions", *Archives of Biochemistry*, 9,401.

Marshall, E. J., Murray, R. M. (1991) "The Familial Transmission of Alcoholism", *Brit. Med. J.,* Vol. 303, pp. 72-73.

Martin, N. G., Perl, J., Oakeshott, J. G., Gibson, J. B., Starmer, G. A., Wilks, A. V. (1985) "A twin study of ethanol metabolism", *Behav. Genet.* 15: 93-109.

Merton, R. K. (1957) *Social Theory and Social Structure*, Free Press, New York.

Messner, S. F., (1988) "Research on Cultural and Socioeconomic Factors in Criminal Violence", *Psychiatry. Clin. North. Am.* Vol. 11(4), 511-25.

Miller, E. (1962) "Individual and Social Approach to the Study of Adolescence", *Brit. J. Med. Psychology*, 35, 211.

Monteiro, M. G., Schuckit, M. A. (1988) "Populations at High Alcoholism Risk: Recent Findings", *J. Clin. Pscyhiatry*, 49 Suppl. (9), 3-7.

Morris, T. P. (1957) *The Criminal Area: A Study in Social Ecology*, Routledge and Kegan Paul, London.

Motoring Offences for England and Wales, 1990, Home Office Statistical Bulletin, July 1992, Research and Statistics Dept., 50 Queen Annes Gate, London.

Murray, C. (1989) "The British Underclass", *Sunday Times,* 26 November 1989.

Murray, J. B. (1989) Alcoholism: Etiologies Proposed and Therapeutic Approaches Tried", *Genet. Soc. Gen. Psychol. Monogr.,* 115(1); 81-121.

Murray, R. M. (1976) "Characteristics and Prognosis of Alcoholic Doctors". *Br. Med. J.* ii: 1537-9.

Norris, F. H., Kaniasty, K. Z., Scheer, D. A., (1990) "Use of Mental Health Services Among Victims of Crime: Frequence Correlates and Subsequent Recovery", Dept. of Psychology, Georgia State University, Atlanta, U.S.A., *J. Consult. Clin. Psychol.,* Vol. 58(5), 538-47.

Nørvig, J. and Nielson, B. (1956). "A follow-up study of 221 alcohol addicts in Denmark", *Quarterly Journal of Studies on Alcohol,* 17, 4, 633.

Notifiable Offences for England and Wales, July 1991 to June 1992, Home Office Statistical Bulletin, July 1992, Research and Statistics Dept., 50 Queen Annes Gate, London.

Offences of Drunkenness for England and Wales, 1990, Home Office Statistical Bulletin, August 1992, Research and Statistics Dept., 50 Queen Annes Gate, London.

Penrose, L. S. (1945) "Mental Disease and Crime", *Brit. J. Med. Psychol.,* 18, 1.

Rees, L. (1981), *Brit. Med. J.* No. 6271, Vol. 282, p. 179.

Road Accidents Great Britain, (1991), "The Casualty Report", Dept. of Transport, Pub. HMSO.

Robins, E. *et al.* (1959). "Some clinical considerations in the prevention of suicide based on a study of 134 successful suicides", *American Journal of Public Health,* 49, 888.

Schachter, M. and Cotte, S. (1950). "Rôle du poids de naissance sur le development mental de l'enfant", *Pediatric,* 215.

Schmidt, W.S. and Smart, R.C. (1959). "Alcoholics, drinking and traffic accidents", *Quarterly Journal of Studies on Alcohol,* 20, 631.

Simpson, K. (1962) *A Doctor's Guide to Court,* Butterworths, London, Ch. 3, pp. 28-30.

Smith, J.J. (1949). "A medical approach to problem drinking", *Quarterly Journal of Studies on Alcohol,* 10, 251.

Smith, R. (1991) *Br. Med. J.,* No. 6777, Vol. 302, 606-7.

Tatum, D. (1988) "Life-long Eccentricity and Social Isolation, Psychiatric, Social and Forensic Aspects", *Brit. J. Psych.* 153, 777-782.

Teanby, D. (1992) "Under-reporting of Pedestrian Road Accidents", *Brit. Med. J.,* Vol. 304, p.422.

Thapar, A. (1990) "Psychiatric Disorder in the Medical Profession", *Brit. J. of Hospital Medicine,* Vol. 42, 480-3.

Trankell, A. (1982) *Reconstructing the Past,* Norstedt, Stockholm.

Vaillant, G. E., Sobowale N. C., McArthur, C. (1972) "Some Psychological Vulnerabilities of Physicians". *N. Engl. J. Med.,* 287: 372-5.

Warr, P. (1989) *Work, Unemployment and Mental Health,* Oxford Scientific Publications, Clarendon Press, Oxford.

Washbrook, R.A.H. (1976) "The criminology of the chronic alcoholic offender", *Journal of Alcoholism,* 11, 1.9.

Whaley, A. L. (1992), *A Culturally Sensitive Approach to the Prevention of Interpersonal Violence Among Urban Black Youth,* Psychiatric Epidemiology Training Program, Columbia University, New York, U.S.A.

Whitty, C.W.M. and Zangwill, O.L., Eds (1966). *Amnesia.* Butterworths, London.

Wilkins, L. T. (1960) *Delinquent Generations: Studies in the Causes of Delinquency and the Treatment of Offenders,* No. 3, HMSO, London.

Williams, L. and Long, R. (1968). "The clinical problem and management of alcoholism", *The Practitioner,* 200, 205.

Williams, R.J. (1951), Pub. Univ. of Oklahoma Press., USA.

CHAPTER V

Memory Recall and the Criminal Law

Engrams, or memory traces, are imprinted somewhere in the central nervous system when people notice things. These engrams are reactivated when the individual remembers. The process of remembering includes reception, registration, retention, recognition and recall.

Bartlett (1932) indicated that perceptions are assimilated into organizations or schemata. Assimilation includes reception and registration. Schemata may be regarded as frameworks of reference and the main specific elements or "landmarks" of learning are first fitted into these frameworks. A general orientation or impression is therefore taken before details are considered.

An individual is quite unable to alter registered material once perceptions have become assimilated into the schemata. The relevance to medico-legal problems is obvious because assimilated material may have been based on false perceptions.

Material for memorizing may be received by any of the five senses which if defective will tend to prevent accurate reception.

Lack of interest, mental fatigue, the effects of alcohol or drugs, organic brain disease, psychoneurotic states and some psychotic states cause defective registration. Preoccupation with matters unrelated to learning will have the same effect. Registration is facilitated if the individual appreciates that he is expected to remember certain material.

Retention decreases during the interval between the original perception and recall. This decrease is more rapid earlier in this interval than later. Memory traces may atrophy as a result of disuse. Interference with traces may also be caused by newly learned material due to retroactive inhibition.

There is a close relationship between recall and recognition. Recognition is the identification of something previously perceived. It is a complicated process involving time-ordering of experiences based on association of the ideas stemming from past and present experiences. This association may be by similarity or contiguity. Perception is based on attentive awareness. "Pastness" is the quality of memory by which an individual appreciates that past experiences occurred in the past. "Pastness" may become erroneously associated with a present experience which is then believed to have been lived through previously. This false sense of familiarity, also called *déja vu*, is characteristic of epileptic attacks originating in the uncinate gyrus but can also occur in normal people, Brain (1955). Errors of recognition may also be caused by failure to distinguish between two similar experiences. Witnesses may make identifications on parades because they believe that this is what is expected of them by authority. These identifications may be inaccurate. Furthermore, good demeanour and sincerity on the part of a witness will not eliminate wrongful identification. A witness may think that he has a good memory for faces when in fact he has a poor one and there is no way of detecting this failing. These considerations are relevant in regard to the validity of opinions given by witnesses when confronted with identification parades. The fact that people differ in memory ability is also relevant in this context. A witness will not correctly recognize a suspected person if he does not accurately remember the suspect. Recognition is therefore dependent on recall.

Recall *per se* is remembering something which is not present and usually takes the form of memory images. However, visual images may be lost after a head injury while visual recognition of objects remains unimpaired (Brain, 1955).

The condition of the temporal lobe also influences recall. Milner (1958) showed that left (dominant) hemisphere temporal lobectomy may be followed by verbal memory deficit such as delayed recall of prose passages and word associations, whereas right temporal lobectomy showed defective delayed recall of visuospatial figures. Channon *et al* (1990) expressed the opinion that the advent of such investigations as CT and MRI imaging should lead to more accurate surgery for temporal lobe epilepsy, consequently minimizing future recall defects.

Difficulty may be experienced in distinguishing between defects of retention and recall. A person may be able to describe how he sustained a head injury shortly after the actual trauma but later claim amnesia. The memory of the injury may however, be revived under hypnosis indicating a defect of recall rather than retention. The mechanisms of repression and dissociation may prevent recall as, for example, when an hysteric wanders away from his normal surroundings and acts and speaks in an apparently rational manner for a period of days or weeks, during which time he loses his sense of personal identity. He will claim complete amnesia for the period of the fugue, but the memory is usually recoverable under hypnosis or during a twilight state induced by intravenous pentothal. Again, the defect is one of recall as opposed to retention.

Recall may be inaccurate under the following circumstances: (i) when an effort was not made specifically to observe the original material; (ii) when details are distorted to fit in with an individual's erroneous original perceptions. Experiments with "nonsense figures" indicate that people have a distinct tendency to make this mistake, Woodworth *et al* (1958).

Recall is influenced by the following factors, Lovell *et al* (1970):

(i)   A tendency to simplify details of the original perception so as to make them fit into the total impression which may have been faulty. This is in agreement with the Gestalt theory which postulates that the whole of any perception is more than the sum of its parts.

(ii) Effects due to the individual's preconditioned outlook in regard to race, religion, politics and sex. In other words, the end products of our thinking may be unintentionally biased. These considerations may lead to mistaken identification.

(iii) The mind has a tendency to fabricate by filling in memory gaps relating to the original perception.

(iv) A tendency for repeated reproductions in the form of memory images to be more in agreement with a first defective reproduction than with the original perception.

Elements of volition, emotion and motivation strongly influence recognition and recall. The more quickly the response is made the more likely recall is to be correct.

Yuille *et al* (1986) indicated that stress levels at the material time of the relevant events do not have negative effects on subsequent memory. This opinion was based on a study of 21 individuals who witnessed a shooting incident on a main thoroughfare in mid-afternoon. They were interviewed immediately after the material time and five months later and recall was found to be "very accurate" after this interval.

A concept is the extraction and recombination of the qualities of a group of ideas. Accurate conceptual thought, judgment and reasoning are all based on accurate recognition and recall.

Good memory is also dependent on satisfactory mental and physical health.

Relationship of amnesia to crime

The following section is mainly devoted to the relationship of amnesia to crime and some observations already made will be repeated to fit into the general context.

Memory disorders encountered in clinical practice may be considered under the headings of amnesia, hypermnesia and paramnesia.

Amnesia may be total or partial, depending upon the extent to which normal cerebral function is disturbed. Varying degrees of inattention in the course of everyday life may be voluntary or due to mental fatigue, which may be accompanied by anxiety, irritability and distractability.

Preoccupation with personal problems may result in varying degrees of forgetfulness for events which took place during these periods.

Memory disorder may be due to defects of registration, retention and recall of experiences in the immediate or remote past. These processes will be considered separately but they are in fact closely related to each other.

Memory disorder caused by defective registration and retention may take the form of amnesia which may be temporary or permanent and complete or partial, depending upon the causative agent and the degree of severity with which it operates. Head injury, electroconvulsant therapy and the effects of drugs and alcohol may cause varying degrees of amnesia, depending upon the extent to which consciousness is impaired. There is obviously total amnesia for events which occur during a toxic confusional state.

Those suffering from mental disorder are likely to develop memory defects because their ability to attend and concentrate is more readily impaired. Acute psychoneurotic illness is accompanied by irrational fear, tension and anxiety and perceptions are inadequately registered due to defective attention and concentration.

Pathological lying was believed by Bleuler (1924) to be due to a disorder of "fantasy life". The lying usually occurs in response to certain situations and auto-suggestion plays a part as the deceiver often "lives himself into" the role which he wishes to play. The lying obviously gratifies some emotional need.

Epileptic furor and episodes of violence by the aggressive psychopath are accompanied by clouding of consciousness and consequently perceptions are inadequately registered, resulting in varying degrees of amnesia for events which took place during these periods.

Hypermnesia means that experiences are retained and recalled with undue facility. This condition is evident in certain prodigies and also in hypomania and paranoia where the mind is overactive and details of events are more easily registered and retained. However, Scrivner *et al* (1988) indicated that other eyewitnesses who are not mentally disordered may show hypermnesia for details of violent events. Some 90 undergraduates watched a video portraying burglary and the shooting of three innocent people. Increasingly more details of significance were recalled on each of four successive showings of the video for the purpose of recall trials, including one 48 hours after the last showing of the tape. Emotionalism and guessing did not influence the accuracy of recall. Consequently, eyewitness accounts may become more accurate with repeated attempts to recall information.

Concussion due to head injury causes varying degrees of amnesia for events which took place immediately before trauma. This period of memory loss may vary from hours to days and is referred to as retrograde amnesia. Memory loss may also occur for events immediately after the trauma causing anterograde amnesia. Some are capable of describing the manner in which they were injured but only when questioned within one or two hours of the trauma.

Hysteria may be accompanied by partial or complete amnesia due to defects of recognition and recall. Gross forms of hysteria may be accompanied by loss of personal identity due to repression and dissociation. Hysterical individuals over-react to pleasant and unpleasant experiences and, in conversion hysteria, the memory loss invariably concerns unpleasant events which may be recalled under hypnosis. Hopwood and Snell (1933) studied 100 patients detained in Broadmoor who had claimed amnesia when charged with the crime which resulted in their detention in the special hospital. Some of these patients were malingerers and hysterics whose "recollection waxed as the need for repression waned". Hays (1961) believed it was quite impossible to distinguish hysterical amnesia from apparent memory loss due to conscious deception, as both conditions may exist in the same individual and appear to subserve the same ends, namely, forgetfulness of a crime with which the person is charged in the hope of being found not guilty or successfully appealing against conviction or sentence.

Catatonic schizophrenics suffer from an *apparent* defect of registration of experiences during their stuporous periods as indicated by the observation that some of these patients are subsequently capable of accurately describing events which took place during their inert periods.

Patients have memory defects for events experienced during the depressive phase of manic-depressive psychosis. The degree of amnesia will vary directly with the intensity of the illness which causes retardation of thought, which in turn interferes with the normal functioning of registration, retention and recall. Memory defect also occurs in the involutional form of endogenous depression.

Mathews (1986) indicated that depressed patients exhibit a consistent negative bias in memory, favouring negative material about themselves. Recall of happy personal memories becomes progressively slower as the degree of depression increases. The negative self-assessments include beliefs and feelings of hopelessness, guilt, fear and they tend to view themselves, the world and the future with futility. It has not as yet been established whether the negative bias in memory is a cause or result of the depression. The Dysfunctional Attitude Questionnaire gives abnormal results when applied to genuinely depressed patients. Perhaps this questionnaire would help to clarify the genuineness or otherwise of allegations of depression made by those charged with lawbreaking or already serving sentences. It is reasonable to assume that the depression under consideration is endogenous to a pathological degree, as opposed to being reactive in nature.

Mentally impaired persons may develop varying degrees of functional amnesia more readily in stressful situations than individuals of average intelligence who are usually less vulnerable to the effects of stress.

Memory is quite faulty in the severely impaired owing to lack of attention and poor concentration due to serious defects in all essential mental functions.

Senile dementia is initially characterized by loss of memory for recent as opposed to remote events. This amnesia is due to defective registration of recent experiences caused by degeneration of cerebral neurones. Memory for remote experiences is retained for a time but eventually also becomes defective as senile dementia is a progressive illness.

Varying degrees of amnesia form part of the symptomatology of cerebral tumour, cerebral arteriosclerosis and pre-senile dementia where memory for recent and remote events tends to be uniformly defective. These conditions progress more rapidly than senile dementia.

Paramnesia means false recollection, and Brain (1955) attributes this condition to a disorder of the mental processes responsible for correct appreciation of feelings of familiarity. The *déja vu* experience which immediately precedes the ictus of temporal lobe epilepsy is an example of paramnesia and the sufferer is subject to some degree of clouding of consciousness and experiences unaccountable feelings of familiarity for persons, places, sounds and/or odours. These experiences are also referred to as fabrications or "illusions of memory". Korsakov's psychosis is another example of paramnesia where, in addition to the above symptoms, there is impairment of correct "time-ordering" of recent experiences. Memory gaps are "filled in" by imagined experiences and this is referred to as confabulation. This psychosis is an "end-state" of a number of illnesses such as chronic alcoholism, arsenical poisoning, pellagra, cerebral tumour, cerebral arteriosclerosis and megaloblastic anaemia.

Amnesia may be falsely alleged by an individual charged with a crime. I would again refer to the study by Hopwood and Snell. Their study of 100 patients revealed that in 78 cases the amnesia was genuine, there were 14 malingerers and the authors could not reach a conclusion in eight instances.

The references to functional mental disorders refer to schizophrenia, manic-depressive psychosis, involutional depression, psychopathic personality and the neuroses. However, difficulties usually arise only in differentiating an hysterical from a fraudulent amnesia.

The genuineness of alleged amnesia is decided by studying its character. A genuine memory loss *due to functional mental disorder* is usually gradual and blurred in onset and termination. An amnesic episode of sudden onset and termination is suggestive of feigned memory loss.

The genuine case of amnesia due to functional mental disorder is characterized by memory loss, of varying degree and duration, for events which took place prior to and after the time of committing the crime, but the *duration of amnesia for events before the offence is usually much shorter than that for events which took place after the material time.*

Amnesia *per se* is not a defence, nor is it a bar to trial if the accused is capable of pleading to the charge. In the event of a trial, the onus is on the prosecution to prove guilt of the accused. *Memory for the material time of a crime is not an essential ingredient of culpability,* as otherwise a person could commit a most heinous crime and have a ready-made defence.

Whitlock (1963) expressed the opinion that if amnesia is but one symptom of an acute psychotic illness, whether of functional or organic origin, the accused may well be unfit to plead.

Brisby (1960) stated that *total amnesia* for the whole of an individual's past life is very rarely genuine except when the defendant suffers from the most gross form of hysteria, advanced dementia, severe mental impairment, chronic and irreversible psychosis or serious brain damage. Such an individual would almost certainly be unfit to plead to any charge. One would be suspicious of an accused person claiming this type of amnesia if he was able to manage his affairs and play an intricate game of cards or chess during the remand period in a prison hospital.

Cartlidge (1991) indicated that transient total (global) amnesia is an established specific clinical entity and considered to be associated with temporary lack of blood supply to the temporal lobes of the brain. However, associations with epilepsy and migraine have also been recorded. The onset is sudden in middle-aged or elderly persons and each episode lasts for some hours and during this time there is no loss of personal identity or rational language and difficult functions such as driving a motor vehicle may be easily undertaken. However, there is subsequent total amnesia for events which occurred during the material time of the episode. There is some resemblance to hysterical fugue which is purely functional but the amnesic episodes considered here have some organic basis. Recovery is complete and recurrence unusual and these features are against cerebrovascular or hysterical causes. This condition could be put forward as a defence for crime perpetrated during the amnesic episode but the evidence would be difficult to unravel in court.

The character of the crime gives valuable information as to whether an alleged amnesia is genuine or feigned. A motiveless crime may be committed impulsively, without premeditation or attempt at concealment, with needless violence and even in the presence of witnesses. Under these circumstances one could reasonably assume that the accused was suffering from a disorder of the mind which could account for some degree of amnesia for the material time of the alleged crime. Offences committed in states of acute schizophrenia, epileptic furor, aggressive psychopathy and mania come within this category.

Finally, one studies the accused person and any statements which may have been made by him in relation to the alleged amnesia and/or the offence with which he has been charged. One judges the feasibility of his statements by comparing his story with that given to the police. These procedures should be repeated in order to detect inconsistencies. One tries to determine if the accused is a truthful person and this is indicated by studying details of his life history with particular reference to previous amnesic episodes and the circumstances in which these occurred.

The Guilty Knowledge Test (GKT), in the detection of deception, Bradley et al (1984) could have been criticized on the grounds that innocent people who were merely told the details of a crime, could achieve high scores on the test, suggesting genuine guilt. However, a controlled study involving 20 guilty subjects and 26 innocent ones strongly indicated that only a small minority of the latter group could be classed as guilty on the basis of the scores which they achieved. The test scores indicated guilt in 19 out of the 20 guilty subjects but in only three of the innocent ones.

Personality and intelligence tests are helpful in formulating an accurate diagnosis. The accused is given a thorough physical examination and X-rays, electrocardiograms, electroencephalograms, blood counts and biochemical investigations are carried out as indicated.

Management of amnesia

Memory loss which is not due to organic pathology can be treated by using one or more of the following procedures which are not indicated if the subject is in a confused or aggressive state, psychotic or suffering from organic cerebral pathology:

(i)   By direct discussion and encouragement, the patient is helped to extend the history of circumstances which led up to the amnesic episode until forgotten details are recalled spontaneously.

(ii)   Under hypnosis the patient can be encouraged to relive known emotionally toned incidents of his past life. During this procedure the patient will abreact and he is subsequently encouraged to continue talking. The hypnotic state is then terminated and the "forgotten" material may then be recalled.

(iii) The slow administration of 250 mg. of sodium pentothal diluted in 10 ml of sterile water for intravenous injection may be successful in terminating an amnesic episode. During this procedure the subject should be encouraged to relive some remembered event which is related to the forgotten material. Suggestion is given to the effect that total memory will be regained when the patient emerges from the twilight state. Abreaction usually occurs during the course of this investigation.

The following case history indicates that alleged amnesia may not necessarily influence the course of a murder trial, despite the presentation of reliable biochemical evidence indicating the probability of a genuine memory loss at the material time of the crime.

Case 5: A man in his twenties was charged with the murder by strangulation of a teenage girl. He drank about seven pints of beer within four hours of the time of the alleged crime. He recalled walking down a side street with the victim when they kissed and he interfered with her clothing and he alleged that at this point his mind "went blank" and he next remembered walking alone from the side street to a nearby main road. He retraced his steps back to the side street within minutes and discovered the girl's dead body on the ground. His memory for subsequent events was quite clear and he remembered returning to the main road to seek help from a passing motorist.

The court was informed that the alleged amnesic episode probably lasted about 15 minutes and was of sudden onset and termination. The position of the girl's stockings in relation to her wrists indicated attempts at tying, meaning organized purposive behaviour on the part of her assailant. This type of behaviour could not be regarded as connected with confusional states associated with epilepsy or hypoglycaemia.

About two weeks before the crime, the accused indicated to the deceased's brother that he had designs upon her and the court was informed that such statements by the accused indicated an element of premeditation. The court was also told that the alleged amnesia for the actual crime could be accounted for on the basis of shock due to realization of the possible consequences of his behaviour. An electroencephalogram taken during the remand period did not suggest epilepsy, cerebral trauma or neoplasm.

The defendant's childhood appeared to have been reasonably happy and secure. There was no family history of mental disorder or epilepsy. He stated that he was subject to nail-biting and nocturnal bedwetting until late childhood, and that he had attended school regularly and got on well with the other pupils. He was an average scholar and testing during the remand period indicated average intelligence. He worked regularly as a labourer for several years after leaving school. He was happily married and heterosexual. There was no history of psychiatric illness or suicidal attempts. He gave a history of striking his head on a wall about two years before trial when he felt dizzy and fell to the ground but did not lose consciousness. He did not require hospital treatment, but he alleged that he experienced two "mind-blanks" about two years after the latter injury and within three months immediately before the homicide. The "mind-blanks" could be interpreted as amnesic episodes, each lasting 15 to 20 minutes, and were associated with aggression and drinking about 10 pints of beer on each occasion. There was no clinical history of epilepsy. There was no history of illicit drug-taking. He took alcohol to excess, but he was not an alcoholic in the Jellinek sense.

The defendant conducted himself in an orderly manner throughout the remand period and there was no evidence of epilepsy or other abnormal disturbances of consciousness.

On one occasion during the remand period he tended to sleep more deeply than one might expect, but was quite rousable. He was never regarded as mentally disordered at any time before arrest and no signs or symptoms of mental disorder during the remand period were detected. An interview with his mother revealed that she never regarded him as epileptic or mentally abnormal and his general medical practitioner shared these opinions. Blood tests indicated that he did not suffer from venereal disease. His physical health was quite satisfactory.

I made the following conclusions in my report to court:

1. The accused was fit to plead and to stand trial.
2. At the material time he was capable of knowing what he was doing and that what he was doing was wrong.
3. The other consideration that arose was that of mental abnormality as defined in Part I, s.2, para.1, of the Homicide Act 1957. I could not think that his state at the time of the alleged offence could be described as mentally abnormal within the meaning of the definition, that is to say, due to arrested or retarded development of mind, inherent cause or induced by disease or injury. I could not therefore think that in this case there was mental abnormality sufficient to substantially impair his responsibility for his actions in doing the killing.
4. It automatically followed that s.60 of the Mental Health Act 1959 (now s.37 of the Mental Health Act 1983) was not applicable to him on the grounds of mental disorder.

A leading forensic pathologist advised the defence to have a fasting blood-sugar estimation on the accused during the remand period. The result was 58 mg. per 100 ml of blood and indicated a tendency to hypoglycaemia which was confirmed by three subsequent glucose-tolerant tests. A professor of metabolic medicine was briefed by the defence and gave an opinion to the effect that the accused was suffering from reactive hypoglycaemia but there was no evidence of an insulin-secreting tumour. Plasma insulin assays were also undertaken and the professor said that reactive hypoglycaemia was "not an uncommon condition".

The court was also informed that electroencephalographic tracings were taken during blood-sugar level estimations and were found to be normal. Consequently, abnormal brain rhythms were not associated with abnormally low sugar levels in the blood of the accused.

The behaviour of the accused was not disturbed during the hypoglycaemic phases of the glucose-tolerance tests. There was no evidence of the common signs and symptoms of hypoglycaemia during the remand period in the prison hospital which lasted about three months. Consequently, I informed the court that my conclusions remained unaltered. I was asked in court if I had ever seen an individual in a hypoglycaemic state and in reply mentioned my experiences of deep insulin-coma therapy for schizophrenics some years previously.

Written and oral evidence was presented to the court by all the doctors concerned. The plea of diminished responsibility failed and the accused was found guilty of murder by the jury and sentenced to life imprisonment.

References

Bartlett, F. C. (1932) *Remembering: A Study in Experimental and Social Psychology*, Macmillan, Cambridge.

Bleuler, E. P. (1924) *Textbook of Psychiatry for Students and Practitioners*, George Allen and Unwin, London.

Bradley, M. T., Warfield, J. F. (1984) "Insurance, Information and the Guilty Knowledge Test in the Detection of Deception", *Psychophysiology,* University of Brunswick, U.S.A., Vol. 21, No. 6, pp 683-89.

Brain, R. (1955) *Diseases of the Nervous System*, Oxford University Press, London.

Brisby, F. H. (1960) R. v. Podola. A Symposium held on Monday, April 4, 1960. *Medico Legal Journal*, 28, 117.

Cartlidge, N. E. F. (1991) "Transient Global Amnesia", *Brit. Med. J.,* Vol. 302, pp 62-63.

Channon, S., Polkey, C. E. (1990) "Memory and Temporal Lobe Epilepsy: A Review", *J. Roy. Soc. of Medicine,* Vol. 83, 100-3.

Hays, P. (1961) "Hysterical Amnesia and the Podola Trial", *Medico Legal Journal* 29, 27.

Hopwood, J. S., Snell, H. K. (1933) "Amnesia in relation to crime", *J. of Mental Science,* 79, 27.

Lovell, K., Vernon, P. E. (1970) *Educational Psychology and Children,* University Press, London.

Mathews, A. (1986) "Cognitive Processes in Anxiety and Depression: Discussion Paper", *J. of Roy. Soc. of Medicine,* Vol. 79, pp 158-61.

Milner, B. "Psychological Defects produced by Temporal-lobe Excision", *Res. Publ. Assoc. Nerv. Ment. Dis.* (1958) 36: 244-57.

Scrivner, E., Safer, M. A. (1988) "Eyewitnesses Show Hypermnesia for Details about a

Violent Event", *J. of Applied Psychology,* American Psychological Assoc. Inc., 73, 3, 371-377.

Whitlock, F. A. (1963) *Criminal Responsibility and Mental Illness,* Butterworths, London.

Woodworth, R. S., Marquis, D. G. (1958) *Textbook of Psychology,* Methuen & Co. Ltd., London, 17, 566-7.

Yuille, J. C., Cutshall, J. L. (1986)"A Case Study of Eyewitness Memory of a Crime", *J. of Applied Psychology,* (American Psychological Assoc. Inc) 71, 2, 291-301.

CHAPTER VI

Young Offenders

Delinquency is used in a general sense to describe the behaviour of young offenders against the law. It can also be used with regard to an offence of a minor kind as is often but not always the case with regard to juvenile delinquency when the law is violated by offenders below the age of legal responsibility. A "delinquent" is here defined as an individual with a criminal conviction record. The aetiology of delinquent behaviour has a sufficiently diverse theoretical background to warrant a clear and practical definition as a starting point. I shall collectively regard individuals as "young offenders" up to the age of 21 years and confine the term "juvenile" to delinquents under the age of 17 years.

The following classification of delinquent behaviour indicates the possible causative factors involved:

(a) *Marauding offences* indicate spontaneous and unplanned lawbreaking which include truancy, petty theft and individuals brought to court as "beyond parental control".

(b) *Proving offences* are committed to prove manhood and to promote an image of self which will establish self-respect. These offenders often come from "well-to-do" homes and usually have respectable but over-strict and unsympathetic parents who are insensitive to young people's feelings. Examples are taking and driving away cars ("joy-riding"), offences of violence and sexual offences.

(c) *Comforting offences* mean lawbreaking perpetrated to compensate for loss of affection. Typical examples are stealing from shops (shoplifting), to gain parental attention and car theft to gain friends in the peer group.

(d) *Well-planned offences* are usually due to inherent selfishness.

While there would appear to be no significant relationship between delinquency and actual economic status, Nazario's (1988) studies have especially highlighted the incidence of delinquency where contributory factors such as poverty and unemployment are present.

Environmental conditions tend to influence delinquent acts which increase when domestic, social and economic conditions are unfavourable. West (1973) reported that delinquency, as measured by self-report independently of official records, was very significantly correlated with parental criminality. Delinquency is more common in cities. Moving from high- to low-density parts of a city and breakdown of social values and authority within the family predispose to lawbreaking. An American study by Perales (1988) found that poverty, violence, illegal drugs and despair dominate the lives of many inner-city children, most of whom are black and Hispanic.

Intellectual levels among delinquents do not appear to follow any significant pattern and low intelligence is not an essential factor. Poor motivation for schooling and frustration with educational expectations are much more likely to be contributory factors. Temperament alone cannot account for behaviour disorder. There does appear to be a correlation between delinquency and brain damage occurring during pregnancy, e.g. foetal anoxia and rubella. Delinquency is twice as likely to occur in such cases as compared with persons who have not sustained such brain damage (Pasamanick (1956)). Some psychometric studies of young delinquents have found a characteristic pattern of slight deficits suggesting neurological impairment, Fromm-Auch et al (1980)). It is also the case that with the so-called hyperkinetic syndrome of childhood, characterized by a combination of overactivity, restlessness, hostility to discipline and general anti-sociability, there is a suggested connection between this form of neuro-psychiatric disorder and juvenile delinquency.

A small percentage of maladjusted "problem" children may become delinquent in later life because their cerebral hemispheres may be overwhelmed by average sensory stimuli and, consequently, they lose control of their behaviour. Intra-utestine damage has been implicated.

The pathological basis for these opinions is apparently based on double blind trials in which one group was subjected to perfusion techniques involving inhalation of Xenon "133" and emission tomography which indicated decreased blood flow to the striatal regions of the hyperactive children and especially to the corpora striati of their right cerebral hemispheres (Lou et al, 1989).

This decreased blood flow is taken to mean hypofunction of the striatal regions and over function of the primary sensory and sensorimotor cortical regions which were over perfused with blood as indicated by the above investigations for children aged six years or over. Dexamphetamine in doses of 5 mg. once or twice daily apparently increases the blood supply to the striatal regions resulting in improved behaviour.

It is recognized that the behaviour of hyperkinetic disruptive children is also improved by alteration in diet. Double blind trials have indicated that certain foods militate against controlled behaviour in a minority of children. Avoidance of tomatoes, milk, oranges, citrus fruits, chocolates, bread, eggs, wheat and food additives including colouring substances apparently leads to improved behaviour in some instances (Pollock, 1991).

Investigations should be undertaken to discover the percentage of such overactive badly behaved children who later become delinquent in the absence of earlier treatment.

Types of Juvenile Crime

Homicide

Case 6: A 15-year-old boy strangled a teenage girl. The victim was not sexually assaulted. The accused had never had psychiatric treatment and was not an epileptic. His intelligence was within average limits. He had been asked to leave grammar school because of unruly behaviour. He was reported as having had encephalitis when a few months old. He had made sexual advances to girls a few months before the homicide and had also been found to be in possession of house-breaking implements a short time before committing the homicide. He showed little remorse and was diagnosed as suffering from a serious personality disorder. The charge was reduced from murder to manslaughter on the grounds of diminished responsibility and he was sentenced to be detained during Her Majesty's Pleasure under the Criminal Procedure (Insanity) Act. A doctor told the court that the accused was going through a "sinister" phase in his development. He was not mentally disordered within the meaning of the Mental Health Act (1959).

Case 7: A 16-year-old boy stabbed a young girl to death. He was subject to nocturnal enuresis up to the age of nine. He tended to go to his father rather than his mother for advice and comfort during childhood and adolescence. His mother had a history of residential psychiatric treatment. His school career was characterized by frequent truancy. His intelligence quotient was estimated as 114 (WAIS). After leaving school he worked for a brief period. There was no history of epilepsy, attempted suicide or serious head injuries. He had earlier been found guilty of a comparatively minor offence and committed to a remand home. A consultant interested in chromosomal typing paid routine visits to the remand home and the youth was found to have the XYY chromosome constitution. Price and Whatmore (1967) found that persons with the extra chromosome tend to commit offences against property rather than persons and when a group of XYY offenders was compared with a control group of XY offenders, the majority of the XYY offenders had indeed committed offences against property. There is no specific correlation between the extra Y chromosome and the likelihood of indulging in violent behaviour and this extra chromosome has been found in members of the public who had never broken the law. The accused felt hostile to women from the age of 12 years. He was resident in the consultant's hospital for three months for the purpose of further chromosomal typing. Notes from the hospital did not indicate that a psychiatric diagnosis had been made. There was no history of homosexual behaviour. An electroencephalogram did not reveal any abnormality. He was not mentally disordered within the meaning of the Mental Health Act (1959). The victim was stabbed about eight times with a penknife for no apparent reason. The accused did not experience sexual orgasm at the material time. A plea of diminished responsibility was unsuccessful. He was convicted of murder and sentenced to be detained during Her Majesty's Pleasure under the Criminal Procedure (Insanity) Act 1964.

The link between personality type and delinquency is by no means clear. Eysenck (1950) expressed the opinion that delinquency is characterized by the extrovert temperament: delinquents condition poorly, they evidence clumsy psychomotor performance and they present a mesomorphic physique. These characteristics allegedly have an adverse effect on social learning. Trasler (1962) expressed the opinion that introverts are good conditioners and usually develop respect for property and persons because their autonomic conditioning reactions are strong components of their personalities and act as a learned-drive. These anxiety reactions also inhibit or activate specific types of behaviour which are stongly resistant to extinction and are reinforced by anxiety. The opposite would seem to apply to extroverts.

These assumptions are questioned by other researchers. Farrington (1981) states that contradictory findings have resulted from other investigations seeking to apply Eysenck's inventories to delinquent populations. West (1973) failed to identify a crime-prone group by means of assessments of neuroticism and extroversion.

Arson

The subject of arson in general and in relation to all age groups may conveniently be considered here. Arson is an offence against the Criminal Damage Act (1971). Section 1(1) refers to damage and destruction of property and Section 1(2) to destroying or damaging property whereby life is endangered. It has always been considered a serious common-law crime and arson in connection with H.M. ships and dockyard stores carried the death penalty until 1971.

Case 8: A 19-year-old youth was convicted of attempting to burn down a church. He filled a bottle with paraffin, inserted a rag in the neck of the bottle and, having set it alight, threw it through the church window. He drank alcohol to excess shortly before the offence. His intelligence quotient was 62 (WAIS). He had received psychiatric treatment on six occasions. He had attempted suicide on at least three occasions. He had suffered from epilepsy since he was six years old. He was incapable of managing his affairs in the community. His parents were intellectually dull and his father's aggressive attitude aroused feelings of intense violence and self-destruction in him. He attempted to fracture the skull of a peaceful member of the community with a large stone, shortly before the arson. This victim was picked at random and provided an outlet for this young man's aggression. He was admitted to a psychiatric hospital under s.60 of the Mental Health Act 1959 (now s.37 of the Mental Health Act 1983). A restriction order, without limit of time, was imposed under s.65 of the 1959 act (now s.41 of the 1983 Act).

The offence of arson, which may carry a life sentence if committed in its aggravated form, whereby life is endangered, is most frequently committed by members of the male sex. The great majority of such crimes are accounted for by motivations such as vandalism, profit, jealousy and revenge by those who are *not* mentally disordered.

Case 9: I have personal knowledge of an impaired person who stole money from his aunt's house and then set fire to it in order to avoid detection. He hoped that she would not associate him with the crime, and did not attempt to confirm her absence from the house at the material time, nor did he appreciate the importance of so doing. Impaired individuals who indulge in arson usually prefer to set fire to buildings which are unoccupied by people but the impaired psychopath would not be so scrupulous.

Schmideberg (1953) made the pertinent observation that the "violent thread of sadism runs through the majority of cases of arson". Those (of any age) who indulge in malicious firesetting may or may not be compulsive arsonists (pyromaniacs) and they are not necessarily disordered within the meaning of the Mental Health Act. The pyromaniac regards arson as an end in itself and derives pleasure from planning and starting fires and witnessing the results. From a psychological standpoint arson is an act of fulfilment associated with a host of sensations such as excitement, creativity in originating a spectacle, empathizing with a process of destruction of the old and re-birth of the new as in the legend of the Phoenix, ecstasy and pure enjoyment in the warmth and glow of the flames.

Exhibitionist and sado-masochistic tendencies are particularly strong in pyromaniacs and fires may enable them to experience vicarious sexual pleasure. Males predominate (the "Macho" effect), and the offence tends to be repeated. The pyromaniac ruminates on and exults in the fantasies of firesetting in the form of memory images of flames, fire engines, police cars, panic-stricken victims and the sense of emergency. They like to be present at the scene and often subsequently gather information about it from the media.

It is most important to question arsonists as to the nature of their fantasies in relation to fire and their apparent disregard for the safety of others. Some individuals may masturbate whilst enjoying the memory of fires or studying photographs of them.

Psychotics, mentally impaired and psychopathically disordered individuals may indulge in arson. Psychotics include schizophrenics, manic depressives and dements. Mentally impaired individuals may indulge in firesetting as a simple act of revenge.

It should be pointed out that the great majority of individuals who are disordered within the meaning of the Mental Health Act do not indulge in arson.

Arsonists may claim amnesia for the material times but such claims are rarely genuine. The tests for amnesia are set out in Chapter V.

Prognosis for Arson
(a) Children and adolescents who are not mentally disordered tend not to repeat the crime of arson. Children may start fires as an experiment or because of emotional conflicts arising out of home circumstances and bad feelings about themselves.

(b)   Malicious firesetting is usually not repeated when indulged as a group activity.
(c)   Pyromania (in the sense of compulsive and repeated malicious firesetting) tends to be repeated by mentally impaired individuals.
(d)   Arson secondary to mental illness is not likely to be repeated if the illness is successfully treated.

The pyromaniac who starts fires to satisfy some inner need might come within the definition of psychopathic disorder in the Mental Health Act. Scott (1974) referred to a special type of pyromaniac with sadistic tendencies, called the fire-fetishist who tends to be a "loner" in the sense that he is relatively isolated from society. Scott stated that fire-fetishists are usually vagrants or mentally impaired individuals who are not particular as to whether they set fire to buildings which are occupied or empty, while other pyromaniacs usually choose empty buildings.

I have seen large butterfly tattoos on the backs of some pyromaniacs. Perhaps the butterfly wings symbolized flames. Pyromaniacs are a serious danger to the public and they are best treated in conditions of maximum security as provided in a special hospital if they are mentally disordered within the meaning of the Mental Health Act 1983.

Lewis and Yarnell (1951) indicated that older vagrants tend to repeat the crime of arson.

Malicious firesetting may also be associated with alcoholism and drug addiction, including solvent abuse. It may also be associated with varying degrees of dementia due to cerebral injury, arteriosclerosis, epilepsy or senility.

Psychoneurotics *per se* rarely indulge in serious crime including arson. Conversion hysteria may be an exception to this statement but the existence of this condition as a clinical entity is now in question.

I have known pre-menstrual tension successfully used in mitigation of a charge of arson.

Statistics
(a) Tennent *et al* (1971) studied 56 female arsonists and found that 34 were psychopathically disordered, 12 were mentally ill, seven suffered from mental impairment and three from severe impairment. All were patients in special security hospitals and therefore mentally disordered within the meaning of the Mental Health Act 1959.
(b) The following statistics of arson are from Lewis and Yarnell (1951)

and concern males.

(1) Of 1,108 studied, 154 were mentally ill and 155 of defective intelligence.

(2) Of 174 studied, 13 repeated the offence.

(3) Of 688 studied, 447 admitted a compulsion to start the fires and 241 admitted experiencing emotional satisfaction, expressed as a desire to help firemen extinguish the fires and thus become heroes. They also admitted that they enjoyed the destruction of property.

(4) Of 447 studied, 98 were classed as low-grade defectives. Of the remainder, 120 acted in response to the "irresistible impulse" and 40 derived sexual satisfaction from watching the flames.

(5) Of 154 studied, 34 were epileptics, 27 were arteriosclerotic and senile psychotics, there were 27 cases of alcoholic psychosis and four individuals suffered from manic-depressive or involutional psychosis.

(6) Of 91 studied, the average age was 39 years. The group included middle-aged men on the verge of impotence and others approaching senility and expressing delusions of infidelity.

Rix, (1994), studied 153 arsonists and found that 70 suffered from personality disorder, 15 were mentally handicapped, 11 abused alcohol, 8 were psychotic and 20 were regarded as "normal". The remainder had various other diagnoses.

Bourget *et al* (1989) studied a sample of 15 female arsonists. A review of the literature suggests that arson is seen more frequently in males, with female firesetters usually comprising 10 to 18 per cent of the samples of firesetters studied. As a result, female arsonists have been studied less often, and only a few authors have reported on their clinical features. This retrospective study demonstrates that female arsonists do not fall into any particular age group and are mostly either single or separated. Some psychosexual aspects of their behaviour also appear to be clinically relevant. In contrast to previous studies, they were more often diagnosed as personality disorder – and an association with suicidal behaviour was found.

Kolko et al. (1989) indicated that a model of firesetting-risk poses that high curiosity, involvement in fire-related activities, expression of negative emotions, limited knowledge and skill related to fires, poor parental supervision, early experiences with fire, and exposure to others' involvement with fire are characteristic of firesetters as opposed to non-firesetters. Some 343 children (ages 6-13) were studied.

Webb *et al.* (1990) undertook a study in which assessment, preventive intervention, and interdisciplinary collaboration between the fire department and mental health services are highlighted as key factors in the identification and treatment of juvenile firesetters and their families. An interagency pilot programme in New York City is described and the importance of "aggressive" outreach is emphasized in motivation.

However, Quinsey *et al.* (1989) studied the penile responses ; the responses of 26 firesetters and 15 non-firesetters to audiotaped narratives were compared. The categories of narratives were: neutral, heterosexual sexual activity, and firesetting motivated by sexual excitement, general (unspecified) excitement, insurance, revenge, heroism, or power. Responses to all of the categories were of small magnitude, although both the heterosexual-activity and the sexual-excitement firesetting categories elicited larger responses than the neutral category. There were no significant differences between the firesetters and non-firesetters to any of the categories. These data contain no support for the idea that sexual motivation is commonly involved in arson. Some 3,167 persons were convicted of arson in England and Wales in 1988 as compared with 2,807 in 1978.

A small minority of children and adolescents indulge in arson and most frequently between the ages of 13-17 years. A minority of adolescents apparently find communal satisfaction in "playing with fire" which has been alleged to symbolize sexual behaviour. I have noted several instances where arson occurred in the domestic setting because of familial conflict. These individuals were intellectually retarded but could not be described as pryomaniacs.

There are strong associations between arson, sexual offences and mental impairment.

Offences concerning illicit drugs
Case 10: A young man of average intelligence was addicted to morphine, cannabis, methedrine, LSD, barbiturates and Mandrax. He also took alcohol to excess. He did not suffer from epilepsy. He earned his living in the building trade. The current charge concerned illegal possession of cannabis. He was heterosexual and quite promiscuous. He had treatment at a psychiatric hospital for three months. He also had an unhappy childhood and his father suffered from schizophrenia. The history also

indicated that he had been in an approved school for theft. He was admitted to the addiction unit of a psychiatric hospital as a condition of probation. He was diagnosed as a drug addict and he also suffered from a schizo-affective disorder.

This case history illustrates that drug-dependence may be secondary to a serious mental disorder which will also require treatment. Solvent abuse by young persons is dealt with in Ch. VII on illicit drug-taking.

Notifiable Offences Recorded by the Police in England and Wales July 1990-June 1991:

Statistics:
    4.9 million notifiable offences were recorded in the 12 months to the end of June 1991, a rise of 18 per cent over the previous 12 months.
    94 per cent were crimes against property, 5 per cent were crimes against the person.
    The 5 per cent increase in violent crime was small compared with previous years.
Car crimes accounted for more than a third of the overall increase of 756,000 offences.
    Recorded crime increased in all police force areas.

Offences of taking conveyance

Taking and driving away cars (joy-riding) is a common offence which may be motivated by:

(i)   an intention to steal and sell the cars for profit;
(ii)   a desire to have a joy-ride and then abandon the car so that the owner is only temporarily deprived of his property (which constitutes about one-third of all conveyance offences);
(iii)   a vindictive desire to steal the car, drive it, and then smash it up before abandoning it;
(iv)   a desire to commit suicide by reckless driving;
(v)   stolen cars may crash accidentally, especially when pursued by the police when the occupants may be killed or injured.

Individuals who commit these offences may or may not be under the influence of intoxicating substances such as drugs or alcohol deliberately taken to excess. They may also be mentally disordered.

There is much current concern to the effect that some car dealers may unwittingly issue replica alarm control boxes to potential car thieves who obtain same by quoting the alarm model numbers. They arrange to view the cars afters seeing same advertised for sale and open the alarm control boxes and note the model numbers, usually when the owners leave them alone to fetch log books. Ignition key numbers are also noted and duplicates obtained by quoting these numbers at the appropriate garages. The cars are stolen after switching off their alarms by using the replica control boxes. Owners could remove identification numbers from control boxes and the makers of the latter should only accept orders from accredited dealers who in turn should not take orders without proof of ownership.

It is also alleged that insurance companies tend to pass on the heavy costs of car thefts in increased premiums so that a substantial proportion of innocent drivers face a considerable increase in their policy renewal premiums. Lower premiums should be charged to the owners of models with adequate anti-theft protection and there should be an increase in the detection of fraudulent car insurance claims.

Case 11: An 18 year-old youth, with an intelligence quotient of 50 (WAIS), was charged with taking and driving away cars without their owners' consent. He was unable to earn a living in the community. The history indicated that he had attacked his mother with a pair of scissors and also indulged in bestiality. He did not suffer from epilepsy. He was not addicted to any drugs or alcohol. Psychopathic elements were evident in his personality. He had been a resident patient for six months at a hospital for the mentally sub-normal. His parents were described as "stable dullards". He tended to wander from place to place. He was sent to a mental hospital under Section 60 of the Mental Health Act 1959 (now s.37 of the Mental Health Act 1983) on the basis of sub-normality. A restriction order, without limit of time, was added under s.65 of the 1959 Act (now s.41 of the Mental Health Act 1983).

Sexual Offences
A case history of rape is described in Ch. VIII. Saunders et al. (1986) divided male adolescent sexual offenders (under age of 16 years) into three groups:

(i)   courtship disorders such as exhibitionism, "toucherism" and obscene telephone calls. These offenders tended to come from a less disorganized family background, were better adjusted to school and in the community, and were seen by clinicians as less seriously disturbed than the adolescents in the other two groups. In addition, these adolescents did not experience the offence as a sexual act. Toucherism refers to sexual offences consisting of a brief touching of a woman's breasts or genitalia.

(ii) Those who committed sexual offences such as rape and indecent assault came from a more disturbed family background characterized by a high rate of long-term parent-child separations, committed more violent offences and had a higher frequency of intellectual functioning in the Borderline Range of Intelligence meaning 42 per cent had IQs of 70 to 79.

(iii) Paedophiliac offenders who had witnessed physical violence between their parents were described as having been infants who did not enjoy being cuddled and had siblings who were truants.

Sixty-three offenders were studied and distributed between the three groups in reasonable proportions. Some 30 were regarded as sexual "recidivists" and very few of these committed offences which fall into more than one group.

A sexual offence committed by an adolescent should always be treated as a sign of psychiatric disturbance and a careful clinical assessment, including psychological testing, should be carried out.

A report by investigators representing the National Childrens Home 1992 indicated that the number of children who are sexually abused by other children may be grossly underestimated because complaints of sexual abuse are frequently dismissed by parents, police and childcare authorities. Furthermore children exposed to such evils as pornography and telephone sex lines may well experience premature sexual arousal which they are unable to understand or control resulting in life-long personality damage.

Child sex abusers are often victims of abuse themselves in the first instance and their tendency to abuse other children tends to become obsessional.

The report also emphasizes the drastic shortage of treatment facilities including staff training and research.

Recommendations include:

1.   All suspicion of abuse should be investigated by social services or police as part of an overall systematic approach.
2.   Schools must be told if a child has sexually abused another youngster.
3.   Known abusers should never be placed with foster parents if there are younger children in the home.
4.   All child-care workers should be trained in how to handle the problem.
5.   Intensive treatment should be given to all those in custody and should be offered to all young abusers.
6.   A telephone should be available for youngsters in care where they can talk in private.

The 200-page Warner Enquiry (1992) concerning children's homes in England made 83 recommendations with the object of raising the level of qualifications and training for staff. It was noted that 80 per cent of care staff and 40 per cent of those in charge of these homes lacked any relevant qualifications. Furthermore, training, supervision and assessment left much to be desired after appointments had been made.

Unsatisfactory recruitment gave much cause for concern. Applicants should not be offered posts before references are received and written references should be followed up by telephone enquiries with the object of confirmation. Checks should be made to discover if applicants have criminal records or histories of psychiatric treatment. It is also very important for employers to try to establish how applicants relate to children and to detect incidents in their past which might give cause for concern.

Sexual propensities and behaviour of candidates should also be investigated.

These recommendations should be implemented urgently and child carers should be required to have a licence to practise.

Differential Diagnosis of Delinquency

Psychopathic disorder is characterized by serious impairment of the normal capacity to co-operate with others, by lack of concern, guilt or anxiety about the consequences of misbehaviour, grossly impaired capacity for making relationships, and a paucity of satisfying life experiences. Psychopathically disordered individuals are a potential danger to themselves and others and a minority are capable of explosive violence which may be unmotivated and accompanied by clouding of consciousness.

Acute behavioural crises may occur during adolescence and these may or may not be an outcome of the emotional stresses of the post-pubertal changes in the physiological and psychological constitution of the individual.

The symptoms of *psychoneurosis* need not be enumerated. Delinquency must be differentiated from psychoneurosis. A crime can only be attributed to psychoneurosis when the following criteria are satisfied:

1. The illegal act must be the outcome of an emotional conflict and one side of the conflicting forces must be social conscience, however primitive in structure.
2. One should be able to understand the offence as an attempt to resolve the emotional conflict.
3. Material gain must not be the primary object of the illegal behaviour.
4. Other recognized symptoms of psychoneurosis should be evident (Gillespie, 1944).

Prognosis

The prognosis for an individual delinquent should be assessed by studying all available information. Foxe (1948) postulated that the prognosis of delinquency in general would be facilitated by considering the subject from the criminologic, sociological and statistical aspects.

The criminologic approach

The following questions should be asked:

1. Why did he break the law?
2. Do the various factors which caused him to break the law persist?
3. Is his basic preference for legal or illegal behaviour?
4. Is he willing to mend his ways by giving up associates and localities which influenced previous lawbreaking? Good resolutions are not of much value as the delinquent usually overestimates his ability to control his behaviour. A study of his police record would indicate the number of previous convictions The illegal behaviour might follow a pattern.

The sociological approach

This approach involves a study of the subject's home environment, availability of work, marital disharmony and attitude towards children.

The "battered-baby syndrome" means that some delinquent parents subject their children to severe physical violence. Records indicate that 622 such cases occurred in Chicago in one year and 27 per cent were fatal. The parents usually felt isolated and depressed and unable to cope with the ordinary stresses of life and had usually been subjected to cruelty during their own childhoods.

The influence to which the delinquent was subjected during childhood and adolescence should also be studied. Was the individual separated from his or her parents? If so, at what age? Was there genuine affection from the parents? The degree of parental supervision and the type of discipline experienced in the parent-child relationship should be taken into account. Studies indicate that prognosis is improved if delinquents are helped by professional social workers.

The statistical approach

O'Neal *et al.* (1960) assessed 227 adults some 30 years after they had been referred (as children) for treatment of behaviour disorders and obtained the following results:

(i)	34 per cent of those considered to be delinquent as children eventually developed "sociopathic" personalities.

(ii)	20 per cent had a history of psychopathic disturbances.

(iii)	42 per cent were not mentally disordered as adults and these were originally referred for neurotic complaints.

In a comprehensive study by West (1973) it was found that of those male juvenile offenders who were convicted more than once for a juvenile offence, a high proportion (47 out of 209) had been exposed to unsatisfactory parenting and 38 out of the sample of 209 came from poor-income families. Further it was found that those in the sample who had as children between the ages of eight to 10 years been rated as extremely troublesome by class teachers were more likely to develop as persistent recidivists later. Very large family size (defined as six or more children born to a boy's mother before his tenth birthday) appeared also as an important link to persistent recidivism in West's sample. From among the early assessments which appeared to be predictive of long-term recidivism, West selected three criteria:

(a)	Very troublesome according to teachers' reports;

(b) Father with at least two criminal convictions in adult courts before the boy was ten;

(c) Mother with an adult conviction record, or a sibling with a conviction record (juvenile or adult) before the boy was 10 years old.

Oldham (1964) studied 50 male prison inmates remanded on charges of theft and who admitted their guilt. The thefts were committed without the use of violence in all instances. Twenty-four had good homes and happy childhoods. Forty-seven had previous convictions. None suffered from mental disorder. Thirty-one were aged between 17 and 21 years. In 41 instances the motive was simply acquisitiveness in the sense that they wished to obtain goods or money without the effort of labour. None were in dire financial need. Alcohol was held to be directly responsible in only five instances. Thirty had given no consideration, at the time the crime was committed, to the risks of detention, apprehension or punishment and were less likely to benefit from attempts to reform them. Not one of the 50 cases studied expressed remorse, and each of the thieves spoke readily about their crimes and past history. Marked self-pity was evident in 25 subjects of the study group.

Prognosis can only be improved by undermining the lawbreakers' confidence in their criminal abilities and this can be done in three ways:

1. by increasing the probability of custodial sentence;
2. by implying intensive suggestion that crime does not pay;
3. by employing psychotherapeutic techniques when the thief is first detected and before there is opportunity of association with hardened criminals.

Individuals who indulge in sex crimes and crimes of violence were excluded from the study group and each member of the group was endowed with average intelligence.

Management
The Home Office proposes (1995) to accommodate up to 200 persistent young offenders in England and Wales, in 5 secure units equivalent to jails and managed by the private sector. Supervision will be shared with the probation and social services. It is also proposed to discontinue the university-based training of probation officers. These units have yet to be built.

Delinquent behaviour may be *sociological* in origin. It is motivated, goal-orientated and involves learning from experience usually through trial and error. It may also be regarded as adaptive in nature. Sociological delinquency usually entails "group-endorsement" of anti-social behaviour by the minority subculture in which the delinquent lives. This type of delinquency does not require psychiatric treatment. Use could be made of the following means to combat sociological delinquency:

1. Neighbourhood citizens' committees;
2. Recreational and group work facilities on a large scale;
3. Job upgrading projects;
4. Home study programmes;
5. Youth group activities.

The urgent need is for the provision of opportunities for positive non-delinquent relationships. Sociological delinquents are bonded in loyalty to the delinquent group. Awareness of the self-defeating aspects of delinquent behaviour and of the option of non-delinquent alternatives should be promoted as wholesome and healthy outlets for youthful energies. The recidivism rate might be lowered if further means could be devised of helping delinquents to become accustomed to life and work in the community by the increased use of pre-release youth custody and probation hostels. The socialized delinquent is rejected by other members of the gang if there is a refusal to take part in delinquent behaviour and this rejection by the peer group is a formidable obstacle to the avoidance of future lawbreaking.

Delinquent acts are reinforced and established as behaviour patterns due to the increased prestige and self-esteem of successful criminal activities (Weiner, 1962). Symptomatic delinquency is due to emotional conflict. This type of delinquency is maladaptive and induced by frustration. The resulting anti-social behaviour tends to be stereotyped and uninfluenced by punishment.

Prevention is not only better than cure; it is easier and more economic. McCormick (1989) in an American report on "research related to children at risk" suggests the importance of parental involvement and early education as influential factors in preventing juvenile crime and related problems such as substance abuse. Weikart (1989) in the USA analysed the long-term benefits, to children and society, of high-quality early childhood education. The study indicates that good pre-school programmes can lead to consistent improvement in poor children's achievement and a subsequent reduced delinquency and arrest rate.

Symptomatic delinquency may be an expression of psychopathic disorder as defined in the Mental Health Act 1983. Psychopathic disorder is characterized by a gross failure of conscience in an emotionally disturbed individual with an abnormally low tolerance of stress. Abnormal lack of inhibition, unrestrained impulsiveness, bitter resentment of society, and pathological aggression also characterize the disorder. In attempting to treat the psychopathic delinquent the therapist should become sympathetically involved with the delinquent's current needs in order to win the offender's confidence. An authoritarian yet supportive relationship with the delinquent is advised. The psychopath is characterized by boredom with the familiar short-term perspective and a non-verbal orientation. Consequently, regular, orderly psychotherapeutic sessions tend to be ineffective. Treatment sessions should be varied and stimulating. The psychopath expects the therapist to demonstrate by deed as well as word. The therapist should be ready to give of self and personality for the patient's benefit, and should display a deep and sustained interest in all aspects of the psychopathic delinquent's life. Sufficient anxiety must be generated and treatment for the delinquency *per se* can begin at this point. The aim is to arrive at a stage where the psychopath freely identifies with the therapist's non-delinquent type of model behaviour and attempts to suppress or control some of his or her anti-social tendencies. Delinquency as an expression of a neurosis or psychosis requires treatment of these conditions.

Psychiatrists should obviously be aware of management facilities available for juvenile offenders under the age of 18 years, in their areas of residence.

I would like to digress slightly here to refer to Feltham which was a borstal until it became a Young Offenders' Institution under the Criminal Justice Act 1991. It also provides psychiatric facilities to help young offenders who are emotionally disturbed but not mentally disordered within the meaning of the Mental Health Act 1983.

The Home Office report on Feltham (May, 1992) indicated that this young offender institution was occupied by 500 male remand prisoners all under 21 years. They often spent 21 hours per day in their cells. Bullying amongst inmates was not uncommon and the use of control and restraint techniques was not lower than in any other establishment in England and Wales. Four young inmates of Feltham committed suicide by hanging between August 1991 and June 1992.

It is alleged that potential suicides are "missed" at reception at Feltham and a psychiatrically trained nurse should be employed and stationed permanently in the reception area . Cell beds should also be secured to the floor so that they cannot be used as gibbets. "Helsinki Watch" is a human-rights group and justifiably condemns the British preoccupation with sending so many offenders to penal institutions. There is a connection between overcrowding and suicidal attempts. Fine defaulters should not be sent to prison and remand periods should be drastically reduced. Some of the vacant army camps could be used to relieve overcrowding in penal institutions.

The court may also send a juvenile delinquent to a community home or to a special youth treatment centre established by the Department of Health under s.30 of the Children and Young Persons Act 1969. Such a centre provides, in secure accommodation, many of the treatment facilities of a school, a children's home and a hospital.

Treatment Centres
The first youth treatment centre in the United Kingdom was opened at St. Charles Hospital, Brentwood, Essex in July, 1971. Accommodation is provided for 30 children. The minimum age for admission is 12 years. Individuals over the age of 17 years are not admitted. Psychiatrists, psychologists and occupational therapists work at the centre, whose aims – like those of youth treatment centres generally – may be summarized as follows:

1.   To provide long-term care under secure conditions for young people suffering from "serious psychological damage" and who are not suitable for detention under the Mental Health Act 1983.
2.   Treatment with a view to improvement or at least prevention of further personality deterioration.
3.   Rehabilitation.
4.   Research.
5.   Staff training.

Prescribing in these centres is the exclusive prerogative of the visiting general practitioner. The two visiting psychiatrists may, of course, recommend treatment.

The following research summary by the Dartington Social Research Unit (1989) analyses the background characteristics and experiences of all leavers from two youth treatment centres – Glenthorne and St Charles – between 1982 and 1985 inclusive and involving 104 children. It also scrutinizes the career outcomes and destinations of those difficult young people who, for a variety of reasons, failed to take up a place at the Centres, although they met all the criteria for admission.

During the planning of the Centres and in the initial years, the needs of difficult young people in local authority care, particularly girls, were viewed as a priority. But, by the time of the research, boys out-numbered girls by three to one and s.53 cases – that is children who were convicted of grave offences – occupied a third of Centre places. Indeed, boys almost entirely predominated among this latter group.

The average age of entrants was 15 years and children stayed until 17.4 years on average. However, Section 53 children are usually older than care-order cases on leaving the Centres. One in five of all leavers is from an ethnic minority.

On many criteria, such as persistent offending, absconding, aggressive and difficult behaviour, the Youth Treatment Centre population clearly emerges as very difficult indeed. Nevertheless, there are risks assuming that residents present similar problems; it was found that a wide variety of backgrounds and presenting difficulties characterize those admitted. Indeed, each child has its own avenue leading to entry, career in the YTC and outcome on leaving. For example, while many Section 53 cases presented few problems at school or in the community before the serious offence which gained them admission to the Centres, others had been highly problematic in the outside world prior to entry. On admission many children on care orders were aggressive, prone to abscond and had a long history of delinquency. On the other hand, some were more a danger to themselves than to others. In addition, 37 per cent of boys and 57 per cent of girls displayed problematic sexual behaviour. Thus, in behaviour terms, the children presented the Centres with an unenviable and complex task.

While three-fifths of the young people had serious delinquent histories, some had committed very grave offences indeed. Thirteen children at the Centres had indeterminate sentences under Section 53(1) legislation usually for murder, manslaughter or arson. In addition, the 24 young people under Section 53(2) legislation were sentenced to detention for up to six years. While all Section 53 cases have been convicted of serious offences and adolescents on care orders have been generally disruptive, the individual problems presented by the entrants vary. For example, two-fifths of the Section 53 children were first offenders, although others had a long history of delinquency and deprivation typical of adolescent offenders in care. Similarly, the care-order entrants had a range of problems although a quarter of them are technically non-offenders. For many, their difficult behaviour was compounded by risks posed to the public or by self-inflicted injury, a pressing problem with many girl entrants.

Findings show that the young people entering the Youth Treatment Centres have experienced and failed in a wide variety of provisions offered by numerous agencies, such as social services, child guidance, special education, health services, prison department and voluntary oganizations. The young people can clearly be seen to have taken a number of different routes towards referral to the Centres.

Thus, prior to entry, the young people had experienced a wide variety of previous placements as well as breakdown, transfer and frequent movement between settings. For many children, the YTCs offer them their only stable experience for many years. While not strangers to separation, the majority have spent a considerable time with their natural families, particularly in comparison with other adolescents in care. The majority of young people have living close relatives, for example, only eight children were entirely bereft of family support during their time at the Centres. Nevertheless, their families of origin are highly and continuously stressed and a cluster of difficulties seem to have driven their children out of control and into conflict.

Mindful that heterogeneity is the characteristic of these children and that there are dangers in making generalizations, nevertheless, YTC entrants seem to fall into four distinct groups: (i) Section 53 cases, 40 per cent of whom are first offenders; (ii) one in five of the care order children are long-term child guidance and special education cases, well-known to the statutory services and proving increasingly recalcitrant in their mid-teens; (iii) two-fifths of the care order children have been in long-term care, their frequent changes of and breakdowns in placement contributing to their unmanageability in adolescence; (iv) in contrast, two-fifths of the care order cases to the Centres have come to the notice of statutory authorities late in their careers and had precipitated their admission to security by a rapid rake's progress which had exhausted other welfare, educational or health provision. Many of these children had been sheltered from view by parents or long-suffering institutions prior to an eruption of uncontrollable difficulties during mid-adolescence. Indeed, nearly a third of all parents of YTC entrants were assessed as being over-protective of their children.

As no single feature dominated the families of all the 104 young people we scrutinized, the best scenario that can be constructed from the evidence was that of a young person seriously beyond control, in conflict with family, neighbourhood, school and the law. Children came from unstable families with rapidly changing membership whose difficulties were often compounded by chronic economic, health and relationship problems. It was the context and combination of all these problems that had affected the care career of the child and the ways in which the support agencies had responded to their needs, such as seeking secure accommodation.

The study shows that the majority of children were assessed on admission to the YTCs as being immature and impulsive, many had poor social skills which affected both their educational experience and vocational choice. For example, on entry to the Centres 55 per cent of the children were markedly failing to exploit their academic potential, one-third had very irregular attendance at school and nearly half had been either expelled or suspended for poor behaviour.

With such unpromising recruits, any hopes for marked and rapid amelioration while in the Centres must be modest. Nevertheless, during their stay the behaviour of the majority of children greatly improved; absconding and aggression diminished, the children developed better social skills and their family relationships settled down. Naturally, there were considerable differences in adaptations to the Centre experience between groups. Section 53 cases were relatively quiescent during their stay at the Centres, girls settled more slowly and care order boys remained likely to commit offences.

A follow-up scrutiny illustrates what happens to the young people when they leave the Centres. All the leavers we looked at have left the Centres for more than 12 months and three-quarters for more than two years. Naturally, on leaving, not all children went directly to the community; for example, many Section 53(1) cases went straight to prison establishments and several children were admitted to secure mental hospitals. Of the 104 leavers studied, 79 moved to live in the community, over a third to rejoin their families (30 children), nearly one-third to open residential care (23 children), while ten children were fostered and a further 16 children went to their own accommodation.

The Centres continued to support many leavers during their early months in the community and clearly make a considerable contribution to a reconciliation between child and family. When they left, more than half the children had come to view their parental households as home, a great improvement on the perspectives they entertained on entry to the Centres. Indeed, as many as three-fifths of them shelter with parents, wider families and siblings some time after leaving the Centres. While the families were often stressed and their offspring continued to present them with problems, they nevertheless remain very important in terms of providing shelter, emotional and material support and in giving their offspring a sense of belonging.

Although the conduct disorders that demanded intervention at the outset and which precipitated the young person's entry to the Centres do not entirely disappear over time, they do moderate and change. Aggressive behaviour, sexual problems, difficulties in relationships with adults and peers and the committing of grave crimes greatly diminish in significance as time passes and as young people move to the outside world. But, if some problems evaporate, others, such as persistent offending, endure and new difficulties emerge, such as drug abuse, inability to hold a job, chronic social isolation and general rootlessness.

Curiously, on entry to the Centres, those young people destined to have the poorest outcomes seem to excite far less anxiety than difficult girls or those young people convicted of grave offences. It is encouraging to note that many of those who provoked the greatest apprehension at the outset fare well after they leave the Centres. On the other hand, the continuing dependency, delinquency and inadequacy of care-order boys is very evident from this study.

Thus, it is important to realize that many of the young people are not only difficult when they enter the Centres but that they are also problematic when they return to the community, although in rather different ways. It is not surprising, therefore, that many leavers need help from statutory and voluntary services for a considerable period after leaving the Centres. A quarter remain particularly dependent, notably Section 53 cases and boys who have been long in care. At present, after-care is limited by the absence of any clear policy and by a dearth of provision for such young adults. There also seems to be room for better liaison between social services and probation and a greater recognition that many of these young people will require support for some time after leaving the Centres.

But, if the behaviour changes, family relationships and growing independence of Centre leavers offer us encouragement, a scrutiny of their offending once out in the community brings us down to earth. Offending is one aspect of these young people's general conduct disorders which seems to remain intractable, partly because of the detrimental influences of homelessness, poverty and social isolation.

Prior to their arrival at the Centres, some of the young people will have committed very serious crimes, some are persistent serious offenders, others commit frequent minor offences, while a few are very difficult but have not offended. Thus, presenting a combined picture of their offending on leaving the Centres obscures important differences between young people as, for example, some Section 53 cases do very well indeed and girls do much better than boys. However, boys who have been long in care have very disappointing outcomes indeed. Our predictive exercises have also highlighted those variables associated with subsequent conviction. These are gender, ethnic origins, perception of dangerousness, social isolation and contact with parents.

Our follow-up study shows that one-fifth of the leavers from the Centres who return to the community are convicted of an offence within six months of leaving. As time passes, the conviction rate rises so that by the time two years have elapsed, 59 per cent of such leavers will have received a conviction and by four years, the proportion rises further. This offending rate is very similar to that of other leavers from custodial situations.

Although this picture of offending is gloomy, the scene brightens when the seriousness of offence is considered. One-fifth of leavers subsequently committed a serious offence which, in view of the threat posed by many of the children on entry to the Centres, is very encouraging. Indeed, the overall picture of offending amongst leavers is less that of serious crime and more that of occasional lapses into minor offences, a pattern which differs little from other young offenders. The trivial nature of many offences committed by YTC leavers is further reinforced when court disposals are scrutinized. Many leavers offend but fewer are incarcerated. Half of those YTC leavers convicted of an offence within two years received a custodial disposal, which contrasts favourably with other young people re-offending after release from other secure accomodation, where the majority return to custody very rapidly.

While criminality always commands a disproportionate significance in studies of people at risk, the vulnerability of Youth Treatment Centre leavers is once more reinforced when other dimensions of their careers are considered. While the majority of those leaving the Centres enjoy good health, a larger minority than might have been expected experience illness. Indeed, the proportion of those who develop an identifiable mental illness subsequent to leaving the Centres is high in comparison with morbidity in the general young adult population. The evidence on suicide attempts among leavers is also disquieting.

The educational and employment careers followed by leavers from the Centres are less than satisfactory. One must accept that in educational terms the YTC leavers are not particularly promising, however their failure to exploit the educational opportunities offered by the Centres is regrettable. Educational failure also contributes to a poor employment record amongst leavers as much classroom experience socializes and prepares young people for future working roles. The high unemployment among leavers reminds us not only of their poor social skills and low levels of frustration tolerance, but also of the inadequate support and encouragement they receive in the community. Sadly, an inability to hold a job must greatly contribute to their overall poor life chances.

The Centres were set up to provide therapy and containment for those difficult children for whom no other appropriate asylum existed. While the characteristics of young people sheltered by the Centres has changed considerably over the past 20 years, for example, there are fewer girls, more older adolescents and those convicted of grave offences, nevertheless, the need for Youth Treatment Centres still remains.

Certainly, developments within mental health, and better use of social services secure accommodation have improved facilities for difficult children generally. However, some adolescents are too young for prison and the sad backgrounds of many of those that are eligible arouse sufficient guilt to make punitive disposals difficult. The pressures on youth custody provision mean that the considerable problems of difficult young people are not likely to be approached in such settings.

The Centres also have important wider functions for the child-care system, reassuring social services departments that they are not end-of-the-line organizations and providing a back-up for all those working with difficult children in open conditions and short-stay secure units. The Centres' contribution is also much appreciated by the prison system, particularly in the unenviable task of preparing and reconciling Section 53 children with their long sentences. The YTCs also have a potentially high international reputation in a field where interesting and creative initiatives are very few.

It is also clear that those local authorities who do not use the Centres fail to make adequate alternative arrangements for difficult children. Indeed, their poor provision is constantly under criticism. Those problematic young people who fail to find refuge in the Youth Treatment

Centres or other secure treatment settings persist in their rake's progress through the care system. Difficult children who are not referred to the Centres or who, for a variety of reasons, fail to find a secure niche for treatment continue to display careers characterized by placement breakdown, traumatic relationships, delinquency and periodic sojourns in custody.

In spite of the failure of difficult children in other settings, the study demonstrates that some social workers are very reluctant to use the Youth Treatment Centres. Some authorities have few difficult adolescents or are discouraged by cost, by the prospect of close scrutiny of their child care practice, by strict no "out county" policies or by the delay in gaining admission to a Youth Treatment Centre. Some social services departments are very hostile to ideas of treatment in security or prefer to use their own provision or that provided by other local secure units.

Neither are the debts which these children incur for social services negligible. Difficult young people are very costly wherever they are placed, not only in terms of the cash and resources demanded but also in terms of the stress and anxiety generated in social workers and other care staff.

The study demonstrates that in the Centres most young people come to terms with their difficulties, conflicts with their families diminish, their problematic behaviour is moderated and their social skills improve. Thus, in stabilizing children's difficult behaviour and diminishing on release the dangers they pose to the community, the Centres make a valuable contribution.

It is the hallmark of a compassionate society that efforts should be made with these difficult children, even in contexts where complete success is very unlikely. The major difficulty is to convince all those working with problematic young people that there is little to be gained from endless disputes about treatment, entry criteria and cost and to accept that only limited success is the essence of the job.

Some 75 per cent of young offenders who receive custodial sentences are convicted of another offence within two years of release. The alternative use by Courts of supervision orders, requirement to attend day centres, community work such as cleaning up graffiti and rubbish or helping the mentally or physically disabled and compensating victims, would reduce reconviction rates to at least 40 per cent. However, magistrates' courts may have to be convinced of the benefits of these alternatives for young people charged with non-indictable offences. The number of youth custodial sentences increased by 500 per cent between 1966 and 1986 and the crime rate has also increased substantially.

This research was produced by Social Information Systems, an independent organization commissioned by local authorities to examine the success of alternatives to custody.

The Government is about to close an additional major loophole from the point of view of protecting children. As from 1992 independent Lay Inspectors will work with 200 local professional teams and the National Unit from the Social Services Inspectorate, in England and Wales.

The Inspectorate already carry out periodic unannounced inspections when problems are identified in council homes, but additional safeguards are needed.

As a general principle, the *causes* of maladjustment which result in some children being made the subject of care orders and admitted to children's homes, should be investigated on a broad basis and evidence should be taken from criminologists, psychiatrists, psychologists, probation officers, social workers, ministers of religion, police, teachers, politicians, official visitors to establishments for offenders and from the relatives of the offenders.

Young people who are expected to adapt to useful community life will require considerable help after release from the regimentation of such places.

The majority of children in these homes are subject to Care Orders under Section 1(2) of the Children and Young Persons Act 1969. Such children are regarded as in moral danger, beyond control, having their proper development avoidably prevented or their health neglected.

Children's homes may be managed quite badly as illustrated by the Levy Report (1990) which criticized the excessive discipline at some such homes in England. Delinquents and "difficult" children were admitted to these homes. The discipline was referred to as the "Pindown" regime. Discipline was enforced by locating the young person in an isolated room also referred to as a "crash pad". The "offender" was not allowed to wear shoes and deprived of some clothing, ate alone whilst so located and furthermore, television, music and telephone calls were banned. Those under this discipline also had to get up at 7 a.m. and go to bed at 7 p.m. The following extracts of the report are relevant and based on a study of 132 children between November 3, 1983 and October 2, 1989.

"The impact on the children was likely to be wholly negative and was so in that the regime imposed was fundamentally dependent on elements of isolation, humiliation and confrontation. Pindown in our view falls decisively outside anything that could properly be considered good childcare practice. It was in all its manifestations intrinsically unethical, unprofessional and unacceptable." It continues: "The regime had no theoretical framework and no safeguards. No psychiatric, psychological or educational advice was obtained before or during the time pindown was used." The absence of professional advice in dealing with children who were "disturbed, depressed and in despair was inexplicable." Children subjected to the above conditions could subsequently suffer from post-traumatic stress disorder.

The report continues: "We noted that on occasions critical comments made by a statutory visitor on the forms used would be missing from or couched in more anodyne language in the report which was later sent to the district advisory sub-committees." Government inspectors who visited three of the homes as part of a survey were not told about pindown but with hindsight it is clear there were a number of clues available, particularly in log books and measures of control books to alert them to something out of the ordinary.

Top and middle management of the relevant social services departments were held responsible.

Recommendations

(i) Greater monitoring of the methods used to control such young people and statutory visitors should pay special attention to control methods and visits without advance notice. Log books dating back over the six months immediately before the visits should be studied. These books must be strictly kept.

(ii) Immediate introduction of suitable and efficient supervision of offenders and urgent review of the staffing policies of the relevant social services departments.

(iii) A five-year training strategy for staff.

(iv) Immediate establishment of complaints procedures for the staff, young persons and their relatives. These procedures need not encourage unjustified complaints but fear of complaining must be eliminated.

Social workers are employed by councils to inspect council homes and consequently they may feel compromised in the contexts of identifying and reporting child abuse in such homes.

The Children Act, 1989, became operative on October 14, 1991. Care Orders may be issued on the basis of this legislation or under section 1(2) of the Children and Young Persons Act, 1969, which is still operative from this point of view. Care Orders may be applied up to the age of 18 years.

Furthermore, section 53 of the Children and Young Persons Act, 1933, is still operative and orders for the admission for treatment in secure accommodation are made under this section for children aged from 10-17 years who have committed serious offences and are regarded as suffering from "serious psychological damage". The Secretary of State makes the decision to admit to a Youth Treatment Centre.

A Criminal Justice Bill is now before the House of Lords. This Bill will authorize the issuing of Youth Treatment Orders for 1-2 years in respect of young offenders. Five secure training centres will be established for this purpose and each will accommodate 40 young persons. Authority will also be given for such offenders to be admitted to secure Local Authority accommodation.

Juvenile Liaison Bureau
The Northampton and West Juvenile Liaison Bureau has achieved encouraging results. It was established in 1984.

Before atttempting to describe the ideology and function of the bureau it is necessary to describe the framework within which they were originally conceived and now operate. Although the 1982 Criminal Justice Act has made some important changes to the legal context of the bureau, the key starting point remains the 1969 Children and Young Persons Act. This legislation brought together two orientations, the existing justice system and the emerging treatment and welfare models.

The object of the bureau is to help juveniles avoid the stigmata of criminal records under certain circumstances. The age range referral is 10 years to 17th birthday. All juvenile offenders from the Borough of Northampton and the west of the county of Northamptonshire, who are charged with appropriate non-indictable offences, are referred by the police directly to the bureau in the first instance.

The bureau team is composed of two police constables, two social workers, one probation officer, one teacher and youth workers. It is headed by a director to advise them.

Parents are always present when offenders are interviewed. The offender and the offence are studied by the team which makes a recommendation to the chief inspector of prosecutions. The latter may agree or disagree with this recommendation.

The director has authority to liaise directly with the superintendent if he or she cannot come to an agreement with the chief inspector. Persistent offenders would be answerable to charges in court. The majority of referrals are for theft and usually of the petty kind. Pleas of guilty or not guilty may only be made in court but the juvenile may admit or deny responsibility for an offence. The bureau can deal only with those who admit offences. The basic function of the bureau is to resolve offences and resolution should be acceptable to offenders and offended. The bureau is supported by Home Office guidelines (H.O. Circ. 14 (1985)).

Offenders are expected to make voluntary reparation to victims but punishments *per se* are not imposed. Facilities are available for fire- and road-safety counselling. Advice is also given in the contexts of controlling violence and aggression and consumption of alcohol. Apologies and returning stolen money and property are also advocated. Offence analysis is also practised with juveniles and the benefits of choosing not to offend are indicated in the hope of helping offenders gain a sense of social responsibility. Some 70 per cent of first offenders have not reoffended during the past six years (Pragnell (1990)).

The bureau undertakes supervision of offenders for up to six weeks but referrals are made to the social, youth, career and family guidance services as necessary.

The bureau cannot caution offenders. Cautions can only be given by the police to juveniles who are not dealt with by the bureau. The juvenile and his or her parents or guardian must have explained to them the procedure of cautioning and its significance, and that a record will be kept, that the fact of a previous caution may influence the decision of the police whether or not to prosecute if the juvenile should offend again, and that the caution may be cited if the juvenile should subsequently be found guilty of an offence by a court.

Offenders serving youth custody may have psychiatric investigation and treatment for emotional problems at Grendon Underwood, Aylesbury, Buckinghamshire, or at one of the training establishments where psychiatric facilities are available.

Suitability for admission to Grendon Underwood may be considered from two points of view but those admitted must *not* be mentally disordered within the meaning of the Mental Health Act 1983.

The Diagnostic Label

(i) All neurotics (except anxiety neurotics who have not responded to drug therapy).

(ii) Alcoholics, as defined by Jellinek (1960), meaning individuals who specifically take alcohol to counteract feelings of depression, tension and anxiety and who later develop a compulsion to take more alcohol once a drinking bout has been initiated.

(iii) Potential psychotics in the younger age group.

(iv) Sexual exhibitionists and fetishists.

(v) Individuals who should respond to ordinary prison discipline but keep returning to prison for obscure reasons.

(vi) Homosexuals between the ages of 17 and 25 years, where the homosexuality is an expression of a general physical and emotional immaturity, and when practised as a substitute activity, as when the deviant finds women more difficult to approach than members of his own sex, because of fear.

(vii) Individuals who suffer from epilepsy. Their epilepsy may be associated with temporal lobe lesions, personality disorder, neurotic reactions, psychotic episodes, or automatisms.

(viii) Individuals who are pathologically depressed.

(ix) A man whose first crime is committed in middle age, or a man of good personality who commits a crime out of character.

(x) Arsonists.

(xi) Those convicted and sentenced on the basis of a successful plea of diminished responsibility. About one-third of these cases require transfer to a special hospital during the course of sentence.

The individual's attitude

Treatment at Grendon is usually not successful if the patient adopts the passive attitude or the extra-punitive attitude, or both.

The individual who adopts the passive attitude expects the psychotherapist to say the "magic words" which will make everything all right and resents any situation in which he is expected to make an effort to work with the therapist with the object of changing his basic attitude to life. The prospect of making such an effort makes him anxious and despondent. He seems to prefer his psychopathology to cure. The passive individual's idea of cure is indicated by the not uncommon request "Please can I be given the truth drug?"

The extra-punitive attitude means that the patient is so intent on expressing his resentment towards authority, that he has no emotional energy left to direct against himself in the form of self-criticism or guilt. The aggressive psychopath is an example of this type of individual. A patient must look at what is wrong internally if he is to benefit from a therapeutic atmosphere. There is no basis for treatment if there is no capacity for self-correction. Undue aggression and resentment against external figures swamps any capacity for self-criticism and, therefore, self-change. These excellent criteria of suitability and unsuitability for treatment at Grendon were formulated by the late Dr H.P. Tollington.

Statistics

Deer (1986) indicated that Research by Social Information Systems, an independent organization commissioned by local authorities, indicated that 75 per cent of individuals under the age of 17 years are convicted of another offence within two years of release from youth custody and detention centres. This reconviction rate could be reduced to at least 40 per cent if magistrates used supervision orders (involving community work, attendance at day centres and making reparation to victims) instead of custodial sentences.

Overcrowding in the British penal system has become a very serious problem. The United Kingdom has 96.5 prisoners of all ages per 100,000 of the population, as compared with 34 per 100,000 in Holland.

The Children and Young Persons Act 1969 meant that as from January 1971 care orders were substituted for approved school orders for individuals under the age of 17 years and such persons are now cared for in community homes.

Detention Centres for females closed in 1969 and were abolished for males in 1988. Borstal training was abolished in 1983.

The number of offenders (mostly males) aged 17 and under 21 sentenced to immediate custody increased each year from 18,900 in 1979 to 26,500 in 1985 but fell to 16,736 in 1989 and 14,515 in 1990, but increased in 1993 to 33,000 for those aged 14 and under 18.

The following persons were sentenced to Young Offenders Institutions:

Table IX

Aged 17 and under 21	Year ending December 1979	Year ending December 1985	Year ending December 1989	Year ending December 1990	Year Ending December 1993 (ages as above)
All cases	18,900	26,500	16,736	14,515	33,000

*(Statistics 1 Division of Home Office, Research and Statistics Dept., Home Office, (1993).

References

Alternative Care Careers: The experience of very difficult adolescents outside Youth Treatment Centre Provision, 1989, University of Bristol.

Bourget, D., Bradford, J.M. (1989) "Female Arsonists: A Clinical Study", *Bulletin American Academic Psychiatry Law*, 17(3) pp. 293-300.

Campling, W. (1990) St. Charles Youth Treatment Centre, Brentwood, Essex.

Choosing with Care, Report of Committee of Enquiry into selection, development and management of staff in Children's Homes in England (1992) [Committee Chaired by Norman Warner] HMSO ISBN O 1132 1539 2.

Deer, B., "Study says Bails Fail with Young", *The Guardian*, March 23, 1986.

Eysenck, H.J., (1950) in *Recent Progress in Psychiatry*, ed. Fleming, G.W. Churchill, London.

Farrington, D.P. (1981) "The Prevalence of Convictions", *British Journal of Criminology* 21, 173-5.

Foxe, A.N. (1948) *Studies in Criminology*, Williams and Wilkins, Baltimore.

Fromm-Auch, D., Yeudal, L., Davies, P. and Fedora, O. (1980) "Assessment of Juvenile Delinquents: Neuropsychological, Psychophysiological, Neurological, EEG and Reading Test Findings". In West, D.J. (1982) *Delinquency, Its Roots, Careers and Prospects*, Heinemann, London.

Gillespie, R.D. (1944) "Mental Abnormality and Crime". In *Psychoses and Criminal Responsibility*, eds. Radzimowicz and Turner, J.W.C. Macmillan & Co., London.

H. M. Young Offenders' Institution and Remand Centre, Feltham, [Pub. Home Office, (May, 1992), HMSO] Social Information Systems (1990).

Home Office, Criminal Statistics (1988) CMW 847.

Home Office Statistical Bulletin, Statistical Dept., Lunar House Croydon, Surrey CRO 9YD. Issue 18/91. Criminal Statistics, September 13, 1991.

Kolko, D.J., Kazdin, A.E. (1989) "Assessment of Dimensions of Childhood Firesetting among Patients and Nonpatients: The Firesetting Risk Interview", *Journal of Abnormal Child Psychology*, 17(2); pp. 157-76.

Levy, A. and Kahan, B. (1990) *The Pindown Experience on the Protection of Children*, Report on the Staffordshire Child Care Enquiry.

Lewis, N. and Yarnell, H. (1951) *Pathological Firesetting, Pyromania, Nervous and Mental Disease*, Monographs No. 82., Coolidge Foundation, New York.

Lou H.C., Henriksen, L., Bruhn, P., Berner, H., Nielsen, J.B. (1989) "Striatial Dysfunction in Attention Deficit and Hyperkinetic Disorder", Department of Neuropaediatrics, J.F. Kennedy Institute, Glostrup, Denmark, *Archives of Neurology*, 46(1): 48-52.

McCormick, K. (1989) *An Equal Chance: Educating At-Risk Children to Succeed* pp. 52. Available from: National School Boards Association, 1680 Duke Street, Alexandria, USA, VA 22314.

Nazario, T.A. (1988) "What do we know about Delinquency?" *Law-Related Education*, v.12; n.2; pp. 8-9 Spr.

Oldham, W.M. (1964) "The Common Thief", *Criminal Law Review*, Sweet and Maxwell, London.

O'Neal, P., Bergman, J., Schafer J. and Robins, L.N. (1960) "The Relation of Childhood Behaviour Problems to Adult Psychiatric Status: A 30-year follow-up of 262 subjects", in *Child Development and Child Psychiatry*, ed. C. Shagass and B. Pasamanick, [American Psychiatric Association] New York, Robins, L.M. (1958) "The Relation of Childhood Behaviour Problems to Adult Psychiatric Status: A 30-year follow-up study of 150 subjects", *American Journal of Psychiatry*, 114, 961, and (1959) "Childhood Patterns Predictive of Adult Schizophrenia: A 30-year follow-up study", *American Journal of Psychiatry*, 115, 385.

Pasamanick, B. (1956) "Pregnancy Experience and the Development of Behaviour Disorders in Children", *American Journal of Psychiatry*, 112, 613.

Perales, C.A. (1988) "Minorities, Equality, and America's Future", *Journal of State Government*. Vol. 61; no.2; pp. 45-48.

Pollock, I. (1991), Hyperactivity and Food Additives", St. George's Hospital, London, U.K., *Bibliotheca Nutritio Et Dieta*, (48): 81-9.

Pragnell, S. (1990) *Northampton and West Juvenile Liaison Bureau* (1990) Personal Communication.

Price, W.H. and Whatmore, P. (1967) "Crime and Chromosomes", *World Medicine*, March 7, 13.

Quinsey, V.L., Chaplin, T.C., Upfold, D. (1989) "Arsonists and Sexual Arousal to Fire Setting: Correlation Unsupported", *Journal of Behavioural Therapy Exp. Psychiatry*, 20(3); pp. 203-9.

Rix, K.J.B., (1994)., "A Psychiatric Study of Adult Arsonists"., *Med. Sci. Law* (1994) Vol. 34, No 1, ps. 21-34.

Saunders, E., Awad, G.A., White, G. (1986) "Male Adolescent Sexual Offenders: The Offender and the Offence", *Canadian Journal of Psychiatry*, Vol. 31.

Schmideberg, M. (1953) "Pathological Firesetting", *Journal of Criminal Law and Criminology*, 44, 30.

Scott, D. (1974) *Fire and Fire Raisers*, Duckworth, London.

Tennent, T.G. *et al.* (1971) "Female arsonists", *British Journal of Psychiatry*, 119, 497.

The Care Careers of Young People in Youth Treatment Centres: A Research Proposal, 1984, University of Bristol.

The Characteristics of Young People in Youth Treatment Centres: A study based on leavers from St. Charles and Glenthorne between 1982 and 1985, (1988) University of Bristol.

The Experiences and Careers of Young People Leaving the Youth Treatment Centres: A retrospective study of 102 leavers from St. Charles and Glenthorne between 1982 and 1985, (1989) Universtiy of Bristol.

Thorley, A., Davies, B. and O'Connor, D. (1985) "Progression of Addiction Careers in Young Solvent Misusers", *British Medical Journal*, 290, pp. 109-110.

Tollington, H.P. (1966) "Grendon Prison", *British Journal of Criminology*, 6, 39.

Trasler, G. (1962) *The Explanation of Criminality*, Routledge and kegan Paul, London.

Warner N. (1992) *Choosing with Care:* A Report of the Committee of Enquiry into Selection, Development and Management of Staff in Children's homes, HMSO.

Webb, N.B., Sakheim, G.A. Towns-Miranda, L., Wagner, C.R. (1990) "Collaborative Treatment of Juvenile Firesetters: Assessment and Outreach 1990", *American Journal of Orthopsychiatry*, 60(2); pp. 305-10.

Weikart, D.P. (1989) *Quality Preschool Programs: A Long-Term Social Investment.* Ford Foundation, Office of Communications, 320 East 43 Street, New York, NY 10017 (free).

Weiner, H.R. (1962) "Some Effects of Response Cost upon Operant Behaviour", *Journal of Experimental Analysis Behaviour*, 5, 201.

West, D.J., Farrington, D.R., (1973), '*Who Becomes Delinquent*', Chap. VII, ps. 113, 129., Chap. VIII, ps. 132-4. Pub. Institute of Criminology, Cambridge.

CHAPTER VII

Illicit Drug-Taking

DR J.M. HUGHES

Definition

We need to ask ourselves first "What is a drug?" It is easier to ask the question than to answer it. However, perhaps the best attempted definition is that adopted by the World Health Organization – a drug is any substance that when taken into the living organism may modify one or more of its functions.

Drug abuse or drug dependence is today a serious public health problem throughout the world. A variety of manufactured drugs and naturally occurring substances are abused and they have widely differing effects on human beings. Many of these drugs can produce both psychological and physical dependence. From the point of view of the law, the consequences of psychological dependence are especially important.

Many forms of drug dependence can lead to serious deterioration in the physical and psychological health of individuals. Drug dependence also leads to serious social problems for society with the emergence of an alienated subculture living in a shady world frequently crossing the boundary into illegal acts.

Another feature of much of drug addiction is the development of tolerance to the particular drug involved. This means that an individual gets used to a given quantity of the drug and needs to increase the dose to obtain the desired effect. They are thus sometimes able to take quantitites that would be lethal to non-dependent people.

Another characteristic, particularly in those obtaining their drugs illegally is the tendency to take widely varying doses from day to day. They "binge" some days when supplies are plentiful and then have to manage at other times on what they see as an inadequate quantity.

To obtain their supplies many indulge in criminal activities – forging prescriptions, stealing (even from their families), prostitution, etc.

We can therefore see drug dependence as a state of periodic or chronic intoxication produced by the repeated consumption of a drug. Characteristics include:

1.   an overpowering desire or need to continue taking the drug;
2.   a tendency to increase the dose although some remain on a steady dose;
3.   physical and psychological dependence on the effects of the drug;
4.   the development of a characteristic and striking abstinence syndrome when the drug is withdrawn;
5.   an effect detrimental to the individual abuser, to his family and to society as a whole.

Notification of drug abusers (of certain drugs) to the Home Office is compulsory for doctors whether the individual is prescribed for or not. These drugs are: Cocaine, Dextromoramide (Palfium), Diamorphine (Heroin), Dipipanone (Diconal), Hydrocodone (Dimotane DC), Hydromorphone, Levorphanol (Dromoran), Methadone (Physeptone), Morphine, Opium, Oxycodone, Pethidine, Phenazocine (Narphen), Piritramide (Dipidolor).

This notification is confidential and the information collected is intended to give the Government some indication of the size of the problem and, equally important, of the trends in drug abuse. The information obtained about individuals is, however, available to other doctors. It is widely recognized that only a minority of drug abusers are notified, as many do not obtain their supplies legally.

Incidence and Patterns of Drug Misuse
The number of "hard" drug abusers notified to the Home Office is just under 15,000 (1989 figures). Field surveys would tend to show that the true numbers of regular "users" is at least five times that figure. A commonly quoted figure for the number of drug abusers is 100,000, but it must be recognized that no-one really knows.

The commonest drug misused is Cannabis and almost all persons with a serious drug problem start off by using this drug. The 1982 Crime Survey suggested that 5 per cent of the sample of the general population over the age of 16 had taken Cannabis. Of those in their twenties the figures were one in five of men and one in ten of women. Rates of recent use were much lower.

Maden *et al.* (1992) published a survey of pre-arrest dependency in sentenced prisoners in 25 prisons in England and Wales. 11 per cent met the criteria of the investigators for habituation or addiction to drugs. The representative sample of 1,751 prisoners was studied. The incidence for various types of drugs was as follows:

Cannabis 34 per cent
Opiates 9 per cent
Amphetamines 9 per cent
Cocaine 5 per cent
Crack 1 per cent

Payne-James *et al*, (1994), indicated that approximately 11 per cent of individuals seen by forensic medical examiners in police custody in London are drug misusers.

Obviously some took more than one drug.
The crimes of burglary, theft and drug offences were more common than offences of violence in the study. However, the investigation *could* mean an incidence of about 5,500 pre-arrest drug dependents in prisons in the United Kingdom if one accepts a prison population of about 50,000 at any particular time. These individuals had been living in the community and dependent on drugs prior to arrest, but one could reasonably assume that they constituted a minority of the general population and consequently the incidence of drug dependency in the community in general would hopefully be less than 11 per cent. Otherwise one would have the colossal number of 6,600,000 drug dependents in a population of some 60,000,000 in the United Kingdom.

Such evidence as there is suggests that the incidence of drug-taking in the U.K. has remained at a stable level during the last five years.

Cocaine misuse has probably increased a little in recent years but on nothing like the scale that was feared and predicted a few years ago.

Cannabis
This drug is used extensively by young people, many of whom regard it as an acceptable relaxant. A minority use it heavily with potentially serious ill-effects on their mental health and probably on their physical health. Cannabis forms 80-90 per cent of all drug seizures and drug offence convictions.

It is relatively cheap to buy in the street. About £1.50 is enough to make 2 Cannabis cigarettes ("joints"). Resin costs from £14.00-£25.00 for one quarter of an ounce. Most Cannabis is imported to the UK but some is grown here.

Amphetamines

This drug is widely used by young people as a stimulant and is commonly injected. It is relatively easy to manufacture. The drug is little used in medical practice now.

Bought illegally it costs about £10.00-£15.00 for a gram – sufficient for 1-2 weeks for an occasional user. Heavy users develop considerable tolerance and may spend £50.00 a day or more on their addiction.

Heroin and Opiates

The use of these drugs has increased substantially in the last 20 years, but appears to have been more or less constant in the last few years. Much of it is imported illegally. However, it is known that much of the Methadone used comes from diverted legally prescribed supplies from drug clinics. Good practice in such clinics should help to reduce this diversion to a minimum.

A Heroin user might spend £20.00 a day in purchasing the drug, costing about £80.00 a gram. The price of Methadone is about £2.50-£5.00 for a 5 mgs tablet with the Methadone mixture being half that price. An addict might spend £20.00-£30.00 on his habit daily.

Cocaine

This is a more expensive drug whose use tends to be restricted to better-off people. Its use is wide-spread in the USA but despite doom-laden predictions, has not really taken off in this country.

Pure Cocaine costs about £80.00 a gram. A 'recreational user' might use one quarter of a gram over a weekend but a more heavily addicted person might use 1-2 grams daily.

Benzodiazepines

Dependence on these drugs can readily develop in those treated medically with them. In addiction, many 'junkies' use them regularly, including frequent use by injection. Diazepam might sell for £1.00 for four 5 mgs tablets.

Use of other narcotic drugs is now low – partly because they are so little used in medical practice.

Hallucinogens and Lysergic Acid Diethylamide (LSD)

These drugs produce marked effects on the mind. In the case of Lyseric Acid minute quantities only are needed to produce psychotic-type distortions of the mind. LSD tablets cost £2.00-£3.00 each.

The Aetiology of Drug Abuse

Although the abuse of alcohol and of drugs goes back very far in human history, the simple truth is that we do not know the precise causes of addiction. There are plenty of theories.

Hereditary Factors

Drug abuse occasionally occurs as a complication of serious mental illness – in which heredity is an important causal factor. However, in general, there is no evidence to support causation.

Personality Factors

The personality of an individual is one of the important determinants of the course of addictive behaviour and certainly of the response to treatment. One cannot, however, with any certainty paint a picture of a distinctive personality type in addiction.

What one can say is that people with personality disorders of psychopathic type are over-represented. The personality disorder can be shown to precede the drug abuse and not to be a consequence of the life style typical of a drug subculture.

Researchers have suggested, with some supporting evidence, that dopaminergic pathways in the brain are involved in reward circuits and can facilitate the emergence of dependency patterns of behaviour.

Psychological Factors

Drug addicts can come from any sort of family and any sort of class structure. However, the majority seen in drug clinics tend to come from poorer families and from families where bonds are not strong and where role-modelling is difficult because of parental inadequacies.

Psychological factors certainly seem important. The natural curiosity of youth – the temptation to try out experiences that society (and families) frown upon – is often the first step.

The common need to rebel in adolescence and the attraction of rejecting what are seen as hypocritical standards of parents and society are common factors. Peer group pressures can then become increasingly important especially if the individual becomes part of a drug subculture – a frequent occurrence.

A common pattern is for the young person to start smoking Cannabis and to graduate over a period of a few years to more destructive drugs. However, only some Cannabis users progress in this way.

The Environment
In some ways drug abuse is like an infectious disease – when the appropriate circumstances exist, it can spread rapidly amongst the vulnerable. The existence of a drug subculture is a dangerous aspect of society for some young people.

The superficial attraction of "opting-out" of a society they do not understand or approve of seduces them into a downward spiral of a drug lifestyle.

We live in a society where some believe there is a drug for every human difficulty and so to drug abusers, using a drug to "blot out" society seems natural.

Seeing alcohol and tobacco as freely available legally, can be used by abusers as a justification of their habit.

Factors related to the drugs themselves
There are broadly three groups of drugs that are seriously abused:

1. sedative and painkilling drugs, e.g. opioids;
2. stimulant drugs, e.g. amphetamines;
3. hallucinogens, e.g. Lysergic Acid Diethylamide.

These drugs have a powerful effect on the mind and can rapidly become established as a harmful habit. Abuse is facilitated by modern technology. Purer forms are produced that have a stronger effect on the mind. Some of these drugs can be easily manufactured illegally. The transportation and importing of such drugs has become easier and is difficult to detect and stop.

The availability of drugs is of crucial importance for the emergence of abuse. For example, in Third World countries in Asia and South America that produce and export these drugs, widespread dependence has occurred amongst their own young people.

We should not forget that in pre-war days, serious addiction was virtually confined to those who had access to drugs, i.e. doctors, nurses and pharmacists.

A notable feature of the problem is the poly-drug misuse that is so common. For most abusers, it seems that if the favoured drug is not sufficiently available, other drugs will be (and commonly are) used.

Legally prescribed drugs
Addiction to legally prescribed drugs is an old problem. They are

principally drugs in three categories:

1. sedative drugs – mostly sleeping tablets;
2. tablets prescribed for slimming – mostly amphetamine-type drugs;
3. painkillers e.g. opioids.

The whole area of abuse of legally prescribed drugs has been high-lighted in recent years by the recognition of a major problem with the widely prescribed Benzodiazepine drugs.

Profiles of Commoner Drugs of Abuse

Cannabis

Cannabis is a drug obtained from the Indian hemp plant *Cannabis Sativa.* It is grown in many climates, particularly tropical countries, but can be grown in the UK. Its effects depend on the presence of psycho-active substances called carbinoids of which the most important is Tetra Hydro Cannabinol (THC).

Various forms of Cannabis are used, often with different names in different countries e.g.:

1. Bhang – the dried leaves and flowers which are used to make an infusion.
2. Marijuana – dried leaves and flowers that are smoked.
3. Ganja – a stronger preparation which is smoked.
4. Hashish – a form of Cannabis resin that is still stronger and is usually smoked.
5. Liquid Cannabis/hashish oil – a syrup-like fluid in which cigarettes are dipped before smoking.

Pharmo-kinetics

When smoked, Cannabis is quickly absorbed giving higher blood concentrations than when taken by mouth, producing a more dramatic effect on the user.

THC is fat soluble and is slowly released in the body so that complete elimination of the drug may take a month. It can, therefore, accumulate in heavy or regular users.

When smoked, the effects are apparent within minutes and last for two to three hours. When taken by mouth a larger dose is needed to produce the same effect and the onset of that effect is slower.

Anandamide is a chemical in the human brain which may act as the body's "natural" cannabis and possible mediator of brain activity. Consequently Anandamide may influence the normal functions of memory, perception and mood and its imbalance with cerebral hormones may be a factor in mental disorder, (Pertwee, 1993).

The effects of Cannabis on humans
It commonly produces a number of physical effects – a dry mouth, redness of the eyes, hunger and a more rapid heartbeat.

The psychological effects are the reason why it appeals to some. Such effects are notably dose-related.

One smoke ('a joint') is likely to produce a sense of calmness, well-being and even euphoria. Perception of time, sense of taste and smell, and powers of concentration and orientation are impaired.

Sometimes feelings of anxiety, agitation, suspicion and even violence occur.

With a greater exposure to the drug, as in heavy users, much more marked psychological effects are apparent. These include considerable distortion of perception, including hallucinations, feelings of depersonalization, paranoia and confusion. A Cannabis psychosis can occur.

Tolerance is well substantiated in countries where heavy usage of Cannabis is common. Dependence is also reported in those countries.

Both these effects have not commonly been reported in the Western World, probably because the level of dosage used is so much smaller.

Cannabis psychosis and its relationship to schizophrenia
A Cannabis psychosis, characterized by delusional thinking, hallucinosis, emotional instability and sometimes confusion, is well recognized in countries where heavy use of Cannabis occurs. It has also been reported in the Western World but less commonly. A few observers deny its existence.

These differing conceptions can be explained on the basis of the quantity of THC consumed. In some countries where heavy usage occurs daily intake may be as high as 400 mgs daily, whereas a self-styled 'recreational' user in the West may take 3-8 mgs daily from one smoke. Such psychotic episodes are fleeting, lasting a few hours or exceptionally 1-2 days. More debatable is the occurrence of a schizophrenia-like psychosis of longer duration occurring in a setting of clear consciousness.

Many observers are adamant that such psychoses occur. They could well be pre-existing psychoses precipitated by foolish use of Cannabis or whose course is altered by its use.

'Flash backs' – i.e. the recurrence of drug-induced psychological phenomena, after the use of the drug has ceased – is generally recognized. However, there is no evidence that a chronic psychosis occurs, persisting after the drug is no longer used.

An amotivational syndrome is seen in heavy users – a condition of apathy and virtual withdrawal from every-day life – the so-called 'drop out' behaviour. There is no conclusive proof that brain damage occurs in Cannabis users.

How dangerous is Cannabis?

This is a controversial subject that generates a lot of emotive arguments. It is an important topic in view of the widespread usage of Cannabis in young people. In some surveys, as many as 17 per cent of young people have reported using Cannabis (higher in males than females). Much of this use is short-lived.

The Wootton Report on Cannabis (1968) concluded that the dangers of Cannabis use had been exaggerated – but certainly dangers did exist. The 1982 report of the Advisory Council on the Misuse of Drugs reached much the same conclusion.

A similar debate occurs over whether use of Cannabis can lead to escalating drug abuse with progression to 'hard drugs' like Heroin and Methadone. Although almost all 'hard drug' users start off by smoking Cannabis, it is also a fact that only a minority of Cannabis users go on to use more destructive drugs.

Most doctors believe it would be wrong to legalize Cannabis. Cannabis seizures fell by 8.5 per cent in 1991.

Amphetamines and similar stimulant drugs ("Speed")

These are a group of drugs which produce "sympathomimetic" effects in the body, i.e. they produce similar effects to that of adrenaline, a naturally occuring chemical produced in the body itself in the adrenal gland.

Its effects, both physical and psychological are those needed to raise temporarily the level of effectiveness of the body. This has been described as the 'fight and flight' reaction of the body to danger and fear.

Adrenaline is a transmitter substance in the sympathetic nervous system and also produces a series of physical and psychological changes in the body.

Amphetamines produce feelings of elation and self-confidence and diminish the need for sleep and relaxation. Hunger is reduced and there is increased talkativeness and restlessness. Blood pressure, respiratory rate and heart rate are increased with a dry mouth, sweating and dilated pupils. The concomitant release of sugar enables a greater level of activity to occur.

Such effects are short-lived and are followed by a rebound phenomenon with depression of both physical and psychological activities.

Side effects
When taken in an addictive manner, serious psychological complications can occur. These commonly take the form of a psychotic illness with delusions, hallucinations and over-activity and may be difficult to distinguish from schizophrenia.

Ritualistic behaviour also occurs – repetitive pointless activity, tidying some article of clothing repeatedly or scratching continually a part of the body.

There can be weight loss because of suppression of appetite often followed by failing health standards because of self-neglect.

Tolerance and dependence
Dependence can develop rapidly because of the superficial attractions of the "high" that occurs – high confidence, seemingly abundant energy, diminished need for sleep and food, etc.

Just as night follows day, the high is followed by the "low" – apathy, poor concentration, depression and despair. There is a risk of suicide and the "low" feelings are often intolerable, leading to a compulsion to take more of the drug.

Remarkable tolerance to the psychological and physical effects occur quite rapidly in abusers, leading to the use of very large doses i.e. 250-1,000 mgs daily compared to a therapeutic dose of 10-60 mgs daily.

Injecting Amphetamines
Abusers commonly take the drug by mouth but many graduate quickly to injecting the drug, because the stimulant effect then becomes more intense and more rapid.

Most Amphetamine abusers are young people in their teens and early adult life. However, there are a minority of middle-aged users who develop their dependence following legal prescriptions of Amphetamines earlier in their lives.

Other Ampehtamine-like drugs

Methamphetamine (methedrine)
Benz amphetamine
Methyl phenidate (Ritalin)
Phenmetraxine (Preludin)
Diethyl proprion (Apesate)
Phentermine (Duramin)
Mazindol (Teronac)
Pemoline

The historical development of Amphetamine abuse

There are preventative health lessons to be learnt from the rise and fall of Amphetamine abuse. In the 1960s, these drugs were not only freely prescribed, but could be legally bought over the counter in various forms. At one time, such drugs were used extensively for the treatment of depression and obesity. The therapeutic uses today are very limited.

Not surprisingly, Amphetamine abuse in the young was then common and increasing. A combination of voluntary changes by doctors, pharmacists and manufacturers combined with legislative changes (The Drugs, Prevention of Misuse Act 1964), have changed the situation. A consequent reduction in Amphetamine misuse has occurred.

However, Amphetamine is a relatively simple substance and is easy to manufacture illegally. This has hampered control of abuse and it is probable that Amphetamine abuse is again on the increase. Certainly, police seizures of the drug have increased threefold since 1985.

Cocaine

Cocaine is a drug half as old as time. In recent decades it has taken on a completely new form. This is a consequence of new methods of administration giving a much more striking and dramatic effect compared to the traditional mode of usage.

Native populations in Central and South America used to chew (or suck) a pad of leaves from the coca bush to alleviate tiredness, hunger and cold. This way, the alkaloid was absorbed slowly and did not have such an addictive effect.

The coca bush, *Erythroxylum coca*, grows in mountainous regions. Its leaves are harvested and the Cocaine alkaloid is extracted in illegal factories set in relatively inaccessible areas. The refined form is easy to transport and to import illegally.

Effects and tolerance

It is a stimulant drug producing increased confidence, energy and wakefulness. Its powerful euphoriant effect gives it a reputation for facilitating social life.

Physical effects include raised pulse rate, raised blood pressure, raised temperature and dilated pupils. Cocaine also has local anaesthetic effects (once investigated by Sigmund Freud) and produces vaso-constriction.

Large doses can produce cardiac arrhythmias, hypertension and epileptic convulsions.

Abusers develop considerable tolerance and can therefore take what would be toxic quantities for the unitiated. Probably psychological tolerance develops less readily, so that a syndrome of irritability, suspiciousness and restlessness develops in heavy users.

Symptoms of dependence

Physical dependence shows itself through a variety of symptoms when the drug is withdrawn (the "crash"). Lethargy, depression, anergia, social withdrawal, tremor, insomnia, anorexia and muscle pain are prominent.

Evidence of psychological dependence is equally striking. Users quickly seek to convert occasional weekend use to regular daily use of increasing quantities. Intellectual life is dominated by the need for ever greater supplies. Such drug-seeking behaviour gives the lie to the concept of the safe "recreational" drug – a concept once widely held in the USA.

Methods of administration

Cocaine can be self-administered by almost any route – by mouth, by injection, by smoking or by sniffing ("snorting") the powder.

In the last few years a new form of Cocaine has appeared – Crack. This is a pure crystaline form of the drug produced easily by 'cooking' with baking powder.

It has two extra dangers – it is a cheap form of a traditionally expensive drug and it produces a quicker and a heightened effect. Despite this, it is not certain that alarmist fears about its high potential for addiction are justified.

Ill effects

With increasing doses, symptoms of anxiety, foreboding and restlessness proceed to suspiciousness and paranoia. Simultaneously muscle twitching, nausea, vomiting, high pulse and blood pressure, respiratory difficulties and sometimes convulsions occur. Coma and death are well recognized sequelae.

These effects are so unpleasant that they drive the addict to become even more dependent and often to look for sedative drugs or alcohol to counteract these feelings – thus compounding their problems and leading to additional dependence.

Khat

This is a type of leaf, similar in effects to coca leaves, which is cultivated and used in East Africa, Somalia and the Yemen. Its use in the UK is likely to be confined to Somalies and Yemenies and its effects are milder than those of Cocaine.

It readily produces a psychosis with paranoid ideas, hallucinosis and disturbed and aggressive behaviour. Somatic symptoms also occur in the first few hours after ingestion. Fortunately, all symptoms disappear within a few days of ceasing to use the drug.

Cocaine seizures by Customs Officers in 1991 were 89 per cent up on 1990 and over one ton was confiscated at street value of £138,000,000.

Cocaine users tend to be young with numerous problems including family difficulties, criminality, unemployability and a tendency to take a variety of other illicit drugs. Cocaine addicts fall foul of the law earlier than heroin-takers and therefore seek treatment sooner. Sexual perversion including prostitution can lead to infection with HIV, in turn causing development of AIDS in some 50 per cent of HIV "carriers" in an average 2 to 10 years after infection. The basic cause of AIDS is destruction of the "T" lymphocytes in the blood which protect the body against viral and fungal infections and "switch on" other immune systems. This disease is also spread by the use of dirty infected syringes by drug abusers.

Firth (1991), referred to some conclusions reached concerning Cocaine abuse in particular and illicit drug-taking in general at a meeting of the Royal Society of Medicine. The importance of case comparison studies to gain an understanding of the rise and fall of illicit drug-taking epidemics including Cocaine in the contexts of the influence of varying social attitudes, economic factors, market prices of drugs, "street" chemistry and criminal organizations which influence such epidemics, were stressed.

Hypnotic drugs

These are drugs that are widely used in medical practice. They can readily produce dependence. There are two main categories:

1. barbiturates and other strong hypnotics;
2. benzodiazepine drugs.

Barbiturates

These drugs were extensively used to treat insomnia, epilepsy and in certain treatments in psychiatry. Their use declined with the introduction of the safer benzodiazepines and they are now seldom prescribed. They are still available on the 'illegal' market but are not today common drugs of abuse.

Effects and tolerance

They have a strong sedative effect, inducing sleep and, in overdose, can readily cause death. Tolerance develops in weeks or months and this characteristic can lead to a steady increase in the dose taken.

Both physical and psychological dependence occur and can lead to a syndrome of chronic intoxication. This state is characterized by drowsiness, irritability, poor concentration, loss of appetite and weight, 'blackouts' and falls, leading to bruising of the body and epileptic convulsions.

Abstinence

Abrupt withdrawal of the drugs gives rise to a very unpleasant condition with anxiety, insomnia, confusion, delirium and epileptic convulsions.

Benzodiazepines

When introduced into medical practice in the 1960s, these drugs seemed to have many advantages. They were certainly much safer.

It was claimed that they could control symptoms of panic and anxiety without producing sedation. This is not so, but the degree of sedation is certainly less than with barbiturate-type drugs.

Apart from their use in psychological medicine, they have many other uses – treatment of status epilepticus, in anaesthetic practice, as muscle relaxants, etc.

Their capacity for producing dependence was not recognized for a long time. A source of confusion was the fact that withdrawal symptoms were very similar to the anxiety symptoms that led to the original prescription. Hence the drug tended to be re-prescribed on the assumption that treatment had not continued long enough.

One should not, however, over-estimate the tendency to addiction. It is a minority of patients who become "hooked" i.e. about 15 per cent.

Tolerance
Tolerance to the effects of these drugs can develop rapidly (i.e. after 4-6 weeks) in some patients.

Dependence
The length of action of these drugs is crucial both in determining their clinical effects and also in influencing the development of dependence.

Drugs like Diazepam (valium) have a long half-life and can accumulate in the body when prescribed daily, leading to drowsiness, impaired concentration, etc. "Half-life" means that blood levels are reduced (on average) by 50 per cent some 48 hours after ingestion. When combined with alcohol the effects of both alcohol and drug are increased, leading in some to aggressive and anti-social behaviour. In these longer-acting drugs, withdrawal symptoms do not show themselves for 4-8 days.

With shorter-acting drugs like Lorazepam, (Ativan) withdrawal symptoms occur within hours and commonly last about a week.

Withdrawal symptoms last longer with longer-acting drugs and can persist for several months.

Injecting
Addicts commonly use a number of Benzodiasepine drugs by injection, e.g. Temazepam and Triazolam. This gives these drugs a "street" value. Using them by injection makes the addiction more difficult to treat. The attraction of injection – as with so many drugs – lies in the enhanced effects that the abuser experiences – the "buzz".

The size of the problem
Benzodiazepine addiction is now a major and widespread problem. Clearer guidelines for their use in neuroses have emerged. Doctors are encouraged to use non-drug methods of treatment, e.g. psycho-therapy, relaxation training, anxiety-reduction programmes, etc.

When such drugs are prescribed it should be for only a few weeks – certainly less than a month.

Two main groups of patients are encountered in clinical practice:

a.   a middle-aged group – mostly female – who have been prescribed Benzodiazepines for anxiety and who become dependent.
b.   A younger population of poly-drug abusers where abuse of Benzodiazepines is part of the picture.

A convicted killer who stabbed a fellow prison inmate 17 times after drinking tea spiked with the Benzodiazepine (Halcion) has been acquitted of attempted murder, in the first British case to raise the side-effects of the drug as a defence (Dyer, 1992).

By a majority verdict a jury at the High Court in Edinburgh found the charge against James McLeod (30) not proven after hearing that his tea had been drugged without his knowledge. Staff at Perth prison gave evidence that they witnessed the attack on 22-year-old Paul McGuire in August 1991, but McLeod, now in Peterhead jail, said that he had no recollection of the incident. Another prisoner told the court that he had slipped Halcion and an unidentified drug into McLeod's tea to calm him after rumours swept through the prison that McLeod was about to be beaten up.

McLeod's Counsel, Mhairi Richards, asked the jury to accept that he was entitled to rely on the "robot" or "temporary madness" defence, established in an historic Scottish appeal ruling in 1991. This established that automatism could be a complete defence to a charge, not just a mitigating factor affecting the sentence, if it was due to something external, such as drink or drugs, which was not self-induced, which the accused did not foresee, and which caused a complete loss of self-control.

Hallucinogens
These are drugs that can seriously distort the mind – altering perception and leading to illusions and to hallucinatory experiences. They can be considered under three headings:

a.   Lysergic Acid Diethylamide;
b.   Other hallucinogenic drugs;
c.   Phencyclidine.

Lysergic Acid Diethylamide (LSD)
Effects and tolerance
Very small quantities of this drug i.e. 25-100 micrograms can produce striking, often alarming effects, on the mind. The effects are influenced by the mood and expectations of the user and by the setting in which the drug is taken.

Distortion of perception is common – both the perception of the environment and the perception of the user's own body. For example, an unexciting, mundane object like a chair, may take on an entirely new significance. Often these changes are illusions, i.e. distortions of real objects or situations, but true hallucinations also occur.

There are changes in thinking – the user may see life, religion and society in an entirely new light – hence the term "mind-expanding" drugs. The drug can lead to loss of contact with reality and occasionally this leads to early disaster, for example, a person may think he can fly leading to death by jumping out of a window. Such much publicized happenings are rare.

Tolerance develops so rapidly that physical dependence on the drug does not develop. The form of abuse tends to be that the user will take the drug perhaps once a week.

Adverse effects

These are psychological, i.e. the "bad trips" that occur in many. The user experiences frightening psychological effects lasting 12 hours or more. Such "bad trips" often lead to the user giving up LSD.

"Flash backs" are another feature – psychological "re-runs" of the drug's effects occuring long after the drug is out of the body.

Psychotic episodes can occur after taking LSD. Whether these are truly caused by the drug or whether it merely precipitates a psychosis in a predisposed person is a matter for debate.

Other hallucinogenic drugs

There are a number of naturally occuring substances which have marked effects on the mind. Some have been used traditionally in religious and tribal practices – e.g. the use of Mescaline in indigenous communities in Mexico.

The only such drug commonly used in Britain is Psilocybin occuring in "magic mushrooms". The legal position relating to "magic mushrooms" is unusual – it is not an offence to possess or eat the mushrooms but it is illegal to make preparations like infusions from them.

The effects of these preparations are similar to those of LSD. The major difference is that LSD is so much more potent – it is 200 times more powerful in effect than Psilocybin which is in turn 30 times stronger than Mescaline. Bad trips, flash backs and, rarely, psychotic episodes can occur.

Phencyclidine ("Angel dust") (PCP)

This drug is used in America and Canada but hardly ever in the U.K. It can be readily synthesized illegally and impure forms are often sold.

Phencyclidine has distinctive features in that it combines an intoxicating effect (like alcohol) with the attributes of an hallucinogenic drug. In addition it can cause serious neurological problems – impaired speech, ataxia, visual defects, convulsions and coma. It is a highly dangerous drug.

So-called "acid house" parties almost exclusively held in the home counties, became a cause for concern in the United Kingdom in 1989. Some 10,000 young people apparently attended one of these parties and were allegedly protected by 60 guards with "walkie-talkie" radios hired from private security companies, at a fee of £250 per night with an extra £25 for each savage guard dog. CS gas, knives and baseball bats were allegedly used against intruders in order to ensure that the cash customers were not interrupted. A variety of drugs were taken, including Lysergic Acid and 'Crack'. Cancellation of an acid house party in Harlow, Essex, in December 1989 resulted in a number of revenge attacks on police. The police are also very concerned about other guards who act as doormen at certain night clubs or similar establishments. These people are also known as "bouncers". However, a sinister element may be introduced because those who manage illicit drug syndicates know that control of these doormen means control of the quantity and type of illicit drugs which may be sold to those who frequent such places. Competition for doormen "contracts" has recently resulted in violent confrontations between interested parties.

Designer Drugs

These are drugs that are produced clandestinely in a chemically modified form that then places them outside the control of strict national and international laws on the control of drugs.

These manufactured analogues are mostly derivatives of Pethidine, Fentanyl and Amphetamine. Fentanyl is itself a potent synthetic opiate. Disasters have occurred because of impurities produced in their manufacture. For example, in the manufacture of MPPP, a derivative of Pethidine, another product is produced that is a neurotoxin (MPTP). This has caused Parkinson's disease in abusers.

Two Amphetamine derivatives have been commonly abused in North America (and sometimes in the UK), MDMA, known as "Ecstasy" or "Adam" and M.D.E. known as "Eve".

Legal steps have now been taken in the USA and in Britain to bring designer drugs within the reach of the law.

Ecstasy (MDMA)

MDMA (Methylene dioxy methamphetamine or Ecstasy) has attracted considerable media attention recently. It is unusual in having a combination of sympathomimetic (stimulant) and hallucinogenic activity. A feature of its illegal use in recent years has been its association with acid house parties or raves.

Studies of brain function in users suggests abnormalities of 5-hydroxy tryptamine (5HT) metabolism.

Adverse reactions include a variety of somatic symptoms, distortions of perception, hallucinosis and occasionally more serious physical symptoms, including hypertension, vascular coagulation and rhabdomyolysis.

The "recreational" use of Ecstacy has real risks to health, even occasionally to life itself. It should be emphasized, however, that most users come to no great harm.

Ecstasy, also called the "love" drug, has become a cause for serious concern in Britain since 1991. This "trendy" drug is illegally imported mainly from Holland. Seizures by customs increased fivefold in 1991 and 1,200,000 tablets with a street value of £24,000,000 were confiscated as a result of one search. Some 500,000 people aged between 15 and 21 years are estimated to be currently taking this drug. Henry (1992), also indicated that those who take the drug say it is often mixed with Crack or ordinary amphetamine. A single tablet may cost beteen £5 and £25. Those habituated or addicted to this drug are distributed among all social classes and they may live in homes where virtually all expenses are paid by their parents. Petty crime could also provide necessary funds. Addicts are unemployable. Ecstasy has amphetamine-like effects which have already been described but may usefully be summarized again.

The nervous system is stimulated and psychological effects include feelings of alertness, self-confidence and well-being. Decisiveness tends to be restored or increased. Drowsiness and sleep are prevented. Mood elevation and fantasy thinking are common effects and sexual excitation has been described.

Scott (1964) identified two types of amphetamine taker and Ecstasy takers may be similarly typed:

1.   Narcissistic individals with mild personality disorders who take the drug mainly at the weekends.
2.   Those with severe personality disorders who drift into criminal

and/or homosexual circles and take large amounts daily and may progress to opium and/or Cocaine addiction.

Paranoid attitudes and delusions may be caused by excessive and prolonged Ecstasy indulgence and schizophrenic-like psychosis with fear, ideas of reference, visual and tactile hallucinations are not uncommon. Impaired memory, depression and suicide may also occur.

Physical effects are due mainly to stimulation of the sympathetic nervous system, resulting in increased heart rate, palpitations, dilated pupils, dry mouth, sweating, headache, pallor, poor appetite and diarrhoea. Cramp-like pains in stomach and muscles and weight loss are also evident. General muscle stiffness including trismus has been recorded. Serum Hepatitis and liver abscesses would result from insanitary injections if and when Ecstasy becomes injectable, when AIDS may also become a danger. Oral Ecstasy causes liver damage and jaundice. The immediate and long-term effects of Ecstasy may not be known for some years, but this drug alone or mixed with others may induce cardiac and or respiratory failure more readily than some other drugs which are illicitly taken.

Rapid rehydration, cardiac and respiratory resuscitation and active cooling measures are essential for treating acute withdrawal phase and its complications which usually last for 48 hours.

Tolerance develops rapidly and an addict may take large daily doses resulting in confusion, delirium, psychomotor overactivity to the point of exhaustion and convulsions. Dependence tends to be psychological rather than physical and recovery is possible if the patient can be denied the drug for between six months and one year. The withdrawal period is made easier with Epanutin 100 mg. TDS and Phenergran 50 mg. *nocte*. Psychoses usually respond to Chlorpromazine 100 mg. TDS.

Seven people are known to have died and a greater number made seriously ill since the drug became available in Britain about two years ago. Excessive physical exertion and disturbances in temperature regulation may well contribute to fatalities (Henry, 1992).

Pan *et al.* (1991) indicated, on the basis of animal experiments, that injection of the drug Ecstacy suppressed the discharge rates of nerve impulses from the majority of nerve cells in the frontal lobes and they also found that the chemical fluoxetin prevented this suppressant action but the brain hormone 5-Hydroxytryptamine did not have this suppressant effect. These effects of Ecstasy could possibly be correlated with the stupor eventually induced in humans by this drug.

Mandrax

Mandrax contains two synthetic components called methaqualone and diphenhydramine. The drug has a powerful hypnotic effect and it is alleged to produce its effect by selective action on the thalamocortical part of the ascending reticular activating system by reducing the inflow of sensory impulses to the cerebral cortex. This results in a state indistinguishable from normal sleep. The drug also produces antihistamine effects.

Psychological rather than physical dependence tends to occur. Mandrax dependents indicate that the drug initially induces a period of euphoria which last for about four hours and sleep then supervenes. Dependents also complain about an effect called "stonewalling", meaning that several Mandrax tablets cause insensitivity and drowsiness to such an extent that an individual may walk into a wall or other barrier or crash a motor vehicle. Sleep is maintained for about seven or eight hours after taking one tablet.

The effects of Mandrax are potentiated by alcohol.

The drug is no longer prescribed or legally manufactured in the United Kingdom but may still be obtained illegally.

Mandrax was implicated as a cause of peripheral neuropathy.

Opiates

These are drugs based on Opium, a naturally occurring extract obtained from the seeds of the opium poppy *Papaverum Sativa*. Opium contains a variety of pharmaceutically active substances including Morphine (10 per cent by weight) and Codeine.

The term opiate covers naturally occurring alkaloids, semi-synthetic derivatives and wholly synthetic drugs with similar activities. These are amongst the most powerful and destructive drugs that are abused in Britain.

Effects and tolerance

They have a powerful pain-relieving property – one of the principal reasons for their clinical use. This is combined with an euphoriant effect that doubtless is a cause of their high degree of addictiveness. They also have a marked sedative effect.

Opiates are also used in medicine because of their ability to suppress coughing, which is useful in the treatment of terminal lung cancer. High doses can cause respiratory failure. They are also used to treat diarrhoea.

They have some stimulatory effects on the brain – producing the highly characteristic pin-point pupils and also producing nausea and vomiting.

Tolerance develops to many of the drug effects so that an addict may be taking a quantity that would kill a non-addict. Tolerance does not develop to constriction of the pupils.

The psychological addiction that develops is particularly strong.

Methods of administration

These drugs can be taken in a variety of ways – by mouth, by injection, by snorting, by inhalation and by smoking. Some addicts become very drawn to heating heroin and inhaling the fumes – known as chasing the dragon. This is one of the methods employed to produce an enhanced effect (a "high").

Opiate drugs that are abused

Morphine – a naturally occurring alkaloid.

Omnopon – 'papaveretum', a mixture of Morphine and other alkaloids.

Diamorphine (heroin) – a man-made derivative of Morphia that is more powerful and more addictive.

Methadone – a synthetic drug that has a long duration of action – 24 hours or more. It has properties that make it the drug of choice for treating opiate addiction in many clinics.

Pethidine – a synthetic analgesic opiate sometimes abused by members of the medical and related professions.

Dipipanone (Diconal) – a synthetic analgesic.

Dextromoramide (Palfium) a synthetic analgesic.

Dextropropoxyphene (Dolexene) – a derivative of Methadone.

Codeine – a naturally occurring alkaloid, weaker than Morphine but nevertheless addictive. Unfortunately, it can be bought over the counter in certain cough medicines and antidiarrhoea preparations.

The withdrawal syndrome

This is so unpleasant that addicts will virtually "sell their souls" to obtain a supply of drugs to counteract it.

The syndrome starts with anxiety and drug-seeking behaviour. Soon other characteristic symptoms emerge – yawning, sweating, running nose and eyes, and restlessness. Later comes dilated pupils, "goose flesh", hot and cold flushes, muscle twitching, loss of appetite and irritability.

When an addict comes off opiates without any "covering" drug, the above syndrome is known to them as "cold turkey". It is the reason why many are unable to give up the drug without professional help.

Heroin seizures fell by 39 per cent in 1991 at street value £40,000,000.

Treatment

Before undertaking treatment, a detailed assessment is necessary. The assessment covers the social, psychological, medical and legal aspects of the addict's life. Blood and/or urine tests are undertaken to establish what drugs a person is currently taking. Relatives (including spouses) are interviewed if possible.

The first line of treatment is counselling about drug addiction and its complications, and includes also more formal psycho-therapeutic techniques, designed to treat all aspects of the addict's personality.

This treatment is usually carried out on an out-patient basis and can include a *detoxification* programme leading to a gradual reduction in the dose of drug taken. Often *substitute medication* is used, e.g. in the case of opiates, Methadone is prescribed as it is easier to progressively reduce the dose of this long-acting drug (see Table X).

<u>Table X</u>

On the 1st day give 30 mg of Methadone intramuscularly		
	8 a.m.	2 p.m.	8 p.m.
On the 2nd day give	20 mg orally	20 mg orally	20 mg orally
On the 3rd day give	20 mg orally	-	20 mg orally
On the 4th day give	10 mg orally	-	20 mg orally
On the 5th day give	10 mg orally	-	10 mg orally
On the 6th day give	10 mg orally	-	-
On the 7th day give	10 mg orally	-	-

Librium 10-20 mg tds and Dichloralphenazone 1,300 mg *nocte* may subsequently be given for a 14-day period.

Treatment with Lomotil and Heminevrin is an alternative to the Methadone treatment. The dose of Lomotil is two tablets four times daily and gradually diminishing over a six-day period. Heminevrin is a derivative of the thiazole group of drugs and it is also an anti-convulsant. The dosage is three tablets three times daily for two days, two tablets three times daily for three days and one tablet four times daily for four days. Heminevrin has low toxicity but should not be given with other sedatives. Attention is also paid to treating toxaemia, cardiovascular collapse, dehydration and electrolyte imbalance.

Special measures such as daily dispensing are used to ensure that the addict takes a regular dose and to limit any tendency to divert legally prescribed drugs to the illegal market.

This type of treatment is long term, perhaps 12 to 18 months, giving time to build up a relationship with the addict that will help him to give up his addiction.

In-patient treatment can be much quicker, enabling the addict to come off drugs in a few weeks. Unfortunately, the relapse rate is high unless the in-patient treatment is the climax of a longer period of out-patient treatment and counselling. When the addict is off drugs, "blocking agents" can be prescribed – drugs that block the effect of the addictive drug should the abuser be tempted to restart drug-taking.

Drug clinics prescribing treatment of this sort have been largely used for the treatment of opiate, hypnotic and Benzodiazepine abusers. However, in recent years, prescribing regimes for amphetamine abusers have been increasingly used by a number of clinics.

Amphetamine abuse usually leads to a very chaotic life style and sensible prescribing over 1-2 year periods can lead to major changes in the abusers for the better. A minority give up drugs altogether and most start to lead more sensible, more productive and more law-abiding lives.

Longer term residential facilities are available in Therapeutic Communities where a person lives in a drug-free environment for perhaps a year with plenty of work and other activities built into the programme. Most of these units will only take patients who are off drugs. An important part of the treatment lies in the abuser being taken out of the drug subculture that is so potent in tempting him back on to drugs.

Self-help organizations can be very useful. Narcotics Anonymous and Families Anonymous are groups of 'cured' addicts who aim to help those who are still hooked on drugs.

All these treatment approaches are multi-disciplinary in nature, relying on the co-ordinated approach of a number of professionals of widely differing backgrounds and training.

Prevention is particularly important. Educational approaches are used in schools and for groups of young people who may be vulnerable.

Reducing the availability of drugs is vital. This involves trying to prevent the growing and the importing of drugs. Prevention of the diversion of legally prescribed drugs into the illegal market can be achieved in great measure if drug clinics adopt strict prescribing methods.

It is hoped too that intense effort to treat existing addicts will help to stop the spread of the problem.

Politicians readily approve of research into illicit drug-taking but those in power are far more reluctant to accept that this evil is influenced by adverse or manipulated market forces. Illicit drug-taking may be managed from the sociological, legal, pharmacological and psychological points of view. Unsuccessful attempts have been made to discover which of the neuronal actions of Cocaine has the effect of making the addict crave for more and the effects of dopamine, serotonin and noradrenaline have been studied in this context.

The discovery of chemical substitutes which would give the psychological joy of "hard" and "soft" drugs to the takers without the mental and/or physical side effects and without impairing social responsibility and work efficiency would presumably be the ultimate Utopian goal of the pharmacological industry on the grounds that having created the present pernicious drug menace to society, chemistry should therefore find a solution to do it. From the long-term prognostic point of view, adequate social engineering may be successful without medical intervention because drug abuse is an interaction beween the organism, the drug and the environment. The unskilled and those without hope have the worst prognosis which also applies to life-long poorly integrated personalities.

Young Offenders and Solvent Abuse
I include a section by Denis O'Connor of the School of Education, University of Newcastle-upon-Tyne, dealing with this topical and troublesome problem.

Background
O'Connor (1992) indicates that it has long been known that inhalation of vapours emitted by certain substances causes people to experience

altered states of consciousness. In ancient Greece the prophecies of the Delphic Oracle were achieved partly due to the inhalation by the priestess of mysterious gases escaping through a crevice in the rocks. There are biblical references to religious rituals in which incense and perfumes were inhaled by the hebrews as a means of achieving spiritual enlightenment. But it was in relatively modern times, when Sir Joseph Priestley in 1776 discovered laughing gas or nitrous oxide, that a new era was started in which synthetically produced chemicals could be inhaled for purposes of intoxication. During the latter part of the nineteenth century there were reports, (Brecher, 1972), of university parties at which ether and chloroform were abused before the medical applications of these substances as anaesthetic gases were fully realized.

In the USA there were some references to children inhaling petrol fumes in the early 1950s but it was in 1959 that the glue-sniffing craze really began (Susman and Kupperstein (1968)). It all started with a widely publicized case involving the wilful inhalation of glue vapour by schoolchildren in Denver, Colorado, and over the next two years it spread rapidly through the teenage populations of most states. From Western Europe there were reported cases of glue-sniffing incidents in Sweden at Ska (the children's village) as early as 1948. During the mid-fifties an inquiry into the abuse of paint thinner resulted in 1969 in a Royal Ordinance prohibiting the sale of "thinners" in Sweden to persons under the age of 18 years (NSBHW, 1978).

In the United Kingdom the evidence from Dr Joyce Watson's research in the Lanarkshire area of Scotland has served to emphasize the growing danger to the young. Since 1970 when the police in Lanarkshire first became aware of the problem the practice has continued to spread at an alarming rate through all the school age groups and has even affected children as young as five or six (Watson, 1979). It is significant at the present time, as solvent abuse is spreading to many areas of the country, that each local community is left to cope alone without the benefits of nationally worked-out strategies supported by financial aid where needed, despite the fact that the dangers of such practices have constituted a world-wide problem for at least the last decade. There are official reports on incidents occurring in places as far apart as Australia, Japan, Africa, Mexico, USA, South America, Canada, Finland and several countries of Western Europe, (Werner, (1979)). In view of this, it is surprising that so little reliable information is available to professionals working in child care, such as school doctors, social workers, teachers and police who encounter at first-hand emergencies involving young people intoxicated by solvents.

Research into glue-sniffing

At the University of Newcastle-upon-Tyne the problems encountered by teenagers involved in solvent abuse are being carefully researched. Within the School of Education a Counselling Clinic was organized in 1980 to receive referrals of young people suffering from the ill-effects of solvent inhalation and related abuses. The response to the service offered has been overwhelming, due largely to the lack of any real knowledge on how to tackle the problem anywhere else. In the past whenever decisions regarding policy towards glue-sniffing incidents have been made there has generally emerged a concerted effort by the agencies concerned to minimize the seriousness and underestimate the extent of the problem. The need has always been for clear information on all aspects of solvent-abuse practices by young people so that a proper course of action can be adopted, which will include treatment and care of those who develop an unhealthy dependency on these chemicals. Work at the clinic has been aimed at meeting these needs at the simple practical level by studying glue-sniffers in person.

The counselling clinic

The clinic is housed in a converted terraced house of Georgian design owned by the University of Newcastle-upon-Tyne. At these premises mature students drawn from teaching, social work and residential care are reading for advanced qualifications in Counselling Psychology. As part of their practical studies in developing caring skills they are required to counsel young people with problems. In the early months of 1980 the referrals of glue-sniffers to the clinic increased so much that it was decided to offer counselling, especially for those clients involved in solvent abuse, at a separate clinic organized with voluntary help and held principally on Saturdays (although clients are sometimes seen during weekdays or in some cases individuals are visited by a counsellor at home).

The clinic opens at appointed times every week. Referrals, including self-referrals, are accepted from anywhere in the region; where possible, appointments are made, but no one is turned away. Parents often turn up alone or with their teenager son or daughter and very often they need counselling also. Social workers, teachers, general practitioners, probation officers, youth workers and police from the community welfare branch are among the professionals who send young people to the clinic and who sometimes actually accompany a teenager on a first visit.

On arrival a new client is shown to the reception area where he can sit in a relaxed atmosphere and have a cup of tea or coffee in the company of other clients. Within this group there are at least two counsellors who work hard at creating a receptive client-centred atmosphere. Also in the group will be a few individuals who have been successfully weaned from the dependencies on solvents and who are now able to help others through peer counselling, since teenagers are more likely to identify positively with each other than with adults. Each client is seen individually for counselling and a further appointment is made for the following week. When a client has been attending the clinic for several weeks and it is considered opportune, he will be asked to join others for group counselling. The atmosphere is engineered to be as informal as possible in order to reduce stress for the client. As one 15-year-old summed up his first impressions:

> "I didn't really want to come. But things were getting so bad I was ready to try anything to stop. I expected to be criticized and preached at but everyone was so nice to me that I couldn't believe it. I knew then if I kept coming I might be able to stop glue-sniffing."

Possibly it is because the clinic has no formal status (there is no funding or payments to counsellors) and is run as described through voluntary effort that it has principally achieved its effectiveness. The absence of any compulsion to attend or formal labelling of the premises (e.g. child and family psychiatry unit, etc.) helps to convey the messgage that clients need to make up their minds to help themselves in partnership with the counsellors who are guiding them. Whilst the primary function of the clinic is to provide a counselling service for young people troubled by solvent inhalation and abuses, it also has the purpose of gathering research data which will improve knowledge in this area. The following information is derived from study of the information collected about the clients coming to the clinic.

Who are the glue-sniffers?
The majority of young people who inhale and abuse solvents are in their mid-teens, 13 to 16 years old. An increasing number of children younger than 13 years have been referred and some older individuals up to 30 years

have attended the clinic at some time. The majority of clients in attendance are boys, in the ratio of three boys to every one girl. This statistic may be misleading for two reasons. First, girls seem to be better at disguising their glue-sniffing activities than boys. For example, some teenage girls said they spread face cream around the mouth and lips to avoid the skin rash caused by the practice. It was the girls who first inhaled through paper funnels and straws in order to avoid skin contact with the solvents. Secondly, it is possible that generally girls do not respond in the same way as boys to intoxicants and the effects are therefore less noticeable. The popularity of gas lighter-refill aerosols for sniffing may well also stem from girls, who wished to avoid the after-smell and skin sores of glue-sniffing.

Since the clinic started in 1980, there have been 1,200 referrals for counselling, but 283 of these have attended for only four sessions or less. The average number of attendances (more or less consecutive) is 15. Over 200 clients have so far succeeded in overcoming the dependency for periods varying from two months to over 18 months. Two hundred approximately who were well on the way to giving up completely have suffered relapses: most have undertaken to try again. These figures are as accurate as it is possible to verify, but it needs to be understood that it is extremely difficult for many reasons to follow up some cases. It is sufficient to mention that the clinic is operated on the trust generated between client and counsellor and it is this relationship which is regarded as providing the effective therapy, even though therapy does not always constitute a complete cure.

The single most identifying feature of the dependent glue-sniffer (reference here is to clients who inhale regularly, i.e. four times or more per week for sessions comprising in total at least two hours per day) is that he or she is experiencing strong negative feelings about self as witnessed by the following statements taken from case reports at the clinic:

"There is nothing I can do. I'm useless."
"Nobody likes me. I can't get on with anybody."
"I've got no life. Nothing's worth doing."
"I even hate myself."

The profile which emerges is of a person who suffers agonies of rejection and dislike. Problems have to be avoided at all cost and any behaviour which reduces stress is to be indulged. It is estimated that there is a latent population of glue-sniffers who only dabble in the abuse and who never become seriously attracted to the practice. While this is undoubtedly true for the majority of young people who experiment with solvent inhalation, it would nevertheless be unwise to become complacent about the dangers of solvent abuse because of this. It is not possible to predict who will only dabble and who will develop dependency on the solvents. It needs to be noted that every case of chronic abuse attending the clinic started out as a dabbler.

How are solvents inhaled?
The methods of solvent inhalation and abuse involve deliberately breathing solvent vapours into the lungs, where the toxic chemicals are distributed to all parts of the body including the brain within seconds. It is as fast as an intra-venous injection.

Empty containers such as plastic bags, milk bottles and empty crisp packets are used. The glue or solvent is poured or sprayed into the container which is then held to the mouth and the vapour inhaled. Some substances are inhaled directly from their containers and aerosols are sometimes directly sprayed into the mouth. Other substances, such as dry-cleaning fluid, are dabbed on the coatsleeves or lapels and inhaled from there. Large plastic bags are sometimes placed over the head of the sniffer to maximize the concentration of gases in the air to be breathed. Sometimes the residues in near-empty glue tins are heated to obtain a further concentration of fumes. In some cases, solvents have been consumed together with alcoholic drinks or taken in conjunction with tablets or other drugs. Needless to say, all these methods are potentially life-threatening.

Where does it happen?
Glue-sniffing is chiefly a secretive group activity in which young people are encouraged to inhale through the example of their friends and contemporaries. When an individual becomes habituated to the practice he or she will often hide away or inhale alone. Although the activity is not illegal, it seems that most glue-sniffers wish to avoid attracting adult attention and interference. Places in common use are public parks, waste ground, corporation tips, public toilets, derelict property, houses when parents are out, garden sheds, near railway lines, and underneath road bridges – anywhere that is sufficiently remote or enclosed to offer privacy and seclusion. Recent trends, however, indicate that at least some sniffers

prefer public places for their activities, possibly as an open challenge to authority.

What motivates the glue-sniffer?

There are no simple solutions as to why young people inhale solvents. The causes of the practice vary from the superficial need of one teenager to be in the fashion to the profound feelings which motivate another to seek escape from every-day frustrations and anxiety into an experience which is pure fantasy and wish fulfilment. Fundamentally, solvents are inhaled for the feelings of pleasure and relief which they give the person. But developing from this there are a multitude of motivations which may lead an individual to inhale solvents, for example:

(i)   to experience dreams and bizarre sensations;
(ii)   to escape from conscious reality;
(iii)   to relieve embarassment, loneliness and inferiority feelings;
(iv)   to copy adults who regularly use alcohol, tobacco, stimulants and tranquillizers;
(v)   to calm the nerves and soothe aggressive feelings;
(vi)   to get drunk;
(vii)   to challenge authority;
(viii) to gain confidence;
(ix)   to take risks;
(x)   to make home, school, unemployment and financial insecurity bearable.

Some of the remarks made by teenagers at the clinic are worthy of note in this connection:

"When I've been sniffing I forget all my worries."
"It's better than sex."
"My friends sniff glue."
"I was with my friends and we were in this dark place where there was a kind of dim red light. Horrible things started coming out of the walls and up from the floor, draculas and monsters. We were screaming and yelling for help. There was blood everywhere. It was great when we knew that it hadn't really happened."
"I could hear voices and I thought I might be dead."
"I was cold and the glue made me warm all over."

Underlying all these quotations is the obvious need of the young people concerned to escape into an imaginary world where nothing was "for real". One of the dangers of this is that the young person learns to "switch off" from life and cannot bear to "switch back" and find ways of coping with his problems. A further trend is for sniffers to progress to careers of multiple substance abuse (e.g. solvents, alcohol, illicit drugs) and to need to sniff just to feel normal again.

The effects
An important part of counselling the glue-sniffer is to consider carefully the different ways in which the practice has an effect upon the person. In this respect it is quickly realized that the practice of solvent abuse is symptomatic of underlying disturbances and troubles rather than a sickness in its own right. The mistake is often made of considering only the physical effects of solvent abuse as if it were solely a medical problem when it is apparent that the ill-effects on the social and personal life of the individuals involved are just as critical. It is convenient therefore to discuss the effects under three main headings (reference here is to cases where sniffing has reached chronic or acute proportions and where the sniffer is experiencing dependency).

(a) The physical effects
Solvents have a poisonous effect on the body, the symptoms naturally varying depending on the strength and type used. At their most vivid, the experiences affecting the central nervous system are such that the sense organs do not function properly, hearing and vision become distorted and consciousness is so affected that the person begins to experience dreams and hallucinations. This mental state deteriorates until all contact with every-day reality is lost and the individual becomes unconscious. Death can result from severe solvent poisoning but such cases are comparatively rare. Usually the poisonous effect causes a gradual decline in the health of the body.

Evidence from medical research, summarized by Werner (1979) and O'Connor (1983), indicates that solvent intoxication, over a period of prolonged exposure, may damage the structure and function of the soft organs of the body. The liver, kidneys, and the brain are alleged to be especially susceptible to these harmful outcomes. It must be mentioned here that some teenagers have died due to accidents indirectly caused by solvent abuse, such as plastic-bag suffocation, choking to death on vomit, road accidents and injuries suffered through falls from high places.

The latest figures released (July 1990) by St George's Hospital and Medical School for deaths from glue-sniffing and solvent abuse practices are the highest ever recorded since the surveys were started in 1971. In 1988 there were 134 recorded deaths from solvent abuse, an increase of 18 per cent on the previous year. In 1988, 51 per cent of all deaths were of individuals aged 16 years or under, (including the first recorded death under the age of ten years), and 87 per cent of those who died were under the age of 25 years. The majority of deaths (90 per cent), were of males. Volatile substance abuse now accounts for about 4 per cent of deaths from all causes, of people aged between 10 and 19 years of age. It would appear that there has been an important and statistically significant increase in the numbers of young people dying as a result of inhaling gas fuels and aerosols.

(b) The social effects

The most damaging effect on the social life of the person is the way in which normal relationships are disrupted. Family quarrels flare because of glue-sniffing incidents and the teenager can become so dependent on inhaling these substances that everything else is neglected so that more time may be spent "sniffing". Further to this, anti-social behaviour may develop, such as petty theft (often of products containing solvents), vandalism, burglary and assault.

(c) The personal effects

An ill-effect of solvent abuse which results in long-term harm to the person is the force of the habit itself. Once a teenager has learned to escape from facing up to real life by becoming inebriated on solvents it is easy for him to respond this way again when he is under stress. Other ill-effects for the person may be summarized briefly as follows:

(i)   becomes increasingly isolated;
(ii) loses interest in life;
(iii) avoids intellectual stimulation;
(iv) does not play sports;
(v)   neglects recreation;
(vi) develops a morbid attitude to personal health.

Comments from sniffers.

Comments by the "sniffers" themselves serve to illustrate and clarify important aspects of the practice:

'The first time, sniffing for me was magic. Things stopped being heavy and slow. It got brighter and nicer. It was out of this world. I'd never felt so good. All my troubles just vanished.'

'If I wanted to go anywhere I could go. I could fly and make things go very fast.'

'There was this buzzing noise like helicopters coming. Voices started to echo in my head and I couldn't see things at first. Sometimes my feet would go really cold and my hands, jaws and knees started to shake. I was frightened!'

'At first I only got headaches but then I got these pains in my back and chest and they wouldn't go away!'

'You can only stop glue-sniffing if you make up your mind to do it yourself. Nobody can make your mind up for you.'

'Sniffing really makes you one of the gang.'

Individual cases

The cases given below are typical of many clients.

Case 12: Philip is 14 years old. He lives at home with his mother and younger brother. His father does not live there any more. Philip says inhaling glue fumes helps him to think about his life. Also it helps him feel good and to forget his worries. He does not attend school very much because he says he detests the place. Recently he has had a lot of body pains after heavy glue-sniffing sessions. He loses his temper easily and has been in trouble for fighting. He does not read any more as it hurts his eyes. He would like to spend all his time inhaling glue fumes and playing records. The other day he passed some blood in his urine and this upset him a lot. On average Philip spends four to six hours a day by himself inhaling and needs a full tin (medium size) of glue each day. A month ago he committed burglary with a friend and he has to go to court soon. He says he feels tired most of the time and cannot always remember what he has just done. His mother says he is out of control. Philip was banned from the youth club for bringing solvents inside the club premises and smoking "pot". He expects to be taken into care.

In contrast the case of Sheena shows the influence of group pressures on the individual:

Case 13: Sheena is 15 years old. She belongs to a punk group and dresses accordingly. She has a stud through the right side of her nose, four studs in the lobe of the right ear and six studs in her left ear. On her arms and hands there are signs of self-mutilation as well as lots of self-inflicted tattoos. She inhales glue fumes and butane gas lighter fuel. She does this because the group expect it of all their members. She started inhaling when she and another girl were tattooing themselves. She was told it would ease the pain and it did . She has a nasty burn mark on the back of her right hand which she did while intoxicated on solvents. She is in care because of the 'glue habit', but is allowed home most weekends. She does not wish to stop inhaling solvents even though she believes the fumes are damaging her eyes. She has been charged twice with shop-lifting.

Counselling the glue-sniffer
In order to be able to help the teenager who has developed a dependency on solvent fumes it is necessary to be alert to the signs which identify his appearance and behaviour so that he can be made aware of these and motivated towards overcoming them himself. With this in mind the individual is encouraged to see himself as others see him, e.g.:

'Pallid, tired-looking; dilated pupils; skin rash; glue smell and marks on skin, hair and clothes; slurred speech and loss of co-ordination; the apathy, indifference and neglect of his person are everywhere apparent.' (O'Connor (1981)).

In this respect the information can either be gently and, over a period of time, fed back to him, or in appropriate cases it may be more effective to use video-tape recorders. The use of television in this way can have an immediate good effect on the progress of the counselling.

The form that counselling at the clinic takes is briefly summarized below:

1. Help the person to relax in a friendly atmosphere and to build a warm trusting relationship.
2. Listen to him and encourage him to talk out his problems.
3. Mobilize family and professional help by engaging as many responsible adults as possible to support and care for the individual.
4. Offer help: talk to relatives on telephone or home visit; contact school or social services – anything that will help the individual to gain relief from stress.
5. Advise on diet, hygiene, breathing exercises, daily routine in order to boost the self-concept.
6. Advise and guide the person on how to modify his own behaviour.
7. Counsel on how to plan a gradual weaning away from the dependency without demanding immediate abstinence and without threats of punishment.
8. Consider alternative courses of action to solvent abuse in response to boredom, frustration and anxiety.
9. Structure discussion groups in which the client can hear how others have successfully coped with problems like this.
10. Educate the person to his own psychological condition and prepare him for withdrawal symptoms like depression and irritability. In this respect it is necessary to eventually devise a treatment programme which will be based upon established approaches to therapy as long as it is understood that any therapeutic intervention arises from an initial impact of tender loving care (TLC) in the relationship as a prerequisite for good caring practice.

Finally, it is always pointed out to clients that they should ask a doctor for a medical examination to assess their present state of health. It is also impressed upon clients that simply to trade a dependency on solvent vapours to become dependent on something else, such as tobacco, alcohol, drugs (such as amphetamines and tranquillizers), overeating, over-dieting, etc., is no solution. The most effective results are achieved when the client is able to adopt a positive attitude to his self-behaviour and to look to ways of making the most of himself.

It is also relevant to add here that habitual sniffers tend to have tried inhaling more than one solvent and usually have experienced a variety of products containing volatile substances *in combination* with other intoxicants such as alcohol and illicit drugs. It is clearly the case with chronic cases of solvent abuse that glue-sniffing activities can involve or lead to multiple substance abuse, e.g. poly-drug abuse (Banks and Walker, 1983). It follows that because of the range of substances involved, glue-sniffing can easily become a habitual pattern of experimentation with intoxicants. Further to this, an outcome of such multiple substance abuse can be that the substances misused may give rise to increased ill-effects for the sniffer because they are combined. An example from what is common practice will serve to illustrate.

The liver can only convert one toxin to an aldehyde at one time and the rate of conversion for alcohol is 10 mls per hour, which is a slow means of breaking down the substance so that it can be cleared from the body. If, therefore, the sniffer has been drinking alcohol and subsequently starts glue-sniffing then the solvent toluene which is present in some of the glues abused will remain active in the body system longer and it will be an abnormal concentration because little of it will be broken down until the alcohol is no longer present. Emerging from considerations of these chemical actions within the body is the fact that the sniffer who drinks alcohol prior to a sniffing episode will intensify the intoxication effects.

Modern trends show that young people are increasingly likely to develop habits of taking intoxicants as part of the social settings in which they live and in response to peer group pressures. Glue-sniffing and the consumption of alcohol for recreational purposes are practices which expose the youngster to the dangers of becoming dependent on chemicals for enjoyment in life. Once this connection has become established in the person's mind it is easy for him or her to experiment with other forms of intoxication which are available, such as illicit drugs. The likelihood of serious addiction problems can start with the simple childhood act of glue-sniffing.

Anabolic Steroids

The abuse of these substances has come to the fore in recent years, especially in the context of international athletics, Perry et al(1992).

Those who abuse anabolic steroids fall into two categories:

1. Athletes who take these substances to enhance performance.
2. Those who take these drugs to change their physical appearance, and in the case of men users, it is probably to make themselves more attractive to members of the opposite sex.

The steroids may be taken by mouth or by intramuscular injection.

Dependence may be induced and many times the therapeutic dose taken.

Human Chroionic Gonadotrophin and Somatotropin may be taken concurrently. Clenbuterol is a sympathomimetic agonist with anabolic properties in animals, and is taken by some athletes.

Complications may be physical and psychological.

Physical side-effects:

(i)   Hypertension, atherosclerosis and irregularities of heart.
(ii)   Oesophageal varices.
(iii)   HIV infection and possible AIDS, due to shared needles.
(iv)   Gynaecomastia.
(v)   Avascular necrosis of head of femur.
(vi)   Tremor.
(vii)   Serious hypokalaemia.

Psychological side-effects become evident, namely psychotic episodes including manic-depressive reactions, irrational anger and fears, violent paranoid thoughts and aggressive behaviour, expecially after withdrawal of the drugs.

Anabolic steroids should come under the Misuse of Drugs Act 1971.

Special Problems in Addiction
1. Pregnancy

Pregnancy in an addict raises special problems. Most of the drugs used can cross the placental barrier and affect the developing foetus. Too abrupt withdrawal of the drug can lead to miscarriage. In consequence, more intensive care needs to be given to pregnant abusers with close liaison between drug clinics and obstetric services.

Many pregnant addicts become highly motivated to come off drugs or at least, to materially reduce the daily dose taken. Pregnancy thus offers a useful treatment opportunity.

2. Addiction in the Caring Professions

This is an old problem, predating the rise of addiction in young people in the last three decades. There are special difficulties because doctors, nurses and pharmacists have easier access to pure drugs than others. There are special worries about the condition in view of the special responsibilities that these professionals hold.

Professional people have strong reasons for concealing their problem but, nevertheless, it usually comes to light. Losing their professional registration gives them strong motivation to actively pursue treatment.

3. Drugs and Driving

Citizens have an obligation to report to the Driving and Vehicle Licensing Centre (DVLC) any medical condition which may affect their fitness to drive. This includes drug abuse. Drug abusers are not allowed to hold HGV licences and there is a 10-year restriction after giving up drugs before they can reapply for their licence. In theory, they may apply for a private vehicle licence but they are likely to be refused, if they reveal their habit.

Under UK legislation, the onus is on the abuser himself to report his habit and not on his attendant Medical Practitioner. The doctor has a moral responsibility to report the patient's habit to the Medical Adviser of the Vehicle Licensing Authority if he considers the patient is a danger on the road. It should be remembered that the statistics, as far as they are known, indicate that the accident rate for Methadone abusers is less than that of the general public.

Under EEC regulations, abusers are not allowed to drive and it is proposed that they should not be allowed their licences back until they can show that they have been off drugs for 5 years. Representations from doctors will probably be allowed.

Now under EEC regulations, addicts are not allowed to drive and cannot get their licences back until they have been off drugs for 12 months.

4. Children of Addicts

Many children of addicts are put on 'At Risk' registers by the Social Service Departments of Local Authorities. They are then subject to regular review by multi-disciplinary conferences representing a wide variety of professions. The aim is to ensure proper care for those children with the ultimate deterrent through the courts of power to take the children into care.

Despite their chaotic life-style, many addicts are caring and reasonably good parents.

5. Addicts who Inject

Injection of drugs is common in addicts because of the powerful and rapid effect of drugs taken this way. The injection habit increases the seriousness of the problem and makes treatment more difficult.

There are many complications of injecting. Infections leading to cellulitis, endocarditis, hepatitis and AIDS are a consequence of using unclean needles or of sharing syringes and needles. Thrombosis of veins is also common.

Most drug services now offer a needle exchange service whereby addicts can obtain sterile equipment free, the objective being to reduce the complications of injecting.

6. AIDS and Hepatitis B

These two viral infections can be spread amongst addicts by injecting or by heterosexual or homosexual activity. Pregnant mothers can infect their unborn children.

There are no effective treatments for these conditions. Blood testing and counselling services are available in most drug services.

Legal Control on Drugs

There is a long tradition of legal controls on certain dangerous drugs in most countries, e.g. the Hague Convention of 1912 relating to opiates and Cocaine. The explosion of illicit drug-taking in the 1960s showed that existing legislation was inadequate to control the problem, leading to new legislation i.e. The Misuse of Drugs Act 1971.

Drug abuse is an international problem, that no one country can adequately control in isolation. The imperative need is therefore for international co-operation and international controls.

1. International Controls

The Single Convention of Narcotic Drugs

This was agreed and adopted by a number of countries in 1961 and extended by its protocol of 1972.

It lists four schedules of drugs and signatories of the Convention undertake to institute certain standards in the production, distribution and storing of scheduled drugs to ensure that they are used for medical and research purposes. It covers serious drugs of abuse.

Convention of Psychotropic Substances 1971

This convention defines the need for co-operation to control the use of drugs like hallucinogens, amphetamines, barbiturates and tranquillizers.

2. United Nations Drug Abuse Controls

The United Nations Secretariat have taken a lead in many fields of drug control.

Commission on Narcotic Drugs

This 40-member body is important in determining United Nations recommendations to constitutent governments and in deciding what substances merit special controls.

Division of Narcotic Drugs
This is a professional body concerned with drug control laws and with law enforcement. Governments are expected to submit annual reports on drug trends in their countries.

International Narcotics Control Board
Its aim is to limit international cultivation, manufacture and use of controlled drugs to what is required for medical research and scientific purposes.

Governments are expected to keep records of the use of these drugs and also of illicit drug-dealing and to report their findings to the U.N.

World Health Organization
A scientific body that co-ordinates international research on drug effects and effectiveness. In return, it provides advice and guidance to governments and to doctors.

U.N. Fund for Drug Abuse Control
This is a voluntarily funded body which aims to make the international fight against drugs more effective. It advises, for example, on crop substitution for poppy growers in Third World countries, helps to train law enforcement officers and to develop effective treatment programmes for abusers.

3. *United Kingdom Controls*
The Misuse of Drugs Act 1971
This Act replaced all earlier legislation. It concerns itself with a wide variety of drugs liable to misuse, laying down regulations for prescribing, custody of drugs and record-keeping and defines offences in their production, supply and possession.

Drugs are listed in three categories:

Class A – including opiates, Cocaine, LSD and injectables;
Class B – includes amphetamines, Cannabis and barbiturates;
Class C – includes appetite suppressants and tranquillizers.

Offences concerned with Class A drugs are regarded as more serious than those with drugs of classes B and C. Drug-dealing is made a more serious offence than drug possession.

The Home Secretary is empowered to make the regulations needed to control the changing drug scene.

Misuse of Drugs Regulations 1985

Drugs are divided into five schedules, more along clincial lines than legal lines. It defines the people who can hold and use these substances.

Schedule 1 – concerns drugs not used clinically but for research purposes.

Schedule 2 – this concerns drugs that are particularly harmful in producing dependence, e.g. opiates, Cocaine and amphetamines.

It makes regulations for the safe storage of these drugs and defines closely how prescriptions are to be made (e.g. in the doctor's own handwriting). It also lays down stringent controls for the dispensing of these drugs by pharmacists.

Schedule 3 – includes barbiturates and appetite suppressants. There are less strict rules about their storage.

Schedule 4 – includes Benzodiazepines. The controls are less strict.

Schedule 5 – includes low-dose preparations from other schedules that are not subject to controls.

Obligations to Notify

The regulations impose a statutory obligation on all doctors to notify to the Chief Medical Officer of the Home Office any patient who consults them about abuse of certain listed drugs – opiates, Cocaine and some synthetic analgesics.

The doctor has to notify whether he prescribes or not. There are agreed regulations about the confidentiality of the information obtained.

The obligation is designed to enable the government to have some idea of the size of the drug problem and of changing trends in drug abuse. It is estimated that only about one fifth abusers are notified; most do not consult doctors.

A new system of drug notification is being introduced from May 1991, which should give much more reliable and valuable indications of the extent of the drug problem in the UK. It will lead to the setting up of a

Regional Database in each of the Health Regions. The new system will provide information on all potential drugs of abuse, not just opiates and Cocaine as previously. In addition, notification must be made by social workers, probation officers and drug counsellors and not just doctors. Other valuable information is included in the notification as for example about the prevalence of injecting.

Prescriptions
There are arrangements whereby prescribed drugs of abuse can be dispensed daily.

Only named, licensed doctors are able to prescribe Heroin, Cocaine and Dipanone for addicts.

Advisory Council on Misuse of Drugs
This is a 20-strong body of experts who advise the government on many aspects of the drug problem – e.g. on education about drug abuse, on best methods of organizing treatment, about research needs, etc.

It also advises about developing changes in drug abuse so that government can respond quickly and adequately.

The Relationship of Drug Abuse to Crime
Like many medical legal issues, this subject is a complex one. Undoubtedly there are strong links between drug abuse and crime. In reports from clinics as many as 90 per cent of males and 70 per cent of females attending have previous convictions. However, reports from many countries indicate that about 1/3 of males and about one in eight females have previous convictions for abusing drugs – substantially higher levels than in the general population. It seems that anti-social traits are built into many addicts rather than being a consequence of their habit.

The offences they commit are almost invariably petty crimes – larceny, shop lifting, prostitution and minor drug related offences. Less often, offences involving violence occur. Offences are often committed to obtain money to pay for drugs.

About 50 per cent of males attending drug clinics have been in prison. In June 1985 male drug offenders formed 6 per cent of the prison population and female offenders 16 per cent. The females are, of course, smaller in actual numbers and their offences tend to be less serious. About 16 per cent of drug offenders are given a custodial sentence in court hearings.

Results of Treatment

Treatment of drug abuse is difficult with poor compliance and a high relapse rate. Compulsory treatment under the Mental Health Act is not possible, except occasionally for complications like confusional states and psychosis. Nor is it desirable as the co-operation of the abuser is essential for successful treatment. However, sensible use of probation orders with or without a condition of medical treatment is helpful.

Treatment is theoretically possible in prison where abstinence should be easier to ensure. However, lack of sufficient trained staff and of sufficient staff time, make it a pipe dream in most cases.

Treatment in drug clinics does not eliminate offending behaviour even in those who are abstinent. However, the rate of committing offences is usually reduced perhaps by as much as a half. There are good reasons, therefore, for courts to recommend medical treatment.

Legalization of Drugs

This has been tried in various parts of the world, e.g. in some American states and in Holland where the law is more tolerant than in the UK. There is no hard evidence of benefit and legalization of drugs cannot be recommended medically.

Drug Dealers

Offences concerned with importing and marketing drugs are regarded as much more serious than crimes of possession in abusers. Much of it is large-scale international crime where it is extremely difficult to "nail" the big-time offenders. It is usually the small fry who are caught. Maden *et al* (1991) interviewed 1,751 unselected men serving prison sentences during 1988-89 and 189 were considered to suffer from 'drug dependence' during the six months immediately prior to arrest. This would represent an incidence of about 10 per cent or 4,000 prisoners if one accepts that the average day-to-day prison population of England and Wales is about 40,000.

Penalties

Table XI shows the maximum penalties for certain offences under the Misuse of Drugs Act 1971.

Table XI

Misuse of Drugs Act 1971: Maximum penalties for certain offences

Class of drug	Supply		Possession with intent to supply		Possession	
	Magistrates Court*	Crown Court	Magistrates Court*	Crown Court	Magistrates Court*	Crown Court
A	6 months or £1,000 fine, or both	Life imprisonment or unlimited fine, or both	6 months or £1,000 fine, or both	Life imprisonment or unlimited fine, or both	6 months or £1,000 fine, or both	7 years or unlimited fine, or both
B	6 months or £1,000 fine, or both	14 years or unlimited fine, or both	6 months or £1,000 fine, or both	14 years or unlimited fine, or both	3 months or £500 fine, or both	5 years or unlimited fine, or both
C	3 months or £500 fine, or both	5 years or unlimited fine, or both	3 months or £500 fine, or both	5 years or unlimited fine, or both	3 months or £200 fine, or both	2 years or unlimited fine, or both

*Sherriff's Courts in Scotland

Medical Reports to Courts

Medical reports about abusers are of great value to courts in deciding the disposal of convicted offenders. They are particularly valuable, especially if the abuser is well known to the clinic, as is often the case. Reports are more difficult to prepare if the accused is not known to the clinic. A prognosis is much more realistic if the accused's response to a treatment programme has been studied over a period of several months.

Table XII

All drug addicts notified to the Home Office during the year by age and sex

Opiate addiction is largely a young man's occupation

	Number of persons. UK				
Age	**1987**	**1988**	**1989**	**1990**	**1991**
Under 21	1,450	1,547	1,443	1,695	1,755
21 and under 25	2,730	3,124	3,380	4,072	4,569
25 and under 30	2,711	3,407	4,332	5,411	6,441
30 and under 35	2,059	2,325	2,754	3,208	3,820
35 and under 50	1,438	1,925	2,581	3,067	3,839
50 and over	134	121	143	143	192
Nor recorded	194	195	152	159	204
Total of all ages	10,716	12,644	14,785	17.755	20,820
Average age	28.1	28.3	28.9	28.8	29.2
Males	7,766	9,093	10,479	12,807	15,138
Females	2,950	3,551	4,306	4,948	5,682

Comparable statistics not available for years before 1987
Source – Home Office, Statistical Bulletin, Issue 6/92. March 1992

Table XIII

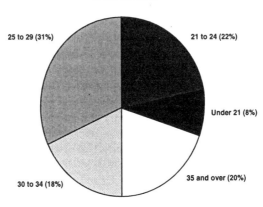

Addicts by age, United Kingdom 1991

Deaths of drug addicts notified to the Home Office, have increased in recent years:

Table XIV

1987	1990
257	325

Table XV
DRUG MISUSE IN BRITAIN, ISSN, 1992.

Drug addicts notified to the Home Office during the year and/or in treatment with notifiable drugs

	Number of persons. UK						
	1985	1986	1987	1988	1989	1990	1991
New statistics							
1. New addicts	6,409	5,325	4,593	5,212	5,639	6,923	8,007
2. Renotified addicts	n/a	n/a	6,123	7,432	9,146	10,832	12813
3. All addicts notified during the year	n/a	n/a	10,716	12,644	14,985	17,755	20,820
Old statistics							
4. Addicts in treatment on 31/12	7,052	8,435	10,389	12,977	n/a		
5. All addicts – addicts in treatment on 1/1 plus those notified during the year	14,688	14,758	16,128	19,179	n/a		

Sources – Home Office, Statistical Bulletin, Issue 6/92, 19 March 1992.
Home Office, Statistical Bulletin, issue 7/90, 19 March 1990
Home Office, Statistical Bulletin, Issue 13/89, 11 April 1989

Table XVI

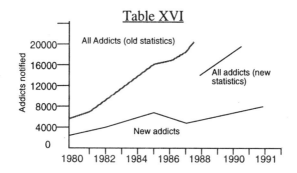

Addiction Tables
Addicts returning to or continuing in treatment account for rising totals in the late 80s. In contrast, the number of new addicts (now the only continuous statistic) has stablized.

Continuity broken
Table XV reveals that the presentation of addiction statistics changed in 1989. Two of the most important indicators available up to that time are no longer being published (lines 4 and 5 in Table XV), while two new statistics have been introduced (lines 2 and 3), backdated to 1987. The result is that long-term trend analysis is now only possible for the number of addicts notified for the first time in 1987 – the so-called 'new addicts' in line 1 of Table XV – as this is the only figure computed on the same basis before 1987 and after 1988.

The new statistics also include (line 2) the number of previously notified addicts renotified during the year. These plus newly notified addicts give (line 3) the total number of addicts notified during the year.

What this total now excludes is addicts in treatment at the end of the previous year who were not subsequently renotified. Excluding these means the figure for the 'total' number of addicts is now smaller than it would otherwise have been. How much smaller can be seen by comparing line 3 (new total) with line 5 (old total) for the years 1987 and 1988 when the two statistical regimes overlapped.

Some 3,050 persons were under sentence in Prison Service establishments in the United Kingdom for drugs offences during the period 1 July, 1991 to 30 June, 1992. The figure for the corresponding period 1981-82 was 1,000. The Home Office Statistical Bulletin (1992) indicates that the number of drug offenders in England and Wales is underestimated by up to 17 per cent.

Testing for Drugs
by Dr D. Berry (1994)

Introduction
Drug-screening is undertaken not only to detect overdose, but also to assist with the clinical management of registered addicts and the diagnosis of abuse in any patient who exhibits symptoms which might be drug-induced. Requests for analysis are increasing as the laboratory service proves its value and the range of abused compounds expands.

Which substances to test for?
Cannabis and alcohol are the two most widely misused substances and should be included in any screening programme. Narcotics are also abused and can be subdivided into two groups:

(a) Opiates, i.e. Heroin (which is rapidly metabolized to Morphine) and drugs of similar structure such as Codeine and Dihydrocodeine.
(b) Opioids which are synthetic drugs with morphine-like action, e.g. Methadone, Pethidine, Propoxyphene and Dipipanone etc.

Illicit ingestion of stimulants is also quite common and the most important drugs in this category are the Amphetamines, although there are a number of related compounds with similar pharmacological action which are taken as amphetamine substitutes, e.g. Phenylpropanolamine, Ephedrine, Methylphenidate, Pemoline, and Caffeine. Also the abuse of Cocaine in its various forms is widespread and in this case one must test for a metabolite, Benzoylecogonine, because very little parent drug is excreted unchanged in urine. Similarly one tests for cannabis absorption by means of a carboxylic acid derivative of the active principal, tetrahydrocannabinol (THC).

Sedatives, e.g. Barbiturates, Benzodiazepines and Methaqualone are also misused and screening for these drugs is required. Some very potent compounds such as the hallucinogen LSD, and the newer synthetic opioids e.g. Buprenorphine and Fentanyl, are particularly difficult to detect and currently their routine analysis is not available, although tests have been developed for Phencyclidine (PCP) which is widely abused in the USA but rarely encountered in the UK. Finally the misuse of volatile substances such as solvents is increasing particularly among the younger generation and it is necessary, therefore, also to have tests available for these substances.

Collection and submission of samples
Urine is the best biological material to examine initially for drugs because concentrations are normally higher than in blood, and metabolites are present to aid identification. Fifty ml of urine is required for comprehensive screening. However, a blood sample should also be collected and is vital for detecting solvent misuse. Urine collection should be closely supervised to ensure validity and security, especially as tampering with samples to falsify results in both a positive and negative way is well documented. It

is wise to measure the temperature of a 'freshly produced' urine sample and always treat it as potentially infectious. A blood sample should also be collected. Ideally a glass-stoppered bottle containing fluoride should be completely filled with blood and the bottle sealed with a cap containing a metal-faced wad.

Both samples should be sent to the laboratory accompanied by a letter which outlines the problem and details all prescribed medication.

Analytical methods

Qualitative screening examines the samples to see if they contain any of the wide range of commonly abused substances outlined earlier and the tests are usually designed with sufficient sensitivity to detect a single therapeutic dose (or normal recreational use) of a compound. However, depending upon the analytical techniques used, it is possible to detect and identify many other drugs (some of which might be legitimately prescribed to the patient). Quantitative analysis is rarely necessary, although it can sometimes be helpful in a case where a patient is overusing a prescribed drug.

Two main method options exist for drug analysis, *immunoassay* and *chromatography,* and one should make use of both techniques in a complementary way. Immunoassay tests are commercially available with a variety of different labels: radiolabelled (RIA), enzyme labelled (EMIT), and fluorescence labelled (FIA). Currently the range of tests (which are all specific for a particular drug or group of drugs) is limited to those listed in the official Appendix. It is important to realize, therefore, that eliminating negatives by immunoassay would fail to detect drugs outside these groups, e.g. an opiate immunoassay would not detect Pethidine, Methadone or Dextropropoxyphene (which have opiate effects). Also most immunoassay antibodies have broad specificity in that they cross react with all drugs containing the core structure. This can cause difficulties when the prohibited substance has an analogue which is available over the counter (DTC) e.g. an opiate test will not distinguish between Morphine and pholcodine which is widely available in OTC medications. A less important problem is caused by antibodies which co-detect minor metabolites of a drug in addition to the major one against which it is targeted, e.g. the test for Cannabis is aimed at Δ-THC-acid, the major metabolite of the active principal Tetrahydrocannabinol. However, the antibody also binds to several other inactive cannabinoid structures and minor metabolites which will be present in the urine and this affects the quantitative rather than qualitative findings.

Chromatographic methods are more selective than immunoassay and are not only able to distinguish between commonly abused drugs, but can also detect a wider range of substances. Unfortunately, the technique is slower than immunoassay, laborious and requires considerable expertise, but is the preferred initial approach when workloads are small. All of the drugs and other substances which are abused can be detected by chromatography and several variations in technique are available e.g. Thin-layer (TLC), Gas-liquid (GLC), High-Performance liquid (HPLC) with each variant enabling the analyst to utilize a range of stationary and mobile phases together with alternative detectors. Having established the optimum chromatographic conditions for a particular screen the drugs are usually first separated from the biomatrix by liquid or solid phase extraction prior to introduction into the chromatographic system. TLC is a relatively cheap and simple method for preliminary screening. GLC with either packed or capillary columns and a range of detectors (flame-ionisation, FID; electron-capture, E.C.; and nitrogen-specific, (NPD), is particularly valuable for more complex identification problems. GLC with headspace sampling of blood and split FID/EC detection is the only way of comprehensively screening for volatile substances, and simple aqueous dilution of blood or urine prior to GLC with FID is an effective means of testing for ethanol although various enzymatic methods are also available. The ultimate chromotographic detector is a mass spectrometer which is extremely sensitive and has the power to unequivocally identify a compound, but it is a costly, sophisticated piece of equipment which requires a skilled operator. However, *mass spectrometry* must be used to confirm findings if the testing has medico-legal implications and in addition it is the only effective way of confirming the presence of Buprenorphine and LSD-25 at the present time.

A chromatographic test demonstrates that a *particular* drug is present, and some immunoassays are quite specific giving similar information e.g. Benzoylecgonine (the major cocaine metabolite and test target). Others respond to a group of drugs e.g. opiates, but sensitivity to the various members of the group might be quite different and depends upon the characteristics of the antibody e.g. commercial opiate immunoassays calibrated against morphine are known to exhibit cross-reactivity to codeine ranging from 30-21 per cent.

False positive results can occur for a variety of reasons:

(a) unusual biological matrix effects;
(b) prescribed medication sometimes cross-reacts with immunoassays e.g. NSAIDs, Anticonvulsants, Antihistamines, some antibiotics;
(c) some OTC medications contain substances which test positive by immunoassay;
(d) environmental exposure, e.g. passive inhalation of marijuana smoke, but this should not produce a positive result if a sensible cut-off concentration has been specified;
(e) samples can be contaminated: (1) by products leaking out of the plastics and rubbers of specimen containers (2) by the target drug being spiked into the sample.

Despite these problems, the application of appropriate confirmatory techniques will eliminate false positives. However, true positive tests can result from dietary exposure, e.g. poppy seed products contain morphine, but quantification of a positive finding will usually enable one to differentiate low-level dietary intake from genuine drug misuse.

False negatives can also occur, but these are more difficult to detect. Adulterants added to the sample might either interfere with the test or dilute analyte concentrations to below the limit of detection. Sometimes other drugs are ingested which dilute the sample, e.g. diuretics; alternatively the target drug concentration can be decreased artificially by phramacological manipulation, e.g. supervision of sample collection. Probably the greatest number of false negatives occur when initial screening is done by immunoassay, which specifically targets a limited range of drugs, and therefore, many urines containing drugs from other groups are not selected for a more comprehensive examination.

Interpretation of results may be done with care especially as individual differences in pharmacokinetic response to drugs make it impossible to give a precise answer to such questions as: (a) when was the drug ingested, and (b) how much was taken. However, test sensitivity is normally set to detect the ingestion of a single therapeutic dose for at least 24 hours, although many drugs can be detected for longer when regular use is stopped.

In conclusion, drug screening is now a speciality in its own right and should only be undertaken by people with expertise in the relevant techniques. The best services employ a range of immunoassay and chromatographic techniques and a commanding knowledge of both the methodology and drug metabolism are essential to correct interpretation of results. These techniques are commercially available and detect the presence of the following drugs or their metabolites in blood or urine: amphetamines; cannabis (THC-acid); cocaine (Benzylecgonine); opiates; methadone; barbiturates; benzodiazepines; methaqualone; Propoxyphene; LSD 25 (RIA only).

References

Banks, A. and Walker, T.A.N. (1983) "Drug Addiction and Polydrug Abuse", *The Role of the General Practitioner;* ISDD.

Brecher, E.M. (1972) *Licit and Illicit Drugs*, N.Y. Consumers Union.

Cannabis: Report of the Advisory Committee on Drug Dependence (1968) Chairman, Baroness Wootton, HMSO, London.

Dyer, C. (1992) "Halcion as a Defence in Britain", *B.M.J.*, Vol. 305: 672.

Firth, M.E. "1991 Meeting Reports, Cocaine as a Biological and Medical Problem", *J. Roy. Soc. Med.* Vol. 84: 753-756.

Henry, J.A. (1992) "Ecstasy and the Dance of Death", *B.M.J.*, Vol. 305: 5-6.

Henry, J.A., Jeffreys, K.J., Dawling, S. (1992) "Toxicity and Deaths due to 3, 4 Methylenedioxymethampetamine ("Ecstasy")", *Lancet* (in press).

Henry, J. (1992) *National Poisons Unit*, Guy's Hospital, London.

Maden, A., Swinton, M., Gunn, J. (1992), "A Survey of Pre-Arrest Drug Use in Sentenced Prisoners", *B.J.Addiction,* Vol. 87: 27-33.

Maden, A., Swinton, M., Gunn, J. (1991) "Drug Dependence in Prisoners", *B.M.J.*, Vol. 302, p. 880.

NSBHW (1978) *Actions Against Sniffing*, Nat. Swedish Board of Health and Welfare, Stockholm.

O'Connor, D.J. (1981) *Glue-Sniffing and Solvent Abuse in Children and Young Adults*, Netherton Park, Stannington, Northumberland.

O'Connor, D.J. (1983) *Glue-Sniffing and Volatile Substance Abuse,* Gower.

O'Connor, G. (1992) "Young Offenders and Solvent Abuse", *Personal Communication.*

Pan, H.S., Wang, R.Y. (1991) Further Evidence that the Action of MDMA in the Medical Prefrontal Cortex is Mediated by the Serotonergic Systems. Output generated from Compact Cambridge: MEDLINE 1991 Annual Search Strategy; Ecstasy (TI, MJ, MW, AB, MN) Document 9 of 14.

Payne-James, J.J., Dean, P.J., Keys, D.W., Group IV Forensic Medical Research, Metropolitan Police Service, London, UK. "Drug misusers in policy custody: a prospective survey", *Journal of the Royal Society of Medicine*, Vol. 87, January 1994.

Perry, H.M., Littlepage, B.N.C. (1992) "Misusing Anabolic Drugs", *B.M.J.* Vol. 305: 1241-42.

Pertwee, R. (1993) "At last, the secret of internal bliss is revealed", *The Independent,* February 15, 1993, Newspaper Publishing PLC, London.

Scott, P. 1964 *Lancet*, ii, 452.

Shephard, G. 1992 Statistics, Treasury Minister Responsible for Customs, U.K.

Statistics of Drug Addicts Notified to the Home Office, United Kingdom (1992). *Home Office Statistical Bulletin,* 19 March, 1992, Research and Statistical Dept., Lunar House, Croydon, Surrey.

Statistics of Drug Seizures and Offenders Dealt With, United Kingdom, 1992. *Home Office Statistical Bulletin*, 22 Sept., 1992. Research and Statistical Dept., 50 Queen Anne's Gate, London.

Susman, R.M. and Kupperstein, L.R. (1968) "A Bibliography on the Inhalation of Glue Fumes and Other Toxic Vapours", *Int. J. Addict.,* 3:1.

Watson, Joyce M. (1979) "Solvent Abuse by Childen and Young Adults – a Review", *Br. J. of Addiction*, Vol.75 27-36.

Werner, M., Dec. (1979) "Inhalant Abuse", *Pharm. Chem. Newsletter*, ISDD.

CHAPTER VIII

Sexual Deviation and Crime

The various types of sexual deviation are described and reference is made to relevant case histories. Radzinowicz and Turner (1957) estimated that 68 per cent of the vicitims of indictable sex offences are under 14 years.

A study of 219 inmates at one of HM Prisons revealed a higher percentage of individuals of sub-average intelligence amongst those convicted of sexual offences and/or offences involving non-sexual violence as compared with those convicted of other offences. Sub-average intelligence was indicated by an intelligence quotient less than 85 on the Wechsler Bellevue adult scale and included grades D and E on Raven's test. The scores gained on the tests on abstract thinking and spelling were graded A to E for the purpose of correlation with the scores gained on the Raven's progressive matrices test. The result of the Raven's test and the tests of abstract thinking indicate that there are 8 per cent more individuals of sub-average intelligence amongst those convicted of sexual offences and/or offences involving non-sexual violence, as compared with those convicted of other offences. The results of the spelling tests indicate that there are 10 per cent more individuals of sub-average intelligence amongst those convicted of sexual offences and/or offences involving non-sexual violence, as compared with those convicted of other types of offence. One may conclude that limited intelligence has some association with lack of emotional control.

Of all notifiable offences recorded in 1992, 24 per cent were offences of theft and handling stolen goods and another 24 per cent were offences of burglary but only 11 per cent of violent offences were sexual offences which can be seen in Tables XVII and XVIII.

Table XVII
Notifiable Offences Recorded by the Police
12 months ending June 1992

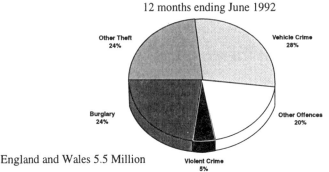

England and Wales 5.5 Million

Table XVIII
Offences of Violent Crime
12 Months ending June 1992

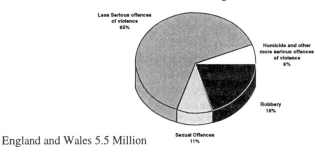

England and Wales 5.5 Million

Sadism
Sadism means the derivation of sexual pleasure from the infliction of pain on others. The majority of sadists belong to the male sex. There are varying degrees of sadism from severe beating to killing in a sexual frenzy. Rape, arson and baby battering may be expressions of sadism.

Diagnostic test
If the infliction of pain is an end in itself which is sexually satisfying then the behaviour is pathological and sadistic. Cruelty means obtaining pleasure from a victim's suffering and humiliation but the pleasure is not sexual. The main object of the sadist is not cruelty but to provide himself with the particular stimulus which arouses him to sexual pleasure. Sadism may affect an individual regularly and periodically in cyclic form and especially in response to periods of stress.

Theories of aetiology

Allen (1961) indicates that the sadist usually has a strong fear of pain and makes his abnormal fear tolerable by associating it with pleasurable sexual sensations. It has also been suggested that men disappointed in love may obtain sexual satisfaction by inflicting pain on other women.

It has been said that a sadist is a person who is kind to a masochist.

Sadism may be due to sexual weakness in the sense that ordinary sexual stimuli are not strong enough to cause arousal.

Sadism may first show itself in childhood and adolescence because of feelings of thwarted affection due to real or imagined parental rejection. The sadist may have the veneer of a mild person and tends to be too compliant in actual life and intensely dominant in fantasy.

Sadism *per se* is not a mental disorder within the meaning of the Mental Health Act 1983 and does not legally excuse or mitigate murder or other serious crimes against the person. It may be an expression of psychopathic disorder, mental impairment, organic brain disease or psychosis.

Alcohol and/or illicit drug-taking may facilitate sadistic behaviour.

Case 14: I examined a man in his late twenties who was accused of murdering his wife by stabbing. There was no family history of mental disorder.

His personality had evidently been abnormal since the age of about eight years when he indulged in ritual slaughter of poultry and killed about 200 birds in all. He also killed a dog and several cats in a similar manner. As he grew older he found that the infliction of pain was closely linked with sexual arousal in himself. His intelligence was somewhat above average. He earned his living in the academic field for a short period but could not tolerate the strain involved. He subsequently worked as a labourer. He tied strings around his throat and inflicted minor wounds on himself with the object of promoting sexual arousal. He was subject to outbursts of extreme violence during adolescence.

The man had considerable religious guilt feelings about masturbation. His masturbatory fantasies mainly concerned plans to murder women of the village in which he lived. He wore his mother's discarded nylons to enhance masturbation and for this purpose their texture was said to be more important than their colour. It was considered that his high degree of insight, social conscience and religion contained his sadistic tendencies up to the time of his wife's death. His views on sex were said to be similar to those of the Albigensians who believed that sexual intercourse was only appropriate when there was deliberate intention to procreate children. He also believed that the temptation to have intercourse should be resisted to the limits of endurance.

He had been psychiatrically examined several years before his wife's death and residential psychiatric treatment was recommended. This treatment lasted several months and he was diagnosed as suffering from sadomasochism and depression. His depression commenced in his early twenties because he could not cope with his academic employment and also because of certain feelings which he had concerning corporal punishment.

He was treated with electroconvulsant therapy and anti-depressant drugs and made a moderately good response to treatment. The treatments had the effect of relieving his depression and fantasies of self-mutilation but the deeper sadistic tendencies persisted.

The psychiatrist indicated that there was a very definite recurrence of sadistic fantasy some months after discharge from hospital. His wife was considered to be in danger if she left him, became permanently frigid or if the accused became interested in another woman. She was not warned of the danger because her husband would not give permission. The psychiatrist attempted to obtain treatment for the accused under secure conditions at a special hospital. The superintendent of the latter hospital was of the opinion that the patient could not be sent to a special hospital under s.26 of the Mental Health Act 1959 because he was not suffering from a mental illness within the meaning of that Act. He could not be detained on the basis of psychopathic disorder because he was over the age of 21 years. A consultant at another special hospital agreed with his opinion. There was a history of two suicidal attempts by self-inflicted incised wounds. These attempts were made a few weeks before his wife's death. There was no clinical history of epilepsy but an electroencephalogram taken during the remand period was reported to be abnormal and revealed generalized dysrhythmia which could have been accounted for by chronic intoxication with drugs or alcohol. There was no clinical or electroencephalographic evidence of localized injury, brain tumour or epilepsy. There was no history of serious head injuries. Tests for venereal disease were returned as negative.

There was a history of a number of marital disputes and his wife suffered bruising on several occasions and sought help from her father. The accused was very upset when their children were not baptized in his faith. He alleged that he had an agreement with his wife that one child would be baptized in his wife's religion and another in his faith. His wife was a member of the Church of England. He could recall all of the events at the material time of his wife's death. He remembered that he visited a local public house and became moderately inebriated on the evening of the crime. He subsequently had an argument with his wife because he came home so late. He admitted that he had stabbed her with a sheath knife he kept in a cupboard drawer in his living room.

The court was advised that this man was fit to plead and to stand trial. The view was taken that at the material time he was capable of knowing what he was doing and that what he was doing was wrong. The other consideration that arose was that of diminished responsibility. An independent psychiatrist agreed with my opinion that his state at the time of the alleged offence could be described as mentally abnormal within the meaning of the definition, that is to say, psychopathic disorder due to inherent causes or disease of the mind. Consequently, his mental abnormality was sufficient to substantially impair his responsibility for his action in doing the killing. Furthermore, s.60 of the Mental Health Act 1959 was applicable to him on the grounds of psychopathic disorder.

The plea of diminished responsibility was accepted. Consequently, the charge was reduced from murder to manslaughter. The court also accepted that s.60 of the Mental Health Act 1959 was applicable to the accused and a hospital order was issued for admission to a special hospital. A restriction order without limit of time was added under s.65 of the Act. Section 64 of the Mental Health Act was implemented and the accused was returned to the prison hospital and transferred to the special hospital within 28 days of the court's decision.

The Mental Health Act 1983 eliminates age limits and consequently s.3 of that Act would apply to psychopathically disordered persons considered treatable.

The Tarasoff case as described by Mackay (1990) may be relevant in view of the above case. Prosenjit Poddar, an Indian national, was infatuated by a young woman called Titania Tarasoff who had rejected him. Poddar took the rejection hard and in the summer of 1969, while Titania was in Brazil, Poddar had outpatient psychotherapy at University of California hospital.

During therapy Poddar expressed fantasies about killing Titania and at this time the therapist learned of the patient's plan to buy a gun. Deeply concerned about Poddar's propensity for violence, an attempt was made to have him committed which proved unsuccessful. After this Poddar dropped out of treatment with no further intervention by his mental health professionals. Two months later Poddar killed Titania at her home by shooting her with a pellet gun and then stabbing her.

Poddar was later charged with first degree murder but the jury accepted his plea of manslaughter (see *People v. Poddar,* 103 Cal Rptr 878, 1973). Since then Poddar has returned to India and is reported to be happily married.

Titania's parents sued the University, claiming that the therapist had been negligent in failing to confine Poddar and in not warning Titania of the danger which the patient posed.

The case first reached the California Supreme Court in 1974 when it was decided that:

> "When a doctor... in the exercise of his professional skill and knowledge, determines, or should determine, that a warning is essential to avert danger arising from the medical or psychological condition of his patient, he incurs a legal obligation to give that warning."

At this stage the American Psychiatric Association (APA) filed an *amicus curiae* brief which voiced grave concerns about the decision and succeeded in persuading the court to rehear the appeal. Accordingly, in 1976, the California Supreme Court by a bare majority, issued a second opinion again favouring the existence of a legal duty owed by a psychotherapist to the potential victim. However, this time the duty was defined more broadly. Thus, Justice Tobriner delivering the majority opinion said:

> "When a therapist determines, or pursuant to the standards of his profession should determine, that his patient presents a serious danger of violence to another, he incurs an obligation to use reasonable care to protect the intended victim against such danger. The discharge of this duty may require the therapist to take one or more of various steps, depending upon the nature of the case. Thus it may call for him to warn the intended victim or others likely to appraise the victim of the danger, to notify the police, or to take whatever other steps are reasonably necessary under the circumstances."

In effect, therefore, this second opinion transformed the obligation from a duty to warn to a duty to protect and was premised on the fact that the special relationship between doctor and patient may in certain circumstances support affirmative duties for the benefit of third parties.

Case 15: Diminished responsibility was pleaded by a middle-aged man charged with murdering a young woman who was not known to him before the day on which she died. The body showed evidence of teeth marks, severe head injuries and sexual interference. The accused was a married man who stated that he had a deep-seated hatred of women since the age of about 14 years. He could not explain this hatred but he held women responsible for "all the troubles since the world began". He had treatment in a psychiatric hospital for a short period before the killing. He admitted that he had assaulted women on a number of occasions during the previous 20 years but not with the primary object of sexual interference. He alleged that he had experienced periodic feelings of acute anxiety and tension for a number of years. He did not suffer from mental impairment, psychosis or epilepsy. He was not under the influence of alcohol or drugs at the material time. He was considered to be an aggressive psychopath who had uncontrollable sadistic urges directed at women.

The prosecution and jury accepted the plea and the accused was sent to a special hospital on the basis of s.60 of the Mental Health Act 1959. The Judge added a restriction order without limit of time.

The majority of sadistic murderers, rapists and paedophiles would not be regarded as mentally disordered within the meaning of the Mental Health Act during the course of their trials. However, hormonal treatment, deconditioning therapy and even surgery may be indicated during the course of a prison sentence as otherwise these individuals would eventually be released from prison and could well repeat their offences.

The sadistic murder may be accidental and unpremeditated. Psychopathic sadistic murder tends to be *repetitive* and has the following features:

1. Periodic killing due to the perpetrator's periodic compulsive sex drive.
2. Cutting, stabbing and biting of breasts and genitals and perhaps drinking the blood and eating the flesh of the victim.
3. Sexual orgasm associated with violation of the victim.
4. Cataclysm of emotion and clouding of consciousness.
5. Normal behaviour until next sadistic paroxysm.
6. Obvious lack of sympathy and empathy for the victims.
7. The victims may be drugged before they are killed.

Masters, (1993), studied the *serial killer* Jeffrey Dahmer who murdered

17 men. He concluded that Dahmer's description of his crimes indicated that he enjoyed committing same but gave no other explanation as to why he killed. This author also indicated that serial killers in the United States tend to select literary agents before attorneys for their defence.

Allen (1961) stated that the personality of the sadistic murderer contains a sinister combination of aggressive and destructive impulses including envy and revenge which are worked out on the victim. This psychopathology was established long before the crime.

Homosexuality
The causation of this condition has never been adequately explained. The "blank slate" theory suggests that sexual propensities are entirely acquired by experience and the "sleeping beauty" theory indicates that sexual responses originate from a built-in neurophysiological mechanism and become evident when the right stimulus is provided at the right time.

Hamer *et al*, (1993), indicated that male homosexuality is linked to chromosome Xq28. This finding will no doubt lead to further arguments as to whether nature or nurture or a combination of both are responsible for male homosexuality. Rees, (1990), quotes a 4 to 4.7 per cent incidence of male homosexuality in England and Wales. Consequently the number of male homosexuals in England and Wales would vary from 2,160,000 to 2,538,000 if one takes the population to be 54,000,000. Homosexuals may be classified as constitutional, conditioned and facultative and one may reasonably assume that the constitutional ones would come under the heading of "genetic linkage". I am not aware of any definitive study of the incidence of "genetic linkage" homosexuals but Hamer, (1993), indicated that 13.5 per cent of the brothers of homosexual men were also homosexual as compared with an expected rate of 2 per cent and consequently, the incidence of "genetic linkage" homosexuality must be at least 13.5 per cent and probably higher. Such "linkage" has profound social, political and legal implications. Homosexuality *per se* (of any type) is not a mental disorder within the meaning of the Mental Health Act, (1983), and consequently, it should not be used as an excuse for lawbreaking.

Heterosexuality in the context of marriage involves a human relationship and a social commitment and unlike homosexuality tends to be productive. It is quite false to assume that all the problems associated with homosexuality are due to social discrimination.

The Sexual Offences Act 1967 excused homosexual behaviour in private between consenting adults of 21 years old or over. Homosexual behaviour involving a male under the age of 21 years was therefore an offence. (The age of consent for homosexuals was subsequently amended to 18 by the 1994 Act).

Homosexuals in general may be classified as:

1. Immature adults who are often sexually deprived but not socially dangerous. These individuals may remain homosexual or become heterosexual. They may need psychiatric support.
2. Well-compensated latent homosexuals who are usually respectable, intelligent and often married. The underlying homosexual tendencies may become activated by depression, anxiety, excessive stress and alcohol.

Homosexuals with severely damaged personalities include:

1. Prostitutes who tend to indulge in robbery and extortion when they grow older and become less attractive to their sexual patrons.
2. The socially dangerous paedophiliacs.
3. Mentally impaired and psychopathically disordered individuals and those suffering from organic brain disease.

Curran and Parr (1957) analysed 100 male homosexuals in private practice and found that 51 per cent were free from gross personality disorders, neurosis and psychosis during their adult lives. Of the 100 studied, 17 were paedophiliacs and usually sought psychiatric advice because of trouble with the law. They tended to be older than the other 83 homosexuals and a higher proportion were married. The homosexuals comprising the group of 83 were attracted exclusively to adult males and did not become sexually interested in boys. The paedophiliacs tended to isolate themselves from the older homosexuals and they had a marked capacity for self-deception.

Paedophiliacs comprise about three per cent of all homosexuals and two types exist, namely those fixated upon sexually immature children and those who choose sexually responsive adolescents: West (1974).

Generally speaking, homosexuality is compatible with subjective well-being and objective efficiency and it is a non-progressive condition. Homosexuality *per se* is not a mental disorder within the meaning of the Mental Health Act 1983.

The paedophiliac is usually shy and timid and may show a wide range of psychopathological behaviour. The commonest psychoanalytical finding indicates that fear has prevented the development of adult heterosexuality and they tend to seek comfort and sexual gratification with children. Their offences may vary from viewing and fondling to the most gross homosexual assault. They tend to be middle-aged when first arrested and have often experienced sexual intercourse for long periods with adult females.

Complications of paedophilia from the point of view of the victim are:

1.   Permanent fear of normal sexuality.
2.   The child may develop into a paedophiliac adult.
3.   The child may feel emotionally deprived and disturbed after a prolonged sexual association with an adult comes to an end.
4.   Premature arousal of sexual desire may lead to neurosis, psychosis or psychopathy because the child is not intellectually or emotionally equipped to satisfy or come to terms with these desires.

Furthermore, children "cared" for by perverted people would tend to imitate their behaviour by example given, and they may even come to regard normal heterosexual activity as abnormal. To take one example, girls who have been raped by their fathers tend to expect the same treatment from other men.

Lesbians and homosexual men are usually promiscuous and would therefore tend to be attracted to and sexually abuse children in their "care".

Paedophiliacs are regarded as the "lone wolves" of homosexuality and are disliked by the majority of homosexuals who are attracted to adult males.

The following case history illustrates that a court need not necessarily accept psychiatric recommendations.

Case 16: A man in his thirties was charged with numerous sexual offences against a male child. The offences took place mainly in derelict houses. He explained his behaviour by stating that he had been the subject of a homosexual assault in late childhood. He also stated that the victim had encouraged him in his sexual misbehaviour. These excuses were obviously rationalizations. He had three previous convictions of offences against boys and two of these were the result of offences committed when on leave from two different mental hospitals. He was one of several children and complained of brutal beatings by his father who had sustained "shell shock" during the First World War.

His intelligence quotient was estimated at 82 on the Wechsler Adult Intelligence Scale and therefore was about equal to that of a 12-year-old child. He was regarded as a good worker during his period of stay in mental hospitals, in one of which he was strongly suspected of indulging in homosexual acts with male patients. He had worked for several weeks as a labourer shortly before the current charges. He was unmarried and strongly attracted to males between the ages of 10 and 14 years. He admitted to having had sexual intercourse with women on a few occasions.

There was no history of epilepsy or serious head injuries. There was no evidence of alcoholism or illicit drug-taking. He was admitted to an ordinary hospital for subnormals in his mid-twenties. This admission was under the old Mental Deficiency Act. He was transferred to a special hospital after five years. He was readmitted to an ordinary hospital for subnormals after six months and re-classified as a psychopath. He was granted home leave after four months' stay but readmission to the same hospital followed after 14 weeks. This readmission was on the basis of s.60 of the Mental Health Act 1959 after sexual offences against male children. An order restricting discharge under s.65 of the Act was imposed. He was regraded to "informal" status and discharged after two-and-a-half years. He remained free in the community for only seven months and was then sentenced to six years' imprisonment for indecent assault on a male child. He gained full remission and served four years. During his imprisonment he was examined by a consultant psychiatrist who was particularly interested in the treatment of sexual offenders and he decided that the accused was unsuitable for hormonal treatment by mouth, because of his unreliability. Appropriate hormone treatment by implant was under consideration but a final decision was not made. He remained free in the community for only 10 months and was then charged with numerous sexual offences involving male children. He stayed with his sister during his months of freedom and worked for about 10 weeks as a labourer. He pleaded guilty and two psychiatrists recommended admission to an ordinary mental hospital on the basis of s.60 of the Mental Health Act 1959. The psychiatrist of the recipient hospital told the Judge that the defendant would not commit further offences or abscond because he would be happy in the hospital environment. He also stated that the hospital was isolated and that security was not provided by locked doors but rather by understanding nursing staff. I advised against this disposal and the accused was sentenced to a substantial period of imprisonment. He surreptitiously obtained sedatives in court and made a serious suicide attempt within hours of his return to the prison hospital. His life was saved with some difficulty.

There have been some 60 incidences during the first six months of 1990, where perverts have tried to persuade parents to undress their children for the purpose of physical examinations. They posed as social workers or NSPCC representatives. About 30 per cent of these individuals succeeded in gaining entry to houses also alleging that they were authorized to remove the children. The offences tended to occur in the north of England. Various theories have been put forward as to the psychopathology of the offenders. It is reasonable to assume that the callers are paedophiles or seeking to abduct children for the use of such individuals. Satanic cults in which illicit drug-taking is endemic have also been implicated. There is also a theory to the effect that these perverts or their representatives manage to "hack" into computer registers of "at risk" children in order to obtain confidential facts on their "targets". This could explain how bogus officials arrive at houses with prior knowledge of the names of potential victims. There is also a suspicion of an association between this perversion and murder cults, and searches were undertaken by the police in 1990 for the bodies of at least four children who mysteriously went missing and presumably were abducted. The searches included digging for graves.

Police and social workers have issued a six-point plan to help parents:

1. Ask to see any social worker's ID card. Ask permission to take visitor's photograph if he or she cannot produce an identity card.
2. If in any doubt close the door and call the police.
3. Ring the visitor's office to make sure he is who he claims to be.
4. Be wary of unannounced visits. Most are arranged with parents beforehand.
5. If at all suspicious, get as good a description of the visitor as possible.
6. Stay calm.

Sexual Exhibitionism

An offence against s.4 of the Vagrancy Act 1824 is committed when a person "wilfully, openly, lewdly and obscenely exposes his person with intent to insult any female". It may occur at any period during adolescence or adult life. The "primary" exhibitionist prefers exposure to normal sexual intercourse and physical contact with the victim is not intended.

Sexual exhibitionism in a public place may be an offence at common law and is also an offence against s.28 of the Town Police Clauses Act 1847, when an individual "wilfully and indecently exposes his person". Proof of intent is not required for conviction. Masturbation may or may not occur during exhibitionism which is closely related to voyeurism. The offence is confined to males.

About 80 per cent of sexual exhibitionists are first offenders. The victims are adult females or children of either sex. Allen (1961) indicated that about 50 per cent of the victims are females under the age of 16 years. It has been estimated that sexual exhibitionists account for 20 to 35 per cent of all sex offenders. The true sexual exhibitionist obtains his satisfaction from the expression of shock on the victim's face. Exposures to children are likely to be repeated. East (1924) studied 91 sex offenders on remand in Brixton Prison and found that sexual exhibitionism was the commonest single type of sexual offence in the group. This offence may be spontaneous or well planned. There is a recidivism rate of 12 per cent for first offenders and 31 per cent for those with similar previous convictions.

"Primary" and "secondary" exhibitionists may also indulge in sexual intercourse with adult females.

Psychopathology
It may be an exaggeration of normal early childhood exhibitionism and a primitive way of displaying masculinity. It may also originate in emotional conflicts in childhood, which are carried into adult life. This is a theoretical cause of primary exhibitionism.

The following are possible causes of secondary exhibitionism:

1. It may be triggered by drunkenness and/or illicit drug-taking.
2. It may be triggered by senility or some other organic cerebral syndrome when it represents a regressive form of behaviour.
3. It may be an expression of epileptic twilight states, when electroencephalograms are helpful.
4. It may be perpetrated by inadequate psychopaths or mentally impaired persons who are conscious of their unattractiveness to females and may therefore be regarded as an invitation to sexual

intercourse. In these instances intelligence quotients and personality tests are helpful.

5. It may also be an expression of hypomanic psychosis or schizophrenia.

Rosen (1964) believes sexual exhibitionism may hold even more undesirable unconscious sex wishes in check. He also describes a *phobic-compulsive* type of exhibitionism associated with severe personality disorder, and a simple *regressive type*, reactive to mental or physical stress with the personality intact.

Primary sexual exhibitionism is explained mainly on the basis of Freudian assumptions. It is otherwise compatible with satisfactory mental and physical health. Psychoanalytic theory postulates that it represents reassurance against the fear of castration which originates in childhood. Consequently, exposure to little girls is safer than exposure to women who might castrate. There may be a sadistic motiviation in the form of suppressed wishes to rape women who are also regarded as dangerous and aggressive as sex partners. Consequently, impotence and homosexuality are not uncommon accompaniments of sexual exhibitionism.

The modus operandi of the exhibitionist tends to be constant from the points of view of dates, times, places, method of attracting victims, type of conversation at material times and facial expression. Masturbation and ejaculation may or may not occur during exposure. The police usually show photographs of known exposers to victims in order to apprehend the culprit.

It is doubtful if sexual exhibitionism should be regarded as a clinical entity because it is frequently associated with other sexual offences and perversions.

The primary exhibitionist does not usually seek medical help unless in trouble with the law. The various treatments are described later in this chapter. The exhibitionist and his wife may need treatment as he may also be depressed and his wife may be refusing sexual intercourse. The fantasies of the exhibitionist may provide help in assessing prognosis. Marriage and legal punishments do not usually influence primary exhibitionism.

Case 17: A man in his late twenties was charged with indecently exposing himself to several female children. His childhood was quite happy and secure. He was one of several siblings. His mother died in his early teens.

There was no familiar history of mental illness, epilepsy or alcoholism. His intelligence quotient was 71 (Wechsler Adult Intelligence Scale), which is equivalent to the mental age of a child of 10 years. He was obviously functioning at a higher level as he was able to earn his living in the community as a labourer.

His wife left him because of drunkenness and cruelty. He admitted sexual promiscuity and he usually met women in public houses for this purpose. There was no history of illicit drug-taking but he admitted to drinking 15 pints of beer and 20 "small" whiskies almost daily.

There was no history of suicidal attempts, epilepsy or serious head injuries. He had treatment at two mental hospitals for a few weeks for alcoholism and malnutrition. He led a vagabond type of existence and lived in caravans.

In regard to the current charge he stated that he left his caravan and went to a nearby fish-and-chip shop where the girls accidentally saw his genitals. This offence was not influenced by alcohol and/or drugs.

This man was an alcoholic dullard who had a number of previous convictions for grievous bodily harm and being drunk and disorderly. He served two prison sentences of moderate duration. He was not mentally disordered within the meaning of the Mental Health Act 1959. He was not a primary sexual exhibitionist as he freely admitted that his exhibitionism represented an invitation to sexual intercourse. He could be described as a chronic social problem.

He was fined £5 in court.

Transvestism

Transvestism is described as the wearing of clothes of the opposite sex for sexual purposes. Transvestism may be indulged in by either sex. The public tends to be tolerant when the female dresses partially or entirely in male clothing but males who dress in female clothing are not usually tolerated by the public or the law. Transvestism may be interpreted as insulting behaviour with intent to provoke a breach of the peace and the individual concerned may be arrested on these grounds.

Randall (1959) studied 50 transvestites (37 male and 13 females). He distinguished (1) a heterosexual group with obsessive-compulsive tendencies who indulged in transvestism as an adjunct to heterosexual relationships, and (2) a group with strong homosexual tendencies who tried to modify these tendencies by indulging in transvestism. Members of this group tended to rationalize their transvestism by claiming that they were undergoing a sex change.

The homosexual male transvestite tends to wear clothes which caricature and mock women. The heterosexual male transvestite wears conventional female clothing and unresolved problems in his marriage or other heterosexual relationships are often evident.

Enelow (1965) classified transvestites into (1) exhibitionistic and (2) non-exhibitionistic types:

(1)   The exhibitionistic group was further subdivided into schizophrenic and non-schizophrenic groups. The schizophrenics attempted to obliterate their true sexual attributes and assume those of the opposite sex. The non-schizophrenics were overtly homosexual or the transvestism represented a substitute phenomenon for overt homosexual behaviour.

(2)   The non-exhibitionistic group suffered from neurotic conflicts and episodes of reactive depression. In this group the transvestism represented an attempt to identify with the parent of the opposite sex in order to overcome "castration anxiety". The psychoanalytic theory assumes that the transvestite male identifies with his mother and refuses to acknowledge that she does not possess male genital organs. Kinsey *et al* (1948), on the other hand, regarded transvestism and homosexuality as totally independent conditions. Women who dress in male clothing do not usually have a compulsion to do so and sexual satisfaction is not the primary objective.

Transvestites do not usually seek help from doctors unless they come into conflict with the law.

They should be examined for any malformation of their genitals. Investigations should also be carried out for endocrine disorder and/or chromosome abnormality. Family doctors, psychiatrists and endocrinologists may undertake treatment. Social workers, marriage-guidance counsellors and probation officers may also make a valuable contribution to therapy.

Epstein (1961) indicated that temporal lobe epilepsy may be associated with transvestism and fetishism.

Case 18: A man in his thirties was charged with indecently exposing himself to several women. He was also charged with stealing from his employers. He explained the latter offence by stating that his employers had promised to provide him with living accommodation in the form of a caravan but this promise was not fulfilled. He pleaded guilty to stealing various types of female underclothing several years previously. He found these garments sexually stimulating and wearing them usually led to masturbation. He felt that he was unattractive to women and admitted that indecent exposure and transvestism were to some extent substitutes for sexual intercourse. He had indulged in transvestism on numerous occasions. He was unmarried and heterosexual. His fantasies were exclusively heterosexual. He had experienced sexual intercourse with women but infrequently. His childhood was reasonably happy and secure. His father committed suicide but the accused was an adult at the time.

His intelligence was described as "low average". He worked regularly for about 12 years after leaving school but developed a defeatist attitude after the death of his mother. Consequently, he did little work and either slept "rough" or lived in reception centres for several years before the current charges. There was no evidence of illicit drug-taking. He took alcohol to excess but was not an alcoholic.

His sexual misbehaviour began after his mother's death and loss of the parental home. He was treated for a period of months in a mental hospital following his appearance in court on the charge of stealing female underclothing. He was diagnosed as a depressive, with a personality disorder and as an inadequate schizoid personality. He threatened suicide on a number of occasions but made no attempt. There was no history of epilepsy or serious head injuries.

This case history illustrates that sexual exhibitionism and transvestism may co-exist but may not necessarily be preferred to normal sexual intercourse. This man's sexual misbehaviour began as a reaction to the death of a loved one and he could be regarded as a facultative rather than a constitutional sex deviant. Psychopathic, depressive and schizoid personality traits were combined with limited intelligence and a low tolerance of stress and one felt that he would need a good deal of medical and social support in the community in order to avoid future lawbreaking.

There was no evidence of mental disorder during the remand period and his physical health was satisfactory.

The court was advised that s.60 of the Mental Health Act (1959) was not applicable to him on the grounds of mental disorder. He was placed on probation for two years without the requirement of psychiatric treatment.

Incest

The definition of incest is sexual relations between those within forbidden degrees of relationship as, for example, brother and sister, father and daughter, mother and son, grandfather and grand-daughter and half-brother and half-sister.

Incest could be punished only by an ecclesiastical court before 1908 when the Incest Act was passed. It is now an offence under ss.10 or 11 of the Sexual Offences Act 1956. Incest may indicate mental disorder.

Incest occurs:

1. between some mentally impaired persons who have low moral values;
2. where alcohol and/or drugs remove the normal inhibitions in a predisposed individual;
3. as an expression of psychosis, psychopathic disorder and organic brain disease (including senile dementia);
4. when a brother and sister have been separated since childhood and meet later as strangers or after being introduced, when mutual interests and attraction to each other lead to sex within the forbidden degrees of relationship;
5. where poverty and overcrowding compel close relatives to live in intimacy; and
6. where there is a breakdown of the sexual relationship between a husband and wife, or pregnancy or illness prevents normal sexual intercourse.

Lukianowicz (1972) found a 4 per cent incidence of paternal incest amongst an unselected group of female psychiatric patients. The fathers who initiated the incest were aged between 30 and 40 years and their daughters were aged between five and 14 years. The average duration of the incest was eight years and several daughters were successively involved in some instances. Most of the fathers were habitually unemployed, psychopathic and alcoholic. The mothers were usually dejected and overwhelmed with family problems. Most victims later became delinquent, psychopathic, depressive, hysterical and/or suicidal. Some of the victims became sexually frigid and some indulged in illicit drug-taking. The offending fathers persistently threatened violence if their daughters disclosed the clandestine relationship. Roberts (1967) showed that the offspring of incestuous unions have a greater mortality and morbidity than the average.

Another study by Kosky (1987) indicated that incest as defined in terms of sexual intercourse, occurs in less than 1 per cent of the population. However, other forms of abnormal sexual activity in families may adversely affect 10 per cent of females before the age of 16 years. It was concluded that incest has very adverse effects on the victims who are usually pre-pubescent females. The damaging effects are aggravated further by violence or the threat of same. This study was based mainly on court or treatment samples.

Williams (1974) indicated that 140 males were convicted in 1971 and 70 received sentences of imprisonment. There were very few cases where the offender could be released to go home to his family. Thirty-five per cent had no hope of reconciliation with their wives. Some of the offenders denied guilt and some expressed remorse. Forty per cent were of low intelligence and there was a high proportion of alcoholics. Incest families are usually social problem families requiring intensive casework. The victim and other female children must be protected.

Incest causes an increase in recessive disorders in the progeny such as cystic fibrosis, cerebral degeneration, loss of vision, congenital cardiac defects, respiratory distress syndrome and mental retardation. Father-daughter and brother-sister unions carry the highest risk. A study of 161 such children revealed that fewer than half were normal (Seemanova, 1971).

Protection of the child is paramount. The social services would investigate with a view to possible care proceedings. The Department of Social Services has a statutory duty to inform the police under the Children and Young Persons Act (1969), and doctors must reveal confidential information if so requested by a court, and refusal could be regarded as contempt.

The victim should be removed from the family home and her whereabouts kept secret from the guilty party because of the probability of recurrence. Marital therapy might help prevent break-up of the marriage but would not necessarily protect the victim if the father was responsible. The girl will need emotional support from all relevant medical, social and legal agencies including the probation service. The children or adolescents may have no apparent emotional disturbances or a whole range of reactions, including severe neuroses, may be evident. Psychotherapy should be on an individual basis and non-punitive. Specially trained foster parents should aim for a long-term trusting relationship and should be supported by psychiatrists, psychologists and social workers trained in the management of child abuse. The foster parents should be advised to explain to the victim that she was not responsible for the perverted acts and therefore guilt feelings are not justified. Psychologists and psychiatrists should never influence the victim to deny the reality of the abnormal sexual experiences as such advice could well result in refusal to continue treatment or even precipitate neurotic or psychotic conditions.

Any form of mental disorder initially discovered should obviously be treated before rehabilitation of the victim can begin.

Gartner *et al* (1988) indicated that many adolescent females who are victims of incest, experience phases of mental conflict as to whether to reveal current sexual involvement with their fathers. They tend to express love and loyalty to their fathers when removed from the parental homes and these sentiments alternate with feelings of loss, rejection, anger, guilt and terror. Severe depression which may be accompanied by regressive behaviour such as rocking, thumb-sucking, enuresis nocturna or carrying a doll or teddy bear, has also been observed. Self-inflicted pain, mutilation and suicide attempts may occur.

The psychoanalytic theory suggests that father-daughter incest may represent a form of revenge by the teenage daughter on her mother who is blamed rightly or wrongly for depriving her father of adequate love and support and consequently causing him to become a bad parent. The mother suffers because of public disgrace and economically if her marriage breaks up. It is not made clear if this "reasoning" by the victim, occurs on a conscious or subconscious level. It is obvious that the mother could not logically be blamed for her husband's perverted behaviour whatever their marital relationship. Freud's original "seduction theory" alleged the universality of incestuous wishes implying that some females who allege incest may have simply fantasized the "event". Presumably such females would have to be old enough to be capable of reasoning before they could experience such fantasies. Freud later abandoned this "seduction theory" which did no service to psychiatry and made treatment and rehabilitation of the victim difficult if not impossible. The sexually assaulted child who is old enough to reason, subjectively interprets the experience as horrifying and evil. Sexual abuse including incest has a very damaging effect on the emotional lives of the victim and innocent members of the family. Psychosomatic symptoms may also follow.

Raskin (1984) described 50 patients with chronic pelvic pain of whom 10 per cent had demonstrable organic disease and 35 per cent had experienced incest. Furthermore, the study by Arnold *et al* (1990) indicated that the history of childhood sexual abuse was recognized only in the later stages of medical and surgical intervention and recommended that the possibility of childhood sexual abuse should be considered earlier in such cases to prevent further unnecessary intervention.

People charged with offences such as incest are usually remanded in custody for psychiatric reports and admitted to the prison hospital from the reception area. Imprisonment would at least temporarily remove the culprit from the source of temptation and make it more difficult for him to excuse and minimize his behaviour. Incidentally, sexual offenders (including those who commit incest) may have a compulsion to molest women and corrupt children but they are usually capable of avoiding sources of temptation if they so choose. Similarly prisoners taking medication to dampen sexual ardour, may simulate responses which the authorities will consider favourable. Consequently such treatments do not necessarily help to decide when a sexual offender may be safely released as a condition of parole. Segregation would usually occur if a sentence of imprisonment is imposed, as this type of offender is most unpopular with the majority of inmates.

Case 19: A man in his late thirties was charged with having sexual intercourse with his teenage daughter on a number of occasions. He made a suicide attempt by wrist-cutting shortly after arrest. He had previous convictions for petty theft.

The man's childhood was rather insecure. He was reared by an aunt because his parents lacked adequate living accommodation. There was no family history of mental disorder, epilepsy or alcoholism. His intelligence was within average limits and he was quite capable of earning his living as a labourer. His marriage was reasonably happy although mutual infidelity was alleged. He was bisexual and he made a suicide attempt after his marriage because of his worry over his homosexual tendencies.

He alleged that in his early teens he had been indecently assaulted by a man. There was no history of voyeurism, transvestism or sexual exhibitionism. His fantasies were bisexual involving adult males and teenage girls. He took alcohol to excess but he was not an alcoholic. There was no evidence of illicit drug-taking. There was no history of psychiatric treatment, epilepsy or serious head injuries.

He was very unhappy during the early part of his sentence mainly because he was terrified of other inmates who do not like offences against children. He was given appropriate protection and sedation, and gradually came to terms with his predicament. His physical health was satisfactory.

He was not mentally disordered within the meaning of the Mental Health Act. He was sentenced to several years' imprisonment and he developed pseudopsychotic symptoms during the early part of his sentence. He declined psychotherapy and treatment with Cyproterone acetate.

His daughter, who was the victim, left home but there was concern for the welfare of another daughter after his release. The social and probation services were appropriately advised. He returned to the family home on release.

This case illustrates the fact that an almost totally amoral individual wished to reform only because he fell foul of the law. He requested psychiatric treatment during the remand period but not after sentence. He was examined by a psychiatrist on behalf of the defence and psychiatric treatment was offered as a condition of probation.

It has been suggested that incest should no longer be regarded as a criminal offence but rather a civil one. This recommendation is made on the basis that imprisonment would not help the guilty party but that psychiatric treatment outside of prison would effect a "cure". However, those of this opinion seldom specify what they mean by "psychiatric treatment" which could consist of one of the various forms of psychotherapy including psychoanalysis, aversion therapy, medication such as hormones, Benperidol or Cyproterone acetate which reduce the strength but not the *direction* of the sexual drive. Offenders cannot be relied upon to continue taking any form of prescribed chemotherapy after release from prison or discharge from a psychiatric hospital. I cannot recall a single instance where any of the above treatments "cured" an incest offender. Incest *per se* is not a mental disorder within the meaning of the Mental Health Act 1983. Even so, psychiatric treatment is available within the framework of the prison service for inmates who are serving sentences and who are *NOT* mentally disordered within the meaning of the above Act.

Obscene Telephone Calls

The great majority of people who make such telephone calls belong to the male sex. From the point of view of psychopathology the call may be the symbolic equivalent of voyeurism which is defined as "looking at sexual happenings" and is somewhat similar to scoptophilia which means obtaining sexual pleasure from watching other people. The call may also have the symbolic significance of rape with sadistic fantasies or made by a timid person with a secret yearning to make sexual contacts. The older caller is more likely to put his sadistic fantasies into practice. The call may be a symptom of latent homosexuality and represent an unconscious projection beyond the woman on the telephone to the "invisible" male in the home. The telephone may serve the unstable, primitive, paranoid person as a "magic" means of influencing people at a distance. The caller usually tries to communicate excitement concerning sexual matters, and tries to involve others in same.

Richards (1989) described the case of an unmarried woman who worked in a college and who could only gain relief of her anxiety and tension caused by her emotional problems by repeatedly telephoning her mother for reassurance and sympathy. The above symptoms were accompanied by what she referred to as "inner pain" in her lower abdomen. She also made persistent calls of an obscene nature to persons she associated directly or indirectly with unhappy experiences during her past life. This woman had experienced lower abdominal and genital pain since the age of eight years. She had bladder and kidney surgery and urethral dilitation during subsequent years but without relief of pain which made sexual intercourse intolerable. Consequently, doctors, nurses, dental hygienists, secretaries at college and even dry cleaners were recipients of her calls as her resentments became so progressively expansive as to include most people with whom she had personal dealings. Her obscene telephone calls were based on her own unfulfilled sexual experiences and desires in which she tried to involve the recipients. The calls also provided an outlet for aggression and became compulsive. Psychonalysis enabled her to accept the limits of her abilities and not become demoralized by variations in self-esteem. Feelings of aggressivity, shame and guilt also reached manageable proportions. Intimacy became tolerable as well. She also became aware of her desire for forgiveness especially from her mother on whom she had been overdependent since childhood and adolescence.

Obscene telephone calls are almost invariably anonymous and have elements of sexual peversion, obsessionalism and neurotic gratification. The perpetrator often feels lonely and neglected. The voice of the victim may also be regarded as the voice of conscience coming from an unseen source (Silverman, 1982). The psychoanalytical theory *alleges* that these calls represent unfulfilled (subconscious) sexual desires and the calls are made to relieve anxiety and tension. A substantial number of anonymous telephone calls are not obscene but made for the purposes of intimidation, blackmail, slander and/or threats of violence by people who are *NOT* disordered within the meaning of the Mental Health Act. Such calls are perverse, meaning that they are obviously wrong and illegal but have no primary sexual motivation. Other malicious people telephone near relatives of people who have disappeared making bogus offers to find them dead or alive at a price or free of charge. This has happened in the cases of Ruth Stevens who vanished in December 1989 and Suzy Lamplugh who has been missing since 1986.

It has been estimated that about 8,000,000 perverse telephone calls are made in the United Kingdom every year. This approximate number includes obscene telephone calls. About 2,000 of the total calls threaten violence. Out of about 175,000 annual complaints about such offensive calls, it is alleged that some 30,000 are traced by organized operator interception from British Telecom's new digital exchanges.

School holidays are favourite times for perverts who make obscene telephone calls to teenage schoolchildren. These callers sometimes pretend to be doctors or headmasters with the object of influencing the children or their mothers to discuss intimate problems. Some victims are driven not only to change their telephone numbers but to move to another area to live. Those who persistently indulge in such calls obviously have psychopathic elements in their personalities as judged by total lack of feeling for their victims and determination to continue the habit unless punished by the law. The great majority are *NOT* mentally disordered within the meaning of the Mental Health Act 1983 and could cease making these calls if they so wished.

Telephone sex chatlines seem to have blossomed in the UK in 1989. These sex lines have been described as "humming with filth" and dealing in perverted fantasy and freely used by perverts. Curiosity and extensive advertising also influence teenagers to use these chatlines and the risk of corruption is obvious. Annual profits for one such telephone organization were estimated at £20,000,000. Officials of a telephone company may plead that they have a statutory duty to provide a telephone line for anyone who has asked for one. The common law dealing with "conspiracy to corrupt public morals" would be relevant. Some of these chatlines have been disconnected and the remainder will hopefully meet the same fate in the near future.

The New Jersey Bell Telephone Company offer caller identification facilities, devices which flash the telephone numbers of callers. Consequently, the recipient can make a return call immediately after receiving any call. The cost is about $12 per month. However, "civil rights" organizations invariably object and as a result an identification blocker became available for selected callers. Obviously, people who use the telephone to make obscene calls, to threaten assault or malicious firesetting, or bomb hoaxers should not be protected by blockers or any other means.

Case 20: A man in his early thirties was charged with indecently assaulting several teenage girls. He also induced them to handle his genitals. He paid each a small sum of money. He had previous convictions for indecent exposure, indecent assaults, making a number of obscene telephone calls to members of the opposite sex, causing false fire alarms by telephone calls and several petty thefts. He also entered local shops and falsely alleged that his mother was dead and asked for some money to assist his relatives.

He was reasonably well cared for in childhood although his parents were of limited intelligence and one sibling was mentally impaired. His I.Q. was assessed as 72, equivalent to the mental age of a child aged about 11 years. He was capable of earning his living as a labourer but needed supervision.

He was unmarried and allegedly heterosexual. He never had a sexual relationship with a woman because of lack of self-confidence. His frustration was expressed in the offences described above. The social inquiry report indicated that parental understanding was not sufficient to counteract his moods and urges during adolescence and early adult life.

There was no evidence of illicit drug-taking and he did not take alcohol to excess. He had suffered from idiopathic epilepsy since childhood. The epilepsy was well controlled by anticonvulsants.

He had two admissions to an ordinary mental hospital and the total time in residential care was under two years. He was admitted on the basis of the old Mental Deficiency Acts and s.60 of the Mental Health Act 1959. He did not abscond from the hospital. He was diagnosed as "an unstable subnormal psychopath subject to hysterical dissociative reactions". He was not followed up by the social services after discharge due to lack of communications between the authorities concerned. He was well behaved in hospital but regarded as a "loner". The accused did not have suicidal tendencies. His physical health was satisfactory.

He pleaded guilty to the charges and the report to court indicated that the accused was quite fit to plead to the charges against him. He was not mentally disordered within the meaning of the Mental Health Act 1959, and consequently s.60 was not applicable to him. His mental condition warranted psychiatric supervision and treatment with Cyproterone acetate as a condition of s.4 of the Criminal Justice Act 1948. He also spent a period in a local authority industrial rehabilitation unit.

The man's sexually deviant tendencies were probably an expression of an underlying psychopathy. He spent a lot of his free time watching children. He was likely to offend again against children because of his poor intellect and lack of moral scruples.

Rape
Williams (1965) refers to destructive forces of instinctual drives originating from the very early phases of emotional development. An individual becomes an active sex criminal if these destructive forces are not integrated with the personality and mitigated by effective counteracting forces such as fear of punishment or concern for potential victims. A potential sex criminal may become an active one as a result of fatigue, physical illness, physical attack, affront or criticism. Alcohol and illicit drug-taking may have the same effect. The resultant of the impelling and controlling factors determine whether a mild or serious sex crime is committed.

Section 1 of the Sexual Offences (Amendment) Act 1976 defines rape as follows:

(1)   For the purpose of Section 1 of the Sexual Offences Act 1956 (which relates to rape) a man commits rape if:

(a)   he has unlawful sexual intercourse with a woman who at the time of the intercourse does not consent to it; and

(b)   at that time he knows that she does not consent to the intercourse or he is reckless as to whether she consents to it.

And reference to rape in other enactments (including the following provisions of this Act) shall be construed accordingly.

(2) It is hereby declared that if at a trial for a rape offence the jury has to consider whether a man believed that a woman was consenting to sexual intercourse, the presence or absence of reasonable grounds for such a belief is a matter to which the jury is to have regard, in conjunction with any other relevant matters, in considering whether he so believed.

Consequently, it is not merely a matter of a man having intercourse with a woman without her consent. In addition to the absence of consent by the victim, knowledge that the victim is not consenting, or at least recklessness on the part of the accused as to whether she consents or not, is an integral part of the prosecution case and without such proof the charge must fail. Sexual intercourse by impersonating a woman's husband or with an unconscious woman would fulfil the above criteria (1)(a) and (b), and therefore constitute rape. Research by Wydra *et al.* (1983) indicated that rapists who are *not* mentally disordered are quite capable of exerting control over their behaviour when sexually aroused and in this context they do not differ from other men. It must be stressed that the largest category of rapists are not mentally disordered within the meaning of the Mental Health Act 1983. It is essential to make this emphasis lest the individuals described in the following "pathological" classifications be thought to include most rapists. In other words *the great majority of rapists are healthy young men who are not mentally disordered and who may or may not have been under the influence of alcohol at the material times.*

Grubin and Gunn (1990) studied 142 men who were convicted of 202 rapes. Some 36 per cent of the group were convicted of more than one rape. The group contained several "serial rapists" meaning men who raped more than one woman on separate occasions, and they were found to be "sexually disturbed". One could reasonably assume that all rapists are sexually disturbed and that rape involves the use of violence to satisfy sexual lust which virtually amounts to sadism. High sexual drive cannot account for rape as the great majority of men manage to control this. About 60 per cent of the sample were considered to need psychiatric attention during sentence. The same authors also indicated that the government agreed that some experimental therapeutic units for sex offenders should be established in various prisons, special hospitals and regional secure units for the investigation and, where appropriate, treatment of sexual offenders, which would include long-term community care after release. These facilities would be provided by the government.

Gebhard (1965) studied 1,356 sex offenders and his classification included the following:

(i)   sadistic rapists;

(ii)   amoral psychopathic rapists who may even regard the act as an entitlement;

(iii) the "explosive" rapist, characterized by episodes of loss of self-control;

(iv)   psychotics and the mentally impaired who rape.

Cerce *et al* (1985) commented on a study of 1,600 "sexually dangerous" adult offenders and indicated that 94 per cent had criminal histories and 64 per cent had psychiatric histories prior to admission to the Massachusetts Treatment Centre. Furthermore, as juveniles, 48 per cent of the sample had criminal histories and 20 per cent psychiatric histories. Perhaps early detection and treatment would have improved prognosis.

Prentky *et al* (1985) based their classification on the relative contribution and interaction of sexual and aggressive motivations in the crime:

(i)   the sexual compensatory type where the amount of aggression does not exceed what is necessary to force compliance. The sexual urge is predominant and injury to the victim tends to be accidental;

(ii)   the expressive type where aggression is uncontrolled and the victim is hurt and humiliated;

(iii) the exploitative type where the rape is an impulsive, predatory act and aggression predominates;

(iv)   the "displaced anger" offender is triggered off by a perceived insult from a woman – again aggression predominates;

(v)   the sadistic offender where aggression is foremost and compulsive and he tends to indulge in a perversity of sexual acts. Sexual arousal will only occur in association with violence.

Lisak *et al* (1988) concluded that the basic motivational factors of convicted rapists were equally relevant to 184 non-incarcerated sexually potent male college undergraduates but only from the point of view of degree of motivation. The latter could control their sexual aggression in the sense that they did not break the law. Evidently the rapists were motivated by such high degrees of anger and need for power that they could not control it. Incidentally, Nasjleti (1980) has shown that adult rapists often give a history of having been sexually abused by their mothers in childhood.

King (1990) also indicated that sexual assaults on males by males occur during the process of torture in foreign countries and also in custodial establishments with all-male populations.

He also referred to cases of male rape which occur in "ordinary" society and indicated that in English law, the offence of rape is recognized only as an offence committed by a male on a female.

However, some states in the USA recognize male rape and Foreman (1982) indicated that such rapes constituted 5-10 per cent of the total reported. Heterosexual men who are subjected to this perversion may well subsequently suffer from the *Post Traumatic Stress Disorder*, as do women who have been raped. Male vicitims will also fear being regarded as homosexuals and may not report the crime. HIV testing should be carried out whenever possible.

Criminal statistics indicate that of 2,855 offences of rape which were recorded by the police for England and Wales in 1988, 2,055 (72 per cent) were "cleaned up" (in the sense of being dealt with by court proceedings). The number recorded in 1978 was 1,243. Even these figures do not tell the whole story since experts estimate that only about one-fifth of the rapes that occur are reported to the police. Some 4,589 were recorded in 1993.

Rapists may or may not be socially competent apart from their sexual behaviour. What differentiates rapists from non-rapists is that they have in common strong arousal images of rape and some are also "turned on" by potential victims. Rape is, on the whole, preferred to seduction and often prompted by hatred leading to aggression. There is also the tendency in rapists to blame the victims which assists them to overcome any inhibitions they may have to commit rape and makes them "blind" to the feelings and suffering of their victims. Empathy is therefore lacking and the victim of rape becomes an object rather than a person, Lowenstein (1989). The same author makes some interesting observations on the treatment of rapists which may to some extent overlap with the section dealing with the treatment of sex offenders in general at the end of this chapter.

In developing a treatment plan, it is important to be aware of the types of rapists that exist in order to formulate an appropriate treatment procedure. Where anger is the prominent feature, treatment must concentrate on anger management. Aversion therapy is likely to be more effective with rapists who are sadistic.

General views on treatment of rapists differ but can be placed in two catagories. The first is the *general or comprehensive approach* to be used with all rapists receiving treatment. This consists of general discussions involving law, philosophy, psychology and sociology in the context of what the great majority of members of any particular community regard as acceptable relationships between the sexes.

The second prefers *specific approaches* to dealing with the individual rapist's particular symptoms and ways of thinking and behaving. These include cognitive behaviour therapy, aversion therapy, empathy development, anger management such as learning to control sexual urges including deviant sexual rape fantasies and seeking to transform them into acceptable manifestations with willing partners. Rapists must be aware of the signals within that lead to the eventual rape behaviour. Hence, inclinations towards rape should be eliminated at the very earliest signs before the act occurs and before they become difficult to control. There are likely to be very specific kinds of stimuli or signals of which only the offender is aware and which must be made clear during the treatment in order to help him overcome his abnormal sexual tendencies. The importance of sympathy and empathy in regard to likely victims is obvious.

While in prison, rapists should be treated by restructuring their thinking and attitudes towards women. Release should not be granted unless:

(a) they accept such treatment;
(b) they respond to the treatment favourably with some assurance that once released treatment must continue to reduce the likelihood of relapse.

The initial treatment should be within the prison system where total control of the inmate is assured. It should begin with intensive individual and group sessions at least five days per week and for three hours a day. This should be for as long as necessary to make changes in the individual. There should be assessments at the end of three and six months to note progress made. Following effective progress being made here, the inmates should be prepared for release. Treatment should continue in the community to prevent relapse, until therapists involved consider there to be no risk or minimal risk. *False responses must be guarded against during assessments.*

As already emphasized, rape offenders need to develop *empathy* with their potential victims and should be made aware of the following: "how do you feel your victim feels about being raped? ... how would you feel about being raped?" If such empathy does not develop, it is senseless to release such prisoners and hence indefinite or indeterminate sentences are most likely to be effective from the points of view of rehabilitation and safety of society.

Lowenstein (1989) found that only 6 per cent of rapists who were treated reoffended but that the recidivism rate for those who did not receive treatment was 38 per cent.

One must be aware of the strong and complex obsessive compulsive aspects related to most rapes and other sexual offences. Obsessive elements are also found in substance abusers, other drug addicts, alcoholics and many criminally inclined individuals.

In order to reduce inhibitions, rapists frequently carry out their offences while under the influence of alcohol and/or drugs. This often combines with their inability to process interpersonal cues from women, especially those who say "no" to their advances, Lipton *et al* (1987). It is in this area that therapy must take an active part by using such techniques as role-playing behaviour (Scully, 1988) and obtain the *in vivo* reactions of women to acts of rape or forced seduction. The rapist must learn to distinguish between females who are for instance friendly and those who actively seek sexual contact, of which there may be very few.

Many rapists tend to forget or ignore the potential punishment of long-term imprisonment for miscalculating female responses or over-reacting to mild responses that they deem to be provocative sexual demeanour. This is possibly because they are overwhelmed by their own sexual and aggressive desires and fail to recognize negative signals from the female, rushing towards what is more than likely mutual disaster and tragedy.

Bestiosexuality

Bestiosexuality is the use of an animal as a sexual object.

Causes

1. Prohibitions such as fear or dislike of women. Dullards who feel they are unattractive to women may indulge in this behaviour.

2. The animal may be used as a maternal substitute to avoid the Oedipus situation which a woman would evoke. This is a Freudian theory.
3. Emotional immaturity, low moral sense and sadism may influence this crime.

Case 21: A man pleaded guilty to an offence involving an animal. His intelligence quotient was estimated at 84 on the Wechsler Adult Intelligence Scale.

His history revealed that he had been well cared for by his parents during childhood. He was a premature baby and the youngest but one of several children. He did not have control of micturition by day or night until he was seven years old. He suffered from rickets during childhood. He attended a special school for the educationally backward but was asked to leave after two months because he was considered to have an undesirable influence on the other children and his personal habits were faulty. His behaviour did not improve as a result of a period of attendance at an adolescent psychiatric unit.

He was 12 years old when his father died and his mother had a "nervous breakdown" as a result of her bereavement. He continued to live with his widowed mother but she was unable to influence his behaviour. Her health deteriorated. The offender was cared for by the local authorities from the age of nine to 11 years. His law-breaking commenced during this period. He was convicted of taking and driving away three motor vehicles and subsequently spent two years in approved school where he was ridiculed by fellow inmates because of his appearance. He stabbed a young girl in the chest with a carving knife during his stay. The victim was a relative of a member of the school staff by whom the accused was under the mistaken impression that he had been unjustly treated. The girl recovered from her injuries and her assailant was transferred to a special hospital under s.8 of the Mental Deficiency Act 1913. He was discharged from the latter hospital after ten years on the advice of a Mental Health Review Tribunal. He subsequently held a number of labouring jobs but was regarded as a poor workman. He was sentenced to 18 months' imprisonment for "assault occasioning actual bodily harm" about two years after discharge from the special hospital and he committed the offence involving the animal after serving this sentence. He was polite and well behaved during the remand period. Psychiatric examination did not reveal evidence of psychosis. The accused expressed marked inferiority feelings. He did not express remorse and his history indicated that he was apparently unable to profit by experience.

He was diagnosed as a sexually perverted psychopathic dullard but he did not suffer from a mental disorder within the meaning of the Mental Health Act 1959. He was sentenced to imprisonment for several years.

Management of Sexual Deviation

If sexual perversion is secondary to mental disorder the latter must be treated in the first instance.

Sex deviants seldom seek medical advice unless they fall foul of the law. A prison sentence may not deter a deviant from committing further offences. Various treatments may be implemented within the framework of the prison service or by community psychiatric services.

Psychotherapy

(1)   Explanation, education and reassurance;
(2)   manipulation of environment;
(3)   suggestion, including hypnosis and persuasion;
(4)   superficial analysis;
(5)   deep transference analysis; and
(6)   sublimation.

Sexual deviation may be due more to nurture than to nature. When the normal sexual outlet is frustrated, the sexual impulses may regress and seek expression in ways abandoned many years previously.

Endogenous depression may release primitive impulses which may be expressed in sexually perverted behaviour which is treated by treating the depression.

Bieber *et al* (1962) indicated that analytical psychotherapy is appropriate treatment for sex criminals in general. Compulsive sex offenders respond poorly to direct suggestion and hypnosis. Sex deviants seldom achieve full sexual satisfaction and they are therefore in a state of constant erotic tension. *Rapists and paedophiliacs may have a compulsion to molest women and corrupt children but they are usually capable of avoiding temptation if they so choose.*

Psychotherapy may prove difficult because the deviant derives pleasure from his perversion and therefore desire for cure may be ambivalent.

There are five essentials of analytically orientated psychotherapy:

1.   The patient must be encouraged to admit freely his sexual difficulties.

2.   The therapist must provide a background of complete acceptance and emotional security against which the patient can mature.
3.   He must be helped to gain some understanding of the origin of his symptoms.
4.   Feelings of isolation, fear, guilt, inferiority and lack of confidence must be counteracted.
5.   The transference situation must be analysed.

The patient first tends to identify the therapist with a Judge or disapproving parent and negative transference is established. Affection for the therapist is later developed and positive transference is established. This positive transference must be eventually terminated by encouraging the patient to make other and more advantageous relationships outside the therapeutic situation where he can give and receive affection freely and correct his own wrong judgments of people.

Explanation and reassurance are used to reduce anxiety and stress experienced in attempting to establish heterosexual relationships. The subject is helped to strengthen mental imagery in heterosexual terms.

Problems arise in psychotherapy because homosexuals have the usual spectrum of personality types and defects such as cyclothymia, neurotic, schizoid and psychopathic personality traits. The psychotherapist may have to settle for control rather than cure. Field and Williams (1971) conclude that psychotherapy has no practical value for the sexual offender as judged by the reduction in reconviction rate.

Imaginal Covert Sensitization is another form of psychotherapy. Each session commences with relaxation training when the patient is asked to imagine a series of events leading to the hypothetical maladaptive (sexual) behaviour. He then imagines that he has a strong urge to perpetrate this target behaviour. He is also then instructed to form mental images of the consequences of this type of behaviour, for example public disgrace and possible poverty for himself and family, being shunned by former friends, imprisonment under difficult conditions, little hope of future employment, etc. These images must be accompanied by feelings of guilt, remorse, despondency, fear, anxiety and apprehension for the future. Finally, the patient is advised to resist the urge to commit the target behaviour and consequently experience feelings of relief, happiness and self-satisfaction. The object is to correct the distorted thought patterns and attitudes to sex which influence the perpetration of sexual offences and also to make the offenders realize the effects on their victims. This realization and insight must be emotional as well as intellectual. Memory images are freely used in this therapy and auto-suggestion is vital.

The patient must be sincere in his desire to mend his ways and persist in implementing the above instructions. Consequently, sexual psychopaths would not respond.

This is worthwhile treatment for sexual deviation because this condition has a strong imaginal component and a socially acceptable alternate response. This provides some reinforcement from the point of view of relapse-prevention, which is obviously most important and involves identifying the circumstances which "trigger off" the commission of these offences and teaching the offender to recognize and cope with the stress and anxiety associated with the temptations to relapse. Appropriately modified group therapy and psychodrama may also be helpful. Simulated responses with the object of gaining early release, must be constantly suspected.

Conditioning

The principle of aversion therapy is to make a specific, pleasant experience unpleasant, so as to discouage tendencies to repeat the particular experience. Aversion therapy has been used mainly to treat homosexuality. Reassurance and persuasion are avoided in this type of treatment and reliance is placed on repeated association of the attractive object with an unpleasant stimulus resulting in an aversion to that object.

Chemical and electrical methods of aversion are employed. The injection of Apomorphine produces nausea and vomiting and electrical stimulation is used as an anxiety-producing stimulus. Mather (1966) expressed the opinion that the therapy most resistant to extinction is anticipatory avoidance where not only is the attractive object associated with the unpleasant stimulus but the subject has to perform a definite operant response such as turning a switch. The following is an example of the use of this type of conditioning treatment for paedophilia.

The treatment is explained to the patient who is then shown a series of slides of male children and adult females in various stages of undress, including nudity. He selects a number which have varying degrees of attractiveness and unattractiveness to him. He then lies on a bed in a darkened room and watches a screen upon which these slides are shown. The slide first used is that of the male child which the patient selected as only mildly attractive, and he has in his hand a switch by means of which he can remove this slide from the screen. If after eight seconds he has not removed it, he receives an electric shock which had previously proved unpleasant to him. The shock continues until he presses the switch to remove the slide. In an endeavour to make adult females more attractive, relief from anxiety is associated with the immediate presentation of the slide of the adult female least unattractive to him as soon as the slide of the male child has been removed. Slide-showing proceeds in such a manner as eventually to condition the patient to prefer the least attractive adult female to the most attractive male child. Each treatment session lasts about 20 minutes and 25 appropriate slide presentations are made. Inpatients receive two sessions daily and out-patients according to their own convenience. The number of sessions varies from ten to 30 depending upon response.

Hormones
Storr (1964) expressed the opinion that prolonged administration of oestrogens may affect many human functions besides sexual behaviour and may also do irreparable damage to other endocrine glands. Consequently, he concluded that the use of oestrogens and similar compounds to lower the sexual responsiveness of the male may amount to malpractice.

Hormonal therapy would be appropriate in certain compulsive forms of deviant behaviour such as paedophilia but it is generally accepted that this form of treatment is contraindicated in the case of homosexual behaviour between consenting adults. Under the Sexual Offences Act 1967 the latter type of behaviour is not criminal. *Therapy with oestrogens, Benperidol and Cyproterone acetate will reduce the strength of the sexual drive but will not change its direction.* It is recognized that homosexuality, and other forms of sexual deviation, are not merely ways of obtaining sexual gratification, but also subserve the deviant individual's need for companionship, admiration or even restoration of self-esteem by inviting punishment. These emotional needs are not likely to be profoundly altered by reduction of sexual drive. Hormonal treatment may not be effective when the deviant is also psychopathic because he cannot be relied upon to report the effects accurately and may discontinue treatment without permission. Furthermore, the oral dose of Stilboestrol sufficient to inhibit libido usually provides an unacceptable degree of nausea and gives an excuse for discontinuing treatment.

Field and Williams (1970) advocated subcutaneous implants of

Oestradiol BPC (100 mg.) for certain types of offenders. The criteria of selection were:

1. The subjective certainty of reconviction if no help is given.
2. Objective estimation that the previous history would strongly suggest the probability of reconviction.
3. Objective estimation that the intelligence level, oral facility and education are too limited for psychotherapy to be beneficial.
4. The likelihood that the next sentence would be a long one.
5. Uncontrollable impulses involving male children or females of any age.
6. He should be physically fit with no history of jaundice or neoplasm.

Implants were given to 25 inmates and a control group of 40 got a placebo. The study was carried out over a two-year period. All 65 inmates were sexual offenders. The results of the study are listed in Table XIX.

Progress was judged by the effects of the Oestradiol on the frequency of masturbation and the ability to obtain spontaneous erection as the result of attempted masturbation or fantasy. The success of treatment depends upon co-operation and the inmates must understand that the treatment will not necessarily influence release dates.

Table XIX

	Control group	Implant group
Convicted subsequently of sex offences	10	1
Reconvicted of non-sex offences	7	8
Not reconvicted of sexual offences	23	16

Sex deviants convicted of murder or manslaughter were excluded from this study because they would be highly motivated to exaggerate the effects of the treatment with the object of gaining early release.

Stilboestrol may be given by mouth in a dose of 5 mg. daily until the strength of the sex drive is adequately reduced and 1 mg. maintenance dosage daily is then sufficient. Slight hypertrophy of the breasts indicates reduction of sexual activity. Testicular underactivity is eventually induced. Stilboestrol treatment may be very successful when applied to the hypersexed male who frequently engages in all sorts of normal and abnormal sexual behaviour and experiences continuous intense sexual fantasy. These individuals appreciate treatment but dosage should be adjusted to allow some sexual activity.

Field and Williams (1971) judged progress of hormonal therapy by assessing sexual responsiveness using a polygraph to measure penile volume, sweat gland activity as indicated by galvanic skin resistance, blood pressure, cardiac activity, respiration rate and forearm blood flow. They then monitored the effect of the Oestradiol implant so that an objective conclusion could be eventually reached to the effect that a patient no longer responds to a sexual stimulus. This method obviates errors likely to arise from depending on subjective reporting by a prisoner serving a long sentence. *This procedure does not help to decide when a sexual offender who has committed a serious offence may be safely released.* The view may be taken that such men should be detained until physiological waning of the sex drive occurs in old age.

Benperidol is a synthetic neuroleptic drug with properties similar to those of Haloperidol. It is relatively non-toxic. This drug was given to 28 paedophiliacs who were carefully selected on the basis of their intelligence, co-operation and stability (Field and Williams, 1973). The Benperidol dose varied from 1/2 to 1 mg. daily. Mild Parkinsonism was controlled by Disipal 50 mg. twice daily. All 28 experienced abolition of sexual desires and inability to obtain erections. This preliminary trial lasted two years.

Reports indicate that Cyproterone acetate (Androcur) may be more effective than oestrogens in controlling sexual drive. This drug is described as specially anti-androgenic as indicated by experiments on rats, and administration to humans does not cause any significant undesirable effects such as gynaecomastia which occurs as a complication of oestrogen therapy. Cyproterone acetate is used in the treatment of sexual exhibitionism, excessive masturbation and paedophilia. The oral dose varies from 100 to 200 mg. daily until control is established when the dose is reduced by 25 to 50 mg. every three or four weeks until the optimum maintenance dose is reached. Long-acting intramuscular injections of Cyproterone acetate are available in oily solutions containing 300 to 600 mg. The injections are given at two-weekly intervals. The contraindications to therapy with Androcur include acute liver disease, diabetes mellitus, thrombosis, embolism, neoplasm, wasting diseases, incomplete bone maturation and incomplete testicular development in immature youths. Androcur should not be given to a sex deviant who is severely depressed because deprivation of his sexual outlet may preciptiate suicide. Alcohol should be avoided with this therapy because reduction of volition may cause the subject to discontinue treatment. Periodic checks of haemoglobin and spermatogenesis should be made.

Surgery

Storr (1964) indicated that castration is fairly extensively carried out on sexual recidivists, especially in Scandinavia. However, adult males who have been castrated may still remain capable of erection and orgasm and the operation does not invariably prevent repetition of sexual offences. Castration is carried out with the consent of the subject in most countries and this consent is often influenced by promises of earlier release from prison or hospital. Some castrated individuals remain embittered and resentful.

The willingness of the offender to co-operate is an essential factor in all attempts to modify sexual behaviour. Reluctant consent given as a result of unfair pressure does not amount to full and free co-operation. Castration was made legally compulsory in Germany for sexual recidivists and individuals with certain hereditary defects but the results were worse than those achieved in Scandinavia.

Storr (1964) also stated that medical or surgical treatment will not necessarily result in the disappearance of certain criminal compulsive forms of deviant sexual behaviour. Castration has no therapeutic effect on psychosis, neurosis, psychopathy or epilepsy, all of which may be associated with sexual deviation. Psychosis may even be precipitated by the operation. Inferiority feelings may be increased after castration and male sex hormones may be illegally obtained to restore sexual drive. The desired reduction of sexual drive may not be established for *six months* after the operation.

Bremer (1959) reported persistence of sexual potency from one to 16 years in 13 of 157 castrated persons. Of 900 men castrated in Denmark between 1929 and 1959, 10 committed sex crimes after the operation. The average relapse rate is 2 per cent. Of 284 castrated in Herstedvester between 1935 and 1967, five committed suicide within five years of their operations (Sturup, 1968). Sturup also indicated that few sex criminals regretted castration. Physical changes included weight gain. Roeder (1970) advocated hypothalamotomy for paedophilia and reported good results in seven out of 11 homosexuals who were mainly paedophiliacs.

Roeder believes that homosexuality results from faulty brain programming due to a severe androgen deficiency in early infancy. His treatment consists of destroying with a series of electrical burns most of Cajal's nucleus which occupies an area measuring about one centemetre in the hypothalamus. Stereotaxic guidance and radiological control are used to facilitate the operation. It is claimed that the subject is "vastly relieved" and often able to resume a normal adult heterosexual role in society. Early treatment gives the best results and hypothalamotomy is an alternative to surgical or chemical castration which may result in loss of self-esteem and confidence and often profound depression. There are metabolic side effects such as eunuchoid obesity or diabetes insipidus. These findings have been supported in East Germany where 17,000 complaints of sex crimes against children and juveniles are reported every year. British reaction to this treatment has not been enthusiastic. Hypothalamotomy is also said to help lesbians alleged to have had androgen excess in early infancy and who wish to become heterosexual.

Hypothalamotomy is a form of stereotaxic surgery which enables small areas of nervous tissue to be accurately located and destroyed and the desired physiological changes are produced with minimal side effects. It has been successfully employed in the treatment of certain psychiatric disorders and the relief of Parkinsonian tremor and has limited application in the relief of intractable pain and the control of aggressive behaviour. Stereotaxic surgery has also been used to control aggressive behaviour in epilepsy and schizophrenia and destruction of the centro-medical hypothalmic nucleus on the non-dominant side gives the best results.

Three male patients had hypothalamotomy for repeated homosexual offences with pubertal boys. There was a distinct and sustained reduction in the level of sexual drive after the operation and complete abolition of homosexual tendencies in two of the patients and substantial reduction in the third. No post-operative metabolic, endocrine or autonomic disturbances were noted. During the follow-up period, which lasted three months, six months and seven years respectively, a marked improvement in emotional well-being and social adjustment was observed, and no further sexual offences were recorded.

Surgical treatments are based upon animal experimentation.

Consent forms should be signed for surgical and hormonal treatments and the rationale of any particular form of treatment explained to interested parties.

The results of treatment of sexual deviation should be satisfactory from the therapeutic, judicial and administrative points of view.

The Home Secretary (1991) announced new initiatives with the object of reforming jailed sex offenders who are a danger to the public. There are about 3,000 sex offenders imprisoned in England and Wales at any particular time and about a third of these are serving sentences of less than four years. About 20 per cent of sex offenders re-offend after release. Sex offenders will be concentrated in about 20 of 125 prisons. Those serving more than four years and assessed as high-risk offenders may also be psychopathic and will be sent to one of six designated prisons where they will receive extended treatment for up to 18 months.

Sex offenders are called "nonces" by prisoners serving sentences for other crimes and they are despised. Segregation under Rule 43 could make them feel persecuted and influence them not to accept guilt. It could also increase their deviant tendencies and focus self-pity on themselves rather than on what they did to their victims. The majority of the offenders request Rule 43 from the Governor who may also order segregation of a minority if he thinks fit. Persons so located are locked in cells for most of their time for their own protection.

Locating these people exclusively on prison wings would be more satisfactory but to some extent they would still be segregated although they would spend less time in their cells. Those who attempt suicide would be admitted to the prison hospital. Successful treatment does not depend on therapy per se but also on the cooperation of prison staff (male and female), psychologists, ministers of religion, psychiatrists, relatives and prison visitors. Probation officers and social workers in association with specialist hostels in the community, have vital roles to play in the context of supervision after release. Co-ordination is also needed between the National Health Service, the National Association for the Care and Resettlement of Offenders, the Richmond Fellowship, and the Prison Reform Trust.

An amendment to the Criminal Justice Bill 1991 provides for released sex offenders to receive additional supervision above that given to other offenders. Adequate funding for all concerned is absolutely essential.

Post-Traumatic Stress Disorder (PTSD)

This disease has received much attention in recent years but whereas there is no shortage of literature dealing with the causes of the condition, symptomatology and prognosis, there seems to be a scarcity of studies dealing with specific treatments. The PTSD consists of three sets of varying types of symptomatology, all of which may not be experienced by any particular individual at any particular time. Reference is made to it in this chapter because victims of sexual offences may suffer from this condition.

(i) Recurrent conscious memory images, dreams and nightmares relevant to the traumatic occurrences. Also insomnia of varying degrees.

(ii) Relative disinterest in environment and a feeling of being detached from people in it. Change in personality is also indicated by loss of interest in activities which were regarded as important prior to the trauma.

(iii) Neurotic symptoms such as feelings of tension, excessive anxiety and irritability. Also unpredictable impulsive episodes of verbal and physical aggression against persons and property. Depression of varying degree and suicidal tendencies are also experienced. Hearst *et al* (1986), as a result of a study covering the years 1974-83, discovered an increase in the suicide rate amongst soldiers who had served in Vietnam in comparison with those who had served elsewhere. Wolf *et al* (1988) indicated that a high incidence of head injury was reported in Vietnam veterans who suffered from this disorder but electroencephalographic studies gave unexpectedly normal results. Psychosomatic symptoms such as chest pains, breathlessness at rest and gastro-intestinal upsets in the absence of organic disease, also occurred. Defective concentration and memory, distractability and feelings of guilt even to the extent of regret for surviving the war. Jensen *et al* (1982) reported cortical atrophy and dementia in a number of young men who had been tortured. Marital and occupational problems and gross indecision concerning life objectives were noted. Finally, excess alcohol and illicit drug-taking were noted.

A joint meeting was convened in 1988 between United States and Soviet veterans of the Vietnam and Afghanistan wars respectively. The Soviet soldiers on returning to their homeland, complained that their friends and even relatives tended to treat them unsympathetically and became embarrassed when they tried to discuss their war experiences. They were even told that they were not entitled to wear medals "legitimately" awarded for the Afghan campaign probably because the Russian people were deliberately kept in ignorance of the war in Afghanistan until comparatively recently. The Soviet veterans were also emotionally disturbed and unsettled in civilian life. They experienced undue anxiety, despondency, nightmares and other symptoms of the PTSD. Their divorce rates were distinctly higher than in other members of the population and impaired ability to persist in civilian employment was also evident. Some joined neo-fascist groups and others indulged in alcohol and drug abuse. The USA veterans on the whole fared similarly.

The post-traumatic stress disorder may be the result of any one of a number of events causing severe mental anguish such as the combat stress syndrome, hijacking on land, sea or air, brainwashing, concentration camp torture, *rape* and transportation disasters of road, rail, air or sea. The survivors of nuclear, bacteriological or chemical warfare could also be affected. Hodgkinson (1988) investigated post-disaster morbidity of Transportation Mass Disasters (TMD), which occur without warning. He reported shock, sense of isolation, and disorientation, feelings of helplessness, anger and future phobic avoidance of the situation in which the stress occurred. The anger tended to be relieved by litigation. Furthermore, long-term psychological disturbances were noted in survivors, bereaved relatives and recovery teams and the figure in this context for maritime disasters was estimated at 71 per cent (Henderson and Bostock 1977). Some members of the various services who attend major accidents may themselves develop the PTSD and need treatment. The children of murdered parents are also subject to this condition.

The first symptoms of PTSD may begin at the material time or after a varying latent period. In the context of battle, the disorder may be regarded as an extension of the combat stress reaction and cannot be diagnosed in the absence of the latter. There is also an obvious connection between the PTSD and the Chronic Identity Diffusion Crisis.

Treatment of PTSD
Victims of the Post-Traumatic Stress Disorder will need psychiatric help. Young people whose personalities are in the process of maturation but not yet "set" at the time of the trauma and who return to an unstable home environment, suffer most. Victims may have been injected with sedatives and females may have undergone sexual interference or even rape. Consequently, investigations such as taking blood, vaginal examinations and electroencephalograms should be kept to a minimum as they remind

patients of the terrifying experiences which they have undergone.

In 1980, a centre for the treatment and rehabilitation of brainwashed and other torture victims, was opened at Copenhagen University Hospital by Dr. Inge Kemp Genefke. Psychiatrists are assisted by psychologists, physiotherapists, social workers, physicians, surgeons, dentists and also financial and legal advisers. Similar centres have been established in Sweden, France, Australia, United States of America and the Philippines. It is surprising that such a centre has not been established in the United Kingdom by the Royal College of Psychiatrists but perhaps its priorities are elsewhere. The Medical Foundation for the Care of Victims of Torture is located at the National Temperance Hospital, Hampstead, London. This centre is quite independent of the Royal College and depends on voluntary donations. Some 500 torture victims were treated there in 1988. The accent is on initial psychiatric assessment and psychotherapy.

Social rehabilitation of victims and their families, including marital therapy, is essential because the whole range of interpersonal relationships are affected in the PTSD. Consequently, holistic psychology has some relevance in treatment. Individual psychotherapy is important for those who suffer from PTSD. Individual patients do best when treated by the same psychiatrist or psychologist. Treatment should be mainly concerned with the victim's personality rather than the trauma *per se*.

The various forms of *psychotherapy* as described under sexual deviation, are applicable (with appropriate modifications) to the PTSD in order to reduce anxiety and stress.

Maciejewska (1987) divided the post-torture psychological symptoms into mood disorders of consciousness involving impairment of intelligence and concentration, and psychosomatic disorders.

Although torture is only one cause of the PTSD it has a distinctive personal content, namely the infliction of pain by one person or another. Consequently, humiliation is an important symptom and also a fear of being disbelieved which may be counteracted by a sympathetic initial pre-treatment physical examination. Every physical scar has its emotional scar. If the victim is an exile, feelings of futility are aggravated by unemployment and inadequate housing.

The object of psychotherapy is to reactivate his or her innate psychological regenerative processes which torturers invariably try to undermine. Communicating with or helping to care for other torture victims, invariably gives relief.

Individual psychotherapy may be combined with group therapy depending on the patient's personality. Group therapy is based on the fact that most people care what others think of them. There are four main issues:

1. The establishment of group cohesion. The group should not be too large and confidentiality is favoured if group members do not change from week to week until therapy is completed. Such an arrangement is referred to as closed-group membership. The group leader should ensure that members take the group seriously and commit themselves to it by not being late for meetings and not forgetting to attend. Group cohesion also means that the members have a sense of purpose. Conflicts between group members mirror those which occur in the community and are ventilated by the group leader sometimes called the "facilitator". Such disagreements are fully discussed in the group and appropriate advice given. Group members reinforce positive and good attitudes in each other by sharing experiences.
   A successful group must be balanced out in the sense that all members must eventually become involved in discussions and the issues and problems that arise. Egos are deflated in balanced groups and arrogance and authoritarianism prevented. Allowance must be made for sensitivities and individual counselling may be a useful adjunct in building confidence in some group members. Group therapy may not be suitable at all for some people.

2. Setting goals avoids vagueness and gives a sense of purpose. Goals must be evaluated and their importance appreciated. A decision must initially be made as to what the group is trying to achieve. A PTSD victim must achieve some very important *new learning* and consequently appropriate therapy must have maximum impact in a comparatively short space of time. Goals are essential even if group discussions are "fluid", meaning free and relatively undirected. Extroverts will tend to dominate static groups and the group leader must prevent "bogging down" on certain issues. Group members also learn not to put their own interests before those of other members.
   A group should consist of not more than eight participants and therapy last for 8-12 weeks.

3. Group members give feedback of information to each other. A member may discuss his own behaviour problems and reasons, for example as to why he did not attempt to rescue a fellow passenger at the time of a transport disaster. A favourable and encouraging group reaction will help an individual member to despise himself less and obtain a new perception of himself. Feelings are shared and individuals learn not to be intimidated by the behaviour of others.

   The group leader feeds back problems recognized during group discussions. Such problems would include issues raised, whether discussion was free, degree of co-operation of group members and whether the right things were discussed.

4. The group must provide opportunities for *learning and practising new behaviour*. Group experiences must have the effect of altering attitudes for the better.

   Psychodrama as a form of group therapy is also helpful for its abreactive element when patients are encouraged to act out their traumatic experiences. Marks (1987) indicated that phobic symptoms are common features of the PTSD especially after torture. The following treatments may also be successful:

   (i)   Desensitization in the form of gradual exposure for progressively longer periods to stimuli designed to reinduce anxiety and fear because these symptoms were originally associated with his or her torture situations. Such stimuli could be the sight of judges, courtrooms, police stations, prisons, police officers and/or army personnel at first in the form of photographs and later in reality. The anxiety and fear will progressively subside and the patient will learn to tolerate same with automatic elimination of the phobic symptoms. This treatment must be accompanied by individual psychotherapy.

   (ii) Fantasy desensitization using appropriate memory images related to the cause of the PTSD and under the guidance of a psychotherapist.

A specific treatment for the PTSD has not as yet been found due, to some extent, to scarcity of controlled studies, in turn due to failure of patients to understand the purpose of the studies with the resulting risk of loss of confidence in therapists.

However, there are few treatments in the whole range of psychiatry which are specific to any particular form of mental disorder. Carbamazepine (Tegretol), decreases agitation, angry outbursts and poor impulse control. Propranolol may have similar effects and Imipramine (Tofranil) usually alleviates the depressive element and prevents panic in the PTSD.

References

Allen, C., 1961, *A Textbook of Psychosexual Disorders*, Oxford University Press, London, 7.104; 8.150.

Archbold, 1969, *Pleading, Evidence, and Practices in Criminal Cases.* Cmnd 2789. HMSO, London.

Arnold, R.P., Rogers, D., Cook, D.A.G. (1990) "Medical Problems of Adults who were Sexually Abused in Childhood", *Brit. Med. J.* 300: 405-8.

Bieber, I., et al (1962) *Homosexuality: A Psychoanalytical Study of Male Homosexuals*, Basic Books, New York, p.220.

Bremer, J. (1959), *Asexualization: A Follow-up Study*, Macmillan, London.

Cerce, D.D., Knight, R.A., Bard, L.A., Carter, D.L., Rosenberg, R., Schneider, B., (1985) "A Descriptive Study of Rapists and Child Molesters: Developmental, Clinical and Criminal Characteristics", *Criminal Justice Behaviour,* U.S.A.

Criminal Statistics (England and Wales) (1988), Home Office, Cm 847, HMSO, London.

Curran, D. and Parr, D. (1957) "Homosexuality: Analysis of 100 Male Cases seen in Private Practice", *Brit. Med. J.* 1: 797.

East, W.N. (1924) "Observations on Exhibitionism", *Lancet* 2: 370-375.

Enelow, M.L. (1965) in *Sexual Behaviour and the Law*, (Slovenko, R. ed.) Charles C. Thomas, Springfield, 749. Illinois.

Epstein, A.W. (1961) *J. Nervous and Ment. Dis.* 133-247.

Field, L.H. and Williams, M. (1970) "The Hormonal Treatment of Sexual Offenders", *Med., Sci., Law* 10: 27.
(1971) "A Note on the Scientific Assessment and Treatment of the Sexual Offender", *Med., Sci., Law* 11: 180.
(1973) "Benperidol in the Treatment of Sexual Offenders", *Med., Sci., Law* 13: 195.

Foreman, B.D. (1982) "Reported Male Rape", *Victimology: An International Journal* 7: 1-14.

Gartner, A.F., Gartner, J. (1988) *Borderline Pathology in Post-Incest Female Adolescents*, The Menninger Foundation, Taylor Manor Hospital, College Avenue, Ellicott City, U.S.A.

Gebhard, P.H., Gagnon, J.H., Pomeroy, W.B., Christenson, C.V. (1965) *Sex Offenders: An Analysis of the Types*, Harper and Row, New York.

Grubin, D., Gunn, J. (1990) *The Imprisoned Rapist and Rape*, Dept. of Forensic Psychiatry, Institute of Psychiatry, London. Pub. Home Office, London.

Hamer, D.H., Hu, S., Pattatucci, A.M.L. (1993) "A linkage between D.N.A., D.N.A. markers on the X chromosome and male sexual orientation"., *Science*, 261: 321-7.

Hearst, N., Newman, T.B., Hully, S.B. (1986) "Delayed Effects of the Military Draft on Mortality", *New England Journal of Medicine*, Vol. 314: 620-4.

Henderson, A.S., Bostock, F.T. (1977) "Coping behaviour after shipwreck", *Brit. J. Psych.* 131: 15-26.

Hodgkinson, P.E. (1988) "Psychological Aftereffects of Transportation Disasters", *J. Med. Sci. Law,* Vol. 28 4: 304-8.

Jensen, T.S., et al. (1982) "Cerebral Atrophy in Young Torture Victims", *N. Engl. J. Med.,* 30 (7): 1341.

King, M.B. (1990) "Male Rape", *Brit. Med. J.* 301: 1345-6.

Kinsey, A.C., Pomeroy, W.B. and Martin, C.E. (1948) *Sexual Behaviour in the Human Male*, Philadelphia Press, Philadelphia.

Kosky, R. (1987) *Australian and New Zealand Journal of Psychiatry*, 21: 430-440.

Lipton, D.N., McDonel, E.C., Mcfall, R.M. (1987) "Heterosocial Perception in Rapists". *J. Consulting and Clinical Psychology.* Vol. 55(1): 17-21.

Lisak, D., Roth, S. (1988) "Motivational Factors in Nonincarcerated Sexually Aggressive Men", *Journal of Personality and Social Psychology* 55, 5: 795-802.

Lowenstein, L.F. (1989) "Understanding and Treating the Rapist". *Criminologist*, Vol. 13: 196-205. Also *Personal Communication,* 1992.

Lukianowicz, N. (1972) "Incest. I. Paternal Incest", *Brit. J. Psych.* 120: 301.

Maciejewska, K., *The Independent*, September 1, 1987.

Mackay, R.D. (1990) "Dangerous Patients" "Third Party Safety" "Psychiatrists Duties" "Walking the Tarasoff Tightrope", *Med. Sci. Law.*, V.30 ps. 52-56.

Marks, I.M., 1987, *Fears, Phobias and Rituals,* Oxford University Press, New York.

Masters, B. (1993) *The Shrine of Jeffrey Dahmer*, Pub. by Hodder and Stoughton Ltd., London

Mather, N.J. de V. (1966) "The Treatment of Homosexuality by Aversion Therapy", *Med., Sci., Law* 6: 200-205.

Nasjleti, M. (1980) "Suffering in Silence: The Male Incest Victim", *Child Welfare* 59: 269-75.

Prentky, R., Cohen, M., Seghorn, T.(1985) *Bull. Am. Acad. Psychiatric Law* 13, 1: 39-43.

Radzinowicz, L. and Turner, J.W.C., (1957) *English Studies in Criminal Science (Sexual Offences),*Vol. 9, Oxford University Press, London.

Randall, J.B. (1959) "Transvestism and Transexuality: A Study of 50 Cases", *Brit. Med. J.* 2: 1448.

Raskin, D. (1984) "Diagnosis in Patients with Chronic Pelvic Pain", *Am. J. Psychiatry* 141: 824.

Rees, M. (1990) *Internat. J. of S.T.D. and AIDS,* vol. 1, pp. 10-17, Royal Soc. Med. Services, London.

Richards, A.K. (1989) "A Romance with Pain: A Telephone Perversion in a Woman", *Int. J. Psycho-Anal.* Institute of Psychoanalysis, London.

Roberts, D.F. (1967) "Incest, Inbreeding and Mental Abilities", *Brit. Med. J.* 4: 336.

Roeder, K. (1970) "Report by a Scandinavian Correspondent", *World Medicine* 6: 42.

Rosen, L. (Ed) (1964) *The Pathology and Treatment of Sexual Deviation,* Oxford University Press, London.

Scully, D., (1988) "Convicted Rapists' Perceptions of Self and Victim: Role-Taking and Emotions", *Gender and Society*, Vol. 2(2): 200-213.

Seemanova, E. (1971) "A Study of Incestuous Mating", *Hum. Hered.* 21: 108-28.

Silverman, M. (1982) "The Voice of Conscience and the Sounds of the Analytic Hour". *Psychoanal. Q.*, 51: 196-217.

Storr, G.A. (1964) *The Pathology and Treatment of Sexual Deviation*, Rosen, L., (ed.) Oxford University Press, London.

Sturup, G.K. (1968) "Treatment of Sexual Offenders in Herstedvester, Denmark: The Rapists", *Acta Psychiatrica et Neurologica Scandinavica*, Supplement 204: 44.

Uniform Crime Reports, 1974, Federal Bureau of Investigation, Washington.

West, D.W. (1974) "Homosexuality", *New Psychiatry* 1: 22.

Williams, A.H. (1965) *Sexual Behaviour and the Law*, (Slovenkar, Chas. C. Thomas ed.) Springfield, 111: Illinois.

Williams, J.E. (1974) "The Neglect of Incest", *Med. Sci. Law* 14: 64.

Wolf, M.E., Alavi, A., Mosnaim, A.D. (1988) "Post Traumatic Stress Disorder", *Biological Psychiatry* 23: 642-644, Pub. Society of Biological Psychiatry, U.S.A.

Wydra, A., Marshall, W.L., Earls, C.M., Barbaree, H.E. (1983) "Identification of Cues and Control of Sexual Arousal by Rapists", *Behaviour, Research and Therapy* 21, 5: 477-483.

CHAPTER IX

Psychosis and Crime

The symptoms, prognosis and treatment of the common psychoses may be found in any standard textbook on psychiatry and I do not intend to deal with these matters in this section. Symptoms will be referred to, but only in the context of forensic psychiatry. I include epilepsy in this chapter because individuals in a state of epileptic fugue, automatism or furore are virtually psychotic and a link has been established between epilepsy and schizophrenia. Clinical descriptions of the various types of ictal episode will only be referred to in the context of the relationship between epilepsy and crime. I will not include management and medication for epileptics, which may also be found in relevant textbooks.

Paranoid Psychosis

Henderson and Batchelor (1961) expressed the view that paranoid schizophrenia is a misnomer and should not be grouped with the schizophrenic disorders. Paranoid delusions may form part of the symptomatology of any functional mental disorder or one secondary to organic cerebral pathology, but these delusions *per se* apparently constitute the disease and are due to defects of judgment and reasoning.

The term paranoid psychosis would of course include paranoid schizophrenia and paranoia. I refer to paranoia in the remainder of this section because I have examined a number of individuals suffering from this monodelusional condition who committed homicide. This is not to deny that the paranoiac may in time develop symptoms of frank (paranoid) schizophrenia.

Clinical experience does not confirm Bleuler's view (1926) that the paranoiac does not become a danger to others. Bleuler also believed that the paranoid trait of morbid suspiciousness did not constitute an emotion. "Suspiciousness" is an idea which is invariably accompanied by the unpleasant emotions of fear, apprehension and anxiety.

Freud (1911) regarded the paranoiac as a "latent" homosexual who developed a hatred for the object of his homosexual desires, because of an inability to accept the consequences of his sexual propensities. The mental mechanism of "projection" is alleged to play a prominent part in the development of delusions of persecution. However, this theory would not explain hatred of a male paranoiac for a member of the opposite sex. I doubt if any psychotic illness can be explained exclusively on the basis of "mental mechanisms" and hereditary factors may be more important aetiologically.

Mowat (1966) studied a group of male and female psychotics who had been convicted of murder and found that the males had been deluded for an average period of 4.53 years before perpetrating the homicides and the corresponding figures for the female group was 9.04 years. Mowat carried out another investigation in order to discover the incidence of paranoia amongst a group of 116 patients in a special hospital. Seventy-one of these patients had been convicted of murder and 39 of attempted murder. Both sexes were represented in the study but only seven of the total group were considered to be "monodelusional" and presumably suffering from paranoia.

Paranoia develops insidiously over a period of years and the diagnosis is usually made in the fourth or fifth decade. Signs and symptoms of the psychosis usually become apparent when "triggered off" by some environmental occurrence which intensifies already established resentment for a person or persons. An individual who misinterprets suspicious circumstances is not deluded, but a delusional distortion of suspicious circumstances would constitute a psychosis. False memories which fit in with the delusional system may be present but hallucinations are not experienced. Intellect is preserved and memory is often superlative. An obsessional element tends to hold the personality together but not for an unlimited period of time.

The word paranoia was first used by Kahlbaum in 1863 and the diagnosis is based upon an assumption that the subject is deluded. Taylor (1966) described a delusion as "an absolute conviction of truth of a proposition which is idiosyncratic, ego-involved, incorrigible and often preoccupying". "Idiosyncratic" means that the false belief is not shared by other members of the same social class and delusion is thus distinguished from a prejudice. Taylor also believes that psychotic delusions possess the quality of "incorrigibility" and that they cannot be eradicated or diminished in intensity by physical punishments or persuasion to the contrary. The same author refers to a delusion as characterized by "ego-involvement", meaning that the false beliefs are "infused with a sense of great personal importance and refer to realities with which the patient's ego is closely concerned". The paranoiac suffers from a basic thought disorder which results in defective reasoning and judgment almost exclusively in relation to the delusional material with which he is obsessed. His judgment is subjectively biased and he is incapable of forming a rational opinion in regard to his delusional beliefs which would appear quite valid to the average "reasonable" person if the original premise was accepted as true. He usually attempts to find objective "proof" in order to satisfy himself that his delusions have some foundation in fact. Additional false beliefs may result from such attempts and Taylor refers to these as "self-verifying" delusions.

Hopwood (1927) makes the important observation that all delusional ideas are intrinsically absurd.

If the paranoiac succeeds in obtaining the eagerly sought "verification" of his partner's infidelity he may react with self-pity, aggression or conclude that the marital partner had named a false lover to ensure that the real object of her affections remained undetected.

Kraepelin (1920) referred to the paranoiac as suffering from a permanent and unshakeable delusional system, but I have noted several instances where the delusions were convincingly denied and feasible reasons given for such denials. These individuals were motivated by a belief that their verbal responses to questioning would result in personal advantages.

Case 22: A plea of diminished responsibility was accepted by a jury in the case of a middle-aged man who shot his sister-in-law and her husband in the erroneous belief that they were trying to break up his marriage. The plea was based on his suspicion concerning his wife's infidelity and he was also said to suffer from chronic anxiety. He did not suffer from epilepsy, alcoholism or mental subnormality, nor was there any history of previous psychiatric treatment. He had not been regarded as mentally ill by his family doctor, relatives, employers or friends at any time before committing of the crime. After the trial he denied all previous allegations concerning his wife's infidelity because he was told unofficially that he might be sent to Broadmoor. He served about 12 months of his life sentence and then developed symptoms of paranoid schizophrenia which necessitated transfer to a special hospital under s.72 of the Mental Health Act 1959 with restriction on discharge without limit of time. He had accused his wife of infidelity over a number of years and she eventually admitted that she had associated with other men in the hope that her husband would discontinue the frequent and intolerable accusations. The matter was further complicated by the fact that a female friend of the family had witnessed this "confession". She had in fact, never been unfaithful to her husband but her false admission caused much difficulty in deciding on the validity of some of his beliefs before and after sentence.

Taylor (1966) described how the paranoiac may "stage" an early recovery soon after admission to hospital but the delusions and morbid jealousies soon "return with a vengeance" if he is allowed to return home. The paranoid psychotic cannot usually feign sanity for more than a few weeks or months as intensity of emotion eventually overcomes intellect and volition. Apart from Taylor's original work on this subject, Mullen *et al* (1985) described a group of emotional disorders based on deep-seated jealousy which tended to dominate the victims' lives. I do not regard morbid and delusional jealousy as identical although the latter may develop from the former.

There is a long-standing view that when a paranoiac commits a serious crime he does so because of an impulse which was based upon a morbid type of affect and corresponding thought pattern. Presumably this morbid impulse is translated into action because volition is also disordered and criminal activity preferred. Paranoia is frequently characterized by periods of depression alternating with periods of elation and a crime of violence is more likely to occur during a depressive episode.

During the stages of hypochondriasis, subjective analysis, feelings of persecution and "transformation" of personality in the development of paranoia, the patient does not hesitate to identify his "persecutors" or explain their methods and motives. Delusions of persecution are usually based upon feelings of "morbid jealousy" which Mowat regards as a syndrome first given verbal, and possibly later physical, expression.

In making a psychiatric assessment of an individual charged with a serious crime, one tests alleged delusions against reality by studying evidence from all possible sources in order to decide if the accused is psychotic. Useful information is obtained by interviewing relatives and studying letters and ward reports pertaining to the accused. One should be able to understand a crime committed by a paranoiac, in the context of this mental illness, and one would suspect deception if the crime did not have a direct connection with the delusions. The examiner should be careful during interview not to take advantage of any over-valued ideas held by the accused person as otherwise he (the examiner), could, during the subsequent trial, be accused of "planting" delusions in the defendant's mind and coming to the wrong conclusion as to the mental state of the accused.

Brief reference may now be made to multiple killers, "Rambo" type or otherwise, who not uncommonly have paranoid and/or psychopathic personality traits. The following features have been noted:

(i)   They are usually young male adults, reared by a dominant natural mother and a hostile, overstrict or indifferent father. They have feelings of continuous frustration in later life.

(ii)   They tend to be socially isolated "lone wolves", and have basic feelings of inadequacy.

(iii)   The actual killings may be "triggered" off by some provocations causing resentment and which are regarded as a serious insult. Examples in this context would be divorce, lack of recognition for achievement and/or a move to another town or city resulting in loss of important relationships. They would lose control of their social behaviour as a result of any or all of these events.

(iv)   They usually try to communicate their fears in advance of the killings.

(v)   They may be very disturbed by sexual problems which they feel unable to solve.

(vi)   Previous history of violent crimes and weapons possession may also be significant as may a history of periods spent in mental hospitals when aggression necessitated seclusion.

Michael Ryan of Hungerford, Dennis Nilsen and Peter Sutcliffe all killed more than once.

However, all of the above features may not necessarily be present in any particular individual.

Latent serial killers become active as a result of the convergence of a number of factors based on genetic predisposition and traumatic experience.

The genetic predisposition must be regarded as one of aggressive psychopathy and reaction to traumatic experiences both physical and psychological. Predisposed children who are subjected to frequent parental quarrelling, broken homes, bullying at school and physical ill treatment including sexual assault, tend to react by repressing feelings of hatred and desire for revenge, in regard to their families and others who misused them.

Serial killers often have a history of malicious fire setting and of torturing or killing animals. They also tend to take refuge in violent fantasy as a reaction to a world which they believe rejects them. These violent "coping" fantasies are enjoyed and may be carried into adult life, translating into violent behaviour when they fail to give adequate emotional satisfaction. Such violent behaviour is obviously facilitated by alcohol, drugs and pornography.

There is a definite association between serial killing and sexual perversion, including sadism. Each killing acts as reinforcement for the next homicide because the desired orgasm is never achieved.

Serial killers usually like to keep parts of the bodies of their victims as "trophies".

Schizophrenia

Two-thirds of all cases occur between the fifteenth and thirtieth year. The incidence of schizophrenia in the general population has been estimated at 8 per 1,000 persons and only a minority break the law. Schizophrenia essentially means failure of psychic function. Intellect, orientation and memory remain relatively intact but ineffectual during the illness which is characterized by withdrawal from reality. The symptoms usually occur in a setting of clear consciousness.

Remissions and exacerbations of symptoms are features of the illness. The onset is not usually related to environmental stress. The symptoms vary from individual to individual. Judgment, reasoning, emotional responses and volition are all involved in the process. Anomalies and poverty of emotion are prominent in the symptomatology. Schizophrenic thought processes tend to be incongruous with prevailing mood. A schizophrenic in a state of remission may commit a serious crime which may show evidence of planning and premeditation. He may be quite lucid when interviewed soon after committing a crime but confused during a subsequent court hearing and vice versa. His mood may be one of severe depression yet he may have joyful, happy thoughts simultaneously and vice versa. Consequently his behaviour may be totally unpredictable during exacerbations. The "affective" component of the schizophrenic psyche may take on a morbid quality which, combined with weakened volition, delusions and hallucinations, may lead to sudden uncontrolled aggression involving self or others. The schizophrenic may later express astonishment at his own behaviour. Varying degrees of amnesia for the material time of the offence is not uncommon.

Early manifestations include "first rank" symptoms which include disorders of the thought processes such as thought blocking, a belief that thoughts are broadcast and ideas inserted into the patient's thoughts by outside agencies which also control his or her feelings, impulses and behaviour. Illusions of perception are also experienced. Depersonalization occurs during the early stage of schizophrenia, but it tends to become incorporated in the delusional system in the later stages of the illness. The patient complains that he has sensations of strangeness and that he has lost feelings of affection for those he previously loved. He often states also that he feels unreal and that the world around him has changed and is unreal.

Feighner's criteria. Feighner *et al* (1972) have proposed a set of operational criteria for a diagnosis of schizophrenia and it is worth quoting these in full, if only by way of illustration.

A. Both of the following are necessary:

1.   A chronic illness with at least six months of symptoms prior to the index evaluation without return to the premorbid level of psychosocial adjustment.
2.   Absence of a period of depressive or manic symptoms sufficient to qualify for affective disorder.

B.   The patient must have at least one of the following:

1.   Delusions or hallucinations without significant perplexity or disorientation associated with them.
2.   Verbal production that makes communication difficult because of a lack of logical or understandable organization. (In the presence of muteness the diagnostic decision must be deferred.)

C.   At least three of the following manifestations must be present for a diagnosis of *definite* schizophrenia, and two for a diagnosis of *probable* schizophrenia:

1.   single status;
2.   poor premorbid social adjustment or work history;
3.   family history of schizophrenia;
4.   absence of alcoholism or drug-abuse within one year of onset of psychosis;
5.   onset of illness prior to the age 40.

The schizophrenic does not usually try to find grounds for his suspicions and unsystematized delusional beliefs. Schizophrenia homicide usually occurs in the early stages of the illness before emotion and volition are completely impoverished. If the basic premise of the paranoiac's delusions was accepted as valid the subsequent development would appear logical to the average person but this general principle does not apply to schizophrenic delusions. Violence tends to occur more frequently in schizophrenics who have frequent exacerbations of symptoms as opposed to those who have prolonged remissions.

I recall an acute schizophrenic who strangled his wife because she swept around his chair. One could attempt to account for this killing by assuming a morbid emotional state sustained by delusions of persecution or omnipotence and appropriate hallucinations. Lack of self-control due to weak volition could be regarded as the final determining factor in this violent action.

An apparently motiveless murder may be the first indication of acute schizophrenia. Auditory hallucinations calling the subject obscene names and making vile accusations such as incest, may be referred to innocent people with disastrous results when the "voices" advise or command killing. Homicidal impulses may be directed against near relatives who are held responsible by the schizophrenic for his sufferings. Guilt feelings during lucid periods may lead to self-mutilation or suicide. A schizophrenic may inflict severe injuries upon himself and apparently feel little pain. A catatonic stupor may be interrupted without warning by a furious outburst of violence.

Green (1981) studied 58 patients in Broadmoor Special Hospital who had committed matricide and found that 74 per cent were schizophrenics. Of the 58 studied, nearly all were sons living a relatively socially isolated existence at home and father was absent from about 75 per cent of the households. "Perspective anticipation" of matricide would be supported by sudden changes in mental condition, delusions (especially of persecution) concerning mothers, threatened or actual violence and statements by mothers that they fear their mentally ill sons.

Naismith *et al* (1990) studied 109 male patients at the Park Lane Special (Secure) Hospital, Liverpool. These patients were admitted because they were mentally disordered within the meaning of the Mental Health Act 1983, and also because they were regarded as an immediate and serious danger to the public. Those suffering from manic-depressive, neurotic or mental disorder secondary to organic brain disease amounted to a total of only 3 per cent whereas 25 per cent were psychopathically disordered and 53 per cent schizophrenic. Arsonists amounted to 1 per cent of the study. Neurotics amounted to less than 3 per cent of the study group. Only a small minority of schizophrenics indulge in violent crime but those who do are an immediate and very serious danger to the public. They are most difficult to assess from the point of view of repetition because of their utter unpredictability based on their psychopathology. Furthermore, treatment may not necessarily make assessment any easier. Potential schizophrenic aggression is usually channelled harmlessly into innocuous delusions and hallucinations.

The simple schizophrenic may become a beggar or a vagrant. He is easily led and steals because it seems the easiest thing to do. The simple, hebephrenic and catatonic forms of schizophrenia may overlap from the point of view of symptomatology. The schizoid personality is unduly vulnerable to stress but poverty of emotional response and thought disorder become evident with onset of the psychosis. Virkkunen (1974) studied two groups of schizophrenics found guilty of serious violence and arson and concluded that only one-third broke the law as a direct response to their delusions and/or hallucinations and two-thirds because of family stresses and frustrations. Schizophrenics tend to be violent to relatives. In the writer's experience, these statistics should be at least reversed. Serious lawbreaking is quite uncommon, and this also applies to paraphrenia, which is a form of schizophrenia characterized by hallucinations, depressive mood swings and delusions of persecution or grandeur which tend to vary during the course of the illness. Paraphrenic delusions are less systematized than those found in paranoia. The paraphrenic's intellect, orientation and memory usually remain intact until the terminal stages of the illness. The age of incidence is about 45 years and the personality and emotional responses remain relatively intact.

Schizophrenic patients were found to be at greater risk of being victims of a violent offence when compared to a control group which seemed to be at a greater risk of becoming victims of non-violent crime, Chuang *et al* (1987).

It may be that mental illness neither adds to nor diminishes dangerousness and that the major determinant of perceived dangerousness and unacceptability by the public, is the seriousness of the offence itself rather than the presence or absence of mental illness. However, a person may perpetrate a violent offence for the first time during the course of serious mental disorder.

A retrospective study was made on 78 men who did not have previous convictions but had at least one admission to a psychiatric hospital of not less than three months before the age of 30 years. Forty-seven of the study group were schizophrenics or manic-depressive psychotics. The conviction rate of the study group (after discharge from mental hospitals and presumably under subsequent community psychiatric care) was found to be comparable to that of men of the same age in the general population. The implication is that ex-psychiatric inpatients transferred to community psychiatric care are probably not more liable to conviction and imprisonment than men of the same age in the general population (Cook, 1983).

Taplin (1985) studied 198 mentally disordered offenders and found their *modus operandi* and types of offences similar to those for the general population but diagnoses were not given. Schizophrenia tends to be a chronic mental illness, so one would think in terms of remission rather than cure. It must be stressed that only a small minority of schizophrenics commit criminal offences.

Having discussed the symptomatology of schizophrenia, the work of Der *et al* (1990) is of some interest. These authors indicated a decline in the incidence of schizophrenia from the point of view of *first admissions* over the past 10 to 15 years, on the basis of relevant data for England and Wales studied for the years 1952-1986. This decline is almost three times greater than for all other diagnostic categories and could be due to more accurate diagnostic methods in recent years. Hypomania has been misdiagnosed as schizophrenia. A good response to Lithium would tend to suggest hypomania and contradict schizophrenia. There have been instances when electroconvulsant therapy was given, without success, to schizophrenics when autism was mistaken for the psychomotor retardation of endogenous depression.

Furthermore, consideration should be given to reactive factors such as provision of better community care for all forms of mental disorder including schizophrenia but first admission rates for other psychoses unexpectedly did not show a similar decline. It is well known that schizophrenics do less well when staying with near relatives. Consequently, improved community care for schizophrenics would presumably not include living with near relatives.

Schizophrenia as an illness is becoming less frequent and the incidence of early onset of schizophrenia is in decline. Furthermore, the incidence of schizophrenia with neurological complications such as catatonia, is also less frequent.

One may conclude that, in time, there may be even more serious doubt as to the existence of schizophrenia as a clinical entity. Confusing diagnoses such as schizofreniform and schizoaffective disorders merely serve to further query the entity.

Pathological mood changes

(a) Manic Depressives: Individuals with the manic-depressive temperature may or may not develop the corresponding psychoses.

Only a small minority of hypomanic and manic individuals indulge in law-breaking, which may or may not be provoked.

The hypomanic, sometimes under the influence of alcohol, may commit offences such as petty theft, disorderly behaviour, deception and non-indictable offences against the person and these are usually dealt with at magistrates' courts. Instability of mood and sexual excitement may occasionally lead to indecent assault or rape but the emotional warmth of the hypomanic usually enables him to satisfy his sexual desires without breaking the law. The hypomanic may indulge in fraud on a considerable scale in order to obtain money for grandiose schemes. Extravagant purchases may be made, incurring debts which cannot be paid. Delusions and hallucinations do not occur in hypomania, which is not usually regarded as a psychosis, although insight is lacking. The mood of the manic is even more unstable and serious crimes may occasionally be committed against persons or property because uncontrolled aggression and some degree of clouding of consciousness may be present at the material times. Hypomania may or may not develop into mania, which is characterized by intense elation, extreme mental and physical overactivity, flight of ideas, irritability, distractibility and grandiose delusions. Hallucinations are uncommon except in delirious mania. The manic phase is less common than the depressive. Only a small minority of persons suffering from the depressive phase of manic-depressive psychosis break the law because psycho-motor retardation, lack of spontaneity and fear act as controlling influences but the "altruistic" type of homicide is occasionally committed. The accused may have recovered from this phase at the time of arrest when the mood may be normal or elevated.

Sullivan (1924) wrote of a woman who killed her three children during the depressive phase and just before the onset of hypomania. She threw the children into a canal and subsequently had a vague idea of having undergone a fearful experience, but she believed that her children were alive and well. The depressive phase was obviously accompanied by clouding of consciousness when the children died, but the confusion cleared a few hours later and a hypomanic phase developed.

Aggressive impulses are normally inhibited by education and training but these effects may be neutralized by any psychotic condition. Delusions of guilt and hypochondriacal delusions are often associated with homicidal impulses when an *endogenous depressive* kills. Consequently, near relatives may be killed in order to prevent them inheriting or developing some serious disease which the depressive erroneously believes that he has contracted or having contracted it that treatment was unsuccessful despite proof to the contrary.

Venereal disease is a common delusion in this respect. The psychotic depressive will use a delusional idea, based on false reasoning, to explain and excuse his abnormal behaviour. He kills from motives which, to his way of thinking, are inherently good, in comparison with the paranoid psychotic who is motivated by spite and a desire to avenge imaginary wrongs. Thought, mood and behaviour tend to be congruous in either phase of manic-depressive psychosis.

Homicidal and suicidal tendencies frequently co-exist in the endogenous depressive and these tendencies stem from acceptance of a fate characterized by hopelessness, futility and despair. Consequently, he believes that killing of loved ones followed by self-destruction is the only practical solution. The following two brief examples indicate obvious defects in judgment and reasoning.

(1)   A psychotic depressive killed her son in order to ensure that he would not grow up and develop a similar condition.

(2)   A psychotic depressive killed her son because he became ill and she falsely believed that he was about to be taken to an "institution". She felt that he would not do well in such an environment.

A psychotic depressive may plan a homicide and act normally beforehand in order to allay suspicion. He may well surrender to the police afterwards when he is more preoccupied with remorse than fear of consequences.

The impulse to kill may be overwhelming and there is usually no prior warning.

The psychotic depressive may, less commonly, act upon a blind unreasoning impulse to take life, regarding suicide as against his moral principles, and perhaps kill a total stranger in order to achieve punishment. He or she may complain of feeling "dead inside" – emotionless, unreal, or like an automaton. This is called depersonalization.

Psychotic depressives charged with murder tend to be calm and well behaved when on remand in prison hospitals. The act of homicide would seem to have the effect of releasing a great deal of pent-up tension.

Both phases of manic-depressive psychosis tend to occur more frequently and with greater intensity with the advance of time. Serious crime is more likely to be committed early in the day in the depressive phase, when depression is most intense and judgment most impaired. The characteristic early morning waking (usually at about 2 a.m.) and insomnia cause progressive mental fatigue leading eventually to exhaustion. Conversation is not spontaneous and questions are answered briefly. Clinical impression is quite distinct from that conveyed by hysterics, malingerers and psychopaths who repeat their stories again and again in order to ensure that the examiner clearly understands what they say. Expressions of self-reproach may indicate knowledge of the crime but not necessarily a realization that what was done at the material time was wrong in the legal sense.

A stage of the illness may be reached when the depressive phase may become constant and the hypomanic or manic phases may not be evident. This is referred to as unipolar depression.

The psychotic depressive may kill under the following circumstances which indicate very defective judgment and reasoning:

(i)   desire not to expose near relatives to imaginary torture and suffering;

(ii)   to secure his or her own death or imprisonment by judicial means in order to expiate groundless guilt feelings which usually have a religious or sexual basis.

The intention is to kill rather than injure.

The phasic incidence of psychotic depression is of importance in relation to psychiatric evidence in court. The depressive phase of manic-depressive psychosis usually lasts six to nine months in the absence of treatment. Consequently, a period of depression lasting only a few days, during which a crime was allegedly committed, would cause considerable doubt on the validity of this diagnosis. However, the duration of the depressive phase of manic-depressive psychosis may be 2 to 6 years immediately before psychiatric advice was sought, Mitchell-Heggs (1971). Brief depressive episodes are unlikely to be an expression of manic-depressive psychosis and one would expect an accused person to have a relevant family history. Special consideration would be required when a diagnosis of manic-depressive psychosis is alleged in regard to an adolescent or young adult as this condition is commoner in later life and the peak age of onset is 50 to 60 years. Arguments based on the above observations tend to develop in court when the defence put forward a plea of diminished responsibility with the object of having a charge of murder reduced to manslaughter.

When a presumptive clinical diagnosis is made of primary depression or when the diagnosis is seriously in doubt the patient should undergo a *dexamethasone suppression test, and a thyroid-stimulating hormone test.* In only 16 per cent of patients with primary depression would both results be normal. If either test is positive, in a doubtful case, this should be regarded as tending to confirm the diagnosis of primary depression, while a negative result should encourage a return to the clinical history and the findings on physical examination. Primary depression in this context means major endogenous depressive illness. Reliable *objective* tests for mental illness are characterized by their scarcity and consequently these tests are important, giving 84 per cent reliability when diagnosis is in doubt, Gold (1981).

Szabadi (1991) indicated that the function of the hypothalamic-pituitary-thyroid axis should be investigated in every patient suffering from chronic or recurrent manic-depressive disorder and especially if rapid (bipolar) cycling of the illness occurs. Lithium carbonate and antidepressant medication aggravate the minority of cases of manic-depressive illness which are caused by deficiency of thyroid hormones when the hypothyroidism may be subclinical.

(b) Involutional depression: Involutional depression is found in an older age group than manic-depressive psychosis. States of anxiety may merge imperceptibility into this type of depression which is accompanied by agitation, intense fear, outbursts of anger, irritability and delusions of guilt. Hypochondriacal delusions are also evident and may lead to suicide or self-mutilation. Suicidal risk may be increased after an unsuccessful attempt because of additional guilt feelings and delusions of persecution. Serious crime by involutional depressives is quite uncommon. The diagnosis is based on the absence of previous episodes of endogenous

depression and the premorbid personality tends to be obsessional and subject to undue anxiety. It is a psychotic depression. Hallucinations congruous with delusions of guilt may occur in any psychotic depression.

The stuperose depressive is of course incapable of law-breaking. Neustatter (1953) indicated that the psychotic depression releases primitive aggressive impulses which may lead to homicide or self-destruction. A chance interruption of concentration may cause a depressive to desist from violent action and consequently spare the victim's life.

A suicidal attempt may be precipitated by a sudden worsening of the depressive state. Suicide is most likely when the depression is developing and during the early stages of recovery when volition and initiative are gaining strength. The psychotic depressive will refute insanity and he is not particularly concerned with saving himself from punishment and will only admit to delusions and/or hallucinations on direct questioning and the existence of these phenomena may well be denied if questioning is too intense.

(c) Senile depression: Senile depression develops after the age of 65 years and the symptomatology is similar to other forms of endogenous depression. Law-breaking is quite unusual but serious crime is occasionally perpetrated. The writer examined a senile depressive who drowned his baby grandson in the erroneous belief that the child had inherited syphilis through him. The Montgomery-Asberg Depression Rating Scale (1979) is useful when taken into consideration with clinical findings. This scale assesses varying degrees of depression and it is also helpful in assessing response to treatment.

The Beck Depression Inventory (1961) is specifically designed for the measurement of depression.

The above tests are not designed for the diagnosis of depression which is made on the basis of clinical criteria.

(d) Puerperal psychosis: Puerperal psychosis, whether depressive, schizophrenic or mixed syndromes, occurs within three months of delivery. The chances are about one in seven that a mother will experience mental illness with a subsequent pregnancy after a puerperal psychosis. The maternal incidence, as quoted by various authors, varies from one to 6.8 per 1,000 births.

Puerperal psychosis is usually preceded by a lucid interval of three or four days after delivery. The onset may be acute and accompanied by clouding of consciousness with delusional and/or hallucinatory experiences. A toxic-confusional state *per se* may occur. A woman may kill her child in a state of puerperal depression or schizophrenia and have genuine amnesia for the material time of the child's death when the charge would be reduced from murder to manslaughter on the basis of the Infanticide Act 1938.

The individual numbers for the categories are printed below (Criminal statistics for England and Wales, Home Office, for 1990).

Table XX

1983	1984	1985	1986	1987	1988	1989	1990	Total
All homicides								
63	76	73	55	59	90	67	54	537
Domestic homicides								
16	18	16	19	20	19	26	20	154
Child homicides								
22	31	33	15	20	38	20	9	188

The figure 188 represents the number of women suspected of killing their own children from 1983 to 1990 (inclusive).

Dementia

Reference is freely made to the excellent section on this subject in *Diseases of the Nervous System* by Sir Russell Brain (1956). Dementia may be defined as an extensive deterioration in the mental functions showing itself mainly in serious defects of thought, memory, feelings and behaviour.

The causes of dementia are:

(1)   Senility and supervening upon other chronic psychotic states.
(2)   Cerebral arteriosclerosis.
(3)   The presenile dementias, a mixed group of degenerative diseases of unknown origin: Pick's disease, Alzheimer's disease (presbyophrenia), Huntington's chorea and Creutzfeldt-Jakob's Disease, which is now thought to be caused by Bovine Spongiform Encephalopathy, commonly called "mad cow" disease.
(4)   Intracranial tumour.

(5)   Non-syphilitic inflammatory diseases: encephalitis (various forms), intracranial abscess, meningitis and disseminated sclerosis.

(6)   Intoxications and deficiency diseases: alcoholism, drug addiction, uraemia, subacute combined degeneration, pellagra and Wernicke's encephalopathy.

(7)   Epilepsy.

(8)   Injury to the brain.

(9)   Syphilis.

Dementia due to the following causes will be considered in some detail:

(i)   *Senile dementia* may be associated with varying degrees of depression. The incidence varies up to 10 per cent, depending on advancement of age beyond 65 years. A small minority break the law. Conditions of profound dementia and physical incapacitation preclude crime. Only a minority of elderly people become demented.

(ii)   *Mental disorder from cerebral vascular disease.*

(iii)   *The presenile dementias.*

(i) Senile dementia

Defective memory for recent events characterizes the early stages of senile dementia and consequently the individual may be charged with an offence such as shoplifting, which he did not intend to commit.

Memory defects combined with confusional episodes occur with increasing frequency as the dementia progresses and may result in unintentional damage to property, including fires accidentally caused. The clinical findings may be further elaborated. The manifestations of senile dementia can be so varied that it may be helpful to explain the chief psychological mechanism behind it. As the cortical degeneration affects the part of the brain associated with the highest levels of mind structure, the disease results not only in the loss or decline of these highest functions, but the release from control of many of the more basic traits in personality. The person who has always been domineering and confident will become aggressive and ill-tempered. The one who has been a secretive, suspicious kind will often show persecutory delusions and begin accusing associates of theft or other misdeeds. The indecisive and dependent personality will become markedly worse and exhibit attention-seeking, and in other ways, exacting behaviour. In addition, the appreciation of increasing mental enfeeblement by the patient himself, even if imperfectly realized, often adds an element of exasperation, a desire to hide the disability or a depressive element, to the general picture. Personal habits fail sooner or later and double incontinence occurs to increase considerably the burden of nursing the patient. Rosandi *et al* (1991) indicated that quantified electroencephalographic and cerebral blood-flow measurements are reliable and currently employed techniques in the functional exploration of the ageing brain and can be routinely employed since discomfort to the patient is minimal. Topographical analysis is accomplished by a full automated mapping system which also enables statistical comparisons in real time. Dementias and cerebrovascular pathologies present characteristic brain functional abnormalities.

Brain (1956) classified the signs and symptoms of senile dementia as follows:

1. *Judgment and reasoning*
   The earliest disability is often an impairment of judgment and reasoning manifesting itself in a failure to grasp the meaning of a situation as a whole and hence to react to it appropriately. At this stage a man's business judgment begins to fail, though in the semi-automatic activities of life no defect may be noticed.

2. *Memory*
   Memory becomes impaired, the recollection of recent events suffering more than that of early periods of life. Even when both are grossly defective, mechanical memory may remain for a time. In more severe stages of dementia, defect of memory linked with defective perception leads to disorientation in space and time.

3. *The Emotional Life*
   Although in some patients the emotional life is little disturbed, in others impairment of higher control leads to emotional instability which finds expression in irritability and impulsive conduct. Acts of violence, alcoholic excess, and sexual aberrations are thus explained. The prevailing mood may be one of euphoria, with hilariousness and hyperactivity, depression, anxiety, or maniacal excitement, and will be influenced by the pre-existing psychological constitution. In the late stages the patient is apathetic.

4. *Delusions*

    Delusions are the outcome of emotional disorder, associated with impairment of judgment and defective appreciation of reality. Delusions centred on the self are likely to be grandiose in a state of euphoria and self-condemnatory or hypochondriacal in a state of depression. Delusions regarding others are often hostile and express fear, suspicion, or jealousy.

5. *Care of the Person*

    In the later stages of dementia the patient becomes careless in dress and in personal cleanliness, and finally incontinent. This may be attributed at first to a decay of the self-regarding sentiment and later also to the lack of perception.

6. *Speech*

    In the later stages also speech undergoes a progressive disintegration. Though the forms of aphasia caused by focal lesions of the brain may be present in dementia, there is also a destruction of the speech function as a whole, so that speech becomes increasingly meaningless and ends in jargon or isolated words or phrases, "logoclonia". Agnosia and apraxia may also develop.

7. *Physical Concomitants*

    The condition of the somatic nervous functions will depend upon the causal disorder, but, whatever the cause, there is usually a general physical deterioration with loss of weight and reduced endocrine function.

(ii) Mental disorder from cerebro-vascular disease may be ushered in by a sudden attack of clouding consciousness, with disorientation, restlessness, confusion and perhaps hallucinations. The onset may be gradual, often in the late fifties or early sixties, with dizziness, headache, fatigue, disturbed sleep and increasing failure of memory. Periods of depression, emotional outbursts and hypochondriacal preoccupation may be seen. The patient may become jealous, easily upset and suspicious of his companions. A lowering of executive ability at work and in the home becomes apparent. Fainting spells, or signs such as hemiparesis which point to a focal lesion of the brain, may precede or follow other symptoms and physical examination may show abnormal neurological signs resulting from this lesion. Aphasia and convulsive seizures may

occur. Tremor of the hands and unsteadiness of gait are often found. The course of the condition is very variable. There is fluctuation in its general severity and in individual symptoms. Each focal attack cripples the patient further. In the early case, differentiation from simple depressive and anxiety states may not be possible. When there is definite dementia and objective signs of cerebral vascular disease, the diagnosis is more certain and also called arteriosclerotic dementia.

Serious brain injury may also cause dementia and the condition may be an end result of chronic alcoholism and/or drug addiction. Dementia may be a terminal effect of frequent epileptic episodes over a prolonged period.

(iii) The Presenile Dementias:
Alzheimer's Disease. This is a progressive cerebral degeneration with the pathological picture of senility occurring in middle life. The essential lesion is a diffuse degeneration of the cerebral cortex involving all its layers and most marked in the frontal lobes. The basalganglia and the cerebellum escape. The brain is atrophic. Histologically, besides degeneration of the ganglion cells of the cortex there is a profusion of senile plaques in the cortex. There are silver-staining masses, often ring- or star-shaped, and probably of neuroglical origin. In addition, there are intraneural fibrillary tangles. These changes are regarded as characteristic of degeneration of the cortex. Their occurrence in middle age is unexplained, but there seems no doubt that Alzheimer's disease is essentially a premature senile change.

About 600,000 people in the UK suffer from Alzheimer's disease which may be an auto-immune reaction on the part of the central nervous system in general and the cerebral cortex in particular. Prednisone and Indomethacin may be of therapeutic value. Rogers (1990) alleged that arthritics treated with these medications had only one-tenth the expected incidence of this form of pre-senile dementia. Alzheimer's disease develops between the ages of 40 to 60. The symptoms are those of a progressive dementia with apraxia and speech disturbances. The onset is insidious. In the early stages the patient suffers from loss of memory and becomes careless in dress and conduct. Epileptiform attacks may occur. Speech becomes slurred, and there is difficulty in recalling words. As the disease progresses there is complete disorientation. The patient does not recognize his friends, becomes restless, and may wander about. A progressive deterioration takes place in the faculty of speech, which, from paraphasic talkativeness, becomes reduced to isolated words and phrases, so-called 'logoclonia'. Movements become stereotyped and the sucking reflect is often elicitable. Spastic contractures usually develop. The duration of the disease is from one and a half to thirteen years. Treatment does not influence its course, once established.

Electroencephalographic studies by Giannitrapani *et al* (1991), demonstrated that the decrease in frequency of alpha activity is perhaps more significant in identifying dementia of the non-Alzheimer type.

Work at Frenchay Hospital, Bristol, (1993), indicates that protein called "Nerve Growth Factor" (NGF) prevents excessive neurone degeneration meaning that reduced production may be a causative factor. A defective gene called APoE4 is also suspected as a cause and this may be connected with NGF.

Charatan, (1994), indicates that Tacrine in doses varying from 80 to 160 mg. daily causes limited improvement of the cognitive and behavioural symptoms.

Pick's Disease. Synonym: Circumscribed cortical atrophy. This condition is characterized by circumscribed atrophy of the cerebral cortex, usually confined to the frontal and temporal regions. The upper three cortical layers are principally affected, exhibiting chromatolysis and disappearance of ganglion cells. There is some glial increase in the atrophic areas, but senile plaques and intraneural fibrils are absent and arteriosclerosis plays no part in causation. The cause of the disease is unknown. It may be toxic in origin or a form of primary degeneration developing in middle life. Multiple cases have been described in one sibship. The age of onset is usually between 50 and 60, and the disease has a duration of from three to twelve years, always terminating fatally. Females are said to be affected more than males. It is characterized by a progressive dementia and aphasia. Restlessness and loss of normal inhibitions are prominent in the early stages. The patient is often voluble and tends to make jokes and puns. At first the more abstract intellectual functions suffer, but the more concrete type of behaviour is well-preserved and the patient emotionally accessible. Memory failure is prominent in the symptomatology.

Epilepsy.
I have included epilepsy in this chapter because various psychoses may be associated with this condition and furors, fugues and automatisms are more appropriately considered with the psychoses than the neuroses.

Some hesitate to define epilepsy because the condition is so complex. However, a court may require a definition. Epilepsy may be defined as an abnormal, transitory and periodic disturbance of consciousness of sudden onset and termination, which has a tendency to recur and may or may not be accompanied by convulsions. A Judge may ask for an explanation of the physiological mechanism of an epileptic convulsion and this question may be answered in lay terms by stating that it is caused by an abnormal and irregular discharge of electrical impulses from certain nerve cells in the brain, which spreads over the surface of the brain, causing hallucinations of sight and hearing, and down the spinal cord causing convulsions which invariably occur when the subject is unconscious. One will usually be required to explain the difference between idiopathic (hereditary) and post-traumatic epilepsy.

The Royal College of General Practitioners (1960) indicated that the incidence of epilepsy in the general population of England was 1 in 200 or 0.5 per cent.

Gunn (1969) conducted a census of the epileptic population being received into prisons and borstals in England and Wales during one month in 1966 and found the incidence of epilepsy to be at least 7.1 per 1,000 men or 0.71 per cent. Consequently the incidence of epilepsy among inmates of prisons and youth custody centres is not substantially higher than in the general population.

Pond and Bidwell (1960) studied 60 epileptics and found that 46 showed psychoses closely resembling paranoid schizophrenia. Fifty-five of the study group probably had temporal-lobe epilepsy. The average age of onset of the psychosis was 30 years and the members of the study group suffered from epilepsy for an average of 14 years before the onset of the psychosis. Hallucinations, thought disorder of schizophrenic type, spells of irritability and aggression, exaltation and/or ecstasy, depression and attempted suicide were all noted giving a general impression of a psychotic illness over a period of years with eventual emotional and intellectual impairment similar to that observed in dementia.

The following psychoses may occur in association with epilepsy:

(i)   manic depressive psychosis;
(ii) paranoia, which may in time develop into paranoid schizophrenia;
(iii) schizophrenia including the paranoid type;
(iv) dementia due to encephalopathy due to anoxia caused by repeated ictal episodes;

(v)   confusional states associated with ictal episodes may result when anticonvulsant medication is suddenly discontinued. Delusions and hallucinations are experienced during such states.

Epilepsy may be idiopathic or secondary to cerebral pathology caused by trauma, tumour, arteriosclerosis or syphilis.

Types (i), (ii) and (iii) tend to be particularly associated with temporal lobe epilepsy. Most acute psychoses related to epilepsy are of the paranoid, catatonic or acute undifferentiated schizophrenic varieties (Ervin, 1967).

Different types of epilepsy may be classified in different ways:

(i)   *grand mal*;
(ii)   *petit mal*;
(iii) psychomotor epilepsy.

The frequency with which epilepsy follows head injury is about 36 per cent in cases of penetrating gunshot wounds (Watson, 1947). The incidence of epilepsy after non-missile head injuries is said to be 5 per cent (Jannett, 1975).

The majority of people who develop post-traumatic epilepsy do so within two years of the head injury. The ictal episodes may develop immediately or be delayed for many years. Epilepsy of late onset usually affects individuals who had depressed fractures and (except in children) is rare with a duration of post-traumatic amnesia of less than 24 hours (Jannett, 1975).

Considerations which apply to idiopathic epilepsy apply equally to post-traumatic epilepsy from the point of view of forensic psychiatry.

The incidence of epilepsy may be 18 per cent when the dura is penetrated and caused mainly by vascularized scar tissue causing the surface of the brain to adhere to the dura. The incidence was only two per cent when the dura was not penetrated (Wagstaffe, 1928).

Jasper (1949) classified epilepsy on the basis of clinical and electroencephalographic observations in relation to the site of origin of the epileptic discharge:

(i)   Epilepsy originating primarily from the cerebral cortex as exemplified in temporal-lobe epilepsy which is invariably preceded by an aura. Convulsion may or may not occur.

(ii) Epilepsy originating in the subcortical regions where the ictus is not preceded by an aura. This type of epilepsy also called grand mal and petit mal but also includes epilepsy due to extracerebral causes such as uraemia, hypoglycaemia, eclampsia, withdrawal effects of alcohol and drugs, infective or other toxic processes, cerebral degeneration which may be primary or secondary to metastatic carcinoma and arteriosclerosis associated with hypertension.

(iii) Discharges spread immediately to subcortical structures from epileptic foci which are usually located on the medical aspects of cerebral hemispheres and in the insula which is a submerged part of the cortex of the lateral surface of each hemisphere. This is called secondary subcortical epilepsy and it is essentially an electroencephalographic concept. Convulsions may or may not occur.

(iv) Epilepsy arising from numerous areas in the cerebral cortex and the subcortical structures giving rise to diffuse dysrhythmias in the electroencephalogram. This type of epilepsy is usually due to extracerebral causes. Loss of consciousness tends to occur with or without local or generalized convulsions.

Judges occasionally ask medical witnesses for information as to the percentage of apparently normal individuals who have abnormal electroencephalograms. Walton (1963) stated that "... usually the electroencephalogram becomes fully mature between the ages of 12 and 14 years, but 10 to 15 per cent of apparently normal adults have immature records".

Hill and Parr (1963) indicate "... whatever criteria of normality are used a proportion of normal subjects ranging from about 5 to 15 per cent in different laboratories, will have abnormal electroencephalograms".

Hughes (1961) gave the following opinion "... in a small proportion of clinically normal individuals an abnormal record is found; in the majority of instances the abnormalities are minor in nature, and as there is some variation in reporting from one department to another the frequency of such abnormal records is still a matter of doubt. The usual figure quoted is from five to 10 per cent. In very occasional instances some gross abnormality is found in the electroencephalogram of a normal person: the assessment of such an abnormality can be very difficult indeed".

Disease of the temporal-lobe is alleged to account for about one-third of all the epilepsies in terms of causation and approximately 50 per cent of temporal-lobe epileptics do not have convulsions but rather equivalents in the form of behaviour disorders (Kiloh, 1961). I am not aware of any statistical study which compares criminal behaviour associated with temporal-lobe epilepsy with similar behaviour in association with other types of epilepsy.

The human brain is an integrated unit but the temporal-lobe has a special association with emotion. Stimulation of the temporal-lobe causes elevation of blood pressure and a rage reaction. A monkey was intoxicated with barbiturate and then killed; the temporal-lobes were found on autopsy to be congested with blood in comparison with the remainder of the brain which is relatively bloodless. The clinical significance of this finding in the context of emotion has not been explained.

Behaviour in epileptic furor has been regarded as similar to that in manic furor when an individual strikes out blindly with violent force and is unaware of what he is doing. Macniven (1944) expressed the opinion that epilepsy permeates the whole personality and therefore a crime committed by an epileptic cannot be completely dissociated from his or her epilepsy.

Section 37 of the Mental Health Act 1983, would be applicable to an epileptic found guilty of manslaughter and who also suffered from psychopathic disorder, psychosis or mental impairment and in this context he would usually be sent to a secure hospital on the basis of a hospital order with restriction on discharge without limit of time under s.41 of the same Act.

Crimes by epileptics only rarely occur during furors, fugues, twilight states and/or automatisms. An angry emotion existing shortly before an ictal episode could theoretically influence behaviour immediately afterwards. Therapeutic drugs such as anticonvulsants may themselves remove inhibitions.

Epileptics who perpetrate crimes in states of clear consciousness may also suffer from mental impairment, psychopathy, hysteria or psychosis. Bleuler (1924) referred to "affective epileptics" as suffering from "psychopathic states with strong affectivity in which psychic influences such as emotional excitement may lead to apparent epileptiform attacks". He also regarded these individuals as "epileptic swindlers" and pathological liars. They did not develop dementia or respond to anti-convulsants.

The following conditions are associated with epilepsy: (i) furors, (ii) fugue states; (iii) twilight states, (iv) automatic behaviour. States of extreme irritability, unjustified anger and sudden uncontrollable rage may be associated with these conditions with the possible exception of twilight states.

(i) Reference has already been made to furor which may occur before, after or replace an ictus, which is defined as a "sudden, severe seizure".

(ii) An individual in a state of fugue wanders from his accustomed surroundings and may claim loss of identity or a lesser degree of amnesia for his past life. Marchand and Ajuriaguerra (1948) studied 1,000 epileptics and found that 64 experienced fugue states which sometimes replaced the terminal sleep after a seizure. Bromberg (1965) indicated that vicious and senseless crimes have been committed by individuals in epileptic fugues but he does not elaborate and one must conclude that such crimes are uncommon. The fugue may last for hours or days. Psychopaths are also subject to fugue states.

(iii) A post-epileptic twilight state is established when post-ictal clouding of consciousness persists for hours or days as opposed to seconds or minutes.

Stereotyped behaviour tends to occur in the twilight state but law-breaking is rare. The post-ictal confusion of grand mal epilepsy may last for 48 hours and fluctuate in its intensity. Monkemoller, (1912) studied 240 arsonists and found that 27 were epileptic. He also believed that epileptics see visions of fire and destruction during periods of confusion. However, an epileptic may perpetrate arson or any other crime during a period of clear consciousness.

(iv) Neustatter (1953) defines automatism as the performance of a number of quite automatic acts which may appear purposeful to an observer. Automatic behaviour may be associated with fugues and twilight states when behaviour may correspond to the subject's personality pattern. Total or partial amnesia for the period of automatism is apparent after recovery. Medico-legal problems may be posed if epilepsy is alleged and the associated ictal episode was unobserved. Automatism means that the individual is capable of action but not aware of what he is doing and therefore lacking conscious intent.

This subject is also considered in Chapter II.

The causes of automatism are:

(1)   epilepsy and associated states;

(2)   acute emotional disturbances such as hysteria;

(3)   schizophrenic psychosis;

(4)   organic brain disease such as cerebral trauma, cerebral tumour and anoxia due to advanced cerebral arteriosclerosis;

(5)   metabolic conditions such as uraemia, hypoglycaemia and the effects of drugs, alcohol and anaesthetics;

(6)   hypnosis; and

(7)   somnambulisms which are related to dreams.

Case 23: A mother who led police to the body of her 11 month-old child, claimed that he had been kidnapped from her car which she had parked outside a bank in a town in Ontario, Canada, where she lived. She alleged that the car doors were unlocked when she left the car. The body of the child was located in nearby woods in January 1988 and the mother told the police that she had seen this location in a dream. The child died from exposure. Her lawyers told the court that she had not at any time suffered from post-natal depression and had no reason to harm her son. Furthermore, amnesia or automatism were not invoked by her defence. Her other son was happy and well nourished and now aged four years. She was charged with murder and acquitted by the jury. A bank clerk gave evidence to the effect that she saw a man speed off in a car with a baby dressed in a blue snowsuit which was similar to the one worn by the victim when the body was discovered.

Buchanan (1991) referred to a man who was convicted of indecent exposure despite a plea of somnambulism at the material time and a well-established history of sleep-walking. Bonkalo (1974) indicated that alcohol influenced one-third of homicides perpetrated during alleged automatisms.

Somnambulisms usually last for several minutes to half an hour but may be more prolonged.

Comment: Instances have been recorded where mothers had dreams about their missing children who, as a result, were occasionally found. Dreams are spontaneous and involuntary and have been described as the "Royal road to the unconscious" and consequently they are utilized to discover and help solve a patient's problems during psychotherapy. They are based on the experiences of waking life and allegedly represent emotionally toned symbolic and distorted expressions of repressed wishes which the dreamer may consciously regard as socially and morally unacceptable. This is the "wish-fulfilment" *theory*. The contents of the dream are out of conscious control and consist of visual and auditory experiences which could justifiably be regarded as psychotic if they occurred in conscious life. The electroencephalogram tracing shows 14 to 17 cycles per second during natural sleep but 4 to 10 during dreaming which may account for 20-25 per cent of sleeping time.

One would regard the wish fulfilment in the case of a mother wishing to locate her child above described as socially and morally acceptable. Jung indicated that dreams which originate in the personal and collective unconscious are of value in psychoanalysis because they reveal the hidden and often violent side of an individual's character and sometimes give clear warnings of danger.

Automatism is considered in Chapter II

The following procedure may be adopted in order to decide the issue of a person's responsibility in a case of alleged automatism at the material time of the crime:

(i) A detailed history from the accused may indicate previous episodes of automatism with stereotyped behaviour and subsequent amnesia, which may not be total. Various details of the history should be correlated with the generally accepted features of automatism and particular note taken of discrepancies. A witness may have observed impairment of awareness, inappropriate gestures, unresponsiveness, irrelevant replies to questions, aimless wandering and/or a dazed vague expression, at or about the material time. A crime quite out of character would lend some credence to this type of defence.

(ii) The surrounding circumstances of the offence should be studied. Automatism may account for sudden, spontaneous and unmotivated behaviour leading to unnecessary violence and no attempt to conceal the crime. A carefully contrived and purposive crime would contraindicate automatism as would a carefully worked out escape plan. These latter features would tend to disprove an allegation of amnesia for the crime and for subsequent incidents.

(iii) The character of the accused should also be studied. The truthfulness or otherwise would be indicated by the individual's background and history (including police record). A family history of epilepsy or serious mental disorder would be significant.

(iv) Full physical and psychiatric assessment is essential. Psychometric tests, electroencephalograms, blood sugar and urea estimations, skull and chest x-rays and tests for venereal disease are implemented as necessary.

A successful defence on the basis of epileptic automatism would require a definite history of epileptic attacks preferably supported by electroencephalographic evidence.

The abnormal (automatic) behaviour usually lasts for minutes rather than hours or days.

The following considerations may be helpful in deciding whether a crime of violence should be attributed to an epileptic state:

(i) An accurate description of at least two attacks suggestive of epilepsy and supporting electroencephalograhic evidence would be significant.

(ii) If the accused is alleged to have had an epileptic episode in close association with a crime, he should in the past have had some similar attacks. Epileptic attacks may not follow the same pattern in the same individual at different times.

(iii) Walker (1961) indicated that an individual undergoing a psychomotor (temporal-lobe) seizure, may appear to a lay witness to be quite conscious and also motivated to react with violence to insults and frustration as though he understood their nature.

(iv) The period of alleged partial or complete amnesia for the crime itself and associated events should be compatible with the type of epileptic attack which the accused usually experiences. Focal motor attacks may not interfere with normal awareness, whereas temporal-lobe seizures may be complicated by a degree of clouding of consciousness quite out of proportion to their motor accompaniments. A relatively long period of loss of normal awareness could be expected if the accused experienced a series of epileptic attacks in association with the material time of a crime which he allegedly committed. Petit mal "absences" are usually of brief duration, occur mainly in children and are invariably associated with immobility and therefore not compatible with crime.

(v) The electroencephalographic findings should be compatible with the clinical type of epilepsy from which the accused suffers.

(vi) The circumstances of the crime should be compatible with assumption of loss of normal awareness for the material time.

All these criteria need not necessarily be present in any particular individual. A major epileptic seizure may occur during the course of hypoglycaemia. A crime committed by an individual under the influence of alcohol cannot be excused in law unless the alcohol causes serious mental disorder such as psychosis including delirium tremens or the accused was known to suffer from a recognized form of mental disorder when not under the influence of alcohol. Defending counsels are particularly interested in the possibility of alcohol reducing the blood-sugar level or further reducing it in an individual who has a tendency to hypoglycaemia. The volume of the alcohol is more important than its strength in this respect. An attempt may be made to excuse criminal behaviour on this basis by invoking automatism.

Pawer (1972) indicated that drinking excess alcohol causes garrulousness, aggression and eventually coma which can be prolonged. Two such patients were admitted to Bridgend General Hospital after having been found unconscious for 24 hours. Their histories are given below. Neither was an alcoholic. An individual's blood sugar may be quite low especially within 12 to 36 hours of taking alcohol and he may become irrational or comatose.

Case 24: A man 82 years of age, was brought to casualty in an unconscious state. His rectal temperature was 35°C. Plantar responses were extensor. The blood sugar was 21 mg/100 ml. He was given 25 per cent dextrose 40 ml intravenously, and rapidly regained consciousness. His muscle tone and plantar reflexes returned to normal, but hypoglycemia persisted for 24 hours. He had drunk about 1,200 mls of whisky.

Case 25: A man, 67 years of age, was found unconscious in his flat. His limbs were rigid. The blood sugar was less than 10 mg/100 ml. Rectal temperature was 35°C. After 80 ml of 25 per cent dextrose intravenously he regained consciousness and his rectal temperature became normal. Hypertonicity, and the extensor plantar responses were no longer apparent.

It seems that he had drunk about 3 litres of beer followed by about 450 mls of whisky the previous night, and his diet had been deficient.

These patients clearly showed hypoglycaemia with hypothermia and responded rapidly to treatment with dextrose. The liver function tests, glucose tolerance curve, blood urea, serum electrolytes, x-ray of chest and blood counts were normal in each case, but the ECG showed flattening of the T waves consistent with cardiac ischaemia.

It is generally accepted that alcohol causes hypoglycaemia by inhibiting gluconeogenesis. These histories do not indicate whether the individuals concerned had a tendency to hypoglycaemia when sober and fortunately they did not fall foul of the law.

Hypoglycaemia causing disturbances of cerebral function is known as neuroglycopenia, and may be caused by an insulin-secreting tumour, the post-gastrectomy syndrome, insulin overdose, sulphonylureas and biguanides especially when a diabetic omits one or more meals. Alcohol and drugs, such as salicylates, paracetamol and antihistamines may also cause hypoglycaemia in susceptible individuals.

Symptoms include acute anxiety, fear, agitation, feelings of depersonalization and realization, lack of spontaneity, drowsiness, memory defects, refractory attitudes, psychotic behaviour usually of a paranoid nature or resembling dementia and confusional states. Lack of response to painful stimuli and absent pupillary responses to light, indicate coma.

Other complications of acute hypoglycaemia include palpitations, increased pulse rate, shallow breathing, sweating, unsteady gait, hypothermia and even transient hemiparesis.

Case 26: The following case history indicates that a plea of diminished responsibility on the basis of the Homicide Act (1957) will succeed when clinical and electroencephalographic evidence indicates that an accused person suffers from epilepsy. In this instance his intelligence was also below average and psychopathic tendencies were evident. He was regarded as an epileptic by his general medical practitioner. He was subject to grand mal and petit mal. The epilepsy was reasonably well controlled by anti-convulsant medication. A consultant neurologist was of the opinion that his antisocial behaviour could be regarded as an expression of his epilepsy.

There was no history of suicide attempts or serious head injuries. One could assume an hysterical element in his personality. He had a history of delinquent behaviour before the homicide but mainly involving offences against property. His childhood was apparently quite happy and secure. His birth was normal and his mother stated that he was well behaved during childhood. He suffered from nocturnal enuresis up to his mid-teens. A cousin suffered from epilepsy.

Part of his school years were spent in an epileptic colony. His intelligence quotient was 79 on the basis of the Wechsler Adult Intelligence Scale. His work record was brief and inconsistent but mainly because he experienced difficulty in obtaining employment as a result of his epilepsy. He was single and heterosexual. There was no history of illicit drug-taking but he took alcohol to excess periodically and he apparently needed alcohol to counteract feelings of despondency, tension and frustration when faced with the stresses and strains of ordinary community life. Consequently, he was regarded as an alcoholic. He attended a mental hospital as a day patient several years before the homicide. Blood tests for venereal disease were returned as negative during the remand period and skull and chest x-rays also proved normal.

He was rather truculent and difficult during the remand period and experienced several epileptic attacks. He was well orientated in place and time and there was no evidence of delusions, hallucinations or serious defects of judgment or reasoning. There was no evidence of incongruity between thought processes, emotional responses and behaviour. His appetite was good but sleep was irregular.

He visited a public house where he drank a moderate amount of beer. He then met the deceased and they started to converse. They then had a drink in a public house and on the way home started kissing and fondling. The deceased was a middle-aged woman and he had not previously been in her company. He alleged that she then accidentally fell down and struck her face on a stone and became semi-conscious. He then panicked and ran from the scene. The woman subsequently died.

He was fit to plead and to stand trial. At the material time he was not suffering from a defect of reason due to disease of the mind and he was therefore capable of knowing what he was doing and that what he was doing was wrong. Consequently, the M'Naghten Rules did not apply to him. The other consideration that arose was that of mental abnormality as defined in s.2(1) of the Homicide Act 1957. I gave the opinion that his state at the time of the alleged offence could be described as mentally abnormal within the meaning of the definition, that is, due to retarded development of mind, as indicated by an Intelligence Quotient of 79. There was also an inherent cause in the form of abnormal personality closely related to his epilepsy. I was therefore of the opinion that there was mental abnormality sufficient to impair substantially his responsibility for his actions in doing the killing.

Section 60 of the Mental Health Act 1959 was not applicable to him on the grounds of mental disorder. He was not psychotic or subnormal within the meaning of that Act.

I did not regard him as suffering from psychopathic disorder as defined in the same Act because this definition is generally taken to mean persistent aggressive psychopathy with the aggression directed against the person. He had only one previous conviction for assault and all other previous offences were against property.

I concluded that he represented a very serious danger to the public especially when under the influence of alcohol. He pleaded guilty to manslaughter on the grounds of diminished responsibility: the plea was accepted by the Crown. He was sentenced to a long term of imprisonment.

The Criminal Procedure (Insanity and Unfitness to Plead) Act 1991 will help people with epilepsy who commit offences during or in the aftermath of a fit. Previously the only plea available to them (apart from guilty) has been not guilty by reason of insanity, which has led to automatic detention in hospital. A new range of orders will be available for people with epilepsy. See Chapter I.

References

Bleuler, E. (1924) "Affectivity, Suggestibility and Paranoia", *State Hospital Bulletin*, New York.

Bonkalo, A. (1974) "Impulsive Acts and Confusional States during Incomplete Arousal from Sleep: Criminological and Forensic Implications", *Psychiatric Quarterly* 48: 400-9.

Brain, R., 1956, *Psychological Aspects of Neurology*, Chap. XXIII, 951-55.

Bromberg, W., 1965, *Crime and the Mind,* Macmillan Co., New York.

Buchanan, A. (1991) "Sleepwalking and Indecent Exposure", *Med. Sci. Law*, 31, 1: 38-40.

Charatan, F.B. (1994) "New tacrine hopes for Alzheimer patients in U.S." *B.J.H. V.*308, pp. 999-1,000.

Chuang, H.T., Williams, R., Dalby J.T. (1987) "Criminal Behaviour Among Schizophrenics", *Can. J. Psych.* 32(4): 255-8.

Cook, D.A.G. (1983) "A Study of Criminal Behaviour in Discharged Psychiatric Patients", *Med. Sci. Law*, 25, 4: 279-82.

Der, G., Gupta, S., Murray, R.M. (1990) "Is Schizophrenia Disappearing?" *Lancet*, 335: 531-15.

Ervin, F.R. (1967) "Brain Disorders IV: Associated with Convulsion", in *Comprehensive Textbook of Psychiatry*, (eds. Freedman and Kaplan) Williams & Wilkins, Baltimore.

Feighner, J.P., Robins, E., Guze, S.B., *et al.* (1972) "Diagnostic Criteria for Use in Psychiatric Research", *Arch. Gen. Psychiatry* 26, 57: 63.

Freud, S. (1911) *Collected Papers*, Vol. 3.

Giannitrapani, D., Collins, J., Vassiliadis, D. (1991) "The EEG Spectra of Alzheimer's Disease", *Int. J. Psychophysiol.*, 10(3): 259-69.

Gold, M.S., Potash, A.L.C., Ryan, N., Sweeney, D.R., Davies, R.K., Martin, D.M. (1981) "TRH-induced TSH Response in Unipolar, Bipolar and Secondary Depressions: Possible Utility in Clinical Assessment and Differential Diagnosis", *Psychoneuroendocrinology* 5: 147-55.

Green, C.M. (1981) "Matricide by Sons", *Med. Sci. Law.* 21: 207-14.

Gunn, J. and Fenton, G. (1969) "Epilepsy in Prisons – A Diagnostic Survey", *Brit. Md. J.*, 4: 326.

Henderson, D.K., and Batchelor, I.R.C. (1961) *Textbook of Psychiatry for Students and Practitioners*, George Allen & Unwin, London.

Hill, D. and Parr, G. (eds) (1963) *Electroencephalograph*, Macmillan, London.

Hopwood, J.S. (1927) "Child Murder and Insanity", *Journal of Mental Science*, 73: 95.

Hughes, R.R. (1961) *An Introduction to Clinical Electroencephalograph*, Williams & Wilkins, Bristol.

Jannett, B. (1975) *Epilepsy After Non-missile Head Injuries*, Heinemann Medical Books, London.

Jasper, H. and Kershman, J. (1949) "Classification of Electroencephalogram in Epilepsy", *Electroencephalograph and Clinical Neurophysiology*, Supplement 2: 123.

Kiloh, L.G., Davidson, K. and Osselton, J.W. (1961) "An Electroencephalographic Study of the Analeptic Effects of Imipermia", *Electroencephalograph and Clinical Neurophysiologi*, 3: 30.

Kraepelin, E. (1920) "Symptoms of Mental Disease", *Zeitschrift fuer die Gesamte Neurologie und Psychiatrie*, 62, I: 29.

Macniven, A. (1944) "Mental Abnormality and Crime", in *Psychoses and Criminal Responsibility*, Radzinowicz and Turner, J.W.C. (eds.) Macmillan & Co., London.

Marchand, L. and Ajuriaguerra, J. (1948) *Epilepsies*, 456, Desclee, Paris.

Mitchell-Heggs, N. (1971) "Aspects of the Natural History and Clinical Presentation of Depression", *Proceedings of the Royal Soc. of Medicine.*, Vol. 64, ps. 1171-74.

Monkemoller, X. (1912) "Zur Psyuchopathologie des Brandstifers", *Hans Cross Archive fuer Kriminal-Anthropologie and Kriminalistik*, 48: 193.

Montgomery S.A., and Asberg, M. (1979) "A New Depression Scale Designed to be Sensitive to Change", *Brit. J. Psychiat.*, 134: 382-398.

Mowat, R.R. (1966) *Morbid Jealousy and Murder*, Tavistock Publications, London.

Mullen, P.E. and Maack, L.H. (1985) "Jealousy, Pathological Jealousy and Aggression", *Aggression and Dangerousness*, John Wiley, Chichester.

Naismith, L.J and Coldwell, J.B. (1990) "A Comparison of Male Admissions to a Special Hospital 1970-71 and 1987-88", *Med. Sci. Law*, 30, 4: 301-8.

Neustatter, W.L. (1953) *Psychological Disorder and Crime*, Christopher Johnson, London.

Pawer, B.P. (1972) "Alcohol and Hypoglycaemia", *Journal of Alcoholism*, 7, I: 26.

Pond, D.A., Bidwell, B.H. (1960) *Survey of Epilepsy in 14 General Practices*, 11.

A report by the Research Committee of the Royal College of General Practitioners, *Brit. Med. J.*, 2: 416.

Rogers, J. (1990) Research Paper, Arizona Institute for Biogerontology Research.

Rosandi, G., Cogorno, O., Marenco, S., Nobili, F., Rodriguez, G. (1991) "Brain Functional Imaging in Senile Psychopathology", *Int. J. Psychophysiol.*, 10(3): 271-80.

Sullivan, W.C. (1924) *Crime in Relation to Congenital Mental Deficiency*, Edward Arnold & Co., London.

Szabadi, E. (1991) "Thyroid Dysfunction and Affective Illness", *Brit. Med. J.*, 302: 923-4.

Taplin, L.A. (1985) "The Criminality of the Mentally Ill; A Dangerous Misconception", *American Journal of Psych.* 142, 5: 593-9.

Taylor, F.K. (1966) *Psychopathology: Its Causes and Symptoms*, J. & A. Churchill, London.

Virkkunen M. (1974) "Observations on Violence in Schizophrenia", *Acta Psychiatrica Scandinavica*, 50: 145-51.

Wagstaffe, W.W. (1928) "A Case of Acute Primary Typhlitis", *Clinical Journal London*, 55: 78.

Walker, A. (1961) "Murder or Epilepsy?", *Journal of Nervous and Mental Disease*, 5: 430.

Walton, J.N. (1963) *Medico-Legal Journal*, 31: 15-35.

Watson, C.W. (1947) "The Incidence of Epilepsy following Craniocerebral Injury", *The Association of Nervous and Mental Disease, Research Publications*, 26, 516.

CHAPTER X

Psychoneurosis and Crime

Some authorities indicate that 15 per cent of the population are significantly incapacitated by neurotic symptoms (Leigh *et al*, 1972).

Psychoneurotic reactions may be regarded as abnormal emotional states caused by mental conflicts involving the social, sexual, aggressive and self-preservation instincts. These conflicts may reach a pathological degree of intensity so as to bring about a disabling condition. Psychoneurosis is usually, but not invariably, susceptible to cure by psychological means. Conflicts involve instinctive desires on the one hand and social requirements on the other.

Transitions between neuroses and psychoses may occur. A patient suffering from an anxiety state may develop an agitated involutional depression. Neurotic anxiety associated with a severe obsessional state may finally develop into a paranoid psychosis (Henderson and Gillespie, 1951). Such transitions are the exception rather than the rule. The aggressive psychopath may be regarded as behaving in a psychotic manner during the course of a frenzied and apparently motiveless attack upon an unfortunate victim.

Some distinctions between psychoneuroses, psychoses and psychopathy are:

(1) The neurotic views his environment in the same way as the average person does, and realizes that his symptoms are abnormal. Genuine suffering is apparent and help is usually sought. Neurotic symptoms usually fluctuate and relief is experienced if the subject's attention is diverted to some activity in which he is interested. The neurotic speaks and usually behaves in a relatively normal manner. The neologisms used by some schizophrenics indicate that language undergoes distortion in that condition. Psychosis involves change of the whole personality and reality is changed qualitatively resulting in abnormal behaviour.

(2) From the point of view of psychopathology, the psychotic behaves as if reality has a different kind of meaning for him than the rest of the community and this change in reality values is often expressed in the form of "projection" when an unpleasant

subjective experience is attributed to some external personal agency resulting in paranoid delusions. Some psychotics "regress" to an infantile level as indicated by defective personal habits. The psychotic does not realize that he is mentally ill and therefore lacks insight. David (1990) made some interesting observations on the subject of insight which is certainly not an all or none phenomenon. He states that insight is based on three overlapping dimensions:

(i)   the recognition by the patient that he or she has a mental illness;

(ii) the patient's adequate co-operation with treatment; and

(iii) the patient's ability to understand in retrospect that experiences such as delusions and hallucinations, were abnormal. Presumably this understanding would be in response to treatment. Autism and premature intellectual deterioration are not evident in the psychoneuroses.

(3)   The response to therapy is different in neurosis, psychosis and psychopathy. Endogenous depression and catatonic schizophrenia will usually respond to electro-convulsant therapy but the same treatment tends to aggravate reactive depression and other forms of psychoneurosis. However, these dividing lines are not absolute because anti-depressant medication may relieve reactive and endogenous depression and an illness with symptoms of both conditions. Debilitating obsessive compulsive neurosis was relieved by "modified" leucotomy but the same procedure removed the last vestige of control if applied to an aggressive psychopath. This operation is no longer practised in this country.

Treatment for the psychoneuroses rests mainly on psychotherapy meaning simple explanations and attempts to find solutions for patients' problems. Long-term support including the teaching of social skills is also helpful. "Aims" should not be set too high lest failure to achieve them results in frustration and relapse.

The psychoanalytic theory alleges that psychoneurosis may be caused by an unconscious death wish towards the parent of the same sex and frustration stemming from a discrepancy between sexual desire and satisfaction.

The Mental Health Act 1983 refers to four types of mental disorder. All are defined except mental illness which is taken to include the psychoses and neuroses. The former are recognized comparatively easily in the great majority of instances and are generally referred to as various forms of "insanity" which is a legal term as opposed to a medical one. Psychotics often require inpatient psychiatric treatment but Zigmond *et al.* (1983) indicated that 21 per cent of all psychiatric admissions to a district general hospital suffered from neurotic disorders.

The Butler Committee (Butler Report, HMSO, 1975) defined severe mental illness for medico-legal purposes, as having the following features:

a)   Lasting impairment of intellectual functions shown by failure of memory, orientation, comprehension and learning capacity.

b)   Lasting alteration of mood to such degree as to give rise to delusional appraisal of the patient's situation, his past or his future, or that of others, or to lack of any appraisal.

c)   Delusional beliefs – persecutory, jealous or grandiose.

d)   Abnormal perception associated with delusional misinterpretation of events.

e)   Thinking so disordered as to prevent reasonable appraisal of the patient's situation or reasonable communication with others.

The above features virtually define the psychoses which are also referred to in ICD9 World Health Organization 1978, as: "mental disorders in which impairment of mental function has developed to a degree that interferes grossly with insight, ability to meet some ordinary demands of life or to maintain adequate contact with reality. It is not an exact or well-defined term. Mental retardation is excluded."

The great majority of neurotics retain intellectual and emotional insight and consequently illegal behaviour would not be excused on the grounds of inability to control their behaviour because of alleged subconscious emotional conflicts and/or motivations. Persons suffering from the acute phases of neurotic depression, obsessional states and anxiety are too ill to break the law because their symptoms, including intense fear, are so overwhelming. The validity of "conversion" hysteria is much in doubt and if it exists, it should not be classified with the neuroses due to absence of insight, fear and anxiety. Furthermore, "anxiety hysteria" is a contradiction in terms.

Various forms of mental disorder, including neurotic illness, may be caused by such conditions as cerebral tumour, thyrotoxicosis, epilepsy, hypertension, cerebral arteriosclerosis, cerebral atrophy, cerebral trauma, Parkinsonism and alcoholism and/or illicit drug-taking. These conditions do not make provision of psychiatric evidence for courts any easier and consequently all relevant investigations for organic pathology should be implemented during the remand period in addition to psychiatric assessment.

Feelings of inferiority, loss of self-respect, overdependence on others, indecisiveness, diffidence, chronic mental and physical fatigue, strong feelings of affection and hatred, sexual conflicts and poor capacity to withstand stress occur in varying degrees in the neuroses.

Gallwey (1992) indicated that "... the neurotic position can decompensate into a delinquent one and the delinquent position can change to a neurotic one". This has not been my experience and I have not encountered instances where neurotic and delinquent states interchanged.

There is no doubt that psychopathic states and law-breaking frequently co-exist and secondary symptoms of anxiety and depression resembling those of the psychoneuroses, not infrequently stem from these conditions. However, I very much doubt if lawbreaking in the form of delinquency or otherwise, can be an expression of neurotic illness *per se*.

Acute neurotic illness is usually associated with some degree of genuine memory defect due partly to inattention and partly to general mental fatigue. The relevance of alleged memory defect in relation to the material time of a crime is obvious.

East (1939) examined 4,000 male delinquents and found that only 24 were psychoneurotic on the basis of commonly accepted criteria. One may reasonably assume that "conversion" hysteria was not included in this study. Martin *et al.* (1985) studied 66 convicted female felons and found that 43 (65 per cent) were anti-social personalities and seven (11 per cent) were anxiety neurotics. This is a much smaller study than that of East, but does not essentially disagree with his findings.

Smart (1969) equated delinquency with emotional immaturity and both with neurosis. The writer is of the opinion that persons suffering from anxiety and obsessional neurosis and neurotic depression *per se* seldom break the law. Such individuals may periodically resort to alcohol or drugs to relieve their sufferings but psychopaths practise these habits in pursuit of pleasure and as expressions of irresponsibility and waywardness. Gillespie (1944) regarded delinquent acts and neurotic symptoms as problem-solving devices. The same writer indicated that an illegal act can only be attributed to neurosis if certain criteria are satisfied. These have been described in Chapter VI but may be repeated here:

1. The illegal act must be the outcome of an emotional conflict and one side of the conflicting forces must be social conscience, however primitive in structure.
2. One should be able to understand the offence as an attempt to resolve the emotional conflict.
3. Material gain must not be the primary object of the illegal behaviour.
4. Other recognized symptoms of psychoneurosis should be evident (Gillespie, 1944).

Varying degrees of neurosis exist and psychiatrists have wide discretion as to whether they regard any neurotic condition as a mental disorder within the meaning of the Mental Health Act 1983.

Slater (1965) formulated the concept of the "neurotic constitution", meaning that liability to neurotic breakdown varies quantitatively from person to person.

Each personality is unique, and some people react to stress with different types of neurosis. Individuals who develop anxiety and obsessional neurosis *per se* tend to be introverted and inhibited and rarely break the law. They learn from their mistakes and develop respect for property and persons because autonomic conditioning reactions are strong components of their personalities and act as "learned drivers" which are strongly reinforced by anxiety and therefore strongly resistant to extinction. The opposite applies to extroverts who are regarded as poor conditioners. This theory attempts to explain why an emotional conflict may cause neurotic symptoms in one individual and lead to delinquent acts in another.

Certain types of delinquent behaviour may compensate for real or imagined loss of affection during childhood and adolescence. Yarnell (1940) indicated that a group of children described as pyromaniacs had suffered more grievous deprivation of affection and security than a control group of neurotic children.

Inherent selfishness *per se* is often the cause of criminal behaviour.

The psychoneuroses may be classified as follows:

1. Anxiety neurosis.
2. Neurotic depression.

3.   Obsessional neurosis.
4.   Hysterical reactions.

1. Anxiety Neurosis.

An anxiety state may be defined as an emotional condition in which the feelings of fear, apprehension and tension predominate. It is a normal defence mechanism mediated by the autonomic nervous system and only activated when an individual believes he or she is or may be in a situation of genuine danger. The symptoms normally subside when the danger passes. The mood ranges from uneasiness to panic. Fear of fainting is common but loss of consciousness unusual. Palpitations, dizziness, perspiration, nausea and vomiting, weakness, trembling, unsteady gait, blurred vision, tinnitus, dyspnoea, stammer and insomnia are the physiological expressions of anxiety.

A chronic anxiety state may develop on the basis of environmental factors, constitutional predisposition and the operation of conditioned reflexes so that symptoms *persist* in the absence of adequate cause. Negative autosuggestion aggravates symptoms. Irritability and defective concentration are common and episodes of acute anxiety may be superimposed on the chronic state.

Anxiety may be regarded as neurotic or pathological when symptoms continue without apparent cause and because of their intensity the individual is incapable of managing his life with reasonable competence from the domestic, social and occupational points of view. This statement also applies to other forms of psychoneurosis and to any serious mental disorder.

Psychosomatic illnesses are commonly associated with anxiety. Examples of such illnesses are bronchial asthma, migraine, duodenal ulcer, and certain types of dermatitis. Diagnosis of psychosomatic illness is based on the premise that organic pathology is secondary to emotional conflict.

Anxiety is frequently associated with other forms of mental disorder and especially depression.

Trait anxiety has been used to mitigate various crimes. However, certain criteria must be fulfilled for such a defence to succeed:

(i)   there must be evidence to the effect that specific stresses (not usually encountered by the accused) were acting on him at the material time of the crime.

(ii)   A history of "out of character" behaviour must be evident such as, for example, overwork followed by unexpected fall off in work performance, recent history of taking alcohol to excess and/ or illicit drug-taking and gambling with resulting serious personal difficulties.

(iii) High trait anxiety means pathological anxiety which may be hereditary.

(iv) Appropriate tests such as the MMPI and the Eysenek personality questionnaire should be positive for abnormal anxiety.

2. Neurotic depression

Neurotic depression is characterized by despondency, irritability and agitation. The basic personality is unstable and unduly vulnerable to stress. The neurotic depressive tends to blame others for his misfortunes. Symptoms become more severe as the day progresses due to mental fatigue but the sufferer may feel tired each morning even after sleeping reasonably well. The condition may progress to a degree where impairment of concentration may lead to defective judgment. Suicide is always a possibility but obviously less frequent than in severe endogenous depression.

Acute neurotic conditions including depression could be regarded as an illness within the meaning of the Mental Health Act 1983.

The American Psychiatric Association (1980) indicated that neurotic depression is more closely related to the major affective disorders than to neurosis but this would depend on degree of depression and possible presence of endogenous elements.

Neurotic depression may be a progressive condition and lead to the endogenous type, but this is the exception rather than the rule. The higher degrees of endogenous depression are characterized by lack of insight and delusions of guilt which may be accompanied by hallucinations.

A charge of murder would be reduced to manslaughter on the basis of diminished responsibility (Homicide Act, 1957) if psychoneurosis was successfully pleaded.

3. Obsessional Neurosis

Obsessions may be defined as imperative ideas which periodically dominate consciousness. These ideas are intrusive and invariably resisted by the sufferer. Obsessions are expressed in the form of memory images, phobias, ruminations and impulses leading to particular types of behaviour and accompanied by fear, apprehension, anxiety and tension.

Phobias are irrational fears and may be classified as:

(a)   claustrophobia meaning fear of enclosed spaces;
(b)   agoraphobia meaning fear of open spaces;
(c)   mysophobia meaning fear of contamination;
(d)   aichmophobia meaning fear of pointed objects;
(e)   pyrophobia meaning fear of causing fire through negligence; and
(f)   homilophobia is a constant tormenting idea that other people might find something wrong with one's appearance, attire or demeanour.

The obsessional personality has the following characteristics (Brain, 1956):

(a)   a primitive emotional life in which guilt demands expiatory rituals;
(b)   feelings of "bondage" to the past;
(c)   sado-masochistic tendencies; and
(d)   a conspicuous tendency to indulge in certain behaviour such as continuous handwashing based on morbid fear of contamination. This type of ritualistic behaviour is designed to ward off anxiety by relieving guilt feelings which may stem from conflicts between the aggressive and sexual instincts on the one hand and exceptionally strong super-ego prohibitions on the other.

Obsessional individuals are usually over-conscientious, meticulous and fixed in their beliefs. Environmental stress may be the determining factor as to whether such an individual develops an obsessional neurosis, meaning a breakdown in adaptation to normal situations.

Ziehen (1926) classified obsessions as:

(a)   disparate obsessions of simple, trivial disconnected ideas which more or less continually and painfully intrude into consciousness;
(b)   connected obsessions of a more complex nature such as notions that a door has been left unlocked or gas not turned off;
(c)   motor obsessions such as handwashing and doing things "in threes".

The obsessional neurotic feels compelled to think certain thoughts which may lead to certain types of compulsive activity. These thoughts and activities can be resisted but only temporarily. The "irresistible impulse" (which has been used in the United States as a defence in some instances of homicide charges), cannot be controlled or resisted for any length of time and it is therefore not an expression of an obsessional state.

There is a fairly strong hereditary element. Lewis (1936) found that one-third of the parents of a group of obsessionals and one-fifth of their brothers and sisters, showed pronounced obsessional traits. He also found that schizophrenia and affective illness occurred with more than average frequency in the families of obsessionals. He also expressed the opinion that obsessions may be symptomatic of cyclic affective states.

Again, Lewis could not discover a relationship between obsessional states and crime. He studied 50 obsessionals and did not find a single instance in which an anti-social (obsessional) compulsive impulse had been put into execution.

Statistics concerning the prognosis of obsessional neurosis indicate high remission rates which are probably independent of treatment given. Lewis followed up 50 obsessional neurotics for five or more years after treatment in hospital, and found that approximately half "did well".

Rudin (1953) found that out of a total of 57 obsessional cases followed up for 15 to 35 years, 28 became symptom-free or totally adapted. He also found that 10 of this study group later developed schizophrenia.

Depression is a common complication of obsessional neurosis but the risks of suicide, alcoholism and drug addiction are small.

Shoplifting
Shoplifting may be considered in this section, as attempts have been made to associate this offence with obsessional neurosis because there is a compulsive element in kleptomania. However, this compulsion is, in my opinion, secondary to basic psychopathic or at least anti-social tendencies in persons who become preoccupied with shoplifting and the same statement applies to other repetitive offences such as pyromania, sexual exhibitionism and homicide.

Epps (1962) indicated that many women who indulge in shoplifting have highly conscientious and mildly obsessional personalities with phobic symptoms. However, Gudjonsson (1988) indicated that although compulsive shoplifting (which relieves tension and is therefore likely to be repeated), may resemble obsessive-compulsive behaviour, there is no evidence that this condition is an obsessive-compulsive disorder *per se* but rather an irresistible impulse at the material time. Probably fewer than 5 per cent of arrested shoplifters fulfil the definition of kleptomania which is a recurrent failure to resist impulses to steal objects not needed for personal use or their monetary value, DSM-111-R (1987).

Buckle *et al* (1984), found that about 2 per cent of customers were shoplifters and men are twice as likely to offend as women.

Some women are frightened by the realization that they are strongly tempted to shoplift and when the offence takes place it may be motivated by a desire to ensure sympathy and help from loved ones.

Stimuli to shoplift may be provided by the excitement accompanying the thought of doing something condemned by society and also by seeing somebody else engaging in the practice. The sights, sounds and smells in a department store may also act as stimuli.

It has been suggested that shoplifting in women may be a less developed and organized equivalent of fetishism in men. People have also been prosecuted for changing price labels on items in stores.

Shoplifting may be perpetrated in order to gain revenge for alleged overcharging.

A group of 313 shoplifters was studied in Chicago and 49 were considered to be psychoneurotic, 50 psychotic, 50 psychopathic and 53 mentally impaired, Arieff (1942).

Arousal enhancement makes shoplifters in general, and kleptomaniacs in particular, feel excited at the material time of the thefts and they subsequently experience relief of tension and anxiety, some mood elevation and a temporary sense of wellbeing. All of these feelings are highly reinforcing, Gudjonsson (1990).

Shoplifting by depressives may be a reaction to inability to give adequate expression of their anger and frustration and consequently, the arousal enhancement and subsequent relief of tension associated with the shoplifting provide alternative emotional satisfaction.

The primary condition needs to be treated when shoplifting is secondary to mental disorders such as schizophrenia, dementia, mental impairment, hypomania, depression, genuine kleptomania and the very rare hysterical fugue, the existence of which is disputed. Treatment includes attempts to prevent further anticipated personality deterioration.

Some professional shoplifters only seek psychiatric advice when they fall foul of the law and in this context they behave like those who are sexually deviant *per se* and break the law.

Moore (1984) found that only 1.7 per cent of all shoplifting was directly associated with depression. In my experience shoplifting by neurotic and endogenous depressives is quite uncommon because of psychomotor retardation in the latter and fears and inhibitions in the former.

Dalton (1961) believes that the hormonal changes of menstruation probably make an individual less amenable to discipline and therefore, possibly, more inclined to offend. Some quite respectable individuals may indulge in shoplifting during a phase of "absentmindedness" and especially when under the influence of sedatives or tranquilizers. The offence may also be influenced by the amount of alcohol ingested and low blood-sugar levels. Shoplifters between the ages of 25 and 40 were found to be otherwise of good character but relatively intolerant of frustration. Depression was particularly common in those between the ages of 40 and 55 years and endogenous depression has a high incidence in this age period. Shoplifting by depressed women may represent a "cry for help". Advice from an endocrinologist should be sought with a view to treating premenstrual tension which has also been alleged to influence malicious fire setting. The Adlerian school indicates that theft in the form of shoplifting is an overcompensation for inferiority feelings.

Epps (1962) studied 200 women in Holloway Prison and could find no connection between the material times of shoplifting and any phase of their menstrual cycles. Systematic studies have not revealed a connection between shoplifting, menstruation, menopause and pregnancy, but Dalton's (1961) studies cast some doubt on these findings. This investigator interviewed 366 newly convicted women under the age of 55 years on the first weekday after their sentences. The interviews took place in one of HM prisons over a six-month period. Nearly half of all crimes (49 per cent) were committed by women during menstruation and the premenstruum (a total period of eight days). On a normal distribution, only two-sevenths (29 per cent) of all crimes would be expected during these periods. This investigation indicated that menstruation tends to be of greater importance in crimes of theft and 56 per cent of such crimes occurred during menstruation and premenstruum. Theft includes shoplifting, burglary, embezzlement and forgery. "Pre-menstrual tension" is defined as headaches, tiredness, irritability, lethargy, mood changes such as depression, bloatedness and/or mastitis occurring during the four days preceding menstruation. These symptoms may be related to fluid retention. Irritability may lead to loss of temper and violence. Lethargy may lead to child neglect.

Motivation may stem from despondency and resentment caused by the loss of a child or desire to conceive. Shoplifting may be an expression or a wish to "keep up appearances" and maintain social status by those who have come into poor circumstances. A mother may steal presents for her children in order to be regarded as a good parent.

Selfish women with rigid views and well-organized budgets may indulge in shoplifting because extra payments are painful and possession relieves anxiety.

Women who shoplift would not usually steal from an individual.

Professional shoplifters are motivated by greed.

Emotionally disturbed juveniles may steal as an act of defiance against restrictive parents.

Shoplifters may be classified as:

1. Those suffering from transitory emotional disturbances. Some individuals in this category may place goods in a shopping basket and unintentionally walk out of the store without paying. Such an occurrence is conceivable in the light of reports concerning prominent people who found themselves in this predicament and indicated that they had been thinking of some important and worrying issue at the time of leaving the store.

2. Mentally disordered individuals, including those with defective judgment secondary to organic cerebral pathology. Moak *et al* (1988) studied a group of elderly first offender shoplifters. All were over the age of 65 years. They concluded that none of the study group were motivated by financial hardship but that the shoplifting was associated with organic and functional (psychiatric) disorders which were acute or chronic. Furthermore Silverman *et al* (1988) undertook a pilot study of 200 legally referred shoplifters who were all females and married. They concluded that they had a recognizable pattern of psychiatric symptoms including those resulting from marital and/or sexual dysfunction, phobic anxiety and depression, but the type of depression was not specified. Another conclusion was that these shoplifters had characteristics more in common with other psychiatric patients than with other offenders.

3. "Down and outs" and vagrants who are tired, hungry and without shelter. I have observed that such individuals not uncommonly steal in order to obtain food or with the specific object of obtaining "board and lodging" in police cells or prisons.

4. Professional shoplifters may be defined as those who to a greater

or lesser extent make their living out of shoplifting and are not deterred by threats of consequences if caught. They are not mentally disordered nor are the great majority of shoplifters.

Mortimer (1991) classified shoplifters from the point of view of *mens rea*, defined as the accused person's state of mind in regard to his behaviour, meaning whether his conduct was voluntary or not and also the accused's state of mind in regard to knowledge of the consequences of his act. On this basis the following classification may be made with reference to Mortimer's excellent article. There is some repetition of material considered earlier in this section.

1. Mens rea present:
(i) Professional thieves who persistently attempt to make a living out of shoplifting and may involve their children.
(ii) Casual thieves who behave with the dishonesty of which most people are potentially capable. This group contains an above average number of first offenders and many are juveniles. There are elements of tension and pleasure in outwitting the shop staff and punishing society for real or imagined unfair treatment and also obtaining attractive goods free of charge.
(iii) People who worry about their poverty and wish to relieve it and help their families.
(iv) People who steal:
    (a) to punish themselves or others by causing disgrace,
    (b) as a cry for help,
    (c) to obtain vicarious sexual gratification,
    (d) with the object of substituting for loss.
    (a) and (b) require being apprehended.
The above would be regarded as having *mens rea* if the shoplifting was voluntary and they were aware of the consequences of their behaviour. *Mens rea* would *usually* be present in personality disorders.

2. *Doubtful mens rea*
Individuals suffering from mental disorder but not to such a degree as to deprive them of insight. Mortimer refers to derealization, dissociation of ideas and depersonalization which is unpleasant with acute onset and gradual termination.
These conditions are symptomatic of abnormal mental

functioning which also applies to twilight states and automatisms which may be associated with epilepsy.

3. *Mens rea absent*
(i)   Serious mental disorders such as psychotic conditions, confusional states and conversion hysteria. The validity of the latter diagnosis has been questioned in recent years. These disorders are characterized by loss of insight.
(ii) Genuine absent-mindedness when people forget to pay due to excessive worry causing preoccupation and distraction whilst shopping. Psychotropic drugs given to these persons may further increase their likelihood of shoplifting. Defending such people may be quite difficult in court.

Careful history-taking and correct interpretation of evidence are vital in reaching a correct conclusion.

Investigations: Intelligence and personality tests, and electroencephalograms are carried out as indicated.

Prevention

There is an increasing tendency for management to discuss with trade unions problems affecting shop staff. Shop owners whose employees are trade union members may well find that consultation with unions about staff rules will not only ensure the smooth operation of the rules but will assist in the desired object of persuading employees to identify themselves with employers in security as well as in other matters. It cannot be emphasized too strongly that losses sustained by the retailer have an effect on the pay and conditions of his employees.

Estimates which have been published in the press of losses in money sustained by retailers as a result of shoplifting in England and Wales have ranged from £56 million to £300 million per year. Estimates of losses from staff thefts range from £135 million to £200 million per year.

The following Criminal Statistics for England and Wales (1992), indicate the number of thefts from shop offences in England and Wales as recorded by Police.

Table XXI

Year	Offences Recorded
1978	203,643
1979	203,122
1980	206,175
1981	225,342
1982	242,304
1983	235,512
1984	248,792 (86 per cent cleared up)
1985	281,557
1986	255,463
1987	247,064
1988	216,242 (83 per cent cleared up)
1989	222,974 (81 per cent cleared up)
1990	250,301 (82 per cent cleared up)
1991	281,276 (81 per cent cleared up)
1994	269,311 (77 per cent cleared up)

In 1988 there were 65,315 less recorded offences of shoplifting as compared with 1985. This finding could indicate more cunning techniques of evading detection.

Increasing public awareness of the consequences of shoplifting and the use of anti-shoplifting signs and posters have been employed with limited success. Parental advice, example and training from childhood are most important for prevention. General medical practitioners and probation officers also have important roles to play.

Store detectives and closed-circuit televisions help to control shoplifting but do not influence its overall incidence.

Shoplifting could be counteracted in self-service stores if personal carrier bags were given to the care of a desk clerk on entering the store. Wiremesh baskets supplied by the store could then be exclusively used to carry store property before payment is made on leaving.

Minute electronic security paper tags can be concealed in the packaging of store products causing alarms to be set off at the front of the store when shoplifters try to leave without paying. The tags are invisible to thieves and contain harmless disposable sensors which can only be switched off when the products are passed over the price codes readers at the checkout. Perhaps the tags will initially be used on the more expensive products. The system is known as Electronic Article Surveillance used at ASDA stores in 1992.

The British Retail Consortium, (1994), reported that shoplifting cost shopkeepers £2 billion in 1993 and 27 per cent of these offences were allegedly committed by staff.

Treatment

Aversive-conditioning procedures are suitable for kleptomania but advice in the form of emotional support and re-education are also necessary. Alternative means of providing relief of tension and emotional satisfaction, must be found or relapse will occur and in this context abreactive techniques including psychodrama are helpful.

For the episodic non-compulsive shoplifter, cognitive therapy with the accent on appreciation of the disastrous effects of further shoplifting on the perpetrator's life prospects is helpful, and Azrin *et al* (1974) advocate over-correction procedures, meaning that the offender returns the stolen item in addition to an identical one which he or she purchases from the same store.

Psychotherapy must always be appropriate for the patient's personality type.

Shoplifting may be an expression of mental disorder or may, of course, be influenced by alcoholism and/or illicit drug-taking when these conditions require treatment.

Problem-solving counselling under psychiatric supervision and with the help of a probation officer, may help some shoplifters but community service or fines may be indicated for those who are poorly motivated. Razzell *et al* (1992) indicated that psychotherapy for shoplifters mainly involves convincing the offenders that their problems and frustrations in regard to shoplifting, are not unique. This is called the "universality" approach. Teaching self-understanding is also important.

Apart from community supervision, carers should accompany mentally disordered persons to shops.

4. Hysterical reactions

Hysterical reactions are regarded as originating from emotional conflicts. Conversion hysteria, now uncommon, is characterized by the "belle indifference" of Janet (1907) when the hysteric may indicate a physical "defect" without showing much concern. Anxiety, tension and depression are allegedly "channelled" or "converted" into physical symptoms and this process is commonly called "displacement of affect". The hysterical reaction with "free-floating" obvious anxiety is called anxiety hysteria and may be interchangeable with the "conversion" type.

Lewis (1936) studied a group of hysterics who were also pathological liars. This group was compared with the average population in respect of the proportion of brothers and sisters who were patients in mental hospitals. Five times as many siblings of the hysterical group required residential psychiatric treatment and one-sixth of their parents had psychopathic personalities. This study indicates that hysteria is not inherited as a disease entity, in contrast to schizophrenia and manic-depressive psychosis which are inherited as entities with high concordance rates.

The hysterical reaction may occur in response to stress in a predisposed personality. Hysterical symptoms may also occur in association with organic pathology such as a cerebral tumour, post-traumatic epilepsy, cerebral arteriosclerosis, neurosyphilis and multiple sclerosis.

Hysterical signs and symptoms are alleged to be due to a conflict in the subconscious between repressed primitive wishes and the social conventions preventing their fulfilment. These signs and symptoms have a meaning for the patient and usually serve the purpose of gaining attention and sympathy, but he or she is apparently unaware of the subconscious motivations.

Lack of libido is frequently evident and they often have little insight and easily deceive themselves. They are highly suggestible and auto-suggestion operates strongly. They may with difficulty be distinguished from malingerers who *consciously* attempt to deceive.

Emotional shallowness, autonomic instability, frigidity, and underdevelopment of secondary sex characteristics may also be evident.

Hysterical reactions in the form of conversion phenomena may be precipitated by financial stress, marital difficulties, childbirth and even minor accidents. These reactions are characterized by a multiplicity of symptoms and signs which have been likened to a series of "masks" adopted by the predisposed personality at different times and in the light of prevailing circumstances:

1. *Sensory*
(a) Anaesthesia of "glove and stocking" distribution.
(b) Parasthesia.
(c) Deafness.
(d) Blindness.

2. *Motor*
(a) Ataxia and dramatic gait.

(b) "Paralysis" which often involves a complete limb.
(c) Tics, stammer and aphonia.
(d) Akinetic mutism.
(e) Pseudo-epilspey. Hysteria, however, may be associated with genuine epilepsy, whether idiopathic or secondary to organic cerebral pathology.

3. *Mental*

(a) Emotional outbursts.
(b) Amnesia.
(c) Fugues, somnambulisms and automatisms are fully considered in Chapter IX.
(d) Dual personality.
(e) Pseudodementia.
(f) Trances.
(g) The Munchausen syndrome where illness is continually feigned and surgical exploratory procedures sometimes carried out. The object is to attract sympathy and attention. The deceiver often alleges pain in the hope that strong analgesics will be prescribed.
(h) Episodes simulating epilepsy.

Ljungberg (1957) found that 20 per cent of hysterics were still ill some 15 years after the original examination but 62 per cent apparently recovered during the first 12 months. Slater (1961) indicated that the outcome was somewhat less optimistic.

Slater (1965) produced evidence to support the view that conversion hysteria is not a disease entity. He suggested that the diagnosis should be abandoned because it is not a well-defined syndrome either clinically or genetically. Follow-up studies revealed that in the majority of cases surveyed, the final diagnosis turned out to be epilepsy, focal brain lesions, endogenous depression or anxiety states. Studies have failed to establish any regular association between hysterical symptoms and hysterical personality (Ljungberg, 1957).

Physical symptoms for which no organic cause can be found may be attributed to hysteria when a "profit motive" is suspected. "Conversion" and "dissociation" are assumed to account for various symptoms. "Conversion" is defined as a mental mechanism, operating unconsciously, by which intrapsychic conflicts, which would otherwise give rise to anxiety, are instead given symbolic physical expression. "Dissociation" is described as a psychological separation or splitting off from each other of different aspects of an idea, situation, or function. One could assume that these definitions may have been designed to fit into preconceived hypotheses by the psychoanalytical school. On the other hand, it has been said that any individual will "dissociate" when he looks down a microscope, but one may point out that "dissociation" in this context is momentary and under control and "conversion" does not occur. Slater (1961) indicated that these mechanisms should not be regarded as specific for any psychiatric syndrome including hysteria and he went on to state that "... the diagnosis of hysteria is a disguise for ignorance and a fertile source of clinical error ... it is in fact not only a delusion but also a snare". Walshe (1965) replied to these observations by commenting on the "unity of hysteria" in the sense that "its essential difference from somatic disease is that it constitutes a behaviour disorder, a human act on the psychological level". He went on "a diversity of symptoms from case to case and, in any single case from time to time, no more destroys the unitary quality of the malady (hysteria) than the same diversities destroy that of disseminated sclerosis or the neurosyphilis". Walshe concluded his defence of hysteria as a clinical entity "... we are liable to frustration in the handling of the subject of hysteria so that when presented with an essentially curable clinical state (that we still cannot banish), we suggest to ourselves that there is no such illness". He regarded hysteria as an "abnormal psychical state" and also countered objections to diagnosing hysteria by a process of elimination by pointing out that this is more or less standard practice in all branches of medicine.

Schneider (1959) says that "there are no neuroses, only neurotics", meaning that rigid theoretical and academic classifications of various types of neuroses are not in accord with clinical practice.

Neustatter (1953) regarded hysteria as the simulation or exaggeration of the signs and symptoms of mental or physical illness in order to gain some benefit which may be material or psychological. He does not deny that hysteria may be a clinical entity, and would probably agree that the condition is a psychoneurosis depending upon an original anomaly of constitution and characterized by a variety of symptoms arising from emotional repression. The repressed emotions, especially in the rare but graver instances of hysterical crime, are almost always related to abnormalities of the sexual instinct.

Hysterical behaviour may be described as an excessive and frequent display of emotion, gesture or illness, out of proportion to the situation in which it occurs.

The hysteric's crime may be motivated by a subconscious desire to excite interest and acquire notoriety. Neustatter (1957) noted that the murderer, John Christie, was quite conscious of being the central figure in an intriguing court case. He murdered four women, including his wife who was buried under the floor-boards of their home, and then gave evidence against Timothy Evans, who was subsequently hanged. Christie was well aware of his feelings of sexual inadequacy which caused him to project feelings of hostility to members of the opposite sex and was observed to be talkative, alert, attentive and to mix freely with others, his motto being described as "out of sight, out of mind" (*R v. Christie*, 1953). In retrospect, one could regard Christie as having been psychopathically disordered within the meaning of the Mental Health Act 1983, as hysterical reactions may be associated with psychopathy. One could only surmise that Christie's mental conflicts were channelled into physical aggression if one accepted that he was subject to the "conversion" type of hysteria.

A minority of hysterics may commit the following crimes:

1. Homicide and other serious crimes against the person.
2. Arson, which tends to be repeated because of the excitement and high drama it provides.
3. Anonymous letters usually imputing sexual misconduct to the innocent.
4. Blackmail.
5. Pathological gambling and lying.
6. False accusations of sexual assault may be made by a female wishing to gain revenge for desertion.
7. Sexual exhibitionism which does not take place in the presence of other males.

Hysteria may be associated with psychopathy and the *degree* of these conditions may influence the seriousness of the crime. Those likely to make *false confessions* may be placed in the following categories (Neustatter, 1957):

1. A person suffering from a severe memory defect combined with confabulation such as in the Korsakow syndrome.
2. A psychotic depressive may "confess" to an "altruistic" type of killing which is in agreement with his motivations and guilt feelings.

3.   Schizophrenics acting impulsively and with poor judgment when under the influence of delusions.
4.   Hysterical psychopaths who enjoy the attention and notoriety involved.

Hysteria and hypnosis are based on suggestion. The question has been asked as to whether a serious crime can be committed by an individual in an hypnotic state and it has never been properly answered, although it is generally agreed that a person under hypnosis cannot be influenced to behave in a manner contrary to his or her deep moral convictions.

There are two forms of simulated insanity:

1.   A crude form akin to malingering where the subject deliberately puts on an act which he thinks represents insanity (Neustatter, 1957).
2.   The Ganser syndrome which was first described in 1898. It is usually observed in prisoners and characterized by varying degrees of amnesia and bizarre behaviour. This syndrome is also called "prison psychosis" meaning simulation of insanity as imagined by a lay person and in some instances controlled by the subconscious. It classically presents with disturbed thought process referred to in German as "vorbeireden", and disturbance of consciousness. The absence of delusions of identity and reference, ideas of passivity and disorder of thought process such as the "knight's move in chess", distinguish the Ganser syndrome from an active schizophrenic process.

An inmate may give answers to simple questions which are the direct antithesis of the correct answers. The syndrome may also be associated with schizophrenia, organic cerebral disease, hysteria, epilepsy and alcoholism. Four cases of the Ganser syndrome were studied in a British prison in 1963. All were basically sane as confirmed by subsequent events, but developed pseudopsychotic symptoms when faced with the prospect of prison sentences. Auto-suggestion operated continuously and intensely and they eventually convinced themselves that they were mentally disordered and lack of insight was apparently genuine. They showed a striking contact with reality when "taken off guard" and especially where personal comforts were concerned. Symptoms disappeared spontaneously after sentence when they realized that they would not be transferred to a mental hospital.

References

Arieff, A.J., Bowie, C.G. (1942) *J. Clin, Psychopathology* 8:56.

Azrin, N.H., Weslowski, M.D. (1974) "Theft Reversal: An Overcorrection Procedure for Eliminating Stealing by Retarded Persons", *Applied Behaviour Analysis* 7: 577-81.

Brain, W.R. (1956) *Diseases of the Nervous System*, Oxford University Press, London.

Buckle, A., Farrington, D.P. (1984) "An Observational Study of Shoplifting", *Brit. J. Crim.* 24: 63-73.

Criminal Statistics, (England and Wales) (1992) Home Office, Cmnd, 9048 HMSO, London.

Dalton, K. (1961) Menstruation and Crime", *Brit. Med. J.* 2:1752.

David, A.S. (1990) "Insight and Psychosis, Discussion paper", *Journal of The Royal Society of Medicine*, 83: 325.

DSM-III-R, 1987, *Diagnostic and Statistical Manual of Mental Disorders*, 3rd ed., American Psychiatric Association, Washington DC.

East, W.N. (1939) "The Modern Psychiatric Approach to Crime", *Journal of Mental Science* 85: 649.

Epps, P., Gibbens, T.C.N., Prince, J. (1962) *Shoplifting*, Institute for the Study and Treatment of Delinquency, (Lon.), 10: 69-89, 16: 162.

Gallwey, P.L.G. (1992) "The Psychopathology of Neurosis and Offending". Section V, V.3, p.361. In *Principles and Practice of Forensic Psychiatry*. Bluglass, R., and Bowden, P. (eds). Churchill Livingstone, London.

Gillespie, R.D. (1944) "Mental Abnormality and Crime", in *Psychoses and Criminal Responsibility* (eds Radzinowicz and Turner), Macmillan, London.

Gudjonsson, G.H. (1990) "Psychological and Psychiatric Aspects of Shoplifting", *Med. Sci. Law.*, 30, 1: 45-51.

Gudjonsson, G.H. (1988) "Causes of Compulsive Shoplifting", *British Journal of Hospital Medicine*, 40: 169.

Henderson, D., Gillespie, R.D. (1951) *Textbook of Psychiatry for Students and Practitioners*, George Allen & Unwin, London.

Janet, P. (1907) *The Major Symptoms of Hysteria*, Macmillan, New York.

Leigh, D., Pare, C.M.B., Marks, J. (eds) (1972) *Encyclopedia of Psychiatry for General Practitioners*, Roche Products Ltd., London.

Lewis, A. (1936) "Problems of Obsessional Illness", *Proceedings of the Royal Society of Medicine*, 29: 325.

Ljungberg, L. (1957) "Hysteria: A Clinical Prognostic and Genetic Study", *Acta Psychiatrica et Neurologica Scandinavica*, Supplement 112.

Martin, R.L., Cloninger, C.R., Guze, S.B. (1985) "Alcohol Misuse and Depression in Women Criminals", Dept. of Psychiatry, Washington University School of Medicine, St. Louis, Missouri, *Journal of Studies on Alcohol*, 46, 1: 65-71.

Moak, G.S., Zimmer, B. (1988) *Hospital and Community Psychiatry*, 39, 6: 648-51.

Moore, R.H. 1984, Shoplifting in Middle America: Patterns of Motivational Correlates, *Int. J. Offender Therapy and Comparative Crimonology*, 28: 53-64.

Mortimer, A. (1991) "Making Sense of Shoplifting", *Med. Sci. Law* 31, 2: 123-5.

Neustatter, W.L. (1957) *The Mind of the Murderer*, Christopher Johnson, London.

Neustatter, W.L. (1953) *Psychological Disorder and Crime*, 4: 48-9, Johnson, London.

Razzell, A., Dolan, D.M. (1992) " Evaluation of Therapeutic Factors in Group Psychotherapy for Non-sensical Shoplifters: A Preliminary Report". *Med. Sci. Law*, vol. 32, no.4, pp.341-244.

Rudin, E. (1953) "Beitrag zur Frage der Zwangskrankheit, insbesondere ihrer hereditare Beziehungen", *Archiv fur Psychiatrie* 191: 14.

Schneider, K. (1959) *Clinical Pshopathology*, Grune, Ne York.

Silverman, G., Brener, N. (1988) "Psychiatric Profile of Shoplifters", *Lancet*, Vol. 2, p.157.

Slater, E. (1961) "Hysteria", *J. Mento Sci.* 104: 107.

Slater, E. (1965) "The Diagnosis of 'Hysteria'", *Brit. Med J.* 1: 1395.

Smart, R.G. (1969) *Neurosis and Crime*, Duckworth & Co., London.

Walshe, F. (1965) "Diagnosis of Hysteria", *Brit. Med. J.* 2: 1451-4.

Yarnell, H. (1940) "Firesetting in Children", *American Journal of Orthopsychiatry* 272.

Ziehen, T. (1926) *Die Geisteskrankheiten im Kindesalter*, Reuter & Reichard, Berlin.

Zigmond, A.S., Sims, A.C.P. (1983) "The Effect of the Use of the International Classification of Diseases (9th Revision) upon Hospital In-patient Diagnoses". *B. J. Psychiatry* 142: 409-413.

CHAPTER XI

Mental Impairment and Crime

The title of this chapter "Mental Impairment and Crime" is in conformity with the Mental Health Act 1983. The selected case histories were compiled when the 1959 Act was operative and when the terms "subnormality" and "severe subnormality" were in use. I consider that these histories are still valid because the individuals described were not only intellectually retarded, socially incompetent and emotionally unstable but also indulged in abnormally aggressive and/or seriously irresponsible behaviour. The term subnormality is retained in the case histories because court decisions were based on this terminology and references to the Mental Health Act 1959 and to the Criminal Justice Act 1948 are also retained in the histories for the same reason.

The 1983 Act indicates that "mental impairment" means a state of arrested or incomplete development of mind (not amounting to severe mental impairment) which includes significant impairment of intelligence and social functioning and is associated with abnormally aggressive or seriously irresponsible conduct on the part of the person concerned.

References in the remainder of this chapter to impairment and severe impairment refer to mental impairment and severe mental impairment respectively.

The above definition implies that mental impairment is not necessarily treatable but there is reasonable hope in the majority of instances that treatment, special care or training will counteract the abnormal manifestations of the impairment or at least prevent further mental and/or physical deterioration. An initial period of residential treatment in an appropriate hospital may be required but the ultimate aim is to restore patients who are not dangerous to the public to normal community life.

Diagnosis is facilitated by a history of attendance at a special school for the intellectually backward and/or residential or out-patient treatment at a hospital for impaired persons. The diagnosis of impairment is based mainly upon clinical criteria which include an inability on the part of the individual to manage his or her affairs in the community at an age when the average person is able to cope adequately with his occupational, social, marital and financial obligations. Interview may reveal lack of spontaneity of speech and poor quality of conversation, and these defects would increase an impaired person's difficulty in establishing rapport with others and decrease his prospects of employment. The psychiatrist employs simple tests to assess ability to read and write, and cope with elementary arithmetic. Ignorance of some items of common knowledge may be accounted for by an individual never having had the opportunity to learn or never having made the effort through lack of interest. Defects of judgment and reasoning are indicated by the subject's lack of appreciation of the effects of his misbehaviour on others.

Limited social competence does not preclude a diagnosis of impairment. A satisfactory work record would present diagnostic difficulties despite the finding of an intelligence quotient which would otherwise suggest impairment and one may reasonably assume that such an individual would be functioning at a higher social level than that suggested by measured intelligence.

An impaired person may also suffer from psychopathic disorder. The impaired aggressive psychopath who represents a serious danger to the public should be admitted to a mental hospital which provides treatment in a setting of adequate security. An impaired person may also be admitted to hospital on the grounds of mental illness.

"Severe mental impairment" will mean a state of arrested or incomplete development of mind which includes severe impairment of intelligence and social functioning and is associated with abnormally aggressive or seriously irresponsible conduct on the part of the person concerned. One may infer from this definition that social incapacity is an essential diagnostic criterion and consequently a severely impaired individual is incapable of providing himself with adequate food, clothing, shelter and medical care. A confident diagnosis of severe impairment may be made if the subject also evinces abnormal unawareness of surrounding events and persistent memory defect which cannot be accounted for by mere absentmindedness or by a confusional state induced by the effects of disease or injury.

Hughes (1994) indicated a continuum extending through mild, moderate and severe to profound impairment. Legally, it is more usual to classify the condition into mild and severe, which makes sense in legal terms as well as clinically.

In assessing mental impairment, it is important to measure not only intelligence but also social competence and educational background.

Mild handicap – only a minority show organic brain damage. Such factors as low parental intelligence and standards, social deprivation, poor education and lower social class are more important aetiologically.

Severe handicap is associated with such factors as brain damage, birth injury, genetic disease and inborn errors of metabolism.

In other words, mild handicap is to be regarded as a lower extreme of the normal distribution of intelligence in the general population whereas severe handicap is related to severe pathology. Severe syndromes can be caused by chromosome abnormalities.

In recent years, the association of other chromosome variations with mental impairment and with crime have been extensively researched. Particular attention has been focused on offenders with abnormalities of the X and Y chromosomes. For example, it has been suggested that XYY individuals tend to be tall and aggressive but the balance of evidence is that the connection is uncertain.

Mental efficiency is largely dependent upon the *speed* at which the intellect functions. Properly constructed intelligence tests should measure this "speed factor" in addition to assessing other inherent qualities of intellect.

The commonly used Wechsler Adult Intelligence Scale (WAIS) consists of a battery of tests and each has been shown to give reliable results. This test, which is applicable to individuals between the ages of 15 and 50 years, estimates general native intellectual abilities and the more specialized abilities which are influenced by the effects of education.

The complete battery consists of 10 tests:

(i)   Information test of general knowledge.
(ii)   Comprehension test which assesses ability to utilize "common sense" in solving standard problems.
(iii)   Arithmetical reasoning.
(iv)   Memory span tests which estimate ability to repeat varying numbers of digits forwards and backwards.
(v)   Similarities test which estimates ability to appreciate superficial and essential likenesses between animate and inanimate objects.
(vi)   Picture arrangement tests which measure ability to assess a total situation. The subject is required to arrange a series of pictures so as to form a story.
(vii)   Picture completion test which assesses ability to appreciate an essential detail. The subject is required to "complete" a picture

by naming the missing part.

(viii) Block design test which measures perceptual ability and memory. The subject is asked to recognize, and subsequently reproduce, designs using coloured blocks.

(ix) Digit symbol test which estimates perceptual ability. The subject is required to reproduce unfamiliar symbols which are associated with particular numerals.

(x) Object assembly tests which measure perceptual ability and judgment. The subject is required to form objects using material of different shapes and sizes.

Table XXII attempts to correlate intelligence quotient with the corresponding non-numerical classification of intelligence level. These intelligence quotients are based specifically on the Wechsler Adult Intelligence Scale. The impaired accomplish higher scores on the more practical Wechsler tests involving perceptual ability and manual dexterity, but their scores tend to be lower on those tests which demand verbal responses and test the higher ideational levels of the mind.

A diagnosis of impairment is suggested by an intelligence quotient below 70, but figures below 80 may be significant when social impairment, emotional instability and/or lawbreaking tendencies are taken into consideration. The normal range of intelligence varies from 85 to 115 and children with intelligence quotients below 85 are eligible to attend special schools for the educationally backward. New terminology as expressed in the Education Act 1981, refers to "children with statements" meaning those with special educational needs.

Table XXII

Intelligence Quotient (I.Q.) (W.A.I.S.)	Non-numerical classification of intelligence level	Corresponding percentages of population
130 and above	Very superior or well above average	2.2
120 to 129	Superior or well above average	6.7
110 to 119	Bright normal or above average	16.1
90 to 109	Average	50.0
80 to 89	Dull – normal	16.1
70 to 79	Borderline (relative to impairment)	6.7
69 and below	Impaired and severely impaired	2.2

Impairment and severe impairment cannot be diagnosed by considering any I.Q. figure in isolation.

Case 34: The following case history illustrates that a comparatively low intelligence quotient in the absence of significant social impairment (as distinct from lawbreaking) did not justify a diagnosis of subnormality.

A plea of diminished responsibility was rejected in the case of a young adult charged with murdering his wife and another woman by stabbing. The killings took place within a few hours of each other and the second victim had been working for a doctor who had been treating the wife of the accused. This doctor had given evidence before a magistrates' court which resulted in the wife being granted a legal separation on the grounds of cruelty some two months before her death. The accused stated that his wife had deserted him about six months before her death and he alleged that he had repeatedly pleaded for a reconciliation. He complained of despondency and experienced some difficulty in sleeping during the remand period. He had been working efficiently and regularly up to the day of his arrest, but had left his usual employment and had undertaken somewhat less complicated work about two months before the killings. Defence counsel alleged that this work record indicated decreased general efficiency due to "reactive" depression caused by separation from his late wife and unsuccessful attempts at reconciliation. There was no history of psychiatric treatment or epilepsy. His intelligence quotient was estimated as 75 on the Wechsler Adult Intelligence Scale. The Raven's test placed the accused in the lowest test category, Grade E, and this result indicated that his intelligence quotient was superior to that of only 9 per cent of the general population.

Evidence on behalf of the Crown emphasized that "reactive" depression should reach a substantial degree of severity before being regarded as pathological in the sense of incapacitating a person from following regular employment or at least causing substantial impairment of working efficiency. The accused managed his general affairs with reasonable efficiency up to the date of his arrest. He was committed to custody on the day on which the homicides were perpetrated and examined on that day. I found no evidence of pathological depression. The jury rejected the plea of diminished responsibility on the grounds of subnormality and/ or mental illness in the form of "reactive" depression. The accused was found guilty of murder and sentenced to life imprisonment.

The concept of percentile rank is commonly used in relation to intelligence quotients. Percentile rank indicates the position of an individual on a numerical continuum representing 0 to 99 per cent of the population. Therefore, to state that an individual is at the hundredth percentile is to state that his intelligence is superior to that of 99 per cent of the population and would be superior to that of 49 per cent if he were at the fiftieth percentile.

Table XXIII attempts to correlate Intelligence Quotient with Percentile Rank.

Table XXIII

Intelligence Quotient	Percentile Rank
135	99
128	97
125	95
119	90
113	80
110	75
108	70
104	60
100	50
96	40
92	30
90	25
87	20
80	10
75	5
72	3
65	1

The Raven's Progressive Matrices Test is regarded as a reliable test of general native intellectual ability which is relatively uninfluenced by the effects of education, social training, muscular co-ordination and speed of performance. The subject is required to complete designs by selecting correct patterns from a number of alternatives. The designs vary progressively in complexity.

The nature of the Raven's test makes it particularly useful for assessing intelligence levels of individuals of foreign cultural backgrounds, and Table XXIV correlates Raven's test results with intelligence quotients and percentile ranks:

Table XXIV

Raven's Test Score Grades	Intelligence Quotients	Percentile Ranks
A (numerical test score equivalent: 48 to 60)	119 and above	90 and above
B (numerical test score equivalent: 42 to 47)	108 to 118	70 and above
C+ (numerical test score equivalent: 38 to 41)	100 to 107	50 and above
C- (numerical test score equivalent: 34 to 37)	90 to 99	30 and above
D (numerical test score equivalent: 26 to 33)	81 to 89	10 and above
E (numerical test score equivalent: 5 to 25)	80 and below	10 and below

The intelligence quotients on the Wechsler Adult Intelligence Scale

Certain circumstances are conducive to inaccurate assessment of the intelligence levels of prisoners remanded in custody. The mental stress caused by the uncertainty of remand may adversely affect test performances resulting in the underestimation of intellectual abilities. An interesting investigation was undertaken in HM Prison, Bristol, during the years 1954 to 1964 inclusive. Some 3,508 inmates were involved in this investigation which did not reveal any significant differences between the Raven's test scores recorded during their remand periods and the scores recorded as a result of re-testing after sentences had been passed, provided the test results of inmates located in the prison hospital were excluded. One may assume that those tested in the hospital would include a significant proportion of malingerers and hysterics whose hopes for leniency from the courts became untenable after sentences had been passed. The hospital inmates included in the investigation also lowered the average of the total test scores, because their numbers included a relatively high proportion of mentally impaired and psychotic individuals.

Psychologists experience most difficulty in assessing the intellectual attributes of immigrants. West Indians seem to perform badly on all types of test with the exception of the Raven's Progressive Matrices.

Formal tests of intelligence are useful but provide only contributory evidence in assessing impairment or severe impairment. Heber (1959) stated that the mental processes other than intelligence *per se* are vital in assessing degree of mental retardation. He defined mental retardation as "sub-average general intellectual functioning originating during the development period and associated with impairment of one or more of the processes of maturation, learning and social adjustment". Maturation is defined as "the rate of sequential development of self-skills of infancy and early childhood". The process of learning is defined as "the facility with which knowledge is acquired as a function of experience". He defined social adjustment as "the degree of ability to maintain oneself in the community and gainful employment, and ability to conform to other personal and social standards and responsibilities set by the community". The upper limit of the development period is taken as 16 years and the term "mental retardation" refers to the current status of an individual.

Campbell (1990) described six important survival skills which should be included in the assessment of mentally impaired persons.

1. What survival skills are limited?
   a. Orientation.
   b. Physical independence.
   c. Mobility.
   d. Occupation.
   e. Social integration.
   f. Economic self-sufficiency.
2. What impairments are present?
   a. Intellectual impairment.
   b. Other psychological impairments:
      (i) intermittent impairment of consciousness if handicapped person also epileptic.
      (ii) behaviour pattern impairment.
3. What disabilities are present?
   a. Knowledge acquisition disability.
   b. Social role disability.
   c. Occupational role disability.
4. Can the survival skills be improved? Can the overall handicap be reduced?
   a. Orientation. *Example:* potential for improved clinical control of seizure disorder if epilepsy also present.
   b. Occupation. *Example:* potential benefit from vocational guidance and from being registered disabled, with possibility of vocational training.
   c. Social integration. *Example:* possibility of specific self-skills training and possible involvement in sports and social clubs.
   d. Economic self-sufficiency. *Example:* reassessment of state benefits and potential for return to regular employment.

Mental impairment is not a disease but rather a disability expressed in the form of varying degrees of functional incapacity.

Hughes (1994) wisely indicates that assessment should include not only an assessment of intelligence but also physical and psychiatric examinations and a detailed assessment of the social background. The educational history is particularly important.

I.Q. tests have to be treated with caution as many such tests are heavily dependent on past education, but should not be discarded.

Kearns *et al* (1988) expressed the opinion that with mentally handicapped people being now moved into the community, information on mentally handicapped criminal offenders is valuable. A group of such offenders was examined by reviewing the case notes of 92 patients referred on hospital orders to two hospitals for the mentally handicapped over 10 years. Compared with the general criminal population, the offenders' ages were higher, the ratio of male to female offenders was similar, and the proportion of married people was lower. The offences committed were for the most part serious, with a greater number of offences against property and public order and their tested intelligence fell almost entirely into the mild mentally handicapped range, suggesting that factors other than intelligence testing, such as social skills, were considered in their admission to hospitals.

These studies are valuable because current policy seems to favour restoring mentally handicapped people to the community whenever feasible. West (1982) described five main factors associated with delinquent behaviour and the I.Q. was only one of them. However, the importance of the I.Q. is not to be entirely dismissed because he also found that 20 per cent of young people who became delinquent had I.Q.s below 90 as compared with only 2 per cent of those with I.Q.s above 110.

Mentally impaired persons are easily led into mischief but only a small minority become involved in serious crime. Appreciation of the moral implications and legal consequences of lawbreaking would depend upon the degree of impairment. An impaired individual has less tolerance of stress than the average person and comparatively minor frustrations may cause impulsive behaviour. Disturbing letters from home or refusal of legal aid may result in refusal of food, unwillingness to work, suicidal gestures or assaults. Fear of consequences may cause the circumstances of an offence to be repressed with resulting amnesia. The prospect of a long prison sentence is particularly feared if the conviction is for an offence against a child because reprisals by other prisoners are common in such instances.

The restrictions and other frustrations inherent in imprisonment may cause transient schizophrenic symptoms or hysterical behaviour. The above remarks pertain to impaired persons who receive sentences of imprisonment because vacancies cannot be found in ordinary hospitals, secure units or special hospitals. Furthermore, a Crown Court may set aside recommendations for a hospital order under s.37 of the Mental Health Act 1983, and impose a sentence of imprisonment.

The impaired have a relatively low tolerance of alcohol which may facilitate lawbreaking by a minority.

Heaton-Ward (1977) studied 1,251 mentally impaired adult patients in the Stoke Park group of hospitals at Bristol. The object of the study was to discover if any suffered from an additional form of mental disorder. He found that about 1 in 20 suffered from some form of psychosis. This incidence would be further increased if the above group had also been assessed for psychopathic personality.

Rao et al (1991) studied 293 persons referred to a hospital for the mentally impaired. It was found that 41 of the total group suffered from forms of mental disorder other than mental handicap and 27 suffered from schizophrenia or endogenous depression. Such studies are important but seldom undertaken.

At one time it was thought that mental impairment was an important cause of crime. This is no longer tenable and it is generally agreed that offending is no commoner in this than in the general population. However, there are exceptions. Crimes involving sex, arson and vagrancy are more common in the mentally handicapped.

Most crime in this group is petty crime but there are exceptions especially in crimes involving sex and arson. Such criminal activity as there is occurs in the mildly handicapped and very little crime is committed by the severely handicapped.

Crime in these handicapped people commonly starts early and can be repetitious. Typical crimes are larceny, and breaking and entering, which tend to occur in the easily led.

Arson is more common than in the general population and in may cases there is no obvious motivation.

The incidence of violence is not high but in a minority it can be a serious problem.

Offending is much more common in males – about 80 per cent. Electroencephalographic abnormalities and minor physical disabilities may indicate a greater liability to crime. The social background is very important, including such factors as broken homes, less intelligent parents and poorer homes financially, emotionally and morally.

In females, offending is much less common, as in the general population. Self-harm and problems in sexual behaviour are however common.

Homicide and Attempted Homicide

Impaired individuals lack self-control and have a tendency to indulge in impulsive behaviour to gratify immediate desires. Homicide may be motivated by a simple desire for gain.

Sullivan (1924) maintained that the perpetration of homicide by a severely retarded person could be explained on the basis of simple imitation as when a child's throat is cut with the object of imitating the killing of a chicken by similar means.

The victim of theft or sexual assault may meet death at the hands of the perpetrator who wishes to escape detection and punishment.

Impaired persons may express concern for their own relatives but not for others and in this context, Neustatter (1957) described a child murderer who expressed concern for his mother but felt no sorrow for his child victims.

Offences such as murder, attempted murder, manslaughter, malicious wounding and assault may be committed by a minority who tend to react with physical violence to real or imagined wrongs or the motivation may be even more obscure. A middle-aged impaired psychopath stabbed a boy in the neck. There was no apparent motive for this crime, which was perpetrated during weekend parole from a mental hospital, and one may assume that the accused derived some perverted emotional satisfaction from wounding the victim. His intelligence quotient was estimated as 60. He persistently denied any knowledge of the crime despite conclusive evidence of witnesses, which may have been a deliberate attempt to deceive in order to escape the consequences.

Case 35: The following case report describes a "revenge-type" killing by a mentally retarded person who developed a hatred of women.

A young adult male pleaded guilty to the manslaughter of a middle-aged woman. He inflicted five stab wounds with a pointed wooden stick and the victim's spinal cord was severed in the cervical region. The accused and victim had lived in the same neighbourhood and were well known to each other. He admitted that he had not disliked her at any time before her death.

The circumstances of the crime were as follows. The accused was walking past the victim's house when he noticed some of her underclothing on the clothes-line and he later stated that the sight of these garments had the effect of "making me have one of my funny feelings and I felt a buzzing noise in my head", which suggested that he had experienced similar sensations under similar circumstances on other occasions. He admitted that he was strongly tempted to steal the victim's under-garments from the clothes-line. He knocked on the front door and asked for "headache tablets" and attacked the woman when she replied that she did not have any. He later stated that he believed that she had lied about the "headache tablets".

He was aware of the reason for his arrest and committal to prison. He was illegitimate. He had been assessed as illiterate on leaving school at the age of 15 years. He subsequently worked as third cinema projectionist for about three months and he was then considered "unemployable".

He was admitted to a mental hospital about 12 months before the homicide as a condition of probation under s.4 of the Criminal Justice Act 1948, after he had pleaded guilty to indecent assault on a young woman. He was discharged from the mental hospital after five months by the supervisory magistrates' court on the recommendation of a consultant psychiatrist.

The following investigations were undertaken:

(i)   Electroencephalography. The recording indicated the "possibility" of temporal-lobe epilepsy. There was no clinical history of epilepsy but the Judge heard evidence to the effect that the "brain-wave test" indicated "unstable brain functioning". About 50 per cent of temporal-lobe epileptics do not experience ictal episodes and their epilepsy is expressed as a behaviour disorder.

(ii) The glucose-tolerance test revealed "an unusually low" curve and the jury was asked to consider whether an abnormally low blood-sugar level could cause abnormal "mental reactions" in situations of undue stress.

(iii) He had an intelligence quotient of 82. He was graded D on the basis of the Raven's test.

(iv) Tests for venereal disease were returned as negative during the remand period.

The psychopathology of this case may be partly understood by considering the accused person's intelligence level and his attitude toward sexually mature females. His resentment of adolescent and adult females was indicated by the remark – "big girls are dirty and they get boys into trouble". He described masturbatory fantasies of locking women in cars and subsequently pushing the cars from cliff tops. Stolen female under-garments were either burnt or impaled on knives which were stuck in tree trunks. These practices commenced after the accused had reached puberty and he believed that he could put "a curse" on women by depriving them of their under-garments and thus "make them feel cold and ill and make them stay indoors". He believed that he would not be tempted to harm women if he could compel them to remain indoors and presumably out of his sight. He was aware of an irresistible desire to attack women and this desire was initiated by the sight of female under-clothing.

The jury found him not guilty of murder but guilty of manslaughter on the grounds of diminished responsibility. Section 60 of the Mental Health Act 1959 was implemented and he was committed to a special hospital with restriction on discharge without limit of time. He was mentally retarded and psychopathically disordered.

Sexual Offences

A study of 219 inmates of Durham Prison in 1958 revealed a higher percentage of individuals of sub-average intelligence (intelligence quotients less than 85), amongst those convicted of sexual and/or offences involving non-sexual violence as compared with those convicted of other offences. The inmates selected for the study had, for various reasons, been referred for psychiatric examination.

The scores gained on the tests of abstract thinking and spelling were graded A to E for the purposes of correlation with the scores gained on the Raven's Progressive Matrices Test and are set out in Table XXV.

Table XXV

	Raven's Progressive Matrices Test		Tests of abstract thinking involving deductive reasoning		Spelling tests	
	Sexual and/or violent offences	Other types of offences	Sexual and/or violent offences	Other types of offences	Sexual and/or violent offences	Other types of offences
	%	%	%	%	%	%
Grade A	4	8	9	9	6	7
Grade B	17	16	13	16	18	24
Grade C (average of + and – scores)	32	37	30	35	37	40
Grade D	27	21	20	20	20	15
Grade E	20	18	28	20	19	24
Percentages below average	47	39	48	40	39	29

The individuals who were scored below Grade C were considered to be of sub-average intelligence.

The results of the Raven's test and the tests of abstract thinking indicate that there were 8 per cent more individuals of sub-average intelligence amongst those convicted of sexual offences and/or offences involving non-sexual violence, as compared with those convicted of other types of offences. The results of the spelling tests indicate that there were 10 per cent more individuals of sub-average intelligence amongst those convicted of sexual offences and/or offences involving non-sexual violence as compared with those convicted of other types of offence.

A minority of impaired individuals may indulge in illegal sexual activities especially after puberty when sexual desires demand expression and volition may be inherently weak.

Impaired male adults may be heterosexually, homosexually or bisexually orientated. They may indulge in homosexual activity with adult males for the purpose of obtaining sexual satisfaction, and the prospect of monetary gain may provide additional motivation. They may also take advantage of children for sexual purposes.

Murrey *et al* (1992) studied the records of sex offenders from Rampton (Special) Hospital. Of the 106 studies, 39 were psychopathically disordered, 32 were mentally ill and 35 were mentally handicapped with an average I.Q. on WAIS scale of 68.42. Paedophilic behaviour was found to be "much more common" among the mentally handicapped offenders in comparison with the other two groups. The latter finding obviously indicates desire for perverted sexual satisfaction but perhaps also sufficient cunning to avoid less helpless adults in their wish to satisfy their desires.

Impaired females may be exploited for the purpose of prostitution or may indulge in this practice on their own initiative.

Sexual exhibitionism may be intended as an insult or an invitation to sexual intercourse. It may or may not be accompanied by masturbation. The perpetrators are invariably males. Severely impaired individuals may inadvertently break the law because they do not understand the social necessity of micturating in private. An impaired person does not usually indulge in the type of exhibitionism where sexual satisfaction is obtained by the perpetrator witnessing the surprise and fear shown by the victim and where such satisfaction is an end in itself.

Indecent assaults may be committed by impaired males who are usually aware that they are unattractive to members of the opposite sex. Females who have reached puberty and children of either sex are the usual victims. Child victims may be tempted by offers of money or sweets or a child's natural willingness to be helpful may be exploited.

Impaired individuals may regard voyeurism as a poor substitute for sexual intercourse, but they usually admit to experiencing pleasure when observing the sexual activities of others. The voyeurism may or may not be accompanied by masturbation.

An impaired person may indulge in rape or attempted rape. These offences may or may not be premeditated. The following case indicates that such an individual may be overcome by sexual ardour and yet retain the ability to foresee the possible consequences of his behaviour.

Gilby *et al* (1989) indicated that there is not a great deal of empirical research on adolescent sex offenders and even less on mentally retarded adolescent sex offenders. Their study provides some preliminary data in this area and is based on results of a survey of the extent and types of sexual problems evident among groups of mentally retarded and intellectually normal adolescents. Some 196 were seen at an assessment and treatment centre in south-western Ontario during a 14-month period. In addition three groups of ten adolescents (mentally retarded and intellectually normal sex offenders and one group of mentally retarded non-offenders with behavioural problems) were each investigated to gain a more in-depth perspective of characteristics of these adolescents and their backgrounds. A high recidivism rate was discovered in the first two groups.

Case 36: A young male adult whose intelligence quotient was estimated at 54 was about to rape a women who increased her resistance when a third party approached the scene of the crime. He then released the woman, ran away and subsequently explained his behaviour by stating that he had a knife in his possession at the material time and feared that he might use this weapon on the victim unless he escaped from the sexual situation. He also stated that "things would go worse for me with the police if I used the knife".

Impaired males may commit incest with daughters or sisters. This type of behaviour has usually been indulged for some considerable time before discovery.

Offences of Fire-raising

Lewis and Yarnell (1951) refer to a study of 447 "pyromaniacs" which included 98 who were described as "low-grade defectives".

Arson may be motivated by desire for revenge arising from real or imagined wrongs or by desire for excitement which is provided by the sight of the flames, the arrival of the ambulances, fire engines and police, and publicity by the media. A profit motive may also influence this crime. I have personal knowledge of an impaired person who stole money from his aunt's house and then set fire to it in order to avoid detection. He hoped that she would not associate him with the crime, and did not attempt to confirm her absence from the house at the material time, nor did he appreciate the importance of doing so. Impaired individuals who indulge in arson usually prefer to set fire to buildings which are unoccupied by people, but the impaired psychopath would not be so scrupulous.

The police are aware that impaired persons have a tendency to start illicit fires in response to provocation but detection may prove quite difficult in the absence of antecedents and the possibility of sympathetic relatives sheltering the culprit. The following case illustrates that an allegedly impaired individual may be detained in hospital although quite capable of earning an adequate living in the community.

Case 37: A middle-aged man pleaded guilty to setting fire to several bales of hay in a barn owned by his employer. He stated that he did so because he believed he had been wrongfully dismissed by the employer and knew that eviction from his "tied" accommodation would inevitably follow. He had been certified as a "mental defective" at the age of 16 when he was committed to a hospital where he was detained for 15 years. He was granted day parole and worked on a local farm during his last five years at the hospital. He was then placed "on licence" and sent to live in hostel accommodation for four years and allowed to reside and work on a local farm at the age of 35. At 38 he was discharged from care under the Mental Deficiency Acts. He married about this time. He supported his wife by working as a farm labourer for 10 years before his arrest on the charge of arson. He committed the latter offence when his wife was seriously ill in hospital and he was concerned about the future welfare of his five-year-old daughter. His wife died of natural causes before his appearance at the assize court. He was well behaved during the remand period and clinical examination did not reveal evidence of psychosis. He did not suffer from epilepsy. His intelligence quotient was estimated at 74.

Two consultant psychiatrists expressed the opinion that he was suffering from subnormality within the meaning of the Mental Health Act 1959 and they recommended detention in a Special Hospital under the provisions of s.60 of that Act. The Judge expressed the opinion that individuals with intelligence quotients below 80 should be regarded as subnormal within the meaning of the Act and issued a hospital order authorizing detention in a special hospital. An order restricting discharge was not made, although a psychiatrist gave oral evidence to the effect that the accused would be well behaved in a special hospital but dangerous when free in the community. The subject of this case did not have a police record, and was known to me during the remand period.

Offences against the Theft Acts

Impaired persons may indulge in petty theft but may also be exploited by others to participate in more serious types of larceny which may or may not involve violence against the person. Apart from gain, theft may also be indulged in with the object of enjoying the state of heightened emotional tension experienced at the material time.

Case 38: A young adult male pleaded guilty to breaking a shop window and stealing several watches which he then hid in various places, which he subsequently experienced considerable difficulty in remembering. His history indicated that he had failed to make reasonable progress during a period of attendance at a special school for the educationally backward. His intelligence quotient was estimated at 50. His mother was described as an individual of "low" mentality who had over-protected him during childhood and adolescence. He had two sisters, one of whom had received psychiatric treatment. He did not remember his natural father and was treated unkindly by his step-father. He attended an adult training centre when 17 years old but was asked to leave after a few weeks because of unruly and violent behaviour and was assessed as incapable of earning a living. He had five convictions for larceny between the ages of 15 and 20 years. He was admitted to a psychiatric hospital when 15 years old on an informal basis but absconded on five occasions during his nine months' stay there. He was readmitted on the basis of a hospital order under s.60 of the Mental Health Act 1959, and a two-year restriction on discharge was added under s.65 of the Act. An intelligence quotient of 50 did not prevent him from appreciating that he was taking property which did not belong to him, and he was also aware of the desirability of avoiding detection. He admitted that the theft of the watches was prompted by feelings of childish excitement and mischievousness. There was no evidence of psychosis or epilepsy.

Impaired persons are fascinated by cars and seem to derive great satisfaction from driving at high speeds. They are sometimes charged with taking and driving away motor vehicles belonging to other people but more intelligent accomplices usually do the driving.

Some are occasionally convicted of making offensive telephone calls which may be made to avenge some real or imagined grievance or in an attempt to establish rapport with a member of the opposite sex. They may be exploited by others to assist in the illegal sale of drugs but they do not usually commit crimes of embezzlement, forgery, perjury, fraud or bigamy as these offences require a degree of constructive planning which is usually beyond their capabilities.

Lewis and Yarnell (1951), state that persons of "defective intelligence" are more likely to indulge in arson and to repeat this crime. They formulated their opinions by comparing intellectually "defective" arsonists with intellectually "normal" members of the community who were convicted of illegal fire-setting.

The Patuxent Institution in Maryland USA, specializes in treating "defective delinquents" who are generally regarded as incapable of being helped. The Institute provides beds for about 400 patients who are "either intellectually defective or emotionally unbalanced, or both, as to clearly demonstrate an actual danger to society". About 20 per cent of patients, at any particular time, are intellectually retarded, the lowest intelligence quotient being 55 (the method of testing is not stated). Each patient received concentrated attention from psychiatrists, psychologists, social workers, vocational and recreational instructors. Therapy is based on a four-tier system and the fourth and highest tier has its own governing council. Patients are punished by withdrawal of privileges.

The staff have good rapport with local employers.

The Institution is surrounded on the outside by heavy iron fences and its windows are stoutly barred, but cell doors are seldom locked and a therapeutic atmosphere exists.

The Patuxent Institution has demonstrated that over a 13-year period many can be treated and rehabilitated, and in more than 50 per cent of cases, returned to society to live adequate, if not overwhelmingly successful lives. The average length of stay is four and a half years.

Day (1988) described a special hospital-based treatment programme for male mentally handicapped offenders, comprising a package of practical and personal skills training coupled with a socialization programme based on token-economy strategies within a controlled and structured environment. Twenty patients admitted to the programme and followed up after discharge for an average of 3.3 years were studied in detail. All had committed serious or persistent offences and showed a high level of psychosocial pathology. A good or fair response to the treatment programme was made by 85 per cent, and 65 per cent were judged well-adjusted or reasonably well-adjusted at follow-up contact. A good outcome was associated with more than two years of in-patient care, a good response to the treatment programme and stable residential placement, regular occupation and regular supervision and support in the community. Offenders against the person (sex and assault) had a better prognosis than property offenders (including arson).

Prognosis

Mental impairment *per se* is irreversible and an established pattern of criminal activity after adolescence is usually permanent. One might be regarded as an optimist if one suggested that some improvement in social behaviour might conceivably result from adequate treatment of mental illness, psychopathic disorder, epilepsy, drug addiction or alcoholism, which may co-exist with impairment.

Lawbreaking may be a symptom of impairment. Illegal behaviour is sometimes followed by a learning process which helps the offender to avoid future lawbreaking and this process is usually initiated by the punishment imposed by the law. Impaired persons are unfortunate from this point of view because they usually profit less from experience than individuals of average intelligence.

The outlook in regard to any lawbreaker may be assessed on the basis of (i) provisional prognosis and (ii) ultimate prognosis.

The provisional prognosis should be assessed between the ages of 15 and 18 years and an opinion as to the ultimate prognosis should not be given before the individual reaches the age of 25 years and not until at least three years have elapsed after official discharge from hospital or release from custody.

Prognosis may also be based on: (i) criminal, (ii) social, and (iii) psychological data.

These criteria are inter-related and should be considered on this basis. The first approach includes consideration of the duration of illegal behaviour and the nature of current and past offences.

Social factors influencing prognosis include prospects of future employment, degree of initiative shown in making plans for the future, willingness to discontinue association with undesirable companions, home environment and marital situation, including attitudes toward marital partner or co-habitee and children. Prognosis would also be influenced by the adequacy of medical and social after-care services designed to assist the individual after discharge from a psychiatric hospital or release from custody.

The psychological approach includes consideration of the impaired person's attitude towards his future, degree of remorse for misdeeds, indications of intellectual and emotional insight into problems and deficiencies and the absence or presence of genuine appreciation of the effects of his anti-social behaviour on others.

Successful rehabilitation would also be influenced by factors such as response to kindness, willingness to help others and loyalty to those who trust him with limited responsibility.

Prognosis should be assessed by careful consideration of the total symptomatology in each individual case.

There is a high incidence of re-offending in the mentally impaired (approximately 50 per cent). Lund (1990) made some interesting observations on mentally retarded criminal offenders in Denmark. Based on data from the Danish Central Criminal Register, the total number of mentally retarded offenders serving statutory care orders on a census day decreased from 290 in 1973 to 91 in 1984. The reduction was caused by shorter sentences and a dramatic decrease in the number of sentenced borderline retarded offenders. The total number of sentences per year slightly decreased, and the number of first-time sentences was stable. Crimes on property are decreasing among this population, while violence, arson, and sexual offences are increasing. Behaviour disorder was found in 87.5 per cent of 91 offenders serving care orders in 1984. Offensive behaviour was significantly predicted by *early institutionalisation*, having *retarded or divorced parents of low socio-economic status*, and *behaviour disorder of social-aggressive type*. Independent significant effects were attributed to behaviour disorder and low socio-economic background. All predictors were closely correlated. Biological factors did not have any significant predictive value.

Factors influencing the repetition of serious crime by the mentally disordered (including the mentally impaired) are considered in some detail in Chapter XV.

Psychiatrists should obviously be aware of *management facilities* available for mentally impaired offenders in their areas of residence.

Hughes (1994) made the following valuable observations on sentencing and treatment:

Sentencing

Every effort should be made to deal with this group along medical and social lines as far as is possible. In recent years, there has been a marked decrease in the number of Hospital Orders used, reflecting the increasing use of community care for the mentally impaired in society. Increasing emphasis is put today on social treatment, training and continued education into adult life in both criminal context and in society. Offenders are often dealt with by means of Supervision Orders (up to 18). Probation Orders and Guardianship Orders are an alternative to Hospital Orders. Guardianship Orders often sound an ideal disposal but in practice lack "teeth".

Treatment

This should include medical, psychiatric and social treatment as well as continued education in the broadest sense of the term. Of these options, the social and educational aspects are the more important in most cases. Treatment is usually carried out in a community setting. For the mildly handicapped, housing needs and training in the skills of daily living are important, as well as training in social skills. Combining this approach with specialized education and employment training by specially trained staff can be very effective. The majority can then lead a fairly normal life – but supervision should not be discontinued too soon.

The severely and profoundly handicapped will mostly need more intensive care in a residential setting. Most will need supervision throughout their lives.

In general, the handicapped are a vulnerable and easily led group of people. They are particularly vulnerable to such social scourges as alcohol and drugs. As in the general public, there is a high incidence of offending in adolescence and young adult life. This is often the very time when they leave the protection of school and family.

Perhaps it is appropriate to conclude this Chapter by referring to some excellent ideas by Perry (1991) concerning the management of the mentally handicapped by social services.

Social Services for People with Learning Difficulties

For centuries people with a mental handicap have been subject to ridicule, misunderstood, treated with fear, and denied basic human rights. They are not ill and very rarely aggressive. Most of them are very affectionate and perhaps better described, as they themselves would prefer to be known, as people with learning difficulties.

Unfortunately services designed to assist them have often in the past added to their problems. Special segregated provision has been developed in order to assist in developing their life skills. This has proved counter-productive in that it has implied, from a very early age, that people with learning difficulties are different, need to be segregated, and has instilled fear of the unknown in others. Segregated education has prevented the acceptance and familiarization developed in children through play and mixing together whilst isolating parents and children from their neighbours through not attending their local school. This has created attitudinal problems which have to be overcome in making a reality of Community Care. Few options have been available in adult life with 80 per cent of the budget going on the 20 per cent in hospital or residential care, leaving many parents to cope in the community with little support or hope.

Objective of Services for People with Learning Difficulties

    (a)   *Impact Objectives.* To restore basic human rights, dignity and self-respect to people with a mental handicap and their carers,

enabling them to exercise choice in deciding:
(i)   with whom they live, with family, with friends or alone;
(ii) where they live, in an ordinary house in the community of their choice;
(iii) what social and recreational activities they wish to participate in;
(iv) whether or not they wish to work and if so for a fair day's pay.

(b) *Service Objectives*
(i)   the counselling of parents of newly identified Down's syndrome children;
(ii) to identify people with a mental handicap and instigate an individual planning system;
(iii) to create opportunities for integrated community living for people with learning difficulties;
(iv) to help people with learning difficulties to develop their life skills;
(v)   to provide support to carers.

(c) *Logistical Objectives*. To redeploy money, staffing and expertise from the large subnormality hospitals and other inappropriate facilities into community care.

References

Campbell, L. (1990) "Impairment Disabilities and Handicaps: Assessment for Court". *Principles and Practice of Forensic Psychiatry*, Blueglass, R., Bowden, P. (eds), Churchill Livingstone, Section V.9: 419-24.

Day, K. (1988) "A Hospital-Based Treatment Programme for Male Mentally Handicapped Offenders". *Br. J. Psychiatry*, 153: 35-44.

Gilby, R., Wolf, L., Goldberg, B. (1989) "Mentally Retarded Adolescent Sex Offenders: A Survey and Pilot Study", *Can J. Psychiatry*, 34(6): 542-8.

Heaton-Ward, A (1977) "Psychosis in Mental Handicap", *Brit. J. Psychiat.* 130: 525-33.

Heber, R. (1959) *Manual on Terminology and Classification in Mental Retardation*, American Association on Mental Deficiency.

Hughes, J. (1994) Consultant Psychiatrist, St. Cadoc's Hospital, Caerleon. *Personal Communications*.

Kearns, A., O'Connor, A. (1988) "The Mentally Handicapped Criminal Offender: A 10-year Study of 2 Hospitals", *Brit. J. Psychiatry,* 152: 848-51.

Lewis, N., Yarnell, H. (1951) *Pathological Firesetting (Pyromania), Nervous and Mental Disease Monographs*. No. 82, Coolidge Foundation, New York.

Lund, J.(1990) "Mentally Retarded Criminal Offenders in Denmark", Institute of Psychiatric Demography, Aarhus Psychiatric Hospital, Risskov, Denmark, *Br. J. Psychiatry*, 156: 726-31.

Neustatter, W.L. (1957), *The Mind of the Murderer*, Christopher Johnson, London.

Murrey, G.J., Briggs, D., Davis, C. (1992) "Psychopathic Disordered, Mentally Ill, and Mentally Handicapped Sex Offenders: A Comparative Study", *J. Med. Sci. Law*, 32(4): 331-36.

Perry, C.J. (1991) Social Services Dept. Director's Commentary and Strategic Planning Statement for South Glamorgan.

Rao, J.M., Sharma, S., Radhakrishnan, G. (1991) "Mental Illness in the Mentally Handicapped: A Study of Ten Yers Referral to a Mental Handicap Hospital", *Brit. J. Clin. and Social Psychiatry*, 7, 3, 148-51

Sullivan, W.C. (1924) *Crime in relation to Congenital Mental Deficiency*, Edward Arnold & Co., London.

West, D.J. (1982) *Delinquency, Its Roots, Careers and Prospects*, Heinemann, London.

CHAPTER XII

Psychopathy and Crime

The term psychopath includes psychopathic personality and disorder. The first part of this chapter is concerned with a review of some of the literature dealing with the concept of psychopathic disorder which is specifically defined in the Mental Health Act (1983). Psychopathic personality may have the same relationship to psychopathic disorder as manic-depressive personality has to manic-depressive psychosis, and schizoid personality to schizophrenic psychosis. This distinction is helpful in court work.

A personal study of 100 inmates, which was undertaken with the object of discovering if psychopathic disorder should be regarded as a clinical entity, is included.

I also refer to a study comparing 18 psychopathically disordered inmates with a control group of 18 normal people. This study was undertaken with the object of discovering environmental influences which militate against normal personality development and predispose to psychopathic disorder.

Five case histories are described.

It is interesting to review the history of the concept of psychopathy. The terms "moral insanity" and "moral imbecility" were introduced by the Bristol physician, J.C. Pritchard in 1842. He believed that certain individuals periodically behaved in a manner harmful to society and their behaviour was not subject to the restraining influences of reason and willpower. Pritchard also believed that the misbehaviour was "uncontrollable" and that insight was lacking. The use of the word "moral" was in keeping with the climate of opinion in the mid-nineteenth century.

John Connolly (1849) described people who were "extremely selfish, cruel and alcoholic and prone to indulge in illegal activity such as fraud, forgery and even murder, which was perpetrated as a result of a sudden homicidal impulse". He also thought that such people were characterized by "irregularity of conduct and insensibility to moral obligations" and they were also considered to be "disqualified" for forming correct judgments or for regulating conduct. Connolly also observed that certain individuals were "all their life long, the subject of one of these fine shades of insanity in which the perceptions are morbidly intense and regard for the ordinary means of worldly success are absurdly absent and at length they become actually insane". Connolly appreciated the significance of a long history of disordered behaviour as a necessary criterion for diagnosing what is nowadays called psychopathic disorder. The comment about "morbidly intense perceptions" is particularly interesting as psychopaths are unduly vulnerable emotionally and often take unwarranted offence at the words, actions or attitudes of others. Their reactions to ordinary stress are frequently exaggerated and abnormal due to feelings of inferiority and compensatory arrogance which co-exist.

The Mental Deficiency Acts 1913 and 1926 referred to "moral defectives" as "persons in whose case there exists mental defectiveness coupled with strongly vicious or criminal propensities and who require care, supervision and control for the protection of others". This description is in agreement with the present-day concept of psychopathic disorder combined with mental impairment.

Bleuler (1924) did not attempt to define the condition. He believed that it represented a deviation from what one may regard as the "normal" or "average" personality. He considered it incorrect to assume that psychopaths possessed this or that quality. He believed that "certain principal features and correlations" frequently repeated themselves in the case histories of socially maladjusted individuals. Bleuler also believed that "many psychopaths are really only in the social sense, not insane". The personality "features and correlations" include nervosity, aberrations of the sexual impulse, abnormal irritability, instability, eccentricity, squandering, swindling, wandering, dipsomania, gambling and compulsive collecting of various articles. Over-suspicious personalities, unduly litigious people and pathological liars are included in Bleuler's abnormal personalities. The pathological liars suffer from "exaggerated activity of their fantasy, with unsteadiness and planlessness of the will" and he regarded these individuals as potential schizophrenics.

The Royal Commission on Mental Illness and Mental Deficiency (1954-57) described psychopaths as "mentally abnormal patients whose daily behaviour shows a want of social responsibility and of consideration for others, of prudence and foresight, and of ability to act in their own best interests and whose persistent anti-social mode of conduct may include inefficiency and lack of interest in any form of occupation, pathological lying, swindling, slandering, alcoholism, drug addiction, sexual offences, violent acts with little motivation and an entire absence of self-restraint which may go as far as homicide". The Commission was also of the opinion that "punishment or the threat of punishment influences their behaviour only momentarily and its more lasting effect is to intensify their vindictiveness and anti-social attitude". No reference is made to the necessity or otherwise of regarding *duration* of abnormal behaviour as a diagnostic criterion but *degree* of abnormal behaviour is appreciated as vital from the diagnostic point of view.

Mayer-Gross, Salter and Roth (1955) were of the opinion that "the psychopathic personality in general is a mosaic of many elements" but presumably a clinical entity. They also stated that the psychopath is prone to develop neurotic symptoms in response to stress.

The Mental Health Act 1983, defines *psychopathic disorder* as "a persistent disorder or disability of mind, whether or not including significant impairment of intelligence, which results in abnormally aggressive or seriously irresponsible conduct on the part of the person concerned". The word "persistent" is not defined, but one presumes that the "disorder of the mind" should have existed for a number of years. Some psychiatrists believe that they should not be bound by any period for diagnosing psychopathic disorder. The individual must also be considered amenable to treatment.

Gould (1959) referred to certain types of criminal behaviour such as sexual assault on a newly dead body and the excessively violent murder involving much force and destruction, even to inanimate objects in the vicinity. This type of behaviour may be an expression of psychopathic disorder or schizophrenia.

Any attempt to define the psychopath is likely to prove very difficult. Psychopathic behaviour is pathological (anti-social) behaviour and may express itself in numerous ways. Bleuler and Kraepelin did not attempt a definition, but confined themselves to descriptions of various types of behaviour which were regarded as abnormal on attaining a substantial degree of persistence and intensity.

The Mental Health Act 1983 refers to the psychopathic disorder in the context of "abnormally aggressive or seriously irresponsible conduct" which results from a "persistent disorder or disability of mind". The word "persistent" presumably refers to a period during which the mind has been disordered or disabled. I recall the case of a young man who was sentenced to be detained in a special hospital on the basis of a hospital order under s.60 of the Mental Health Act 1959. The order was issued by an Assize Court Judge who accepted the evidence of two consultant psychiatrists who stated that the accused was suffering from psychopathic disorder. This man pleaded guilty to charges of assaulting two women within a two-week period. The assaults were not of an indecent nature and the victims were not seriously injured. The accused did not suffer from psychosis, sub-normality or epilepsy, and was in a semi-inebriated state when the assaults were perpetrated. He had not broken the law previously and had never been regarded as mentally disordered.

May one conclude that the Judge decided that the "disorder of mind" had been present for a substantial period in latent form before the "abnormally aggressive conduct" became evident? Otherwise one is forced to assume that a conduct disorder of two-weeks duration is an expression of a "persistent disorder or disability of mind".

The aetiology may be considered under the following headings:

(a) *Genetic factors*. There seems to be a correlation between the sex chromosome constitution XYY on the one hand and criminality, anti-social behaviour and low intelligence, on the other.

(b) *Environmental factors*. Whiteley (1970) of the Henderson Clinic, regards psychopathy as a social disorder and he believes that a study of social interaction would provide clues as to its causation and treatment. Patterns of psychopathic social behaviour are studied by obtaining information from parents, other members of the family and from school records and other early contacts outside the family.

(c) *Psychological factors*. The discovery of illegitimacy at puberty may have harmful psychological effects. Curran and Mallinson (1944) referred to "a persistent abnormality of character frequently, but not necessarily, anti-social". These authors also refer to "continuous psychopathic states" and "episodic psychopathic reactions", and this is a valid distinction, because the former are equivalent to psychopathic disorder as defined in the Mental Health Act, whereas the episodic psychopathic reaction may be characteristic of humanity in general. They sub-divide psychopaths into (i) vulnerable personalities, (ii) unusual or abnormal personalities, and (iii) sociopathic personalities which may be criminal.

(d) *Physical and biochemical factors*. Deformity, cerebral trauma, meningitis and encephalitis may adversely affect the personality leading to psychopathic disorder. Women in the pre-menstrual period are more likely to break the law than at any other time of the menstrual cycle.

The great majority of humans (including psychopaths) are right-handed, meaning that the left cerebral hemispheres are dominant and contain the speech centres. Consequently, the ability to speak is retained when a right-handed person survives a cerebro-vascular accident affecting his right cerebral hemisphere. Hare and McPherson (1984) indicated that the majority of psychopaths despite being right-handed, make greater use of their *right* cerebral hemispheres for processing and expressing verbal information in speech. This leads to under-use or under-arousal of the left cerebral hemispheres. Consequently the two hemispheres become poorly integrated from the point of view of mutual functioning resulting in conflict between language, emotional processes and responses and behaviour. This theory would account for the apparent pathological lying by psychopaths and the useless guarantees which they give with great conviction to the effect that their future behaviour will be law-abiding and considerate of others. Cleckley (1976) refers to "semantic dementia" in this context and studies have indicated that criminals are more likely to have inappropriately dominant right hemispheres than non-criminals.

I studied 100 selected case histories of inmates of Leeds Prison. Their ages varied from 18 to 52 years and included 19 homosexuals and 19 non-addictive alcohlics on the basis of Jellinek's classification. Relevant case notes from various psychiatric hospitals were also studied. This particular group of 100 was selected because each member had been diagnosed as a psychopathic personality at some period during the years 1933 to 1966 (inclusive) and in this context the diagnosis was taken to mean psychopathic disorder as defined in the Mental Health Act 1959, with the added proviso that the "abnormally aggressive or seriously irresponsible conduct" existed for a minimum period of five years.

Twenty-four of the total study group were selected for further consideration because psychopathic personality had been diagnosed at one period and alternative diagnoses were made at other periods. These diagnoses are indicated in Table XXVI.

Table XXVI

No.	Date of Diagnosis	Diagnosis
1	1933	"Mild manic conditions and possible schizophrenia".
	1965	"Psychopathic personality."
2	1940	"Schizophrenic" but within six-month period diagnosis changed to "Ganser Syndrome".
	1965	"Psychopathic personality".
3	1944	"Psychoneurotic".
	1965	"Psychopathic personality".
4	1944	"Mental defective" and spent five years in a hospital for mental defectives, although the I.Q. in 1966 was assessed as 88.
	1966	"Psychopathic personality".
5	1949	"Pathological depression" and in-patient in Rampton from 1949 to 1963.
	1965-66	"Psychopathic personality".
6	1949	"Alcohol insanity with confusion".
	1958	"Confusion with underlying schizophrenia".
	1965	"Psychopath with secondary paranoid psychosis".
7	1950	"Chronic anxiety state".
	1965-66	"Psychopathic personality".
8	1951	"Inadequate personality, anxiety state and depression".
	1965-66	"Psychopathic personality".
9	1952	"Mental defective" and certified under the 1913 MD Act and a patient in Rampton from 1952-65. His I.Q. in 1965 was 105 and he admitted to deceiving the doctors in 1952.
	1965	"Psychopathic personality".
10	1953	"Aggressive psychopath".
	1965	"Paranoid psychosis" – "developing".
11	1956	"Inadequate psychopath".
	1965	"Chronic depressive schizophrenia".
12	1958	"Simple schizophrenia".
	1959	"Inadequate psychopath".
	1965-66	"Psychopathic personality".

13	1960	"Personality disorder".
	1965	"Schizophrenia".
	1966	"Inadequate psychopath with paranoid ideas".
14	1960	"Anxiety state".
	1965-66	"Psychopathic personality".
15	1960	"Hypomania".
	1962	"Endogenous depression and subnormality".
	1965-66	"Psychopathic personality".
16	1961	"Personality disorder and depression".
	1965-66	"Psychopathic personality".
17	1961	"Psychopathic depression".
	1965-66	"Psychopathic personality".
18	1962	"Personality disorder".
	1966	"Psychopathic behaviour" – ? secondary to tuberculosis. Meningitis in 1958.
19	1963	"Psychopath".
	1964	"Endogenous depression and alcoholic".
	1965-66	"Psychopathic Personality".
20	1963	"Depression".
	1965-66	"Psychopathic personality".
21	1964	"Psychopathic and neurotic depressive".
	1965-66	"Psychopathic personality".
22	1964	"Simple schizophrenia and subnormality".
	1965-66	"Psychopathic personality".
23	1946	"Depression".
	1964	"Psychopathic personality with depression".
	1965-66	"Psychopathic personality".
24	1964	"Schizophrenia with depressive episodes".
	1965	"Psychopathic personality".

It is reasonable to regard psychopathic disorder as a defined clinical syndrome but any one of a number of mental disorders may be superimposed upon it during the course of its natural history. A period of unusual stress could be responsible for the development of secondary and usually temporary neurotic or psychotic symptoms and I have noted these developments amongst prisoners.

Psychopathic disorder means persistent abnormal behaviour and constitutes a mental disorder within the meaning of the Mental Health Act 1983. Psychopathic disorder, mental impairment and severe mental impairment are specifically defined in the Mental Health Act, whereas mental illness is not. A single act, however heartless and cruel, would not justify a diagnosis of psychopathic disorder.

The history of the psychopath does not reveal a definite *point in time* when the disorder became apparent and this fact is diagnostically useful in distinguishing psychopathic disorder from the psychoses. Genuine inability to profit by experience is also a helpful diagnostic factor. The history of abnormal behaviour should be long enough to establish that it is not due to an acute illness of sudden and recent onset which is likely to spontaneously abate or be cured in the near future. Police records may indicate that conduct is becoming progressively more violent. Abnormally aggressive conduct means conduct that is entirely unprovoked, and/or so grossly abnormal that no normal person would be a party to it. Seriously irresponsible conduct is judged on the total history with particular reference to drug addiction, alcoholism, sexual perversion and lack of inability to cope with occupational, marital and financial problems. Psychopathic disorder as defined in the Mental Health Act, is usually taken to mean the aggressive type. Table XXVII indicates the difference between the psychopathic and non-psychopathic criminal.

Table XXVII

Psychopathic criminal	*Non-psychopathic criminal*
Tends to indulge in senseless petty crime even when not short of material goods.	No such tendency.
Claims full allegiance to principles of law and morality.	Makes no such claim.
He does not pause to consider the serious consequences of his behaviour.	He considers the possible consequences of his misdeeds.
He often makes little use of his illgotten gains.	He makes good use of his illgotten gains.
His candour, and lack of anxiety and guilt, initially help him more to avoid detection, but he eventually loses interest in safeguarding himself and detection becomes inevitable.	He constructively plans his illegal activity and he is consistent in avoiding the consequences of his misdeeds.
No loyalty to any group.	He shows loyalty to other members of his group and holds a firm antisocial and antiauthoritarion creed.

Table XXVIII

Some Factors in Psychotherapy	18 Diagnosed Psychopaths																		18 Nursing and Prison Lay Staff																	
1 Some relationship in childhood	X										X	X	X	X	X	X	X	X	X	X	X	X	X	X	X	X	X	X	X	X	X	X	X	X	X	X
2 Illegitimate birth		X	X		X														X		X															
3 Parental desertion, divorce or death	X	X	X	X	X	X	X			X		X			X					X																
4 Parental cruelty, drunkenness, neglect	X	X		X	X	X			X	X		X					X																			
5 Family dependence on Nat. Assist.	X			X		X								X						X																
6 Frequent moves in childhood	X	X		X	X	X			X			X																								
7 Irregular schooling	X		X	X	X	X	X	X		X	X		X	X	X																					
8 Large number of sibs.(5 or more)	X	X					X	X	X			X		X																						
9 Residence in slums	X		X	X	X	X	X			X	X	X							X		X		X										X			
10 Early delinquency contacts	X		X	X	X	X	X	X		X			X	X																						
11 An only child			X																							X	X	X			X	X		X		X
12 Low intell., I.Q. under 85 (WAILS)	X					X					X			X		X		X		X																

An attempt to itemize some of the factors in psychopaths as opposed to the same factors in hospital and prison staff, are listed in the table, Factor 1 indicates some relationship in childhood remembered as giving happiness. Factors 2 and 11 register common features in childhood deprivation. Factor 12 indicates intelligence disability.

The Minnesota Multiphasic Personality Inventory is widely used to assess personality disorder and its degree, but only some of its scales are relevant to psychopathy. Furthermore, its standard scales are psychometrically deficient and deviations of personality tend to be confounded with symptoms (Howells *et al* 1989). These authors also indicate that the MILLON Clinical Multiaxial Inventory may well be more useful in assessment as it has a scoring system which takes account of population base rates.

Table XXVIII indicates the results of comparing 18 psychopathically disordered inmates with 18 apparently normal people, from the point of view of environmental influences during childhood and adolescence. The study was carried out before 1959 and lasted for 18 months. The 18 inmates were serving sentences in excess of five years and they were actively or potentially aggressive and regarded as mentally disordered within the meaning of the Mental Health Act 1959. Eight were recommended for special hospitals on the basis of s.72 of the Act. The 18 inmates occupied a hospital landing of a prison. This landing was reserved for psychopaths. These inmates had attacked other inmates and members of staff and they also had histories of suicidal attempts, smashing up hospital rooms and malicious fire-setting. They were located in single rooms where various weapons had been found at different times. Two members of the group committed suicide, two others attempted to murder inmates and a further two did, in fact, murder two fellow inmates. One aggressive psychopath performed what could be described as "a leucotomy with bricks" on another unfortunate inmate who was not a member of the study group.

The following examples of psychopathic behaviour are personally known to the writer, who was responsible for advising courts as to the medical disposal of the individuals concerned.

Case 39: A male in his late teens admitted stabbing two teenage girls with a knife which had a six-inch blade. He followed one of the girls to a park and threatened her with a knife and a toy gun. He held the knife to her throat and stabbed her in the chest when she screamed and struggled. He stabbed a second girl in the neck almost a year later. Both victims survived.

His childhood was rather unhappy and insecure. His father was a drunkard who used violence against the accused and his mother. His parents separated when he was 13 years old.

His intelligence quotient on the Wechsler Adult Intelligence Scale was 83. He was capable of earning his living in the community as a labourer.

An approved school headmaster indicated that he had emotionally matured "a great deal" during his stay at the school, but added that he craved attention. The master concluded that the accused required "a much deeper investigation of home circumstances and the family background". A psychiatrist who visited the school described the accused as "defensive, emotionally very guarded and probably emotionally flat", and his mother as "over indulgent". The psychiatrist concluded that the accused required psychiatric supervision during training.

He was unmarried and did not admit to sexually deviant tendencies. He craved intercourse with a member of the opposite sex but never achieved this ambition and the consequent frustration was expressed in aggression. He believed that members of the opposite sex found him unattractive and enjoyed sadistic fantasies of stabbing girls. He said that he had suffered from a "mind blank" for about ten minutes immediately before each stabbing and alleged that he did not fully realize what he was doing. However, he was able to give a detailed account of the stabbings.

There was no history of psychiatric treatment, suicidal attempts, epilepsy or serious head injuries. He did not take alcohol to excess or indulge in illicit drug-taking.

My report to the court indicated that s.60 of the Mental Health Act 1959 was not applicable to him, and that his mental condition did not justify psychiatric treatment as the condition of s.3 of the Powers of the Criminal Courts Act 1973.

He was fit to plead and he pleaded "guilty".

His physical health was satisfactory.

The Judge sentenced him to life imprisonment with a strong recommendation for the psychiatric investigation with a view to treatment during sentence.

Two isolated acts of violence by a teenager did not justify a diagnosis of psychopathic disorder as defined in the Mental Health Act but such a disorder could develop in future years.

Case 40: A young man pleaded guilty to setting fire to his place of work causing considerable damage but no loss of life. He said that he behaved in this manner because he felt that his colleagues treated him with reserve because they thought that he might be a homosexual. He was well cared for by his grandparents during childhood and adolescence. There was no family history of mental disorder or epilepsy. He received out-patient psychotherapy as a child but details of this treatment were not available. His intelligence was at least average and he was quite capable of earning his living in the community. He was unmarried and heterosexual.

There was no history of residential psychiatric treatment or epilepsy. He sustained a head injury when 14 years old but he was not detained in hospital. He made a suicidal gesture by inflicting superficial injuries on his left hand with a razor blade about two weeks before his remand in custody. He stated that he made this attempt because he was reprimanded by his mother.

He considered throwing himself in front of a moving train when about 15 years old because of "depression" due to arguments which his grandparents had concerning him.

There was no evidence of alcoholism but he used to smoke cannabis fairly regularly and he took lysergic acid on two occasions.

He was clearly aware of the difference between right and wrong. He was well behaved and quite rational during the remand period.

I informed the court that the accused could repeat offences of malicious fire-setting because of morbid fears, emotional immaturity and the frustrations experienced in work situations.

A probation officer regarded the accused as a very disturbed young man who was exhibiting signs of personality disintegration and a detachment from reality which could be indicative of an incipient psychotic condition. A consultant psychiatrist examined the accused during the remand period, and concluded that he was in a pre-psychotic state.

The court was advised that s.60 of the Mental Health Act 1959 was not applicable on the grounds of mental disorder.

The accused pleaded "guilty" and he was admitted to a psychiatric hospital under s.3 of the Powers of Criminal Courts Act 1973. He had not been in trouble with the law previously and the decision of the court was merciful.

Case 41: A man in his late twenties was charged with malicious fire-setting. He admitted setting fire to the curtains of his living room after an argument with his wife during which he smashed crockery. The damage was confined to the kitchen and he was alone in the house at the material time. Police and members of the fire service removed him from the house after a struggle.

His childhood seems to have been reasonably happy and secure. His sister had residential treatment in a psychiatric hospital. He was subject to nocturnal enuresis up to the age of about six years. His intelligence quotient was 62 (Wechsler Adult Intelligence Scale). He could earn his living in the community and cope fairly well with community life. He had good relationships with his children but he admitted beating his wife rather badly on two occasions. There was no evidence of sexually deviant tendencies.

There was a history of residential psychiatric treatment and he was diagnosed as suffering from a "depressive illness with suicidal intent". He experienced abnormal loss of consciousness for brief periods during childhood but an electroencephalogram taken during the remand period was reported as within normal limits. He suffered from temporary amnesia several years previously as a result of a car accident. There was no history of alcoholism or illicit drug-taking.

A consultant psychiatrist who had previously treated him advised admission to a special hospital on the grounds of sub-normality. A consultant from a special hospital disagreed with this view and thought that the accused was not a serious danger to the public for the following reasons:

(i)   The offence was committed in response to specific domestic provocation.

(ii)   The history indicated that the accused was not a repetitive arsonist.

(iii)   He had never experienced enjoyable fantasies of malicious fire-setting.

(iv)   He showed no abnormal interest in fires during childhood.

(v)   He had never before set fires maliciously.

(vi)   He was well behaved, accepted treatment and did not abscond during his four periods of residential psychiatric treatment.

(vii) He had received little community support from the welfare services and it was essential to direct treatment to supporting his inadequacy in his home, so that further stress-induced depressions need not occur.

The consultant who had previously treated the accused refused to re-admit him to his hospital and consequently s.60 of the Mental Health Act could not be implemented.

The Crown Court sentenced him to two years' imprisonment which was served in a prison hospital.

Case 42: A man in his twenties was charged with setting fire to the contents of two dustbins.

His childhood was quite happy and secure. There was no relevant family history. He was a poor scholar and testing during the remand period revealed an intelligence quotient of 61 (Wechsler Adult Intelligence Scale).

He was capable of earning some money by doing simple jobs under supervision in the community.

He was unmarried and there was no evidence of sexually deviant tendencies. He had but a vague idea of the facts of life.

There was no evidence of epilepsy. He stated that he sustained a head injury as a result of a fall during childhood. A prominent scar was evident in the region of his forehead but further details of this injury could not be traced.

There was no history of suicidal attempts. He received residential treatment in a hospital for sub-normals for a few weeks during his teens.

There was no evidence of alcoholism or illicit drug-taking.

An electroencephalogram taken during the remand period revealed an abnormal record and suggested emotional immaturity, but no evidence of local brain damage, epilepsy or cerebral tumour.

He was examined by a consultant from a special hospital who indicated that admission to a special hospital was appropriate. The accused showed an interest in giving fire alarms and in watching fires. He may have indulged in malicious fire-setting on other occasions but the police were unable to prove these offences against him. He was without employment, resources or control. He seemed free to wander and get into mischief. A moderate amount of alcohol sometimes caused him to indulge in malicious fire-setting.

His uncritical attitude and lack of remorse meant that he was a danger to the public.

He was sent to a special hospital on the basis of a Hospital Order under s.60 of the Mental Health Act 1959. A restriction order under s.65 of the same Act was not implemented.

Case 43: I was instructed by a Judge to visit a hospital for sub-normals for the purpose of examining a man in his thirties who was accused of sexual offences involving two female children. He had been admitted as a resident patient to the hospital about three months after committing the offences and he had been a resident patient at the same hospital for two months about 14 years previously. I was asked to carry out the examination because a consultant had indicated that the accused was unfit to plead and too ill to appear in court because of sub-normality and suspected cerebral tumour.

The accused was adopted in early childhood. The adoptive father took alcohol to excess and consequently the home life was unhappy. He attended a special school for the educationally backward and his intelligence quotient was 53 (Wechsler Adult Intelligence Scale). His intelligence level had not altered at the time of the current charges. He was obviously functioning at a higher level. He had undertaken simple labouring-type work under supervision in the community for the greater part of 20 years. The social inquiry report indicated that he was well behaved in hospital but "very obstinate, stubborn, taciturn and truculent" in the community. The probation officer concluded that the accused was liable to "lash out" when thwarted and become "withdrawn and uncommunicative" in response to moderate frustration and "seemed to have little sense of moral values".

There was no history of epilepsy or serious head injury. He did not take alcohol to excess or indulge in illicit drug-taking.

Examination did not reveal neuorological evidence to indicate an organic cerebral lesion. Electroencephalography proved negative for epilepsy.

There was no evidence of homosexual tendencies and he was aware of the facts of life. He was considered capable of having sexual intercourse.

The court was informed that the accused was sub-normal within the meaning of the Mental Health Act 1959, but as he was unfit to plead, a hospital order under s.60 of the Act could not be made.

When written and oral evidence had been submitted, the accused was produced in court where a jury found him unfit to plead "under disability" on the basis of s.5 of the Criminal Procedure (Insanity) Act 1964. He was committed by the Secretary of State to the same hospital and under the same consultant. Theoretically he would have had to stand trial if he became fit to plead at a future date.

The accused had a marked sense of loyalty to the hospital and confidence in the consultant. Consequently, admission to a special hospital was not advised and the court was satisfied that the public would be adequately protected by entrusting him to the consultant's care.

Cases of psychopathic sadism and paedophilia are described in Chapter VIII.

The abused child and wife syndromes
These syndromes are included in this section because individuals with psychopathic tendencies tend to be implicated in these crimes.

Baby and Child Battering
The NSPCC indicate that 738 babies and young children were battered during the years 1977 to 1982 (inclusive). Young children are under four years old.

In a culture where it is acceptable to punish children with physical chastisement, the point at which such treatment becomes abuse is unclear. The children who are the subject of the studies described below are those who have been physically battered to the point where they require medical attention, if not hospitalization. The question has been asked whether every adult is potentially capable of battering a child. The answer is again unclear, for while most adults admit to violent feelings about their children on occasions, there are societies in which child abuse does not occur at all. It has been suggested that cultures in which physical punishment of the child is acceptable are also those in which violent abuse of the child tends to occur.

The NSPCC indicates that it received 42,720 referrals for the UK during the period 1.10.91 to 30.9.92 and a total of 69 per cent were under the age of 9 years and 48 per cent of the total referrals were for alleged sexual and/or physical abuse.

The statistical samples on which the above figures are based may be an underestimate, since it is likely that there are many undetected cases of child abuse, further cases identified but not reported, and still further cases reported but not proven. Most abused children admitted to hospital are both young and seriously injured, so it is possible that many other children with less serious injuries escape detection.

An analysis of the causes of this social problem seems to require a multifactorial approach. The earliest description of the Battered Child syndrome published by Kemp in America in 1962, and the later collection of writings edited by Helfer and Kemp in 1968, which now constitutes a classical study of the subject, tend to emphasize the damaged personalities of the parents, their own emotionally deprived childhoods, and their problematic approaches to child management. Other studies in Great Britain by the NSPCC Research Team from 1969 onwards and by Smith in 1975, note the situation disadvantages of many of these families and the failure of the parents to make adequate adjustments to married life under difficult social, economic and material conditions. It is becoming clear that all these factors are influential and interact one with another to culminate in episodes of violence directed towards the child.

Statistical and clinical studies have produced the following information about the battered child, parents, and family situation.

The parents do not belong exclusively to any social class, educational or occupational grouping. They are to be found throughout society (Helfer and Kemp, 1972). But other studies have found higher numbers of child batterers in the deprived and in working-class groups and a higher number of mothers who indulged in this behaviour were found to be of below average intelligence (Smith, 1975). They frequently showed personality disorders which involved high levels of emotional conflict and anxiety, with some difficulty in tolerating frustration and controlling impulsive behaviour. Most, but not all, had a history of unsatisfactory parenting and childhood experiences. They were emotionally deprived, rejected, and their needs for a dependent relationship frustrated. Their self-esteem, confidence and capacity for trust were correspondingly underdeveloped. Many were punished excessively as children and subjected to physical abuse and they tended to repeat the styles of parenting and child control to which they themselves were subjected. They lacked adequate knowledge on the practicalities of child care, and failed to understand or accept the immature needs and dependence of their children.

A clinical study by Bryant (1963) identified three styles of family relationships associated with child abuse:

(a) *The severely hostile, aggressive parent* who appeared to suffer almost continual anger, had uncontrolled outbursts of temper and violence at any irritation or frustration, including those provoked by the child.

(b) *The passive, inadequate parent* who looked desperately for opportunities to be dependent, and competed with the children for the attention and support of the spouse. These parents were highly anxious and frequently became depressed. They were capable of neglect as well as abuse of the child.

(c) *The rigid, compulsively controlled and orderly parent*, who lacked warmth and tended to reject the child. Their own need for success and order at home made it difficult for them to accept the demands and mess created by the child who was expected to show excellence in behaviour and development to assuage the parents' doubts and fears about their parental ability.

A study by the NSPCC (1976) reported that some families appear to combine a number of the problems in Bryant's three categories.

Finkelhor (1986) referred to preconditions to sexual offending against children from the point of view of the offenders who are usually post-pubertal males:

(i) The offender must be motivated by a desire to satisfy his or her lust.

(ii) The perpetrator must have the ability to overcome internal inhibitions which would normally militate against sexual abuse of children. These inhibitions stem from parental, educational and religious influences and the sexual taboos of society.

(iii) The offender must be capable of overcoming the victim's resistance from the physical and psychological points of view.

Treatment is directed to counteracting the offender's distorted (sexual) beliefs and bringing him to accept responsibility for the crime committed and influencing him to experience genuine personal guilt by not projecting his own frustrations on to the victim and thus holding the latter wholly or partially responsible.

Pathological fantasy thinking combined with frustrations such as marital problems, loneliness, boredom and anger together tend to "trigger" the offence by overcoming internal inhibitions and these factors must also be taken into consideration during treatment.

Situational stresses

Gould (1959) referred to certain types of criminal behaviour such as sexual assault on a newly dead body and the excessively violent murder involving much force and destruction, even to inanimate objects in the vicinity. This type of behaviour may be an expression of psychopathic disorder or schizophrenia.

Parental attitudes

Carefully controlled studies have shown that abused children were not on average more difficult or demanding than other children (Gregg and Elmer, 1969).

However, they were considered to be excessively demanding by their mothers who tended to have extreme and unrealistic attitudes to them and did not enjoy their company most of the time.

They were distinguished from other mothers by the inadequacy and carelessness of their supervision of the child, the inconsistency of their training and the harshness of their punishments including physical chastisement. They tended to show less affection than other mothers. The normal "bonding" process between mother and infant had not been adequately established in cases where the mother abused her child (Ounstead, 1974).

Indices of harm to the child

Bruises and abrasions, especially to the head and face. Fractures, burns and scalds. Loss of hair. Repeated injuries over a period of time. Failure to thrive and/or physical neglect. Good physical care and high standards in the home do not preclude possibility of child abuse. Death may result from starvation and secondary infection in the absence of physical injury. Discrepancies between the physical signs of the injury and the parents' reports and explanations of same, noting particularly the position, extent and types of injuries.

Indices of danger in the parents

Aggressive, impatient, irritable reactions over the child's behaviour, progress and achievements. Extreme reactions to the child's crying, feeding difficulties, incontinence and failure to learn quickly enough to satisfy one or both parents. Delay by the parents in seeking help for an injured child. Some 61 per cent of parents sought medical help for their children 24 hours or longer after the injury, (Smith 1975). Professed lack of knowledge as to the cause of the injury and apparent lack of interest, anxiety or guilt over the child's injury which contrasts with concerned behaviour of parents whose children have genuine accidents.

Particular problems in the management of the battering family

A series of DHSS memoranda and directives (1985) resulted in the management of child abuse by means of two local committees:

(i) An Area Review Committee which is composed of senior members of the medical profession, police, social workers, and administrators of local social services which has the function of collecting information in its own area and making policy decisions on the management of families which abuse children. This includes the organization of a local "At Risk" register containing information on families where child abuse has occurred or is suspected.

(ii) A Case Conference called by the Social Services Department in order to discuss the management of any individual family where there is an abused child or abuse is suspected. The medical, police and social agencies previously involved with the family should be included in this discussion and must arrive at an agreed plan of management. It is usual to appoint a liaison officer to implement this plan, so that all agencies are kept informed of new developments. It is also usual to make one social worker responsible for the supervision of the family, since families already under pressure are better able to respond to the visits of one rather than many professional people. Families overstressed by multiple visiting have been known to re-batter their children.

However, the management of a family by means of an inter-professional committee poses problems. In the initial stages, before treatment commences, the accommodation of the functions of all the agencies involved is the major problem. The police, primarily concerned with the protection of persons and property, have a duty to establish whether an offence has been committed by collecting all evidence for possible conviction. They will wish for early contact with the family since it is difficult to obtain unbiased accounts from other people already interviewed by doctors and social workers. Many other professionals on the committee will not be informed as to the technical differences between charges such as assaults and grevious bodily harm which may be brought against the family or the grounds on which the police may exercise their discretion over whether to prosecute at all. They may also fear that the police will take unilateral decisions by exercising their power of prosecution. The doctors, especially the paediatrician at the local hospital, will be primarily concerned with the physical survival of the child who may require prolonged hospital care. He will need early access to the child in order to carry out a range of medical tests, including the examination of bruising, which only retains its original characteristics for up to 48 to 72 hours after the injury, and the examination of fractures which may only reveal themselves clearly on X-ray two weeks after the injury. The results of these tests help to establish the cause of the child's condition as well as indicating the treatment required. The doctor may be the first person to question the parent about the circumstances of damage to the child. How he and other hospital staff approach the parents at this stage may be a determining factor in their subsequent cooperation with other professionals. It has been observed that hospital staff are not always open-minded and sympathetic to the parent once child abuse is suspected (NSPCC). The clinical material collected by the doctor may be used as evidence in a subsequent prosecution, which may cause him to be more hesitant than usual in the request he makes for information and in the conclusions he is prepared to draw from it (NSPCC).

The social worker is aware that the Social Services Department carries the long-term duty of the care and protection of the child and supervision of the family. He will be concerned that prosecution of the parents, resulting in fines or imprisonment, will reduce the chances of the financial and social survival of the family. He will know that the distress and resistance of the parents are likely to be increased by confrontations with medical staff at the hospital and with the police. He will also be aware that he may be used to collect evidence to establish their guilt. The social worker's supervisory and supportive function requires that he builds with the family a relationship in which trust, honesty about problems and dependence on him are possible. If the child is not placed permanently in the care of the local authority, the social worker must continue to work with the family in an attempt to create a safe environment to which the child may eventually return. What is currently known about long-term social work with these families does suggest that it is not yet effective in many cases and that both more expertise and resources are required (NSPCC).

The 1985 independent Committee of Inquiry into circumstances concerning the death of Jasmine Beckford was chaired by Louis Blom-Cooper, QC. This Committee recommended that all social workers should in future report children who are injured or potentially in danger as their primary responsibility and consideration of the parents in this context should be regarded as of secondary importance. This view is endorsed by the British Association of Social Workers. The Committee also gave the opinion that a council has a trustee function when a child is in care and went on to recommend that social workers should spend at least three years rather than two in training, and devote a large part of that to specialist areas, shifting the emphasis away from generalization.

The Committee also made the following recommendations: social workers should also be taught about child-care law, keep up-to-date with developments, and those who take on a child-abuse case should read up the policy memorandum from their local authority and the procedures laid down, as well as studying relevant literature. Local authorities must tell not only the local education authority but also the headmaster of the relevant school when a child becomes the subject of a care order and in every school one teacher should be designated as liaison officer with the social services to gather and pass on any relevant information relating to children in care or on the child-abuse register.

Senior nurses working for health authorities must discuss all child-abuse cases with the health visitor concerned, even if the health visitor does not think there is any problem.

Health visitors are apparently obliged to consult representatives of the social services if child abuse is suspected in a particular home. Entry may then be gained with police intervention or by means of a Court Order on the basis of representation by the Social Services. One would assume that this system would not lead to disagreements.

Hospital authorities should seek the help of a radiological paediatrician (an expert in identifying and dating injuries in children from X-rays) whenever a child is brought to them with serious, non-accidental injuries.

Taitz (1991) indicated that absence of bruising at the sites of fracture is irrelevant to deciding whether a fracture is accidental or not. He found little evidence to support a theory that fractures due to child abuse and those due to metabolic bone disease could be often confused. He studied 22 abused infants who had fractures and found that two suffered from osteogenesis imperfecta but other evidence of child abuse was apparent.

Family doctors should always be invited to case conferences and the records of social workers and health visitors should be available for all the participants at case conferences. Whenever it is decided to try to rehabilitate abused children with their parents, there should be a requirement, as part of a long-term protection plan, that the parents take children under five years to a clinic at least monthly.

The Social Services Inspectorate of the Department of Social Security, should review the process of decision-making in the management of child-abuse cases.

There should be more effort to recruit black families as prospective foster parents so that local authorities can have a greater choice in placing black children in their care, and such authorities should also set up a residential establishment in their area for children who have suffered abuse so that there is the option to take them there as an interim measure before long-term decisions are made. It is also recommended that local authorities must be under a duty to consult and assist a health authority in child-abuse cases and consideration should be given to the establishment and joint financing of child-abuse training co-ordinators.

Child abuse is a very emotive subject involving public anger and demands for punishment and strict control of offenders. Professionals in this field should be provided with up-to-date information and have sufficient practical experience in the management of battered children and their family situations. It has been estimated that a general medical practitioner will see one case every five years and a senior social worker two or three cases every year (Franklin White, 1975). Consequently, there may be professional hesitations in recording and reporting those suspected of being responsible for child abuse.

Public concern with and the overworking and possible demoralization of social workers could be prevented by the government providing local authorities with adequate funds to back up legislation designed to protect and care for children at risk.

Where child-abuse inquiry is of great public interest, and would be too expensive for a local authority to set up, it should be initiated by the Secretary of State. Finally, the Blom-Cooper Committee recommended that magistrates should be legally bound to give reasons for their decisions in child-abuse cases and should also have a checklist of factors they must take into consideration. The Lord Chancellor should consider ruling that they must not add any recommendations of their own to a care order.

Detailed guidelines for dealing with child-abuse cases were published in 1985 by the British Association of Social Workers which has some 9,000 members. The guidelines include a recommendation that all social workers and their supervisors responsible for child-abuse cases should be professionally qualified and have received specific post-qualifying training in child abuse. The association also advises social workers and supervisors who do not meet these criteria to make representations to their employers.

A child-abuse consultant should be appointed for each local authority, with administrative and supervisory responsibility for the child-abuse register. He or she should offer expert advice and consultancy for the child-abuse register, and may chair case conferences. All children at risk of abuse including sexual abuse must of course be registered. No child in the area of the local authority as a result of child abuse should be returned home before taking into account the views of a full case conference when key people involved in an individual case review circumstances and make recommendations.

David Jones, general secretary of the British Association of Social Workers, indicated that these guidelines offer a national standard against which local services can be judged and may also be used as a potential measure of failure or inadequacy in particular cases.

The NSPCC indicated that 29 child protection teams were functioning in 1985 and recommend that these be increased to 60.

An attempt was made to amend the Childrens Act, (1989) to the effect that a child could only be put back into care of its parents with the consent of the magistrates' court which made the original care order. This refers to a child who had been placed in care on the grounds of cruelty, neglect or moral danger. This amendment was defeated in the House of Commons on 2 May, 1986. Consequently, the decision to return the child to the care of its parents is still at the discretion of the social workers.

Despite the above detailed precautionary recommendations, Kimberley Carlile subsequently met a similar fate to Jasmine Beckford. Social workers may be hesitant to obtain an entry order from a magistrates' court unless armed with one or more medical reports. I find it difficult to believe that magistrates' courts would refuse entry orders unless conclusive proof of child-battering was placed before them. A strong suspicion over a reasonable period of time (as in the case of Kimberley Carlile) would be quite sufficient to obtain such an order.

Sexual abuse of children

Physical abuse of children may of course, include *sexual abuse* which is either on the increase or more frequently diagnosed.

The "Working Together" consultation paper advises social workers as follows when sexual (including ritualistic) abuse of children is suspected:

(i) Parents should be involved at every stage and included in case conferences whenever possible. Openness and honesty between parents and professionals are most important.

(ii) Dawn raids with police to seize children should not occur unless children are in immediate physical danger. Such raids should not take place exclusively for the purpose of collecting evidence.

(iii) Interviews with children should be conducted at their pace and without the type of prompting which would give the impression that the interviewer was "coaching" the child with the object of obtaining answers which he or she wished to hear.

(iv) Social workers should arrive at conclusions more on the basis of intellectual rather than emotional judgments. Specialist advice should be sought if there is any doubt.

(v) The child's welfare must be the first consideration. For example, removal of the child from the family home must be clearly for the welfare of the child and the conviction of the offender. Removal of a child from innocent parents would have a devastating emotional effect on parents and child.

Children cannot be taken from their parents by social workers unless Place of Safety Orders under Section 28(i) of the Children and Young Persons Act 1969 are issued by a magistrates' court. Police accompanying social workers must have search warrants.

The above guidelines were binding and incorporated in the Children's Act, operative in October 1991. The guidelines have been sent to social services directors, chief constables, education officers and other interested groups.

Finkelhor *et al* (1984) indicated that women may be responsible for up to 13 per cent of sexual abuse of girls and nearly 25 per cent of sexual abuse of boys and Faller (1987) found that fewer than one in ten women who sexually abused their children were psychotic. Groth (1979) interestingly observed that only 1 per cent of female sexual offenders are sent to prison. Wilkins (1990) concluded that: Sexual abuse can no longer be considered the exclusive preserve of men".

The following description of sexual abuse of children is taken from an excellent monograph by Dr H.B. Valman, (1987):

> "Sexual abuse is the involvement of dependent, developmentally immature children and adolescents in sexual activities they do not truly comprehend, to which they are unable to give informed consent, and which violate the social taboos of family roles or are against the law. In the past few years the number of cases identified has increased as the public has become more aware of the problem and professional staff have become more skilled at recognizing sexual abuse. A child's statement that he or she is being abused should be accepted as true until proved otherwise. Children rarely lie about sexual abuse. False allegations are, in any event, a sign of a disturbed family environment and an indication that a child may need help. Sexual abuse presents in three main ways:
>
> allegations by the child or an adult;
> injuries to the genitalia or anus;
> suspicious features.
>
> Suspicious features include unexplained recurrent urinary tract infections, and sexual explicitness in play, drawing, language or behaviour. There may be sudden or unexplained changes in behaviour – for example, sleep disturbance with nightmares, fear of men, or loss of trust in those near them. Self-destructive behaviour may occur, including the taking of overdoses of drugs or running away from home. Most of these physical or behavioural signs have other explanations and should do no more than raise the possibility of child sexual abuse for professionals puzzled by a child's behaviour. Presentation may be summarized as follows:
>
> 1) injuries to genitalia or anus;
> 2) recurrent urinary infection;
> 3) sexual explicitness;
> 4) sudden changes in behaviour.

The publication *"Words and Deeds"* by the NSPCC (June 1995) indicates that 1 in 6 children may be sexually abused in this country. The study involved 1032 persons.

Sexual abuse, particularly where a person known to the child was involved and where the abuse continued over a long period, can be followed by serious long-term effects. These include the post-traumatic syndrome, suicidal behaviour, psychiatric illness, and problems with relationships and sexual adjustment.

Increasing the knowledge and awareness of the public and all professionals involved with children will result in the earlier reporting of sexual abuse. Clear local guidelines on procedure and good co-operation between investigating agencies will improve the management of these very difficult problems. Voluntary organizations and self-help groups offering informal counselling through drop-in centres or telephone lines enable some children or families to seek help.

Teaching children how to protect themselves offers the greatest potential for prevention. The prime responsibility lies with the parents, but some schools have started work in this subject within the broad context of health and safety education. Some children have confided experiences to their teachers as a result of these programmes.

Parents may be convicted of sexually abusing their children who must of course be given every possible protection. Innocent parents must also be protected from stigmata which could well be life-long. Consequently, consultant paediatricians, however expertly trained, should not oppose a second opinion especially in cases where some doubt exists. After all, consultants in other medical disciplines welcome second independent confirmatory opinions.

Paediatricians should take the precaution of obtaining written consent from parents before carrying out intimate examinations on children. Implied consent would probably not be sufficient from the legal point of view if children were brought to paediatricians for complaints totally unrelated to physical (and sexual) abuse and especially if the parents were subsequently proved innocent.

Spontaneous evidence given by children in regard to allegations of sexual assault, is usually quite reliable. However, children aged six years and over, who give truthful answers spontaneously, are frequently clever enough to give opposite untruthful answers when the interviewer indulges in persistent prompting if not "grilling" to obtain the required answers and this tends to occur when the interviewer has formed a preconceived opinion of the answers which he or she would prefer to hear.

Whiteley (1993) indicated that the NSPCC has called on the Royal Commission on Criminal Justice to seek to close the loophole which, the charity believes, may have enabled child abusers to escape trial.

The call follows the case of eight-week-old Kid Griffin, of Tower Hamlets who died from non-accidental injuries. Charges against her guardians, who exercised their legal right to silence were dropped in January 1993 after the Crown Prosecution Service decided there was insufficient evidence. No further prosecutions are being considered.

The Head of Policy Development at the NSPCC said it was not campaigning for an end to the right to silence, but was looking at various options for reform. The NSPCC is conducting research based on ten cases it has documented since the mid-1980s. A possible amendment would be to lower the threshold of evidence required before a case comes to court.

The fact that two people are in charge of a child and the child dies of injuries could be sufficient to bring a case to court.

Another option is to give Judges the power to tell a jury it may choose to draw an inference from a defendant remaining silent.

Craig (1993) refers to some interesting material from a meeting of the Section of Clinical Forensic Medicine of the Royal Society of Medicine. The Children Act 1989 came into force on October 14, 1991 and recognized significant harm for emotional reasons in child-abuse cases. Emotional abuse was seldom entered in "at risk" registers in the United Kingdom. Yet it can cause serious personality damage even in the absence of physical abuse, and child psychiatry can help in this context. A speaker at this meeting also indicated that the incidence of child sexual abuse in the United States of America is 1 in 4 girls and 1 in 7 boys. Section 32(a) of the Criminal Justice Act 1988 deals with the admissibility of video evidence in such cases. Another expert at this meeting indicated that brittle-bone disease in the absence of family history and blue sclera, occurs in only 1 in 320,000 people. Multiple fractures usually indicate child abuse. These are helpful diagnostic pointers.

Infant Abduction
The following observations on infant abduction are made by Dr. Denis O'Connor (1994).

The unlawful taking away or otherwise kidnapping of infants and young children is a modern phenomenon although high-profile media coverage in recent years of isolated cases has aroused legal, psychological and psychiatric attention. Infant and child stealing, commonly referred to as "Baby-snatching" is a rare crime which is most often committed by women who have either lost babies in childbirth or who are themselves infertile or otherwise prevented from having babies of their own. In these cases the motivation is the overwhelming desire to mother an infant and to satisfy overpowering maternal needs.

There are other instances of this type of criminal offence where the intention is to cause the baby or child harm for satisfaction of a sexual and/ or sadistic urge. It is alleged that in earlier times infants were stolen to be reared and sold as slaves, or to be trained to be beggars or thieves. Again, it is alleged that sometimes babies and young children were "procured" for abuse and sacrificial purposes in rituals performed during "Black Magic" ceremonies.

In modern times the crime of baby-stealing is most likely to have been committed by women who have recently suffered the loss of an infant or who are unable to have a child of their own, as referred to above. There are cases of a similar nature where the above conditions do not necessarily apply but where the crime is committed by a young woman or teenage girl who is fantasizing about motherhood as the following case exemplifies:

Case 44: A girl of 17 years stole a baby of three months from his pram which was unattended outside a shop while the child's mother was purchasing goods inside. The crime was committed on impulse without intent to harm or keep the infant. The baby was recovered unharmed by the police some hours later. They had been alerted by a suspicious neighbour whose house overlooked the flat where the girl had taken the baby. There was no record of previous offences of this nature in the girl's history although she had several convictions for petty theft from shops. She had been in care at a community home school from the age of 11 years until she was sixteen. In social work reports she was described as being extremely withdrawn and subject to moods of depression in which she morbidly recollected the fact that her own mother had abandoned the family when she was nine years old. At the "Home" she was described as "attention seeking" and "needing lots of love". There was no evidence of psychiatric abnormality or behaviour disorder. By her own account she had wanted someone to love who needed her and when she spotted the baby crying in his pram she took him just for a little while to give him some love.

some love. It appears that in this case the girl was over-identifying with the baby and projecting her own feelings of maternal deprivation on to the situation of the infant who seemed to be similarly abandoned.

The provisions of Section 56 of the Offences Against the Persons Act, 1861 defines child stealing as the unlawful taking away or enticing of any child under 14 years of age with intent to deprive the parent or guardian or any other person having lawful care of the child, or with intent to steal any article from the child. The law specifically excludes the natural parents of the child. Thus, where a couple have separated and one of the parents abducts the child from the other this does not constitute child stealing. This Act was replaced by the Child Abduction Act 1984, ss.11(5) caj and 13(3), as legislation was said to be needed to draw a distinction between the abduction of children by parents and by strangers.

The concern here is with the kind of abduction where a woman for a variety of reasons such as depression, miscarriage, personality disturbance or personal sterility, may remove a baby or child from the parents' safe-keeping, take that child away, care lovingly for that child, and want to rear it as her own.

Edwards (1990) refers to several cases and comments on the legal issues involved.

Case 45: In a similar case, *R v. Whitfield* (21 March, [1975] Crim. L.R: 400; 61 Cr. App. Rep: 209), Whitfield, married for two years, pretended that she was pregnant and when the baby was supposed to be due she stole a seven-week-old baby from outside a maternity home and produced it as her own child to fulfil her own longing and need for a child and to satisfy family expectations. She was convicted and sentenced to two years' imprisonment varied on appeal to nine months suspended for two years.
Case 46: In *R v. Westell* [1979] Crim. L.R: 191, a five month old baby was taken from outside a post office. An hour later Westell returned the baby but a two years' sentence was upheld on appeal. Westell was described as uncommunicative, uncooperative and a woman from whom the public needed to be protected.

Two more cases in recent years are indicative of the dilemma which is posed for the courts who are not sure whether the women who commit this crime are, as Edwards (1990) points out, sick, sad, sorry or manipulative. Public outrage at these crimes tends to exacerbate the legal problems of dealing effectively with these women. For example:

Case 47: Delia McCall snatched a baby from a department store in May 1988 but she returned the child five days later and was sentenced on conviction to three years' imprisonment which was upheld on appeal. She had carefully planned the crime, posing fraudulently as a store detective with the intention of keeping the child.

Case 48: On 11 January, 1990 a woman posing as a health visitor took a two-day-old baby girl, Alexandra, from a maternity ward at St. Thomas's Hospital, London. After a nationwide police search the baby was eventually recovered unharmed and a woman arrested.

The very act of stealing a young baby is so unusual and against the accepted standards of social behaviour that it is suggestive of psychiatric disorder. D'Orban (1972) analysed 13 cases of baby stealing by women and distinguished several patterns of behaviour which could be divided into four clinical groups:

1. Mentally impaired girls who stole babies in order to play with same.
2. Schizophrenic patients whose offence was motivated by delusional ideas.
3. Psychopathic personalities, characterized by a previous history of delinquency, hysterical personality traits, and a preoccupation with their desire to have children. Their baby stealing seemed motivated by an attempt to compensate for their emotional deprivation, and they usually stole children for whom they had previously helped to care.
4. A "manipulative" group with a milder degree of personality disorder, in whom the motive for baby stealing was an attempt to influence a man by whom they had become pregnant and with whom their relationship was insecure. The offence was usually precipitated by a crisis such as a miscarriage or the threat of desertion. These women presented the stolen baby to their partner pretending that the child was his.

It is significant to observe, as D'Orban points out, that baby stealing seems to be an attempt to compensate for emotional deprivation or frustrated maternal feelings, and a real or imaginary miscarriage may be a predisposing or precipitating factor. The offence rarely seems to have been premeditated although there was evidence in some cases of previous planning particularly in the manipulative group. The stolen babies were usually well cared for and were quickly recovered unharmed.

In D'Orban's study, three patients were found to be suffering from schizophrenia. Schizophrenia was first isolated by Kraepelin under the name of 'dementia praecox' as an illness which led to the deterioration of the personality. Later Bleuler introduced the term 'schizophrenia' and included in this illness many cases in which severe deterioration of the personality did not occur (Hamilton, 1985). The disease is characterized by a specific type of thinking, feeling and relation to the external world. It is a disharmony between the functions of the mind, like thinking, feeling and acting (Thakurdas and Thakurdas, 1979). The cases in D'Orban's study had the following characteristics:

1.   All three patients had a history of inpatient treatment for their schizophrenic illness and their offences of baby stealing were committed during periods of severe relapse.
2.   There were no police records of previous convictions.
3.   They all stole young babies from prams which had been left unattended.
4.   The psychological profiles in these cases noted marked feelings of "frustrated motherhood".
5.   In two of the patients the offence was clearly related to their delusional ideas.

The following case is cited from this research study as an example of the schizophrenic syndrome:

Case 49: The patient was a young hebephrenic girl from a disturbed family background who had initially been diagnosed as suffering from a personality disorder with hysterical features but later during subsequent hospital admissions schizophrenic process symptoms became manifest. She had no children of her own but had a persistent preoccupation with pregnancy and childbirth. She had a previous history of baby stealing but no charge was brought against her at the time and she was returned to hospital. While in hospital she had entertained delusions that she had had a baby. Three months before the second episode of baby stealing she had been admitted to another psychiatric unit where she had the delusion that she had suffered a miscarriage. When remanded in custody for taking a baby from a pram she again believed herself to be pregnant but medical examination showed no evidence of pregnancy. She showed gross thought disorder and was unable to give any coherent explanation for her offence. This patient's baby stealing was clearly related to her long-standing wish to have children which had become a prominent feature of her delusions. Her second episode of child stealing may have been precipitated by her recent delusional miscarriage in an attempt to replace the child she believed she had lost.

In D'Orban's study four patients were found to have severe personality disorders with predominantly hysterical features. They were characterized as follows:

1. All four had a history of delinquency both before and after their convictions for baby stealing.
2. They all came from a severely disturbed family background.
3. All had experienced emotional deprivation and felt they had lacked affection and adequate personal care.
4. The baby stealing in this group of patients seemed to be motivated by an attempt to compensate for their feelings of emotional deprivation. Unlike mentally impaired and schizophrenic patients, the girls in this group of psychopathic personality-type seemed to have a deep emotional involvement with the babies they abducted. They showed deep concern for the baby's welfare and stated that their main reason for taking the baby was their conviction that the baby was not being sufficiently cared for. Because of their own deprived background they identified with the unwanted child.

In a further study by D'Orban (1976) it emerged that female child stealers are seen to form a heterogeneous group. Eight patients were schizophrenic, six were of sub-normal intelligence, (two of these suffered from transient psychotic illness at the time of their offence), and ten patients suffered from a personality disorder. Reviewing the histories of the extended series of cases it was observed that while typical patterns of psychopathology were present which transcended clinical diagnostic groups it appeared more appropriate to classify child stealers by *motivation* rather than by clinical diagnosis. Classified in such a way their offences fell into three types:

Comforting. Child stealing in this group of women seemed to be related to feelings of loneliness, deprivation and a desire to comfort themselves by playing with or mothering a young child. A common pattern in this group was the taking away of children who were already known to them and they invariably claimed that the parent was neglecting or ill-treating the baby.

Manipulative. These patients were termed manipulative because by stealing a baby they were attempting to control a crisis in their interpersonal relationships and to manipulate their partners. They were living in an insecure relationship with a man by whom they had become pregnant. They hoped that having a baby would reinforce the bond with their partner, but a crisis then arose which threatened this tenuous link and heightened their fear of being deserted. They then stole a baby and pretended to their partner that he was the father.

Impulsive Psychotic. The offences of patients falling into this category were bizarre and impulsive acts usually committed in an acute psychotic state. A common pattern was the middle-aged schizophrenic patient with children in care who had been sterilized.

The courts may well be considering whether a more punitive stance may deter this crime of baby stealing as Edwards (1990) points out but given the compulsive nature of such crimes then a greater understanding of the nature of the problem by those in the criminal justice system as shown by some of the more caring decisions reached in these cases may well help to induce these women to give back the children and seek psychiatric treatment for their condition.

I can only add to Dr. O'Connor's excellent section by indicating that when this crime is committed by psychotics under the influence of delusions, Hospital Orders under s.37 of the Mental Health Act 1983 would be implemented and a Restriction Order would be added especially if the children died. Forensic psychologists have much to offer in the resolution of these cases, and can be particularly helpful in indicating to the court the psychological characteristics of the child stealer, the motivation underlying the theft, and the treatment or after-care most likely to be effective (Haward, 1990).

Psychopaths may abduct children for the purpose of sexual abuse and/ or to take part in satanic rituals. The victims tend to be older children.

About half of all thefts are from unattended prams, the snatchers usually being unknown to the mother, and a quarter from homes by babysitters or child carers.

The Battered Wife

A battered woman is one who is subjected to physical violence of varying degree by a man with whom she lives and who may or may not be her husband. The violence is usually perpetrated regularly.

Gibbens (1971) studied 350 female inmates of H.M. Prison, Holloway, and found that 60 (17 per cent) could be regarded as battered wives. Harwin (1992) indicated that the incidence of wife-battering is about 2 per cent in the general population of England. This statistic is calculated on the grounds that some 100,000 battered wives seek help every year from the Women's Aid Federation of England Ltd. This is a voluntary charity with co-ordinating office located in Bristol. Hostel accommodation can be provided for only 25,000 of these women, mainly due to lack of funds.

Aetiology

Hereditary factors. Freud recognized four instincts, namely self-preservation, sexual, social and aggressive. Each person is born with these instincts and environmental circumstances may well determine their degree of expression and control. Aggressive psychopaths usually have violent fathers. Studies involving children support the view that abnormal aggression may be inherited. The studies were made on adopted children in order to eliminate environmental influences. The histories of a proportion of emotionally callous psychopaths suggest that they may well have suffered from a typical schizophrenic illness earlier in their lives. The percentage of aggressive psychopaths amongst the relatives of schizophrenics is significantly greater than the percentage amongst relatives of a group of "normal" average people. It is well known that some of the mentally imparied may be easily influenced to behave in an anti-social manner. Hysteria is known to be associated with psychopathic personality. About 50 per cent of people suffering from temporal-lobe epilepsy are subject to aggressive behaviour which may replace convulsions and coma. The incidence of alcoholism, psychopathic tendencies and criminality amongst the children of chronic alcoholics is greater than the incidence of the same conditions amongst the children of non-alcoholic parents (Amarc, 1951).

However, the inheritance of criminality was studied in 862 Swedish men (Bohman *et al*, 1982). The conclusion was that the risk of criminality (including violence) in the study group was determined by the severity of alcohol abuse in members of that group rather than a history of criminality in their biologic parents.

Physical (including biochemical) factors. Various deformities may make a man feel inferior leading to unreasonable attitudes and impulsiveness. Similarly, lack of libido on the part of the male may lead to frustration and aggression especially in response to taunts. Modern contraceptive methods and especially the "pill" enable women to agree more to intimacy and consequently avoid being beaten by aggressive husbands as a result of refusal. Organic cerebral pathology and the effects of alcohol and/or drugs influence some men to subject their female partners to brutality and the epileptic personality is not uncommonly aggressive.

Environmental factors. Men deprived of affection and/or subjected to violence during their childhoods may react with unjustified aggression in later life towards female partners, especially if they hold their own mothers responsible for childhood beatings and humiliations. Perhaps the subconscious mind does not distinguish between individuals of a particular sex.

Emotional conflicts caused by mixing of the classes in marriage may also be relevant, as may be decreased frequency of the "extended family" concept as, for example, an aggressive husband will hesitate to beat his wife if his mother lives in the same house, provided of course that mother and wife have mutual respect for each other. Unemployment, shortage of money, poor living accommodation and "role conflict" leading to arguments as to who should handle the family finances, may result in battering of female partners by males so predisposed. Similar trouble may result when a higher social status is reached due to sudden acquisition of wealth when one or both partners cannot accept rejection by members of the new social stratum into which they have moved.

"Pimps" may cohabit with prostitutes and offer violence for withholding earnings.

A dependent elderly relative may be a source of considerable irritation in a family which lacks the resilience to cope with the stress involved. Similarly, conflict may arise in families because of the tendency to reduce the population of mental hospitals by returning patients, thought to have recovered, to relatives who are not capable of taking on the responsibility of their care, even with appropriate support from the various agencies. The patients may also be put at risk in these circumstances.

Mental Factors. Immaturity, lack of adaptability, conflict and violence are all linked factors in the male when a wife or female cohabitee is battered. Some wives return again and again to violent husbands suggesting masochistic tendencies and also feelings of being "needed". Aggression may also be provoked when the male finds himself unable to satisfy the need of his female partner for excessive dependence on him.

The sadist cannot feel fully potent sexually unless he can establish his authority over a helpless female victim, otherwise he cannot give or receive affection in a manner emotionally satisfying to him, usually due to his own miserable childhood experiences. The sadist may or may not be psychopathically disordered within the meaning of the Mental Health Act 1983.

The non-sadistic wife-beater may have discovered during childhood that violence helped him to achieve his desires and this tendency to aggression may have been reinforced by parental example and certain television and cinema programmes. This learned violence may be carried into adult life and consequenty a female partner is beaten if she behaves in a manner which he selfishly considers to be unreasonable.

Mental impairment associated with psychopathy increases the risk of violence. Morbid jealousy may well lead to battering of wives or female cohabitees.

Psychotic disorders are not usually associated with wife-battering. However, acute schizophrenics, manics and depressives may kill or seriously injure, but usually as a single act.

Relationship between woman-battering and baby-battering
Scott (1973) found that 25 per cent of fathers who battered their children to death also battered their wives or cohabitees. The battered wife is most fearful of her husband's *unpredictability*.

Management
Most of the principles relevant to the management of child abuse also apply to battered women. However, it is obvious that the latter can seek accommodation in appropriate hostels whereas children cannot. Locations of such hostels must, of course, be kept secret from male partners. Husbands, as opposed to male cohabitees, tend to make very determined attempts to track down their wives regarding them as items of their property and they also tend to re-batter.

A decision as to whether to involve social agencies would depend on careful assessment of the nature of interaction within the family (Jones, 1982).

Allegations have been made to the effect that the police are somewhat too hesitant to charge husbands who batter their wives, but then it is well known that some wives do not even call the police for help.

Co-ordination of the various agencies giving assistance is essential.

Brendtro *et al* (1989) investigated 1,000 battered wives and stated that the important correlation was that formal help sources differ significantly in their effectiveness in providing service to battered women.

The Munchausen Syndrome

The Munchausen Syndrome is named after an eighteenth-century German who lied incessantly about heroic deeds. An individual who suffers from this condition repeatedly seeks admission to hospital by simulating the signs and symptoms of illness and most frequently of abdominal disorder for which an operation is usually considered necessary. However, laparotomy reveals no abnormality. The patient is discharged but subsequently presents him or herself at another hospital with similar signs and symptoms when laparotomy is usually repeated. This sequence of events occurs again and again. Psychopathic tendencies expressed as craving for attention and self-directed aggression are evident. Such individuals seldom come under psychiatric investigation and prefer to move from hospital to hospital in their search for admission.

Mercer *et al* (1993) refers to the *Munchausen Syndrome by Proxy* as the diagnosis used to describe a variation of child abuse whereby the parent or adult caregiver fabricates a medical history or induces symptoms in the child, or both, resulting in unnecessary examinations, treatments, hospitalizations, and even death. Samuels (1992) comments to the effect that this diagnosis should therefore be considered in the differential diagnosis of any child with signs or symptoms that remain unexplained after standard investigations or are unresponsive to treatment. This diagnosis was applied to a mother who continued to administer poison through an intravenous drip which was sustaining her child's life when the latter was undergoing treatment in an intensive-care unit.

The pathology of Munchausen by Proxy sufferers may be explained by a desperate need for recognition by, and a good relationship with, people in authority. The physician in charge of the child's treatment would be targeted for attention by the guilty mother. Similar comments apply to the

24-year-old nurse Beverley Allitt who craved approval, attention and sympathy from senior nursing staff, consultant paediatricians and her colleagues by raising alarms and "helping" to save the lives of children whom she had placed in jeopardy. She pretended great concern for these children but she was devoid of empathy and wished their deaths. She was fit to plead and pleaded not guilty. She was sentenced to 13 life sentences at Nottingham Crown Court on 28 May, 1993 after a jury found her guilty of murdering four children, attempting to kill three and attacking six others. Allitt used suffocation and injections of insulin and air to achieve her objectives. She allegedly showed little remorse. She indulged in pathological lying and attention-seeking and personally raised the alarm about the children and sought to be one of the medical resuscitation team. Allitt had made 24 visits to the casualty department of Grantham and Kesteven General Hospital between 1987 and 1990. She was treated for various self-inflicted injuries and apparently made bogus complaints of pregnancy, stomach ulcer and brain tumour. She also claimed that she was sexually assaulted at knife point. However, she *had* apparently had treatment for anorexia nervosa. Physiotherapists allegedly told the hospital of their concern in 1987.

It is easy to be wise after the event but could Allitt have been stopped earlier? The following considerations are of interest:

(i)   alleged delay in taking a blood sample from a baby who had been injected with insulin;
(ii) delay in alerting police;
(iii) alleged delay in recognizing air injection on an X-ray;
(iv) allegedly after 12 children had collapsed, doctors went to hospital managers with their fears. They asked for video cameras on Ward Four but were refused.

Sufferers induce or fabricate illnesses in children and then gain great emotional satisfaction in being praised for helping to treat and solve same.

The two consultant paediatricians who were in charge of Ward 4 where Allitt worked will be redundant as from 30 June, 1993. They will go to the High Court in an attempt to get their jobs back.

Schreider (1993) indicates that the Munchausen by Proxy sufferer has strong sadomasochistic tendencies as a result of which the infants in their care are dehumanized and used as fetishistic objects to control relations with authority figures. This behaviour could be a reaction to emotionally deprived childhoods and feelings of abandonment. The sufferers may also have been the victims of childhood (including sexual) abuse. The presence of a genetic element cannot be discounted, meaning that nature and nurture may be implicated in causation. There is a definite relationship between the Munchausen Syndrome by Proxy, conversion hysteria and psychopathic disorder.

Babe *et al.* (1992) describes a case of the Munchausen *per se* associated with frontotemporal cerebral atrophy and lack of thyroid-stimulating hormone response to thyroid-releasing hormone infusion.

Allitt's behaviour has many parallels with an American killer nurse Genene Jones, who is believed to have murdered 16 children. She was sentenced to 159 years in prison on 15 February, 1983 – exactly 10 years before Allitt's trial began. Allitt could be described as a serial killer.

Conclusion: Aggression is invariably self-directed in the Munchausen Syndrome *per se*. The Munchausen Syndrome by Proxy means aggression directed *at self and others* and should be regarded as symptomatic of psychopathic disorder within the meaning of the definition in the Mental Health Act 1983. The accent would be on aggression. It is not beyond the bounds of possibility that Allitt may become frankly psychotic during sentence.

The following sections on pathological religious cults, killing of children and maiming of animals (rural terrorism) are included because of much recent public interest and because the law-breakers described obviously have or had psychopathic tendencies.

Pathological Religious Cults

The formation of these cults requires charismatic paranoid individuals who have the ability to influence susceptible people to join their groups. Alcohol, illicit drugs, free sex and promises of "eternal happiness" in some after-life are used as bait. Punk – or rap-type music seems to facilitate the process and it is intersting that symphonic music is never used by these cults. Potential cult members are no doubt encouraged to bring their money to the leaders. This money may be used to buy firearms and ammunition to defend the cult. Wire-tapping may also be employed and all incoming and outgoing telephone calls may be monitored to control lower-grade members.

These measures were taken by members of the notorious cult in Oregon and their leader imported many "down-and-outs" from other parts of the USA in order to gain political power by winning local elections, although those imported into the commune were not allowed to vote by law. Members of the cult introduced food poisoning to restaurants in the community which were believed to be frequented by the cult's enemies. The leader of this cult is now dead but two British women who were former members are now in Great Britain awaiting a decision by the Home Secretary as to extradition at the request of the United States government on a charge of conspiring to murder the State Attorney. Extradition was granted on 26 April 1993 but a Judicial Review may be requested. Evidently other members of the Bhagwan Shree Ranjneesh cult in Antelope, Oregon implicated these two women in the context of "plea bargaining."

Certain kinds of people were drawn to these cults, who preach false religions equivalent to modern paganism with hidden agendas designed to control subordinates, if necessary, by fear. The cult leader presents himself as God, although he may hypocritically invoke divine authority.

Cult leaders prefer to recruit intelligent people who can relate to others. Those who are unduly vulnerable emotionally and feel useless, bored and confused by modern society and its values are most likely to be tempted to join. Instantaneous friendship and appreciation from fellow disciples are very important factors in retaining recruits.

Cult members are influenced to believe that sexual promiscuity and polygamy are worthy sacrifices to make for the cult. Recruits are often sought by members going into city streets where they lecture, pray, sing, play guitars and wave copies of the New or Old Testament. Some 500 cults operate at present in the United Kingdom and some tend to infiltrate established churches. Death threats have been received by people who manage Information Centres to counteract the pathological influences of cults.

Brainwashing is an essential part of the inauguration and retaining of members. Misguided adults may bring their children to the cult. The psychopathic leaders of these vicious cults are invariably habituated to illicit drugs and, in time, they usually come to believe in their preposterous theories. They realize that they can only gain from the notoriety which they crave by enslaving their disciples who are pathetically susceptible and often come from disturbed homes. The prospect of earning a respectable living by hard work would be repellent to cult leaders.

Brainwashing is a journalistic concept introduced by the American journalist Edward Hunter in a book called *Brainwashing in Red China* published in 1952. Indoctrination implies the use of psychological methods to influence and change fundamental beliefs (Zehrer, 1959). Brainwashing may be defined as an attempt to alter an individual's thoughts, attitudes and behaviour and involves the use of psychological and physical techniques. Both imply myth creation through interrogation and the constant one-sided communication of ideas and attitudes (West, 1964). The technique is used by the leaders and close associates to influence newcomers who join the cult. Formerly-held social, ethical and religious beliefs are broken down and pathological ones substituted. To these ends the "noviciates" are isolated from relatives, friends and the general public in urban, or more commonly rural, settlements. Assault, prolonged periods of work and enforced fasting, withholding medical treatment, and deprivation of sleep, lower members' physical and mental resistance and increase suggestibility. Confused psychological concepts including the mixing of truth with lies, are fed to the potential disciples in this setting.

Brainwashing techniques are psychologically coercive and used to exert control over the minds of others by neutralising their ability to discriminate. Tapes and videos are used to assist this process.

It is absolutely essential for potential members to *confess* that previous religious and ethical beliefs and generally accepted social values were completely wrong and they may then be *converted* to the abnormal and evil doctrines based on false Christianity or even Satanism. Psychological methods of eliciting confessions involve the creation of fear, anxiety, guilt, tension, insecurity, despondency and mental conflict with the object of impairing judgment so as to make the recipients feel the need for punishment with the hope of salvation. Illicit drugs such as Lysergic Acid (LSD), crack and ecstasy are freely used to assist confession and conversion and virtually obliterate the distinction between right and wrong. Consequently, degenerate sexual behaviour, even involving children, is facilitated. Murder may be committed under the following circumstances:

1. Members of the security forces may be killed during an attack on the cult as occurred in Waco, Texas, in March 1993.
2. Members may indulge in forays outside their settlement with the object of murdering people regarded as having too much money and privilege, as in the case of the murder of actress Sharon Tate and her friends by Charles Manson and his fellow psychopaths. Envy is the obvious motivation.

3.   Leaders may kill members who wish to surrender to the authorities. Members may resort to suicide rather than surrender.

The authorities must have legal grounds to invade a settlement of pathological religious cults which exist in democratic countries. A frontal assault should never be attempted especially in daylight and/or when the members of the cult are known to possess firearms and ammunition and specialist forces should always be used. Police and federal agents tried to storm the "Mount Carmel" settlement in Waco, Texas, under circumstances opposite to those referred to above and with disastrous consequences including four deaths. Furthermore, the assault force made no attempt to disguise their arrival and communications between the attackers tended to break down when the assault was unsuccessful and a satisfactory plan of retreat had not been formulated. The security forces have now changed their tactics and high-tech surveillance is now employed as follows:

1.   Thermal imagers can scan outside walls, track body heat and reveal position of cult members on monitor.
2.   Multi-sensor surveillance aircraft with infra-red scanners and low-light television track from above. Together they pinpoint cult members throughout the compound.
3.   Microphones and fibre-optic probe cameras, less than an eighth of an inch thick, inserted in walls relay sound and pictures back to agents. Lasers detect window vibrations, revealing conversations.

The occurrence of what has become known as the Stockholm Syndrome has important implications for the security forces. This syndrome means that a bond of affection develops between a member of the security forces and cult members. This affection may be on a psychological level or sexual (in the case of a female bank clerk in Stockholm). A member of the security forces could be allowed to enter the compound to negotiate terms and then allowed to leave on condition that he returned in order to prevent the lives of some dissident cult members being placed in jeopardy. He or she could thus betray the plans of the besiegers.

Cult leaders expect worship but preach total freedom and equality for all members, although they tend to supervise work done by the majority. In time, virtually all authority becomes the property of the few who may even dress differently from the others. The cult will collapse from within if the rank-and-file members gain insight into the deception and quarrel amongst themselves. Pressure from outside authority facilitates this process.

These methods would reveal the location of cult members including the areas where they are active and sleeping and also the location of weapons. The tactical plans of cult leaders could also be revealed and could include plans to use dissident members as shields and expose them to crossfire in the event of an all-out assault by the authorities. The seige could end peacefully from boredom as a result of depriving the cult of heat, light, food and water but these measures could also provoke hysterical reactions involving mass suicide or a final foray outside the settlement with all guns blazing. Even so, the successful use of these methods should guarantee a 60 per cent success rate for the authorities. Some 99 followers of the cult leader were besieged in their Waco settlement on 22 March 1993. These included 17 children. Some 31 were allowed to leave the compound from the start of the siege on 28 February 1993.

Psychological assessment of the leaders is most important. The security forces should "play for time" by giving the impression that their demands will be granted. The real intention of the authorities must, of course, be not to capitulate. Efforts should be made to negotiate on terms other than those specified by the cult leaders. For example, a demand for complete withdrawal of the security forces could be counterd by an offer of payment of a substantial sum of money and gradual withdrawal on condition that children were released. It may also be possible to exploit the "internal honour system" of cult leaders in favour of other members who wish to leave the settlement. This can only be done by compiling psychological profiles of the leaders including their ethnic origins and attempting to discover their intentions. Conversations with the leaders and released members would be helpful in these contexts. The security forces may have the records of leaders but such information could only be gleaned by discovering their names when histories of murder and psychosis could emerge. Denial of publicity would be important, but this might not be possible if direct threats to the lives of the potential deserters, including children, are made. Such threats would be important in deciding when to make an assault. It would be important to control the media from the point of view of not giving warning to the besieged of the intentions of the security forces. They will at least have access to radio and will demand regular delivery of newspapers despite roadblocks set up by the besiegers.

The Waco Siege

The Branch Davidian cult at Waco was led by David Koresh, described as a rock guitarist-cum-messiah. He and his 95 followers had been besieged for 42 days in the "Mount Carmel" settlement in April 1993.

It was stated in March 1993 that the cult had powerful thermal-imaging night sights in an extensive armoury, which included machine guns and anti-tank weapons. To counter that threat, federal agents mounted powerful arc lights to blind those inside. The cult was also belived to have enough food and water to last for 12 months.

Koresh has convinced members of the cult that children fathered as a result of polygamy within the cult would be future rulers of the earth. He stated that he awaited a sign from God to end the siege; the end would take the form of surrender or a sacrificial blood-bath.

Federal Bureau of Investigation (FBI) agents attacked the Waco cult compound on April 19, 1993. This attack was made with the consent of the Attorney General and the President. Tanks with giant battering rams were used to punch 12 holes in the sides of the building and CS2 "gas" (a fine powder) pumped through same. Cult members opened fire on the tanks with automatic weapons. The defenders had a supply of gas masks and underground bunkers were also available for refuge and they were also suspected of having rocket launchers. Local hospitals and the county police stations were alerted, but the initiative was taken out of the hands of the attackers when cult members set fire to the compound which was made almost entirely of wood. Ammunition exploded in the compound. The fire brigade services were not used because apparently the FBI did not consider it necessary to make advance arrangement for their presence.

It is suggested that attack was ill-advised and its mode of implementation was disastrously ill-conceived resulting in the deaths of 86 cult people including 17 children under the age of 17 years. Only nine survived. The FBI played very loud music during this holocaust and perhaps this exasperating 'beat' music helped to precipitate the attack. The FBI is now attempting to justify itself by alleging that cult members shot and poisoned each other. The following comments are made on the decision to attack:

(i)   Koresh stated on a number of occasions that he and his cult would be destroyed by a holocaust of fire and the FBI thought he was bluffing.

(ii) The authorities did not give sufficient attention to the history of fanatical cults such as the one headed by Jim Jones in Guyana in 1978 when over 900 people committed suicide when the cult was investigated.

(iii) Ex-cult members, some of whom worked in anti-cult centres, could have been interviewed.

(iv) The 'John Wayne' type of barnstorming used in the attack caused members in the compound to panic which caused their behaviour to become uncontrollable and unpredictable.

(v)   Appropriate advice was not taken as to the meaning of fanaticism and the determination which accompanies it. A strong leader offers a series of certainties to discontented people. Koresh guaranteed the second coming of the Messiah and eternal salvation in the context of mysticism with total obedience to him as a basic essential. This obedience included willingness to commit suicide at the leader's request.

Cult members who survive such an inferno would tend to suffer from the Post Traumatic Stress Disorder (PTSD). The signs, symptoms and treatment of this condition are dealt with in some detail in Chapter VIII.

Killing of Children by other Children

For the purposes of this section, the children involved (perpetrators and victims) will be regarded as under 16 years.

It is reasonable to assume psychopathic tendencies in most children who deliberately kill, but illicit drug-taking and/or alcohol may also be operative in some instances. Sometimes the homicide is preceded by psychological and/or physical torture which may be enjoyed as a "game" by the perpetrators with the object of discovering the extent to which the victim may be persecuted before he or she becomes mentally ill. A small minority of child killers may be mentally impaired or suffer from a mental illness such as schizophrenia. However, one must keep a sense of proportion lest all children who kill be regarded as suffering from serious mental disorder. Psychopathic tendencies are certainly not synonymous with psychopathic disorder as defined in the Mental Health Act 1983.

Psychiatric studies in the context of children who kill children are notable for their scarcity. Walsh-Brennan (1975) studied 10 such children between the ages of 10 and 16 years. They included nine boys and one girl, all of whom killed twice. The girl's father spent long periods away from home; eight of the boys and the girl had mothers who were excessively dominant to the extent of physical aggression and the other findings were as follows:

None of the group had psychological, neurological nor psychiatric abnormalities, although five of the boys showed mild anxiety reactions.

Three of the boys had criminal records.

The father of the girl and those of at least two of the boys had prison records.

It was difficult to elicit information from all parents.

Alcoholism was noted in only one case.

Maternal depression with child rejection was also suspected in several cases.

There were no cases of chronic illness among parents.

All were legitimate.

None of the group was epileptic.

Pathological parental attitudes have been implicated as causes of aggression in children but without conclusive proof. Parental aggression may be overt or take the more subtle form of psychologically punishing the child by setting perfectionist standards which the child cannot possibly attain. Children who live in homes which are located in areas manifesting high crime rates must suffer emotionally. The theory of the "Cycle of Deprivation" postulates that parents of all social classes who have been emotionally and culturally deprived and denied adequate educational opportunities during their formative years tend to pass their emotional traumata on to their children.

Children would obviously get less attention from mothers who have to undertake work outside the home because of economic necessity. Some young people may take to crime when they believe that they are confronted with persistent unemployment, because they feel that they have no real "stake" in society. Other factors blamed for crime in general (including homicide) are the obvious increase in recent years in criminal violence, sexual promiscuity, illegitimacy and venereal disease, including HIV infection. Some of the media do little to discourage free sex and pornography because of the prospect of financial gain.

A careful study of the parents will usually clarify the reasons as to why their children commit crimes, including homicide.

Walsh-Brennan (1975) also studied 1,100 juvenile offenders and found that 25 per cent did not have any significant mental abnormalities. Presumably this study did not imply that the remaining 75 per cent suffered from serious mental disorder.

In February 1993 two 10-year-old boys were accused of abducting and murdering a younger boy and attempting to abduct another child on Merseyside. The magistrates at the Youth Court remanded them to the secure custody of the relevant borough council. One boy obviously dominated the other and he kept looking at the prosecutor, but the other boy who was subservient often looked at his domineering friend during the hearing. This relationship between the boys could be regarded as having a *folie a deux* relationship but not in the context of psychosis. They were closely associated with one another and the antisocial tendencies of the dominant one were communicated to his subservient friend with resulting tragedy. Such tendencies in the non-dominant boy will probably recede if they are separated.

A jury found them guilty of murder and they were ordered to be detained at Her Majesty's pleasure on 24.11.93. They were also named.

Children under the age of 10 years are not considered to be criminally responsible and therefore cannot be charged with criminal offences including homicide. However, such an individual would be regarded as a danger to the public and could be detained in secure accommodation by the local authorities on the basis of a Secure Care Order issued by a magistrate's court under the Children's Act, 1989. This Order lapses at the age of 18 years when detention under the Mental Health Act, (1983), would be an option.

It would be helpful to establish an integrated Health Service for children involving all relevant disciplines.

Some 226 juveniles aged 10 to 16 years were convicted of homicide during the years 1982-1991 (inclusive). The victims were all ages. Nineteen similar cases are pending at May 1993 and may result in convictions.

Eleven suspects under the age of 16 years were convicted of murders of victims also under 16 years, during the years 1982-1991. Two similar cases are pending and may result in convictions.

Maiming of Animals (Rural Terrorism)

Leigh *et al* (1972) indicated that sadism is the sexual perversion named after the Marquis de Sade whose obscene novels are based upon sexual lust and cruelty. It is the exclusive attainment of sexual orgasm through the infliction of pain and cruelty upon other individuals, male or female, or upon an animal (besto-sexual sadism). It mainly occurs in males who are often otherwise impotent. Rudimentary sadistic impulses commonly emerge in the biting and scratching of normal pre-coital sexual arousal. Sadistic fantasies are common and are often sublimated in pornographic literature. True sadism varies from the whipping or beating of prostitutes who cater for this perversion to physical assaults of rape, buggery or murder with mutilation of the corpse. At other times the sadist may subject himself to masochistic stimulation. Sadistic fantasies often date back to childhood and are associated with acts of cruelty for non-sexual pleasure against animals or other children. Treatment is unsatisfactory. The convicted sadist criminal requires supervision in a security hospital.

The unlawful infliction of injuries on horses and cattle became a criminal offence in this country in 1545. This law was strengthened by the Waltham Black Act of 1723 which pertained to harming farm animals and deer poaching. The penalty was death by hanging. This act was repealed in 1832 when imprisonment and transportation became alternative sentences. It is interesting that in those days, a conviction depended on proving malicious intent towards the owners as opposed to the animals, meaning that these laws were really meant to protect the property of the owners and studies indicate that in some instances during the seventeenth and eighteenth centuries, defences were based on allegations to the effect that horses were injured because they tried to repulse the sexual advances of depraved persons.

Investigations by Archer (1993) indicated that 1,000 illegal animal deaths occurred between 1815 and 1870. Going from ancient to modern, 27 criminal injuries were perpetrated against horses between 28 February 1991 and 22 January 1993 and one was maimed to such an extent that it died. Eight additional offences occurred in Hampshire in early February 1993. However, the authorities of other counties in the north and south of England and in the midlands have reported similar offences at various times.

Statistics for England and Wales issued by the RSPCA indicate that 88,632 complaints of cruelty to animals were investigated in 1992. Only

40 per cent of those found guilty in Wales were banned from keeping animals for any length of time.

This section deals mainly with horses but other animals such as cattle, sheep, donkeys and pigs may be the victims of sadistic psychopaths. Little monkeys often have their teeth extracted before being exported to Europe and spend the rest of their lives in cages, when not boosting the profits of organ grinders or photographers. The torture inflicted on dancing bears is well known.

The culprit or culprits who indulge in this savage and barbarian behaviour apparently do not have any *modus operandi* and this fact makes detection all the more difficult. The attacks occur usually, but not invariably, during the night. It has been suggested that the full moon may influence the perpetrator(s) from the psychological point of view and also by providing extra light to facilitate maiming which may be accomplished by one or more persons on one or more animals. The only patterns of animal attacks to emerge are characterized by secrecy, surprise, suddenness, stealth and silent approach, and escape from the scene of the crime. The agonizing cries of the tortured animal are not heard by the owners as often as might be expected. Furthermore, the possibility of "copy cat" maimings and killings cannot be discounted. A 10-strong team of detectives have established an incident room at Alton, Hampshire using the codename Operation Mountbatten and also called the "Special Horse Ripper Squad". However the establishment of a *prima facie* case on the basis of motive, means and opportunity would not be easy. Very few culprits are detected.

Types of Offender:
1. Perpetrators who are not suffering from serious mental disorder
These rural rebels may kill or injure animals as an act of revenge on the rural élite and horses were and are perhaps still singled out because they are regarded as symbols of the wealth of landed gentry who were blamed for low wages, unfair dismissal and unemployment, perhaps due to the use of labour-saving machinery. The crimes cause fear and terror in the landowners and express hatred and envy. The latter feelings were made even more intense by the belief that horses were better fed and stabled than workers in the seventeenth and eighteenth centuries.

2. Perpetrators who are suffering from serious mental disorder
Schizophrenics may commit these offences in response to a delusional

belief that animals in general and horses in particular are possessed by evil spirits who mean to destroy the world. This delusion may be supported by "voices" which give similar instructions.

The sexually perverted psychopathically disordered sadistic psychopath can apparently only gain sexual satisfaction by these practices. He may or may not be mentally impaired. Psychopathic disorder may be associated with paranoid psychosis.

3. Perpetrators who had emotionally disturbed childhoods

Kellert *et al* (1985) examined the relationship between childhood cruelty towards animals and aggressive behaviour among criminals and non-criminals in adulthood, using data derived from personal interviews with 152 criminals in Kansas and Connecticut. A standardized, closed and open-ended interview, requiring 1-2 hours to complete, was administered to all. Aggressiveness was defined by behavioural criteria rather than by reason for incarceration. Results showed that childhood cruelty towards animals occurred to a significantly greater degree among adult aggressive criminals than among non-aggressive criminals or non-criminals. Furthermore, Wax *et al* (1974) indicated that a triad of behavioural symptoms, including enuresis, fire setting and animal cruelty, is highly predictive of adult male violence.

A man suspected of being prominent in attacking and wounding horses in southern England was arrested in April 1993. He is in his late twenties and jobless. It is alleged that animal rights activists interfered with police investigations.

Prevention

Prevention proves very difficult. Floodlighting, locking of paddocks and stables, electric fencing and guard dogs have all been tried with little success. Police could not be spared to give 24-hour protection. Vigilante squads have been suggested. Some owners and stable boys have slept in stables. Imprisonment would act as a deterrent more than time-wasting efforts to discover why the culprits committed these crimes. The culprit would be prosecuted under the Protection of Animals Act, 1911. The penalty could be a fine of £5,000 and/or six months' imprisonment.

Treatment of serious mental disorder might possibly eliminate these vile tendencies in regard to animals.

The human brain has been described as a reptile in the embrace of a dog, the outer layer hopefully providing human self-control.

Introduction to Children and Family Services

This section was contributed by C.J. Perry, Director of South Glamorgan Social Services.

The 1989 Children Act became operative in October 1991. This Act recognizes the importance of security in a child's life, the adverse effect of uncertainty, and the importance of parental understanding. It is legislation which has been, in the main, informed by research and represents best practice. It tightens up the procedures for the removal of children from home, places time constraints on determining a child's future, reinforces parental responsibility which is no longer terminated on the granting of a care order and can only be terminated by an adoption order. It requires social workers to work in partnership with parents, even to the point of accommodating children, in an attempt to resolve situations without recourse to the courts and introduces a new emphasis on Family Support.

The Act aims to protect the child from physical, emotional and sexual abuse and from what may be referred to as "professional" or "agency" abuse. The concept of the mature minor is introduced in conformity with Lord Scarman's words in the case of *Gillick v. West Norfolk and Wisbech Health Authority* in 1985:

> "Parental right yields to the child's right to make his own decisions when he reaches a sufficient understanding and intelligence to be capable of making up his own mind on the matter requiring decision."

Furthermore, such a mature child will have the right in certain circumstances to refuse to be medically examined or to submit to other types of assessment ordered by a court, but a court may nominate an appropriate registered medical practitioner to examine a child.

Children will, *by law*, be supported and cared for by a partnership of parents, social and probation services and health, education and local housing authorities. The role of the general medical practitioner is stressed. Parents will be legally responsible for all factors conducive to the child's benefit.

Family Proceedings Courts will hear cases locally and these courts will be more inquisitorial than formerly and the magistrates will be specifically trained. Strict time tables will be introduced and court orders may be challenged at a much earlier stage, as for example Emergency Protection Orders may be challenged after 72 hours, and will become invalid after eight days.

The first few years of one's life are the formative ones, when we learn to differentiate between right and wrong and form many of the attitudes and prejudices which will remain with us for much of our lives. Children are dependent upon a range of adults with the prime responsibility resting with their parents. Children have a right to know their mother and father, to a happy childhood in a secure caring family preferably with both or one of their natural parents and to love and protection.

Regrettably the sociological changes which are taking place around children are putting them increasingly at risk. One in four children are now born outside marriage. One in five children can expect to experience the break-up of their parents' relationship and one in five of these will experience it twice. One in six families are now headed by a lone parent. Recent longitudinal research has shown that children from single parent families, although clearly there are exceptions, are more prone to illness, do less well at school, are more likely to get into trouble with the police, do less well career-wise and are less likely to form sustained relationships. There is a correlation between single-parent families, particularly of teenage mothers, unemployment, poor housing and child abuse due to the strain it imposes and the likelihood of cohabitees. Parents who abuse their children are likely to have themselves been abused as children. Some research in the United States by Professor Diana Russell (1984) concluded that 34.5 per cent of stepfathers and cohabitees sexually abused the children of their partner compared with 2.3 per cent of natural or adoptive fathers. The majority of child-abuse cases which have been the subject of independent review or inquiry have also involved cohabitees. Social Service Departments across the UK are reporting an increasing bombardment of cases of suspected child abuse, particularly of a sexual nature although not all are substantiated. To become a parent is a responsibility and commitment on both parents, it is an irreversible change in the lives of both of them.

Although our paramount concern is the well-being of the child we believe that this aim is best served by helping parents to shoulder their responsibility. Only where the risk to the child is too great should we seek to remove the child from home and only when the prognosis for change is poor or slow would we seek a permanent substitute home for the child. It is an indictment upon this country that we still look after more children away from home than any other in the Western world. It should also be remembered that, although there are exceptions, children brought up in care also tend to fare less well in life.

Objectives of the Service

(a)   Impact Objective: to ensure that every child has the security of a permanent happy family and upbringing, preferably with both or one of its natural parents or extended family, and is able to make and mix with friends at home and at school.

(b)   Service Objectives:

  (i)   the protection of children;
  (ii)   promoting the welfare and rights of children;
  (iii) support to parents particularly of vulnerable groups, in looking after their children and improving parenting skills;
  (iv)   keeping any period in care (legal status) to a minimum by effective rehabilitation, shared care or where this is not possible, adoption;
  (v)   preserving the positive links in children's lives whilst in care;
  (vi)   support to parents who are unable to look after their children in rebuilding their lives;
  (vii) social education in respect of parental responsibility and commitment.

(c)   Logistical Objective: the redeployment of adequate resources to prevention.

The child's needs and wishes are always paramount and child protection our top priority. However, prevention and resolution of problems before the situation gets out of hand and the child has to be removed is also about child protection. There is little point building a bigger and bigger first-aid post at the bottom of the cliff without attempting to build a fence at the top!

An investigation by the Department of Health (June 1995), indicated that some 180,000 child abuse and/or neglect inquiries are on average, undertaken annually in this country by Social Services but only 15 per cent of the children are considered by the investigators to be sufficiently at risk to be registered. It is concluded that the Social Services spend so much time on these enquiries that adequate time is not devoted to support services for families which need this help.

General Prognosis for Psychopaths

Death by violence and suicide is high in later years, especially in those who suffer from higher degrees of aggressive psychopathy. Robins (1966) indicated that there is a tendency for neurotic depression to predominate over psychopathic drive after a period of years when treatment may be more effective. About 50 per cent of psychopaths undergo spontaneous improvement after the age of 40 years. The presence of other forms of mental disorder such as epilepsy or mental impairment influence prognosis adversely. The degree of psychopathy as expressed by degree of hostility to society, willingness to undergo treatment and age when the therapy is started, all influence prognosis.

The majority of male psychopaths are eventually imprisoned whereas the majority of female psychopaths tend to gravitate to mental hospitals.

Psychopaths tend not to respond to authoritarian-type treatment and intensive psychotherapy may worsen the prognosis of the mentally impaired psychopath. High degrees of inadequate and aggressive psychopathy respond poorly to treatment in the therapeutic community.

Guze (1976) concluded from a study of 223 males that sociopathy associated with alcoholism and/or drug dependence was characteristically associated with serious crime and that schizophrenia, primary affective disorders, anxiety neurosis and organic brain syndromes were not so associated. This study would indicate that sociopaths (psychopaths) are more likely to commit serious and presumably violent crime in contrast to those who suffer from certain other forms of mental disorder. I had personal knowledge of 14 individuals who were admitted to special hospitals on the basis of s.60 of the Mental Health Act 1959 during a four-year period. The original charges of murder were subsequently reduced to manslaughter on the grounds of diminished responsibility under the Homicide Act 1957. The clinical diagnoses were psychotic depression: three; acute schizophrenia: five; psychopathic disorder: four; and sub-normality: two.

Brooner et al, (1993), indicated that antisocial personality disorder among drug abusers has been associated with poor drug abuse treatment outcome and greater human immunodeficiency virus infection risk compared with drug abusers without the disorder.

Gill et al, (1992), examined a sample of 55 consecutive methadone maintenance admissions to their clinic, 42 per cent were diagnosed as antisocial personality disorder (ASPD) using the National Institute of Mental Health Diagnostic Interview Schedule NIMH DIS. They concluded that ASPD patients who drop out of treatment will be at higher risk for contracting and spreading HIV within the IV drug using population. These data also suggest that in this population the diagnosis of ASPD using primarily behavioural traits as measured in the NIMH-DIS-III has little utility in predicting treatment outcome. Methadone is used for withdrawal from heroin and morphine.

Prediction Indices

Prediction indices are based on facts known about the patient's history at the time of admission to a therapeutic environment and assessments during treatment, which together give a Basal Expectancy Rate of Conviction for each person. This Expectancy Rate is compared with Actual Conviction Rate during various periods after discharge in order to assess the effects of treatment. Follow-up periods should be at least two years and longer periods yield more accurate results.

Craft (1966) devised a means of applying prediction indices to groups of psychopaths. The known reconviction rates are associated with such factors as previous convictions, repeated drunkness, illicit drug-taking, repeated changes of employment, serious marital difficulties, homelessness, sexual deviation, affectionlessness, impulsiveness and persistent irritability as judged objectively. These individuals would come high on the prediction index. Conversely, absence of previous convictions, a good employment record, a stable homelife and moderation in the use of alcohol are factors which tend not to be associated with reconvictions and these individuals would come quite low on the prediction index. The two groups should be matched as much as possible in regard to types of crime and duration of sentences and one group would then act as a control on the other. Craft also indicated that the prognosis of psychopaths and delinquents could be expressed in terms of community social adjustment. For example, an employment index could be based on the following statistics:

$$\frac{\text{Months actually worked} \times 100}{\text{Months available for work}}$$

Similarly a wage index indicating improvement of employment position would be indicated by:

$$\frac{\text{Wage level earned today} \times 100}{\text{Wage level earned last year}}$$

Discontent and unhappiness and their opposites may be stated on subjective scales. Using these scales, Craft found that over three-quarters of a group of psychopathic dullards had successful ratings within eight years of admission to his hospital.

Statistics

Maddocks (1970) studied 59 psychopaths who were first seen at out-patient psychiatric clinics in 1961, 1962 and 1963. The average follow up period was 5-6 years. This study was an attempt to discover whether psychopaths could adapt to normal community life. At least three out of five did not make a satisfactory adjustment but the tendency to fall foul of the law became less with increasing age.

Tong and Mackay (1959) found 171 reconvictions out of 587 discharges from Rampton over a 1-12 year follow-up, that is about 30 per cent.

Sturup (1978) indicated that 871 of 900 treated at Herstedvester were finally able to leave that institution and function in the outside community. The "patients" were committed on an indefinite sentence and the treatment followed therapeutic community principles. He does not state how long they survived in the community after release. He confirmed these optimistic opinions in 1978.

Whiteley (1970) indicated that a follow-up study of 122 consecutive discharges from a therapeutic community which specializes in the treatment of psychopaths showed an improvement rate of 40.1 per cent in terms of no further convictions nor psychiatric admissions in a two-year period. Of 87 with a previous history of convictions 38 (43.6 per cent) were not convicted in two years, and of 66 with a history of previous psychiatric hospital admissions 38 (57.5 per cent), had no further psychiatric admission in two years.

Prognostic factors indicative of a good outcome include a history of ability to achieve success in school, work and interpersonal relationships, together with capacity for some empathy. These factors are seen in terms of levels of emotional maturity, and the importance of matching the treatment to the capacity of the subject for emotional appreciation and control is stressed.

Electroencephalographic studies

Gibbens et al (1959) studied the electroencephalograms of 72 adult psychopaths over an eight-year period and found that posterior temporal-lobe theta activity was often, but not invariably, associated with the most severe forms of psychopathic disorder. This study also revealed that 24 per cent of the study group had one or more convictions during the eight-year period.

Hill and Watterson (1942) found that 65 per cent of aggressive psychopaths with suicidal tendencies had abnormal electroencephalograms as compared with 32 per cent of inadequate psychopaths, neurotics, drug dependents and sex deviants.

Stafford-Clark and Taylor (1959) studied the electroencephalograms of 64 individuals charged with murder. The results gave abnormal tracings: in 17 per cent of those who killed in response to strong provocation (compared with five to 15 per cent abnormal tracings in apparently normal adults); in 25 per cent of those who killed accidentally during the course of committing some other crime; in 73 per cent of explosive psychopaths who committed motiveless and unprovoked homicides; in 86 per cent of those who were psychotic when killing their victims. One may conclude that a significant proportion of abnormal electroencephalographic tracings are associated with psychopathic disorder of the aggressive type or psychosis.

Like most of us the psychopath is good and bad in parts – but more so! The psychologists have investigated psychopaths' responses by recording their physiological reactions in various circumstances. In the laboratory, as elsewhere, the psychopath learns by rewards but not by punishment, and he does not show physiological anticipation as others do. Similarly, in psychopaths, electroencephalographic studies show an absence of the "E" wave which has been described as an "electric sign of sensorimotor association and expectancy". He may know what is coming but he does not seem to be able to act on that knowledge (Scott, (1977)).

Raine *et al* (1987) found significantly larger P3 amplitudes in the electroencephalograms of 38 antisocial subjects as compared with a control group of 37 non-psychopaths referred to as prosocials. He concluded that these results indicated reduced conflict and emotional arousal in psychopaths and a heightened ability to focus their attention on matters of immediate interest enabling them to screen out other aversive stimuli. These findings were opposed to those in the proposals. These opinions are consistent with those of Jutai and Hare (1983). These EEG tracings were taken in conjunction with Contingent Negative Variations (CNV) meaning in response to stimuli such as flashing lights, "clicks" heard through earphones and mild electric shocks and facilitated by the use of an oscilloscope. The high amplitude "expectancy" P3 waves are revealed and seen because many waves are manifest in fractions of a second as opposed to the ordinary EEG tracing.

Again Raine *et al* (1990) indicated that previous studies that have assessed a stimulation-seeking theory of psychopathy are open to the criticism that psychopaths may lie on self-report questionnaires. The later study used event-related potential (ERP) augmenting-reducing as a psychophysiological analogy of stimulation-seeking in psychopaths to test this theory. It is also hypothesized that "schizoid" criminals, as defined by poor eye-tracking, would show non-augmenting/reducing, which is a finding characteristic of schizophrenia. Schizoid criminals were found to be characterized by non-augmenting/reducing, but psychopaths were found to be characterized by augmenting. It is concluded that stimulation-seeking is a viable theory of criminality but not of psychopathy, and that the aetiological basis to schizoid criminality may differ substantially from criminality *per se*.

Fishbein *et al* (1989) stated that auditory brainstem evoked response (BAER) and spontaneous electroencephalogram (EEG) were measured in 124 adult male drug-abusers. They examined the relationships between psychiatric diagnoses, paper and pencil measured aggression and hostility, and electrophysiological features. Subjects meeting criteria for antisocial personality disorder (ASP) were not significantly different from non-ASP subjects for either BAER or spontaneous EEG measures. The more overtly aggressive subjects had significant delays in BAER latency. Aggressive subjects also have been observed in "psychopaths" and "criminals". Although ASP and aggression are related, these data indicate that aggressiveness may be a separate, albeit overlapping, trait. As both early aggression and a diagnosis of ASP are predictors of later drug use, the findings that only aggression was associated with EEG slowing and brainstem delays may indicate that ASP and aggression make independent contributions to vulnerability to the development of drug abuse.

Treatment

The Mental Health Act 1983 specifies that psychopathically disordered patients may only be detained in hospital if they are thought treatable, meaning that treatment is considered likely to alleviate or prevent further presumably anticipated personality deterioration and the following criteria would be relevant:

(i)   previous psychiatric treatment led to limited improvement;
(ii) expression of remorse and desire for treatment;
(iii) failure of repeated punishment to alter behaviour.

Investigations by Tennet *et al*, (1993), indicated that psychiatrists had few clear-cut opinions as to the best treatment for psychopathic disorder.

The following types of treatment are available:

1. *Physical treatments* such as sedatives and tranquillisers may be useful at times of crises but the psychopath tends to abuse drugs.

   Medication to suppress excessive sexual ardour may also be appropriate in regard to male sex offenders but medications such as Androcur should be used which will not bring about the development of female secondary sex characteristics. Psychosurgery has no place in the treatment of the psychopath. Antidepressants may relieve a superimposed depression. Imprisonment alone does not influence psychopathically disordered individuals.

2. *Individual psychotherapy* is usually not successful because the psychopath is confronted with an intense "one to one" situation and early memories of mislearning situations are reactivated. He will do all he can to avoid these unpleasant memories by manipulating the therapist and discontinuing treatment.

3. *Group therapy*: The psychopath tends to be a disruptive element in the group but the following systems may be useful: (i) frequent meetings, (ii) peer control groups, (iii) limited goals, and (iv) shared responsibility. These proposals make treatment situations less stressful and lessen the psychopath's scope for manipulation.

4. *The therapeutic community* where the object is to recreate a basic social learning situation which will replace the old mislearned patterns of behaviour. Four social factors are at work:

   (i) limited permission to act in accordance with feelings without accustomed social inhibitions;
   (ii) communalism in the sharing of tasks, responsibilities and rewards;
   (iii) democratic decision-making; and
   (iv) confrontation of the subject with what he is doing here and now.

Therapeutic community work is practised at HM Prison, Grendon and Springhill, Aylesbury, and the Henderson Hospital, Belmont, Surrey.

Grendon Prison

Grendon is a maximum security psychiatric prison built to accommodate 350 male inmates including 250 adults and 100 boys of youth custody age located in a separate wing. The emphasis is mainly on psychiatric treatment but facilities also exist for X-rays, electroencephalography, dentistry and physiotherapy. Cosmetic surgery is also available. Petty lawbreaking sometimes stems from feelings of inadequacy, frustration and resentment due to some unusual physical feature such as large nose or unduly prominent ears. Appropriate surgery has enabled some of these individuals to become law-abiding members of society. Classrooms, hobby rooms, a library and workshops are also provided.

Psychiatric treatment is provided at Grendon for suitable individuals serving sentences of imprisonment or youth custody. These individuals must *not* be mentally disordered within the meaning of the Mental Health Act (1983). A court does not have the authority to order that an individual be treated at Grendon during the course of sentence. This decision is made by the prison medical authorities.

The main objectives of Grendon are:

(i) The investigation and treatment of emotionally disturbed offenders. The offences for which they were sentenced may suggest mental morbidity.

(ii) Research into the aetiology and most effective treatment for the psychopath.

The inmate must be willing to undergo treatment and have at least 12 months to serve excluding full remission.

The habitual criminal may have psychopathic traits in his personality but not to a degree so as to constitute psychopathic disorder as defined in the Mental Health Act, 1983.

Grendon Prison has three adult wings and three wings catering for youth custody boys and young prisoners. The three adult wings and one boys' wing use group therapy as basic treatment and the remaining two boys' wings use individual psychotherapy.

Each wing has in charge a psychotherapist who is responsible for the treatment programme of the wing. Wing staff are made up of uniformed prison officers supported by welfare officers, psychologists and the chaplain.

Prison officers are actively involved in the treatment programme by taking groups and sitting in on treatment discussion meetings. The staff are well informed and kept in touch with decisions concerning policy and treatment.

The prison comprises separate holding blocks for men and boys. The majority are housed in single rooms, although there are a few dormitories to facilitate group arrangements. The inmates are out of their rooms as long as possible in the waking hours which are fully occupied at work, in classes, in treatment sessions and association rooms. Important features contributing to a better atmosphere are the large windows, quite unlike the ordinary prison cell window, and built-in furniture with small writing desks and boards for photographs. This prison is under the immediate command of a senior medical officer and governor. They are supported by an assistant governor and the professional staff includes psychiatrically experienced doctors and psychologists. Other specialist staff will be recruited as desirable and as available. The prison officers have been selected and drawn from both the hospital and discipline side of the service, with the accent on hospital officers. The staff is skillfully trained to form an efficient team.

Consultants from the National Health Service are available as advisers on research and to assist in other specialist fields. An important appointment was that of a woman welfare officer by the Central After-Care Association and contact is maintained with Alcoholics Anonymous, a marriage guidance officer and the local disablement resettlement officer. Cases requiring further psychiatric treatment after release have appointments made for them at out-patient clinics nearest to their homes, as happens at other prisons. There is no guarantee that the ex-inmate will keep such an appointment and he often does not. So much depends on the individual's willingness to accept help after he has left prison. Efforts are made while prisoners are under treatment at Grendon to contact immediate relatives and secure their interest and co-operation.

Grendon is not just a prison for psychopaths or for the collecting together of troublesome and difficult prisoners who are not necessarily psychopathic.

Research into psychopathy, and indeed other psychiatric aspects of criminality call for close liaison with the Home Office Research Unit and collaboration with workers in the mental health services and elsewhere. The patients themselves must not be looked upon as guinea-pigs and research must be married to treatment and after-care.

Inmates arriving at Grendon are often bewildered by the apparent freedom and relaxed atmosphere which pervades the prison, but after a few days of honeymooning, suddenly become acutely aware that it is not the "soft nick" they had anticipated. The inmate is exposed to a great many pressures once he becomes involved in group therapy. A well-orientated group involved in therapy means that a self-analysing process is set up in which the patient is constantly questioning his motives and those of his fellows. Unlike group counselling, group therapy creates tensions within the man which he is encouraged to talk and act out in front of other members of his group. The role of the group leader is to probe and question the emotions and attitudes of his group. Quite often the leader says nothing and the interaction of the members continues without prompting.

Processes characteristic of a group as a whole are an intrinsic and inevitable aspect of all groups, no matter what their size or function. In a therapy group, group processes not only exist, but are a major factor influencing the nature of each patient's therapeutic experience. The manner in which each patient contributes to, participates in, and is affected by the group processes determines to a considerable degree whether he will profit from his group therapy experience, be untouched by it, or harmed by it. The therapist can influence the character and development of the group and thereby influence the individual's therapeutic experience.

Therapeutic groups begin in much the same way as counselling groups with the members critcizing authority, discipline and the establishment before the real purpose of the group evolves.

Groups at Grendon are now a well-established part of the regime.

New arrivals are put in existing groups and, as the group is self-perpetuating, new members are quickly absorbed. Feed-back plays an important part in treatment, for it would be impossible for the psychotherapist to sit in on all the groups.

Wing staff meetings are held where group leaders and therapists discuss their groups and problems arising. Twice-weekly group associates meet to discuss group mechanics and how best to cope with certain common difficulties that always seem to arise.

Wing meetings take place on three afternoons a week at which all inmates and available staff attend. At these meetings, all matters concerning the wing are aired and officers or inmates are liable to find themselves questioned about behaviour or incidents that have occurred. The "hot seat" is frequently used to bring a recalcitrant wing member to task.

This kind of regime does not suit all inmates. Some feel that they cannot cope with the pressures put upon them in a therapy group. Others derive no benefit at all from this kind of treatment and, for a small number, it can even be harmful.

As a general rule, a Grendon inmate must be capable of acquiring insight into his behaviour and wanting treatment. Vacancies are limited and those sent there are carefully selected. Sometimes inmates slip through the selection net and arrive at Grendon without even the need for treatment and some manage to "work their ticket" by devious means in the belief that it is a comfortable way to serve their term of imprisonment.

At any given time, the population at Grendon is about two hundred which is about 0.5 per cent of the total prison population for the United Kingdom. This may seem an expensive programme for a very small return, but like all prototypes, I believe that Grendon is a prototype of future treatment prisons, a great deal of information and constructive ideas are coming from it. In 1970, a special wing was opened at Parkhurst and although there is no outward sign that it is based on the Grendon regime, two of Grendon's senior uniformed staff were sent to Parkhurst to help open it. Further to this, basic grade officers from Parkhurst were seconded to Grendon to observe the methods used there. Feltham also operates a programme of group therapy for some of its youth custody population.

No prison can claim to have pioneered a particular form of treatment, for the majority of the ideas used have been adapted from procedures already in use in hospitals and clinics throughout the world, but Grendon is unique in that it is the first prison in this country to have built its regime entirely on a foundation of psychotherapeutic methods. Criteria for admission to Grendon and further observations on psychotherapy are included at the end of Chapter VI.

Snell (1962) made the pertinent observation that there is a tendency when an individual has broken the law for it to be said that he is mentally abnormal, suffering from this or that in consequence of some adverse influence in his early life. We must be careful not to carry this too far. It may be an explanation but not necessarily an excuse. Many of these so-called abnormalities may well be deviations within what we believe should properly be regarded as the average range in the same way as we include a wide range of variation in intelligence levels as coming within average limits. If these lesser deviations of thought and behaviour are too readily accepted as excuses for crime, the individual's and society's morale will be undermined and the the real task of trying to discover and define more precisely the more serious personality deviations will be obscured. Grendon works on the principle that insight and re-education and not repression and submission are more likely to achieve the desired therapeutic result.

Grendon is sometimes criticized on the grounds that those who have had treatment there subsequently break the law. However, lawbreaking may not necessarily be a symptom of emotional disturbance. Social and psychiatric "backing" services are essential after release. Individuals tend to experience considerable difficulty in obtaining work after release especially if they are honest enough to admit that they have served a sentence.

Any inmate culture is anti-therapeutic but nevertheless 20 per cent only of men who serve one prison sentence will return to serve a further sentence. If we could identify this 20 per cent and predict which first timers will become recidivists and deal with them psychotherapeutically at an early stage, we might avoid a prison tending to make "a bad man worse".

Henderson Hospital

Henderson Hospital is of interest from two points of view, (i) as one of the models for a therapeutic community and (ii) as a treatment centre for people with personality disorders.

The development of the therapeutic community

The basic origins of the unit lie in the experiences gained by Dr Maxwell Jones in the treatment of soldiers with psychosomatic ailments at Mill Hill Emergency Hospital during the 1939-45 war. Here, large group therapy emerged, firstly didactic and authoritarian, and gradually more open to a two-way exchange of ideas. Immediately after the war Maxwell Jones applied a similar social psychiatric approach to the resettlement of returned POWs and their interaction and integration in the industrial scene became the focus of attention. This led to the formation of the Industrial Rehabilitation Unit as a wing of Belmont Hospital in 1947 with great emphasis on industrial liaison and training in the early days until the individual's interaction at work came to be seen as but a facet of his total social adjustment.

Selection for admission

For the "socially deviant" patients for whom physical treatments, individual psychotherapy or formalized group therapy are less appropriate or have failed, the problems of living in society at large are of paramount importance. Thus treatment in a social setting, such as the therapeutic community can uniquely provide, may be most appropriate. People with long-standing histories of emotional or relationship problems are admitted.

There may be associated problems: "acting out" behaviours such as drug or alcohol misuse; episodes of self-harm and impulsive behaviour; delinquency; violence to others; obsessional-compulsive behaviour; eating disorders; panic attacks or social isolation.

The unit excludes individuals with a frank psychotic illness, brain damage, mental impairment or those who are currently physiologically addicted to alcohol or drugs. Around 80 per cent of admissions have had previous in-patient psychiatric treatment. Patients, known as "residents" have informal patient status. No psychotropic medication is prescribed.

About 35 per cent of admissions have a formal forensic history with a further 35 per cent having displayed serious anti-social behaviour related to criminal offending (especially substance abuse, theft and violence to others or to property). Around 25 per cent are on probation when admitted. However, treatment is voluntary and nobody for whom treatment is made a condition of the probation order can be admitted.

There is a lower age limit of 17 years and, in practice, a top limit of 45 years. Clients are referred by psychiatrists (55 per cent), probation officers (20 per cent) social services (6 per cent), psychologists (6 per cent), GPs and other agencies (8 per cent) or self referred (5 per cent). Individuals are admitted on a voluntary basis provided that at selection interview, with senior residents and staff representatives from the multi-disciplinary team, the selection committee are satisfied that the therapeutic community programme is appropriate to the difficulties and needs of the individual concerned, and that the individual is motivated to join the community with the aim of change.

Treatment programme
Henderson Hospital has moved away from a medical model of treatment which puts the patient in a passive position, and represents a community in which the social interaction of one with another can be closely examined and commented upon by all.

The treatment process is a 24-hour living and learning experience, but in order to facilitate exploration it is programmed as follows:

9.15 to 10.30 a.m.: Every day except Sunday, the day begins with a meeting of the whole community (all residents and staff on duty at the time) in which events of the previous day are summarized and discussed, information shared, plans which affect everyone are made, etc.

11.00 to 12.15 p.m.: Monday, Wednesday and Friday, the community breaks up into three small groups, plus a "new residents" group and a "leavers" group. These are nearer the style of traditional psychotherapy groups and are held three times a week. On Tuesday and Thursday there are community elections, progress reviews, community cleaning, visitors' groups or a welfare group.

2.15 to 4.30 p.m.: In the afternoons on two days there are "work groups" of cookery, art work or gardening and maintenance. These are task-oriented and followed by a 30-minute discussion period in which interactions which took place during the earlier activity can be explored.

On two other afternoons there is a reshuffle into psychodrama and art therapy groups which are "group-analytic" in duration and include time for discussion. On one afternoon the selection group is held.

In the evening, when two staff are present, a community meal is cooked (by residents on a voluntary rota basis) and sports and social activities take place. There is a weekly women's group and administrative "floor meetings". At any time of the day or night immediate crises or difficulties can be explored by the "Top Three" residents calling an emergency community meeting to resolve the situation and take any necessary action, including offering support throughout the night.

10.00 to 11.00 p.m.: This final "wind down" group is voluntary for any resident who wishes to talk over problems or share experiences from the day. It is followed at 11.00 p.m. by a meeting of the "Top Three" senior residents and staff on duty, who discuss the community's day and plan the agenda for the community meeting at 9.15 the next morning. Discussions in this meeting are fed back to the community meeting the following day.

The staff, who do not wear uniform or adopt formal titles in order to allow closer yet separate relationships, comprises: one full and one half-time consultant psychotherapist, a half-time senior registrar in psychiatry, a registrar (from a psychiatric rotational training scheme), an art therapist, a part-time social worker, a senior nurse, eight charge nurses (including one also trained as a psychodramatist), three staff nurses, six social therapists. There is also a research psychologist, a liaison probation officer, one full- and two part-time secretaries and a domestic.

The residents (up to 29) elect for themselves a committee responsible for the day-to-day functioning of the unit. This is headed by the "Top Three". It is these three residents who among other duties have a responsibility for conducting the community meetings. The elections occur monthly, and other posts include a general secretary, sports representatives, a treasurer, a catering officer, a research liaison officer, a social work liaison officer, selection representatives and others. Since committee posts are elected by residents this provides further opportunity for role examinations. The committee structure thus serves both administrative and *therapeutic* functions.

Research at Henderson

A great deal of research has been produced from Henderson Hospital which has made valuable contributions to the therapeutic literature on severe personality disorder (Dolan and Norton, 1990). Formal research from Henderson has refined the description, nature and dynamic aspects of personality disorders and psychopathy (Gudjonsson and Roberts, 1985), identified the most beneficial aspects of the whole treatment programme (Whiteley and Collis, 1987), defined characteristics of those who are likely to be selected for treatment (Morton, Dolan and Wilson, 1989) and produced better definition of the patient population who are most likely to benefit from treatment (Whiteley, 1970).

An early investigation of follow-up outcome at Henderson (Whiteley, 1970) considered 112 consecutively admitted male residents between one and three years after discharge. Outcome was measured using the criteria of recidivism and/or re-admission to a psychiatric hospital. In the years following discharge, of those with previous convictions 38 per cent remained free of conviction in the follow-up period and of those with previous psychiatric admissions 38 per cent had no further admissions. The study enabled prognostic factors (both social and demographic) to be identified (Copas and Whiteley, 1976).

In a more recent treatment study, Norris (1983) investigated changes in residents during admission. Repertory grid measures of changes in self-esteem, independence and rule-breaking for 70 men and 33 women were made during their residence. Results showed that over three months residents perceived themselves to have changed with regard to being less rule-breaking and more independent, although change in self-esteem was not so apparent. For the 64 residents who stayed longer than three months the changes in self-esteem were more marked. Comparison was made with residents in a voluntary trust community and a detention centre. It was concluded that the potentially most difficult client group – the Henderson residents – had "benefited" more during treatment than those clients in the other centres.

Grounds *et al* (1987) made some observations on the treatment of psychopathically disordered people sent to Broadmoor Hospital by criminal courts on the basis of the Mental Health Act, 1983. These individuals are considered to be an immediate and serious danger to the public and are sent to security hospitals such as Broadmoor under s.37 with restriction on discharge (usually without limit of time) under s.41. Dangerous patients may also be transferred from ordinary mental hospitals to special hospitals under s.3 of the Act. These authors describe a treatment approach which "integrates psychodynamic behavioural and cognitive principles". Treatment needs and objectives are not formulated until those in charge of treatment understand the patient's personality, including emotional make-up and intelligence level in relation to offences committed. It is an advance towards organizing treatment appropriate to the psychopathically disordered in particular wards or units in Broadmoor. The authors also wisely refer to the abnormal and restricted social setting in which patients are treated in special hospitals such as Broadmoor where there is little integration of the sexes from the point of view of staff or patients, the families of patients are excluded from the wards and alcohol is understandably forbidden. These factors would militate against successful community rehabilitation of patients assessed as having sufficient emotional control to live in harmony with others after discharge.

Grounds *et al* also indicated the psychopathic disorder is not defined or included in the Mental Health Acts of Scotland (1984) or Northern Ireland (1986). This is quite understandable as far as Northern Ireland is concerned, otherwise any terrorist who murdered could have the option of ending up in a secure mental hospital rather than a prison by pleading diminished responsibility on the basis of psychopathic disorder.

Those suffering from mental disorder may be treated in Broadmoor, Rampton and Ashworth special hospitals provided the following criteria are satisfied: (i) The individual is an immediate and serious danger to the public, and (ii) he or she is mentally disordered within the meaning of the Mental Health Act (1983). Secure units (as opposed to Special Hospitals) have varying graduations of security and manning problems are frequent.

They may not be suitable for the really dangerous offenders. Most of the principles for treating psychopaths enumerated by these authors have been practised at Grendon Underwood for many years. Grendon is a psychiatric hospital within HM Prison service. Emotionally disturbed offenders who are serving sentences and are *not* mentally disordered within the meaning of the Mental Health Act 1983 are treated there.

It is appropriate to comment here on special hospitals because of recent criticisms of them. I agree with Bluglass (1992) to the effect that offenders who fulfil the above criteria should be treated in new *high-security* hospital units of 100 to 150 beds situated close to the relatives and friends of the patients. These units should be integrated with local psychiatric and community-care facilities, including rehabilitation. Security should be regarded as part of treatment and efforts made to help patients understand this idea.

The alleged oppressive attitudes of some members of the staff of special hospitals such as Broadmoor, Rampton and Ashworth can only be abolished by the closure of these institutions and their replacement by a sufficient number of high-security hospital units by the Special Hospital Service Authority which has adequate funds to provide for approximately 1,700 patients.

A review of the health and social services for the mentally disordered is now in preparation and should include reference to patients requiring the highest degree of security for the protection of the public.

The report on Ashworth hospital (1992) was led by Sir Louis Blom-Cooper and witnesses had to be issued with subpoenas. The report found evidence of systematic abuse of patients and concluded that Ashworth was a "prime candidate to be visited in the near future by the European Committee for the Prevention of Torture and Inhuman or Degrading Treatment or Punishment".

Coid *et al* (1992) indicated that the Mental Health Act 1983 places responsibility on psychiatrists which in many cases cannot be fulfilled, meaning that psychiatrists should not be expected to take the ultimate responsibility for such clinical decisions as, for example, applying s.47 of the above Act for the purpose of transferring psychopathically disordered persons who are potentially dangerous and serving sentences of imprisonment to National Health Service Hospitals, which could be special hospitals, secure units or ordinary mental hospitals. These writers also remark that the public do not expect people of other disciplines such as Probation Officers and members of the Parole Board to take such responsibility. However, consultant psychiatrists are by law the responsible medical officers who are in charge of the treatment of patients and therefore have no choice but to take the ultimate responsibility for better or for worse. I have on a number of occasions heard consultants complain of being expected to share decision-making. Such sharing was referred to by one consultant as "Democratic Disneyland" or the "Multidisciplinary Con".

References

Amarc, C. (1951) "A Study in Alcoholism", *Acta Psychiat. Scand.* Suppl. 70. Quoted in the *Genetics of Mental Disorder*, 1961, (Eliot Slater and Valerie Cowie) 5: 112, Oxford Univ. Press, London.

Archer, J. (1993) "Breaking the Last Taboo", *Guardian*, 3 Feb., p.19.

Babe, K.S.J., *et al* (1992) "The Pathogenesis of the Munchausen Syndrome: A Review and Case Report", *J. Hosp. Psychiatry*, 14(4): 273-6, Published by Dept. of Psychiatry, Vanderbilt University Medical Centre, Nashville, Tennessee.

Bleuler, E.P. (1924) *Textbook of Psychiatry for Students and Practitioners* George Allen & Unwin, London.

Bluglass, R. (1992) "The Special Hospitals", *B. Med. J.* Vol. 305: 323-4.

Bohman, M., Cloniger, C.R., Sigvardsson, S., vol Knorring, A.L. (1982) "Predisposition to Petty Criminality in Swedish Adoptees. I. Genetic and Environmental Heterogeneity". *Arch. Gen. Psychiatry* Vol: 39(11): 1233-41.

Brendtro, M., Bowker, L.H. (1989) "Battered Women: How can Nurses Help?" *Issues Ment. Health Nursing* 10, (2): 169-80.

Brooner, R.K., Herbst, J.H., Schmidt, C.W., Bigelow, G.E., Costa, P.T. Jr., (1993) "Antisocial personality disorder among drug abusers. Relations to other personality diagnoses and the five-factor model of personality". Johns Hopkins School of Medicine, Baltimore, Maryland. *Journal of Nervous & Mental Disease.* 181(5): 313-9.

Bryant, H.D. (1963) "Child Welfare", *J. Child Welfare League of America*, 42: 125, Pub. Transaction Publishers New Brunswick, U.S.A.

Children Act 1989, H.M.S.O., London.

Cleckley, H. (1976) *The Mask of Sanity*, St. Louis MP, Mosby.

Coid, J.W., Cordess, C. (1992) "Compulsory Admission of Dangerous Psychopaths", *B. Med. J.* Vol. 304: 1581-2.

Connolly, J. (1849) Quoted in the Croonian Lectures, No. VI, 71-85 Published by Royal College of Physicians, London, in 1916.

Copas J. & Whiteley J.S. (1976) "Predicting Success in the Treatment of Psychopaths", *Brit. J. Psychiatry* 129: 388-392.

Craft, M. (1966) *Psychopathic Disorders*, Pergamon Press, Oxford.

Craig, J. (1993) "Child Abuse – continuing problems and different perspectives". Report of meeting of Section of Clinical Forensic Medicine of Roy. Soc. Med.

Curran, D. and Mallinson, J. (1944) "Psychopathic Personality", *J. Mental Science*, 1: 266.

D.H.S.S. (1985) *Child Abuse Inquiries: A Consultative Paper from the Department of Health and Social Security.*

Dolan, B.M., Norton, K. (1990) "Is There a Need for Specialist Psychiatric Units in the NHS? Henderson Hospital: A Case in Point", *Bulletin of the Royal College of Psychiatrists* 14: 72-76.

D'Orban, P.T. (1972) "Baby Stealing", *Brit. Med. J.* Vol. 2: 635-639.

D'Orban, P.T. (1976) "Child Stealing: A Typology of Female Offenders", *Brit. J. Criminol.* 16, 3.

Edwards, S. (1990) "The Child Abduction Agony", *New Law J.*, Vol. 140: 59-60.

Faller K.C. (1987) "Women who Sexually Abuse Children", *Violence and Victims*, 2: 263-76.

Finkelhor, D., Russell, D. (1984) "Women as Perpetrators", In: Finkelhor D, (ed.) *Child Sexual Abuse: New Theory and Research*, Free Press, New York: 171-87.

Finkelhor, D. (1986) *A Source Book on Child Sexual Abuse*, Sage Publications, Beverley Hills, C.A., U.S.A.

Fishbein, D.H., Herning, R.I., Pickworth, W.B., Haertzen, C.A., Hickey, J.E., Jaffe, J.H. (1989) "EEG and Brainstem Auditory Evoked Response Potentials in Adult Male Drug Abusers with Self-reported Histories of Aggressive Behaviour", *Biol. Psychiatry* 26(6): 595-611.

Franklin White, A. (1975) *Concerning Child Abuse (Tunbridge Wells Papers)*, Churchill Livingstone, London.

Gibbens, T.C.N. (1971) "Female Offenders", *Brit. Hospital Medicine*, Vol.6 pp. 279-286. Mark Allen Publishing Ltd., Lon..

Gibbens, T.C.N., Pond, D.A. and Stafford-Clark, D. (1959) "A Follow-up Study of Criminal Psychopaths", *J. Mental Science*, 105: 108.

Gill, K., Nolimal, D., Crowley, T.J. (1992) "Antisocial personality disorder, HIV risk behaviour and retention in methadone maintenance therapy." Department of Psychiatry, University of Colorado Health Sciences Center, Denver. *J. Drug & Alcohol Dependence.* 30(3): 247-52.

Gillick v. West Norfolk and Wisbech Health Authority (Scarman), *All England Law Reports 1985*: 421.

Gould, J, 1959 "The Psychiatry of Major Crime", in *Recent Progress in Psychiatry*, (eds) Fleming, G.W. and Fleming H.J. and A., Churchill, London.

Gregg, G.S., and Elmer, E. (1969) "Infant Injuries: Accidental or Abuse", *J. American Academy of Paediatrics*, 44: 434-439, Elk Grove Village Publishers, Illinois.

Grounds, A.T., *et al* (1987) "A Unit for Psychopathic Disorder at Broadmoor Hospital", *Med. Sci. Law*, Vol. 27 (1): 21-31.

Groth, A.N. (1979) *Men who Rape*, Plenum, London.

Gudjonsson, G.H., Roberts, J.C. (1985) "Psychological and Physiological Characteristics of Personality Disordered Patients", In: *Aggression and Dangerousness*. (Eds) Farrington D.P., Gunn J, J. Wiley & Son Ltd., London.

Guze, S.B. (1976) *Criminality and Psychiatric Disorders*, Oxford Univ. Press, London.

Hamilton, M. (ed) (1985) *Fish's Clinical Psychopathology*, 2nd ed., Wright, Bristol.

Hare, R.D. and McPherson, L.M. (1984) "Psychopathy and Perceptual Asymmetry During Verbal Dichotic Listening", *J. Abnormal Psychology*, Vol. 93(2): 141-149.

Harwin, N. (1992) "Domestic Violence", Women's Aid Federation England Ltd., Bristol, also personal communication from Mrs. Nicola Harwin, National Co-ordinator of Women's Aid Federation.

Haward, L.R.C. (1990) "Babysnatching", *A Dictionary of Forensic Psychology*, Medilaw/ Barry Rose, Chichester, 19.

Helfer, R.E. and Kemp, C.H. (1968) *The Battered Child*, University of Chicago Press.

Hill, D. and Watterson, D. (1942) "Electroencephalographic Studies of Psychopathic Personalities", *J. Neurology and Psychiatry*, 5: 47.

Howells, K., Hollin, C.R. (1989) "Clinical Approaches to Violence", 4: 77, John Wiley & Sons, Chichester.

Jones, C.O. (1982) "The Family as a Conflict-prone Institution", from *Violence in the Family*, 2., Pub. Social Work Services Group, Scottish Education Department (H.M.S.O. Edin.).

Jones, D. (1985) *The Management of Child Abuse*, B.A.S.W., 16 Kent Street, Birmingham B5 6RD.

Jutai, J.W., and Hare, R.D. (1983) "Psychopathy and Selective Attention during Performance of a Complex Perceptual-motor task", *Psychophysiology*, 20: 146-151.

Juveniles Convicted of Offences of Homicide in England and Wales, 1982-1991, Criminal Statistics issued by Home Office, April 1993, Personal Communication.

Kellert, S.R., Felthouse, A.R. (1985) "Childhood Cruelty towards Animals among Criminals and Noncriminals", *Human Relations*, Vol. 37(12): 1113-1129. Published by Yale Univ. School of Forestry & Environmental Sciences.

Kemp, C.H. and Helfer, R.E. (1972) *Helping the Battered Child and his Family*, Lippincott, Philadelphia, U.S.A.

Kraepelin, E. (1921) *Manic Depressive Insanity and Paranoia*, E. & S. Livingstone, Edinburgh.

Leigh, D., *et al* (1972) "Sadism", *Encyclopedia of Psychiatry*, Roche Products Ltd, 15 Manchester Square, London, p.359.

Lord McKay of Clashfern, *House of Lords Official Report*, 1988, 6 Dec., Report No. 1413.

Maddocks, P.D. (1970) "A Five-year Follow-up of Untreated Psychopaths", *Brit. J. Psychiatry*, 116: 511.

Mayer-Gross, W., Salter, E. and Roth, M. (1955) *Clinical Psychiatry*, Balliere Tindall, London.

Mercer, S.O., Perdue, J.D. (1993) "Munchausen Syndrome by Proxy: Social Work's Role", *J. Social Work*, 38(1): 74-81. Published by School of Social Work, University of Arkansas, Little Rock.

Morton A., Dolan B.M., Wilson J. (1989) *Acceptance by the Henderson Hospital Selection Group: Association with Degree and Type of Psychological Distress.* Presented at XIIth ATC/VWAG Conference, Windsor, England.

N.S.P.C.C. Annual Report (1992), 67 Saffron Hill, London.

N.S.P.C.C. Battered Child Research Team, 1976, *At Risk*, Routledge and Kegan Paul, London.

Norris, M., 1983, Changes in Patients during Treatment at Henderson Hospital Therapeutic Community during 1977-1981, *Brit. J. Med. Psychol.* 56: 135-143.

O'Connor, D., 1994, Infant Abduction, School of Education, University of Newcastle-upon-Tyne, Personal Communication.

Ounstead, C., *et al* (1974) "Treatment of Families of Battered Children", *Develop. Med. Child. Neural*, 16: 447.

Pritchard, J.D. (1842) *Forms of Insanity*, Hippolyte and Balliere, London.

Raine, A., Venables, P.H. (1987) "Contingent Negative Variation, P3 Evoked Potentials, and Antisocial Behaviour", *The Society of Psychophysiological Research Inc.* (Printed U.S.A.) 24. 2.

Raine, A., Venables, P.H. (1990) "Evoked Potential Augmenting-reducing in Psychopaths and Criminals with Impaired Smooth-pursuit Eye Movements", *Psychiatry-Res*, 31(1): 85-98.

Report of the Committee of Inquiry into Complaints about Ashworth Hospital is available from HMSO bookshops (1992).

Robins, L.N. (1966) *Deviant Children Grown Up*, Williams and Wilkins, Baltimore.

Royal Commission on the Law relating to Mental Illness and Mental Deficiency (1954-57), Cmnd. 169, HMSO, London.

Russell, D.E.H. (1984) "Prevalence and Seriousness of Incestuous Abuse: Stepfathers vs. Biological Fathers", *J. Child Abuse and Neglect,* 8:15-22.

Sage, A. (1993) "Police Pay-outs to Hunt Saboteurs", *Independent*, 16 Feb.

Samuels, M.P., Southall, D.P. (1992) "Munchausen Syndrome by Proxy", *Br. J. Hosp. Med.*, 47(10): 759-62.

Scott, P.D. (1973) Fatal Battered Baby Cases, *Med. Sci. Law* 13: 197.

Scott, P.D. (1977) "The Psychopathic Patient in General Practice", 1308, 218: 801-4.

Schreider, H.A. (1993) *Bull. Menninger Clinic*, 56(4): 421-37. Published by Dept. of Psychiatry, Children's Hospital Medical Centre of Northern California, Oakland.

Skinner, A.E., and Castle, R.L. (1969) *78 Battered Children*, NSPCC Research Unit

Smith, S.M. (1975) *The Battered Child Syndrome*, Butterworths, London.

Snell, H.K. (1962) "H.M. Prison, Grendon", *Brit. Med. J.*, 2: 789.

Stafford-Clark, D. and Taylor, F.H. (1959) "Clinical and Electroencephalographic Studies of Prisoners charged with Murder", *J, Neurology and Psychiatry*, 12: 325.

Sturup, G.K. (1978) "Changing Patterns of Treatment in Herstedvester: Forensic Psychiatric Considerations in Retrospect and Prospect", *Bull. of Am. Psych. and Law.*, Vol 6(2): 176-194.

Taitz, L.S. (1991) "Child Abuse and Metabolic Bone Disease: Are They Often Confused?" *Brit. Med. J.* 302: 1244.

Tennet, G., Tennent, D., Prins, H. Bedford, A. (1993) "Is psychopathic disorder a treatable condition?", St Brendan's Hospital, Devonshire, Bermuda., *Medicine, Science & the Law.*, 33(1): 63-6.

Thakurdas, H., and Thakurdas, L. (1979) *Dictionary of Psychiatry*, MTP Press Ltd., Lancaster.

Tong, J.E. and Mackay, G.W. (1959) "A Statistical Follow-up of Mental Defectives of Dangerous or Violent Propensities", *Brit. J. Criminology* 9: 276-284, Oxford Univ. Press.

Valman, H.B. (1987) "Sexual Abuse of Children", *Brit. Med. J.* 294: 633-4.

Walsh-Brennan, K. (1975) *New Psychiatry*, 27 Feb: 11. Published by Bradshare Ltd., 10 Northburgh Street, London.

Wax, D., Haddox, V. (1974) "Enuresis, Fire-setting, and Animal Cruelty in Male Adolescent Delinquents: A Triad Predcictive of Violent Behaviour", *J. Psychiatry and Law*, Vol. 2(1): 45-71. Published Am. Psychol. Assoc.

West, L.J. (1964) "Psychiatry, Brainwashing and the American Character", *Am. J. Psychiatry*, 120: 844.

Whiteley, J.S. (1970) "The Responses of Psychopaths to a Therapeutic Community", *Brit. J. Psychiatry,* 116: 517529.

Whiteley, J.S. and Collis M. (1987) "The Therapeutic Factors in Group Psychotherapy applied to a Therapeutic Community", *International J. Therapeutic Communities,* Vol. 8(1): 21-31.

Whiteley, P. (1993) "NSPCC Seeks to Close Child abuse Loophole", *Community Care,* Reed Business Publishing Ltd, Quadrant House, Sutton, Surrey.

Wilkins, R. (1990) "Women who Sexually Abuse Children", *Brit. Med. J.* 300: 1153-54.

Working Together (1991) Consultation Paper 22, Department of Health Stores, Heywood, Lancashire, OL10 2PZ.

Zehrer, F.A. (1959) "Psychological Indoctrination Efforts among Prisoners of War in Korea", *J. Indiana State Med. Assoc.*, 52: 1798.

CHAPTER XIII

Rehabilitation of Offenders

An individual's rehabilitation begins on the first day of his or her sentence. Consequently, I will begin this chapter by making some reference to prison management. John Hughes' section on rehabilitation of inmates from the psychiatric point of view will follow and the chapter will be concluded with a summary of the Home Secretary's proposals for the reorganization of the Probation Service, which plays such an important part in rehabilitation, "the reinvestment of the individual with dignity".

It is generally accepted in a limited context, that a prison is run with the consent of its inmates. However, a riot is unacceptable to the prevailing government which fears accusations of mismanagement. Furthermore, the citizens of a genuinely democratic society are disturbed by such riots which could well provoke sympathy in totalitarian countries where the majority of prisoners would probably be political detainees. Prison staff, police and, if necessary, army personnel would of necessity eventually join forces to bring such riots to an end.

The Prisons Board for England and Wales consists of the Director General of the Prison Service, the Deputy Director, Director of Operational Policy, Director of Services, Director of Personnel and Finance, heads of various other divisions, the Secretariat and two non-executive members who have a special interest in the Prison Service. The Director of the Prison Medical Service would attend when necessary. The Home Secretary has ultimate authority and may be consulted by the Director General who has authority to overrule decisions made by regional directors (future area managers) or governors. Consequently, a governor can, against his better judgment, be prevented from bringing a riot to an end on orders from his or her Home Office superiors, who may decide that "softly-softly" psychological methods are more appropriate. Uniformed prison staff would be very much against the latter solution and the Prison Officers' Association in May 1990 recommended that an emergency task force be established for the four regions of England and Wales. A force consisting of about 1,000 officers could be drawn from the various institutions (including police establishments) in the event of major riots which could be more accurately called mutinies. They would be trained in riot strategy and tactics and armed with CS gas, rubber bullets and stun grenades. The Army, including the Special Air Service, would be summoned to help if prison staff and police failed to terminate a riot. Factors influencing the timing and type of intervention would be the size and scale of the riot, the number of staff and inmates who might be killed or injured if force was used and political considerations such as the attitude of the public to the riot and to the party in power. First choice methods for subduing a riot would be the use of pressure techniques such as sound, lights, and cold water delivered under pressure by fire-engine hoses.

The Prisoners

The average population in custody in England and Wales, including prisons, young offender institutions and police cells, in 1989 was 48,600 representing a fall by about 1,350. This was the first fall since 1973. However there was an increase of 800 in the population of adult males sentenced to over four years' imprisonment. The source of this information is the Home Office, Statistical Bulletin, Statistical Dept, Lunar House, Croydon, Surrey, which gave the population for 1994 as 48,800.

The punishment of prisoners may be concerned under two headings:

Loss of freedom

Deprivation of freedom angers the great majority of human beings even if they accept guilt. Resentment will obviously be increased if the prisoner considers himself innocent and not consoled when correctly told guilt or innocence is not the concern of the prison authorities. Different personalities will react to imprisonment in different ways. The domineering extrovert will tend to be belligerent and bad-tempered, the over-suspicious and over-emotional type may accuse other inmates of stealing his property and the staff of victimization and the dependent, indecisive person who is lacking self-confidence will irritate other inmates and staff by persistent attention-seeking. The latter type of inmate may become an informer. Deprivation of freedom will be even harder to tolerate when bad news is received such as desertion by a wife or girlfriend (letters conveying this information are called "Dear Johns"). The death of a near relative would obviously also be very distressing and occasionally lead to suicidal attempts.

Howells *et al* (1989) made some interesting observations on the behaviour of prisoners. Environmental changes may influence violent behaviour. A prisoner may discontinue aggressive behaviour when segregated from other inmates and vice versa. An adult prisoner may behave violently when located in a prison also housing young offenders, but may control his aggression when transferred to a prison which exclusively caters for adult offenders.

Prisoners may react with violence to peer temptations and pressures, and they experience tension, fear and anxiety because their time is totally controlled during incarceration. They may also react with aggression as a result of anxieties which are aroused on entry into the prison system and/ or when release is imminent. Motives and dispositions and behaviour of even patterned offenders may change temporarily from time to time and may be extreme, as for example, when recidivistic aggressivity changes to helpless confusion.

Overcrowding

The effects of overcrowding make maintenance of internal disciplinary procedures all the more difficult. The majority of offenders are not dangerous to persons and do not need imprisonment. Courts are now being asked to reconsider their attitude to sentencing. Penalties involving community work and appropriate counselling could influence offenders to appreciate the significance of their offences and would be more disagreeable to some than imprisonment. However, police tend to be of the opinion that imprisonment of the great majority of offenders means less crime "on the streets".

Overcrowding and "work to rule" by staff, especially in the larger prisons often means three inmates confined to a cell about 10' x 8' for most of each 24-hour period and the absence of flush toilets during the night hours leads one to ask where does punishment and discipline end and degradation begin?

The Wolds Remand Centre on Humberside is Britain's first privately run prison, (1992). The General, Municipal and Boilermakers' Union will represent the prison staff. Furthermore, a breakaway group from the Prison Officers' Association (POA) called the Prison Service Union (PSU), is seeking recognition from the Home Office. At the time of writing, the POA is allegedly involved in some forty disputes, mainly over staffing levels, at penal establishments throughout the country. This centre will help to reduce overcrowding, which is a serious problem in general in prisons but especially in the hospitals of prisons which serve local courts.

The writer worked in a local prison which provided accommodation for about 500 prisoners and the hospital rooms numbered about two dozen. Up to 12 inmates charged with murder were periodically accommodated in these rooms. A mere 12 rooms remained to accommodate psychotics, psychopaths, the mentally impaired and those with suicidal tendencies. In addition, alcoholics and drug dependents were not infrequently remanded to the prison hospital by the police especially over weekends when local mental hospitals refused to admit them.

The internal conditions in the prison will usually determine whether frustration will develop into fury and the latter progress to riot.

Conjugal visits by wives to imprisoned husbands would be considered by some as an outrageous insult to discipline but would improve morale and reduce nervous tension especially in the large long-stay male prisons and would also reduce the incidence of perversions such as homosexuality.

Prisoners remanded for trial are segregated from those serving sentences and segregation is also applied to the following categories:

(i)   Sex offenders especially those who rape and sexually abuse children;
(ii)   child murderers and those guilty of cruelty to children;
(iii)   informers, also called "grasses"; and
(iv)   former members of the forces of law and order who are serving sentences for any offence.

These people are intensely disliked by other inmates and may well be attacked. They are referred to as Rule 43 inmates. They may make application to the governor to come off Rule 43 and mix with other inmates in the main prison where they may be assaulted despite the vigilance of staff. However, the "internal honour system" amongst the prisoners does not usually allow a second assault to take place on individuals in these categories.

There is concern about the spread of Auto Immune Deficiency Syndrome (AIDS) in prisons in the UK. This spread may be connected with alleged illicit drug-taking in prisons. Education, issuing of condoms and means to disinfect syringes have been suggested as a means of reducing the incidence of AIDS.

The prospect of segregation of sex offenders in prison may influence those who know that they are HIV positive not to admit this information to the prison authorities.

Inmates also suffer for failure to repay tobacco and drug "barons".

It is of paramount importance to give prisoners a sense of purpose and some hope for the future. Industrial training and education by visiting teachers are most helpful in achieving these ends. Padres, psychologists and prison visitors also do invaluable work inculcating social principles and helping to restore dignity. Visiting psychiatrists provide psychotherapy for emotionally disturbed inmates who are not mentally disordered within the meaning of the Mental Health Act (1983) and some of these would have similar treatment at Grendon Underwood or Feltham Young Offender Institution. Psychologists may be in a position to warn governors of troublesome prisoners who may riot.

Those who are mentally disordered within the meaning of the Mental Health Act, whether remanded or sentenced, would be sent to NHS mental hospitals. The first unit for treatment of drug-dependent offenders started functioning at Downview Prison, Sutton, Surrey in December 1992. Members of Alcoholics Anonymous also visit the larger prisons.

Good quality food and efficient medical treatment are most essential for the well-being and contentment of inmates.

Veneralogists are available as necessary and hold regular sessions at the larger institutions. Their investigations include tests for HIV infection.

All inmates suspected of suicidal tendencies are admitted to the hospital of the relevant institution for special observation and treatment.

Recreational activities including football are necessary but more vigorous physical exercises such as weight-lifting and gymnastics are probably not advisable and may be regarded as "building machines" in the event of a riot. An adequate library and a canteen have a calming effect on inmates.

Sanitary conditions including frequency of showers and changes of underwear need improving in our penal system.

Prisoners' rights are also safeguarded by the Right of Petition to the Home Secretary against:

(i)   conviction and sentence during the time allowed for appeal;
(ii)   prison staff;
(iii) conditions in the institution such as medical treatment, food and conditions in workshops;
(iv)   refusal of parole; and

(v)   punishment awards.

Complaints may also be expressed in letters to Members of Parliament and solicitors.

Prison Suicides

Thirty-two suicides, confirmed by Coroner's Courts, were recorded in Prison Service Establishments in England and Wales during the period April 1988 to March 1989, but the total number of self-inflicted deaths was 48 in 1989 as compared with 60 in 1994 and the average prison population some 40,000 per year. An inmate of a Prison Service Establishment is about twelve times more likely to commit suicide than a free person in the community (statistics supplied by Prison Dept. Home Office, 1992).

A more serious view is taken of suicides which occur in prison hospitals where observations of inmates by staff is regarded as superior to that in the main prisons and statistics should indicate the location of suicides. Suicidal attempts usually occur as a result of reactive depression caused by feelings of fear, disgrace, and frustration which a minority of those serving sentences or remanded in custody, are unable to tolerate. The bullying of inmates by other inmates is not sufficiently emphasized as a cause of despondency leading to suicidal attempts. This bullying occurs amongst rival groups of inmates who challenge each other for dominance in various institutions. It is quite common and the tobacco and drug barons are to be found amongst the winners.

Male prisoners sometimes attempt suicide in response to "Dear John" letters which indicate that a wife or girlfriend is seeking consolation elsewhere and similar attempts may also be provoked by feelings of isolation from home due to unsuccessful appeals and failure of visitors and letters to arrive. The above remarks refer to inmates who were not regarded as suffering from serious mental disorders prior to committing suicide, but obviously those who are so disordered are at least as likely to end their lives. All those who are mentally disordered and/or admit to suicidal tendencies or who attempt suicide are immediately admitted to the prison hospital for observation. Reasonable restraint is used as necessary. Straight jackets are never used. Tranquillizers are prescribed if indicated and with the primary object of relieving distress and not to control patients as has been falsely alleged.

When a group of 140 sentenced suicides were examined, a significantly higher proportion were serving longer sentences of four years or more than in the general prison population (57 per cent compared with 18 per cent). Over 25 per cent of sentenced suicides were serving life sentences (Dooley, 1990).

The inmates who kill themselves are more likely to have been convicted of more serious offences than those who do not, and tend to serve longer sentences. It may be that they see little future for themselves either inside or outside prison.

In 1989, 22 per cent of the average daily prison population were on remand and 47 per cent of suicides in that year involved remand prisoners. Of the 242 prisoners who committed suicide between 1980 and 1989, 136 (54 per cent) were remand prisoners.

The above figures are of cases where an inquest returned a verdict of suicide. The total number of self-inflicted deaths in prisons, regardless of the inquest verdict, is higher.

Samaritans are represented in 100 prisons. There are direct telephone links between prisons and Samaritan branches. Samaritans attend group meetings on preventing suicide and visit prisoners on request.

Mentally Disordered Persons in Prison Hospitals

The following observations concern the fate of mentally disordered persons wrongly located in prison hospitals. Long-stay psychiatric patients are likely to be remanded in prisons after discharge from mental hospitals. They are also subject to destitution, disease and death when attempting to live in the community. Eysenck (1987) agrees with these opinions as indicated in her excellent paper "Mentally Disordered Individuals in the Prison System". A minority indulge in crime or even end their lives and usually soon after discharge from mental hospitals. About 17 per cent of schizophrenics commit suicide. Steadman (1985) indicates that during the ten-year period of de-institutionalization of the mental health system in the USA, a large number of psychotics ended up in the prison system. I can confirm that this opinion is also valid for English and Welsh persons. Furthermore, these unfortunate people tend to be blamed for impeding correctional programmes in prisons and consequently causing most concern to the prison authorities, although one would reasonably assume that most concern would be caused by inmates responsible for organized prison riots whether for racial, economic or other reasons.

Coid (1984) indicated that 20 per cent of mentally abnormal men remanded to Winchester prison during 1979-1983 were rejected for treatment by the responsible NHS psychiatrists. Furthermore, Bond (1989) stated that the new Regional Secure Unit for the West Midlands, the Reaside Clinic, had a total of 85 patients referred for admission during the first year of operation, of whom 32 (some 40 per cent) were considered unsuitable for admission. It is reasonable to assume that a significant proportion of these referrals were offenders located in prison hospitals or serving sentences. These studies suggest that the Prison Medical Service can hardly be held responsible for unnecessarily retaining mentally disordered people in prisons. In this general context, Bluglass (1988) commented on a 1987 report by the Home Office and the Dept. of Health officials. This report was concerned with reducing the numbers of mentally disordered inmates of prisons and to facilitate their treatment in custodial institutions and also their aftercare. This report was criticized on the grounds that it was based on limited statistical information supplied by prison medical officers in respect of "mentally disturbed" prisoners. These criticisms are groundless. Mentally disordered prisoners receive satisfactory treatment from prison medical officers with or without the advice of psychiatrists, forensic or otherwise.

Furthermore, I was personally concerned with compiling six-monthly medical statistics in various prisons for many years. These statistics included information on mentally disordered inmates. The various types of disorders were always specifically indicated and vague generalizations such as references to the "mentally disturbed" were not used.

Some 725 beds were available in Secure Regional Psychiatric Units for patients in January 1990. The final target is 921. These figures refer to England and Wales. The calculations are based on 20 such beds per 1,000,000 population. These statistics were supplied by Dept. of Health, January 1991.

The Health of the Nation Report (1992) is a joint effort by the Home Office and Department of Health. It deals with the case of mentally disordered offenders in England and makes 276 recommendations. A multi-agency approach is advised involving prisons, ordinary mental hospitals, regional secure units, regional and district health authorities, probation and social services, general medical practitioners and voluntary services. Chiswick (1992) wisely draws attention to the financial resources needed to implement this scheme during economic recession and possible hesitancy on the part of the Government and in this context he also indicates that district health authorities do not have to pay for mentally disordered patients who are located in prison hospitals and special hospitals such as Broadmoor.

The Report recommends new appointments of 175 general and 80 forensic psychiatrists and also indicates the necessity of 900 extra places in regional secure units. However, these excellent ideas may well remain Utopian without adequate finance especially in the context of aftercare facilities in the community for mentally disordered offenders discharged from inpatient psychiatric care or released from prison hospitals.

Nationwide schemes are proposed to divert mentally disordered persons remanded for psychiatric reports, from prison hospitals to ordinary mental hospitals or to regional secure units. Such schemes are most desirable but beds must be available in these facilities and psychiatrists must be willing to receive them. Consultant psychiatrists have legal authority to *refuse* to admit any mentally disordered person to mental hospitals or secure units and the special hospital service authority may also legally refuse admissions to special hospitals and it is not unknown for such authority to be exercised. These comments also apply to mentally disordered offenders serving sentences. The mentally disordered should not be located in prison hospitals but those with violent tendencies are understandably not well tolerated in ordinary mental hospitals or in the community in hostel accommodation, living with relatives or otherwise.

It is not sufficiently realized that mentally disordered offenders, whether on remand or sentenced, are well cared for in the hospitals of local prisons when beds are not available in psychiatric facilities. Perhaps more attention should be given to increasing the number of psychiatrically qualified prison medical officers.

The Role of Prison Staff

Members of the prison service may reach the rank of governor on the basis of promotion through the ranks when they are sometimes rather uncharitably called "Rankers". Alternatively, they may enter the service as assistant governors after taking an appropriate degree (university or otherwise).

Governors have a very difficult job because they frequently walk on the proverbial "razor's edge" when they must endeavour to please subordinate staff and at the same time ensure that their efforts satisfy their superiors, whether regional directors, the future area managers or members of the prison directorate located in the Home Office in London.

Governors express their opinions on policy through the Prison

Governors' Association. A governor's leadership of an organization such as prison staff, should be such that it ensures in all interactions in all relationships within the organization, each member, on the basis of his or her background, wishes, values and expectations, will view experiences in the work situation as supportive and maintaining his or her sense of personal worth and importance. An individual's interpretation of experiences in the work situation will be a product of intellectual and emotional factors. The principle of supportiveness is built into group decision-making and the relevant groups should meet frequently and regularly. The function of overlapping groups is important and means that one member of a group is also a member of another group in order to ensure that there is sufficient communication between groups and multiple overlapping interdependent group structures would exist in a large organization. Each group has a leader who is expected to successfully employ the relevant talents within each group and at the relevant times. The ultimate aim is to enable group members to act in the interests of the organization as a whole and not just in the interests of themselves and consequently preventing excessive inefficient competition within the organization. The governor has the overall responsibility for allocating tasks to personnel of the various groups in the context of acceptable group decision-making. Staff are quick to sense if a governor is not governing.

Prisons certainly change inmates. Of that there is no doubt. It makes a significant proportion of them more inadequate, more angry and more alienated. Therefore personal change occurs for the worse but change for the better is possible, given that the environment itself is adjusted.

The concept of group work means that prisoners can be influenced and helped by each other in small groups and the extension of this idea leads to therapeutic communities where the total group (staff and inmates) may to a considerable extent be self-regulating and supportive of change. Even violent men can often be managed best by means other than physical. The management role is shared with inmates within the limits of security and with the realities of having to contain a few men and women who are intransigent and irrevocably against society. The fact that a person is highly dangerous and cannot be allowed to escape does not make him someone who cannot be managed by group pressures within a secure environment. Inmates managed in small groups and involved in aspects of the management process of their own environment generate beneficial influences and good communication can occur on any scale. The personal growth process has to be directed at the individual inmate accepting complete responsibility for his actions and as a result doing something about changing himself for the better. This in turn implies that the staff are willing to cooperate. Staff of all grades are reasonable people and will cooperate when adequate and relevant explanations are given. The prison then becomes inmate-orientated and the facilities provided for their management in the above contexts may then be used within the constraints of finance and security.

It is perfectly possible to have effective security and to treat inmates as responsible human beings (with the expectation that they will not necessarily live up to that hope). Grendon Prison does excellent work and has a very good security record despite the fact that it is run as a therapeutic community with a proportion of high-risk prisoners in it.

If such a society was gradually developed over a period in a penal institution certain facilities for individual change would have to be available. Examples are individual psychotherapy or counselling, behavioural therapy, group and community meetings, gestalt, and all the other facilitating environments to help men and women effectively to take responsibility for themselves and then decide on their future lives.

If such an environment and such facilities are provided, the question of effective support in the outside world and an effective leaving process become important.

Prison Riots or Mutinies

Though mutinies occur with unexpected suddenness, their growth normally can be likened to a certain kind of forest fire which burns in two distinct stages. Stage 1 consists of a period of days or even weeks when the undergrowth is smouldering and only the conscientious forester observes the danger. Stage 2 occurs when with apparent suddenness the whole forest bursts into flame and, temporarily, the situation is out of hand.

The governor, having his ear to the ground, takes note of Stage 1 and, taking appropriate action, prevents Stage 2 from developing. A mutiny is never without leaders, though in Stage 2 these are invariably in the background and never in the vulnerable positions where they are likely to be identified, accused and punished themselves. The governor will have his eye on these during Stage 1, and by judicious alterations in labour or locations, or by segregation, will prevent them congregating and so avoid Stage 2. Trouble-makers on their own can be contained in prison, but they form a danger when several are together. Consequently, action in good time is vital. However well Stage 2 is handled, a mutiny is likely to be almost irreparably damaging to staff-prisoner relationships. Never was the old adage, "prevention is better than cure" more applicable than in the case of mutiny.

Most prisoners prefer the quiet life and will only take part in a mutiny with considerable reluctance. Consequently, in the event of mutiny the vital principle in dealing with it is to endeavour to separate as quickly as possible the real trouble-makers from those who are only taking part so that they will not lose face with their fellows. It will greatly help if, as a beginning, a trickle of persons can be persuaded to move out of the mutinous situation, and once some are on the move, others will be likely to follow. It is possible that in the event of a sit-down workshop strike, for example, persons being called for visits or for a bathing parade might provide sufficient initial movement to help others to move who are only supporting the strike because they do not have the courage to do otherwise.

Governors will normally receive some warning of a mutiny even if only of a few minutes, e.g. there will be an interval of some minutes between the time they receive a message that a particular workshop is mutinous until the moment they reach the workshop to deal with the situation. These few moments are vital and it may well be wise to delay entry to the shop concerned for a few minutes so as to think out clearly how the situation may best be handled. If an officer from the shop can quickly put the governor into the picture, suggesting suspected ring-leaders, this will prove vital. For the governor to be armed with a few names is invaluable, for if there is a complete deadlock, he only has to say he wants a word with the following and either call them outside or tell the rest to go to their cells while he talks to them. This shows he knows more than they think and gives the less courageous a chance to move without losing face.

It is important that a governor has the reputation of being fair and having the best interests of staff and inmates at heart.

The Prison Department and also the press office must be kept informed if the situation covers an hour or more. A prolonged siege as opposed to force, would involve the cutting off of vital supplies such as food, water, heating and lighting facilities.

The media thrive on sensationalism and consequently may unintentionally militate against a satisfactory solution.

The Home Secretary introduced a Bill in the Parliamentary Session

(1991) to the effect that prison riot is a criminal offence which could carry a maximum prison sentence of ten years.

Lord Woolf's Report on Prison Disturbances (1991) indicated that at the termination of a major incident within an establishment, the following procedure to deal with the surrender of prisoners will be adopted:

The Commander will appoint a Surrender Area Manager (normally of the rank of Principal Officer) who will:

(a) Establish the identity of each individual prisoner who is surrendering by name and prison number and will initiate Part A of the Individual Incident Log.

(b) Detail two uniformed members of staff, who have not been members of any Control & Restraint Team to escort the prisoner to a designated search area.

(c) Ensure that sufficient property bags and seals have been made available from Reception to hold items of prisoners' property and, where necessary, items of clothing.

(d) Ensure that all items of clothing, whether prison issue or civilian clothing, are itemized and searched.

(e) Ensure that all items of personal property are placed in a property bag and sealed in the presence of the prisoner, the seal number being annotated on the property list. He or she will also ensure that all property removed from the prisoner is correctly stored in the Reception area in the appropriate property box.

(f) Ensure that the prisoner is allocated to appropriate accommodation (preferably cellular if available) and that that has been kitted out to the specified scale with sleeping, washing and toilet utensils.

(g) Ensure that there are sufficient full sets of clothing available to issue to prisoners who have had theirs removed as a result of the "strip-search".

(h) When and where appropriate, liaise with the Senior Catering Officer on duty to ensure that sufficient meals are available to feed each prisoner who has surrendered.

(i) Ensure that the Individual Incident Log is fully completed prior to its being filed in the prisoner's Form 1150/2050.

The "On-Call Doctor" will:

(a) Medically examine each prisoner so as to assess the extent of any injuries or marks and ensure that a Form 213 is raised, as appropriate.
(b) Record details of any treatment which may be prescribed.
(c) Sign and date the relevant section of Part A of the Individual Incident Log and, where appropriate, make comment.

Arrangements should be made for a member of the Board of Visitors to:

(a) See each individual prisoner who has surrendered.
(b) Sign and date Part B of the Individual Incident Log and, where appropriate, make comment.

A Senior Manager of a rank no lower than Governor 4 will:

(a) See each individual prisoner who has surrendered and ensure that:
   (i)   Each prisoner has been medically examined and been seen by a member of the Board of Visitors:
   (ii) Where appropriate, has had a meal;
   (iii) Each prisoner is in possession of a complete set of clothing, having been returned after the "strip search" or being a newly issued set of prison clothing.
(b) Sign and date Part C of the Individual Incident Log and, where appropriate, make comment.

The Government is represented by the Home Secretary.

Four regional directors for the custodial facilities in England and Wales are now located at Woking, Bristol, Manchester and Birmingham. They will be replaced by 15 area managers at the end of September 1990. Most prison governors are not in favour of this re-organization on the grounds that it could delay decision-making and decisive action. The custodial facilities referred to above do not include persons held in police custody.

Registered Medical Practitioners

It is here appropriate to make some comments on the role of registered medical practitioners in Her Majesty's Prison Service. Full-time prison medical officers are employed as established civil servants and may be promoted to senior and principal medical officers on the basis of work records and post-graduate degrees, especially in psychological medicine which is essential for medical officers in prisons which serve courts. Senior medical officers have statutory responsibility for the physical and mental health of inmates who come under their care. Part-time doctors who are usually general practitioners also give valuable support. Forensic psychiatrists are primarily National Health Service appointees with the agreement of the Home Office. They divide their time between penal and NHS psychiatric institutions. Consequently, they are part-timers as far as the prison service is concerned. A certain amount of antagonism exists between full-time prison medical officers and forensic psychiatrists and elements of competition for authority sadly exist. This type of situation makes a difficult working environment even more difficult.

The above remarks do not necessarily apply to all full-time prison medical officers and forensic psychiatrists. Full-time prison medical officers need a sound knowledge of general medicine, psychiatry, administration, the criminal law and the art of giving evidence in court must also be mastered by those who work in local (Remand) prisons. Full-time prison medical officers are conscious of the fact that, at times, they have little option but to skillfully divide their loyalties between "grass roots" personnel and their superiors and hope for the best.

Prisoners suffering from serious physical illness or injury are sent to local hospitals for treatment.

Prison medical officers have the authority to request National Health Service psychiatrists to examine any inmate of a prison or young offender institution with a view to implementing Sections 37, 47 or 48 of the Mental Health Act (1983). The medical officer must first be satisfied that reasonable grounds exist to suspect mental disorder. An article in the *British Medical Association News Review* (March 1990) indicated that "many prisons do not have access to a qualified psychiatrist". This is quite inaccurate. During many years full service I have not encountered a single instance where a psychiatrist did not promptly respond to a verbal or written request for examination of an inmate of any institution.

It has also been suggested that the Prison Medical Service should be transferred to the authority of the NHS. However, disciplinary problems could arise and problems concerning equipment, medications and finance do not occur in the Prison Medical Service. Furthermore, the prospect of prisoners being treated by overworked NHS doctors, deserves consideration.

Incidentally, medications are *not* specifically used by prison medical officers merely to control mentally disordered inmates. Control is an integral part of treatment and practised on a vastly greater scale by general medical practitioners and psychiatrists in the community, but rarely publicized. Such medications are sometimes prescribed for inmates by visiting psychiatrists.

The Prison Officers' Association deals with all matters affecting the working conditions of its members. Staff at "grass roots" level sometimes feel unappreciated and often in the "firing line", believing with some justification that they are at times subjected to undue criticism by their superiors, Members of Parliament, penal reformers and the public in general. I have heard the phrase "we are the keepers of the public conscience" used on more than one occasion. Staff are often of the opinion that critics tend not to appreciate the very difficult conditions under which they work and that criticisms tend to come from outsiders who have never actually worked in penal institutions. However, staff also understand that such criticisms may be made with the object of improving the lot of inmates rather than to score political points. Prison officers do not receive sufficient credit for tempering discipline with understanding of inmates.

Probation officers assist courts with social enquiry reports and supervise offenders (including those who are mentally disordered) in the community. They also try to alter community circumstances which may have persistently militated against offenders and influenced their re-offending.

Magistrates visit regularly to inspect conditions and help inmates with legal problems. They also adjudicate where appropriate, on certain offences committed by inmates. Police are called in to investigate serious offences.

Prisons and young offender institutions may not be visited by representatives of outside authorities without Home Office permission.

There is at present a shortage of about 2,000 staff of all grades in prison and young offender institutions in the UK.

Hospital officers should be encouraged to become General Registered Nurses and they should also be given the opportunity to gain psychiatric experience at the local mental hospitals on a rota basis, as part of their normal duties. Full-time prison medical officers should also assist at least once weekly at a clinic held at a local NHS psychiatric facility.

The following extract from the Report of Her Majesty's Chief Inspector of Prisons and his colleagues for 1988, reads as follows:

"We were impressed by the quality and dedication of staff in all the establishments. We found, however, wide variations in conditions, regime resources, staffing levels and the use made of open prisons. The extent to which some establishments can successfully absorb high proportions of young, short-term inmates coupled with the increasing life sentence population suggests that there might well be scope for increasing the number of open establishments. The differences between the male and female establishments were principally those of staffing levels and costs. It should also be said that the women's prisons are so few and so scattered that the chances of the inmates being far removed from home and family are high. We wondered if there was some scope for developing one or more prisons for men and women, as has been done in Denmark and the U.S.A, for example, for many years. What we found lacking more than anything was a coherent national policy. To enable open prisons to play their full part in the national system, extra care will be needed on matching staff and other resources to the kind of inmate population most likely to benefit."

This summary is interesting for two reasons:

(i)   the idea of having men and women in the same prison but obviously segregated, and

(ii)   there is no coherent national policy for the prison service in all its aspects. For instance, could correct and consistent advice be given by a senior member of the Prisons Board in London to a governor in a riot prison situated perhaps several hundred miles from the capital? "Objective" advice given at a distance could be regarded as of dubious value.

Lord Woolf's Report on Prison Disturbances (1991) made the following recommendations:

1.   Closer co-operation between the different parts of the Criminal Justice System. For this purpose a national forum and local committees should be established.

2.   More visible leadership of the Prison Service by a Director General who is and is seen to be the operational head and in day-to-day charge of the Service. To achieve this there should be a published "compact" or "contract" given by Ministers to the

Director General of the Prison Service, who should be responsible for the performance of that "contract" and publicly answerable for the day-to-day operations of the Prison Service.

3. Increased delegation of responsibility to governors of establishments.

4. An enhanced role for prison officers.

5. A "compact" or "contract" for each prisoner setting out the prisoner's expectations and responsibilities in the prison in which he or she is held.

6. A national system of Accredited Standards, with which, in time, each prison establishment would be required to comply.

7. A new Prison Rule that no establishment should hold more prisoners than is provided for in its certified normal level of accommodation, with provisions for Parliament to be informed if exceptionally there is to be a material departure from that rule.

8. A public commitment from Ministers setting a timetable to provide access to sanitation for all inmates at the earliest practicable date not later than February 1996.

9. Better prospects for prisoners to maintain their links with families and the community through more visits and home leaves and through being located in community prisons as near to their homes as possible.

10. A division of prison establishments into small and more manageable and secure units.

11. A separate statement of purpose, separate conditions and generally a lower security categorization for remand prisoners.

12. Improved standards of justice within prisons involving the giving of reasons to a prisoner for any decision which materially and adversely affects him; a grievance procedure and disciplinary proceedings which ensure that the Governor deals with most matters under his present powers: relieving Boards of Visitors of their adjudicatory role; and providing for final access to an independent Complaints Adjudicator.

Custody, Care and Justice: White Paper, (1991)

Home Secretary Kenneth Baker published a White Paper, Custody, Care and Justice: The Way Ahead for the Prison Service in England and Wales, cmd 1647, *Home Office Publication, September 1991*, which charts a course for the Prison Service for the rest of this century and into the next.

It sets out proposals to provide more effective measures for security and control, more constructive relationships between prisoners and staff and more stimulating and useful programmes for prisoners.

The White Paper identifies 12 key priorities and describes a challenging and far-reaching programme of change in accordance with those priorities.

The proposals focus on three key areas:

Custody. Effective physical security and a well-trained staff are essential to keep in custody those committed to prison by the courts. Maintaining security and control must be based on the quality of relationships between prisoners and staff. It must also provide prisoners with an active and worthwhile day in a secure environment as close to their homes as possible.

Care. Staff have a responsibility also for the care of prisoners which must be demonstrated through the programmes and conditions provided.

Justice. Prisoners should be consulted and given explanations for decisions which affect them and should be required to show responsibility for what they do. Disciplinary procedures must be effective and fair.

The challenge for change presented by this programme builds on the recommendations of the Woolf Report, *Prison Disturbances*, April 1990. cmd 1456. The White Paper confirms the government's acceptance of the central propositions in the Report: that security and control must be kept in balance with justice and humanity and that each must be set at the right level. It has accepted the direction set by the recommendations in the Report and its principal proposals.

The White Paper is divided into ten chapters:

The Work of the Prison Service. This chapter puts the work of the Prison Service in context with the rest of the criminal justice system, sets out the role of the Service and details specific priorities for a programme for the Prison Service in the years ahead.

It includes a proposal for a national forum for the criminal justice system – the Criminal Justice Consultative Council – to promote better understanding, co-operation and co-ordination in the administration of the criminal justice system.

Security, Control and Incident Management. The proposals have two main objectives: to provide appropriate security within which active and relevant regimes can be developed, and to ensure that prison and headquarters staff can respond quickly and effectively to any incident.

This chapter sets out the government's intention to introduce a new offence of prison mutiny and to increase the maximum penalty for aiding a prison escape. It also proposes new security and contingency planning manuals, with annual security audits and regular contingency planning exercises.

The Structure of the Prison Service. This chapter confirms that the prison service should remain directly accountable to Ministers, with clear delegation to governors in establishments. It aims to provide a prison service which is structured to give the best possible service to the public.

The proposals include the publication, in May of each year, of a statement by the Home Secretary and the Director General setting out the annual objectives and resources of the Service.

The Prison Service's Staff. The proposals point the way the government wants the prison service staff to be developed, recruited, trained and employed in the future. It highlights the need for a change in industrial relations in the prison service.

Measures proposed include a new staff handbook setting out the standards for the care and treatment of prisoners and the introduction of a Prison Officer Development Scheme to provide talented staff with more attractive career prospects.

Management of the Prison Population. This chapter sets out the prison service's aims for the management of the prison population. It gives high priority to reducing overcrowding. It recognizes the advantage of locating prisoners near to their homes in community prisons but notes that some prisoners (e.g. sex offenders) may need special allocation which takes precedence over this objective.

The chapter proposes that, as a first step, the prison service will identify a number of new and existing local prisons which could be converted to multi-functional community prisons and other prisons to be grouped into community clusters. It also proposes the introduction of a security classification for remand prisoners to allow more informed judgments of the degree of risk posed by each prisoner.

Standards in Prison. These proposals establish clear priorities on standards and recognize the obligation to provide prisoners with decent as well as secure conditions.

The measures include the introduction of a code of standards on the provision of services to prisoners, encompassing accommodation, food, clothing, hygiene and regime facilities and improvement to health care services.

Programmes for Prisoners. The proposals in this chapter aim to provide a fully active and demanding day for prisoners – relevant to their needs and the reasons why they are in prison. The chapter recognizes the particular needs of unconvicted prisoners arising from their separate legal status. Proposals cover work, access to education and training, links with the family and programmes for certain groups of prisoners with special needs.

Proposals include separate Prison Rules for unconvicted prisoners, statements of the facilities available for prisoners and what is expected of them in return, more openness and consultation with prisoners and increasing prisoners' pay.

Complaints and Discipline. These proposals should ensure that complaints and disciplinary matters are resolved in a fair, just and proportionate manner and so help to provide improved relations in prison establishments.

Proposals include relieving Boards of Visitors of their disciplinary powers and establishing an independent appeal body – a Complaints Adjudicator – to consider disciplinary cases and complaints which have exhausted normal procedures within the prison service.

Relations with other Parts of the Criminal Justice System. These proposals will improve the exchange of information between the prison service and the other parts of the criminal justice system. They will develop closer links with the probation service and other criminal justice services.

The measures include the extension of bail information schemes to all probation areas, as resources allow, and increasing the availability of bail beds in the independent sector from April 1992.

Prison Rules and Legislation. In order to take the prison service into the next century, revised legislation would provide an opportunity for

Parliament to consider the powers required and what is expected of the Service.

The government plans a fundamental revision of the statutory framework for the prison service and a reformulation and consolidation of the Prison Rules.

Finally, written evidence has been given by a prison officer to Lord Woolf's inquiry into prison disturbances. The officer works at H.M. Prison Strangeways, Manchester. He alleged that prisoners with grudges against staff could order attacks on off-duty prison officers through an organization known as the Prisoners' Liberation Army. The usual cause of grudge is when a prisoner is put on governor's report by an officer, for indiscipline.

Prison Escapes

Brixton prison is 173 years old and the escape of two dangerous men on 7 July 1991 has caused much heart-searching as to causes and prevention. The prisoners were remanded for trial. The police are understandably angry because they now have the responsibility of finding and re-arresting these men. A report was submitted to the Director General of the Prison Service for England and Wales at the Home Office, in December 1990 by Judge Stephen Tumim who is the Chief Inspector of Prisons. This report clearly indicated security defects for high-risk Category "A" prisoners at Brixton which now contains about 60 such persons. The Home Office was not under statutory obligation to implement Judge Tumim's recommendations. He will hold a further inquiry as a result of these escapes.

Category "A" prisoners on remand have always presented security problems. Their visits cannot, under normal circumstances, be restricted because they are unconvicted. Furthermore, they are located in prisons which serve courts and are therefore called local prisons. They are sent to non-local long-term prisons after sentence and escape is more difficult because of increased security, restriction on visits and much lower discharge and reception rates. The average weekly number of prisoners received into Brixton in 1990 was about 600 and the number released weekly (directly or via the courts) was approximately the same. This is called the "turnover" rate. The population on any particular day is about 1,000 and the prison is about 50 per cent overcrowded. Efficient supervision of visits is obviously vital. Metal detectors would help to prevent smuggling of weapons by visitors yet only 34 of 124 custodial institutions in England and Wales are equipped with them. X-Ray facilities in reception and visiting areas would be similarly helpful but they cost £20,000 each and they are not available in the above institutions. Category "A" prisoners should be strip-searched after each visit. Pieces of weapons may be concealed in hollowed-out heels of shoes or the centres of books and sent by post to prisons where they are re-assembled by inmates. Frequent routine searches of cells are also essential. Electronic locking of prison cells would make escape more difficult by eliminating the use of keys. Prison staff and their families may be threatened and even blackmailed with the object of influencing them to smuggle weapons, drugs or messages to inmates and such dangers would be increased in Northern Ireland. I hasten to add that prison staff are honourable, dedicated and reliable. Frequent routine searches of cells is also essential. A hand grenade was found in a cell in Brixton prison some two days after the above escapes.

The Prison Officers' Association complain that staff shortages prevent officers performing their duties efficiently. However, the Prison Department of the Home Office indicates that the official capacity of all 124 custodial (including prison) establishments in England and Wales is 44,180 but the numbers of prisoners in custody in July 1991 was 45,171 which is 3,700 fewer than in 1987 and allegedly there are now 4,000 additional officers to deal with them. I should prefer not to take sides in this matter. Over-crowding is obviously the problem.

We live in a liberal society and consequently restriction of visits to remand prisoners and the arming of prison and police officers for the purpose of escorting potentially dangerous prisoners to and from courts would not be tolerated.

Apart from increasing staff and provision of more suitable equipment, other suggestions have been made to prevent escapes. Category "A" prisoners both on remand and sentenced, should be located at the new Belmarsh prison in South-East London, about six miles from Brixton. It has a self-contained unit for high-risk inmates and the prison now has accommodation for 380 and will eventually care for 800. It has also been suggested that prison governors should wear uniform and that senior ex-army officers should be appointed as governors. I would agree with this recommendation, having served in the army for some years. However, they should not replace all civilian prison governors and should perhaps take charge of prisons where high risk prisoners are detained whether on remand or sentenced. The Inspector of Prisons intends to make regular unannounced visits to Category "A" prisons in order to check security.

Perhaps special prisons should be provided for the exclusive custody of remanded and sentenced Category "A" prisoners but those sentenced should be kept in separate sections from the unsentenced. Remand periods should be reduced especially for potentially dangerous persons. Overcrowding of our prisons is a menace especially as some 60 per cent of inmates are not dangerous to the public in the sense of potential physically harming them. The United Kingdom has the highest prison population of all the countries in Western Europe and much more use should be made of alternatives to prison such as attachment of earnings, suspended sentences, conditional discharges and probation orders for petty offenders. The morale of prison officers is now at a very low ebb and can only be helped by reducing the prison population and increasing the number of prison officers.

Prison chapels deserve special mention as they are regarded by prisoners as the best places in which to start prison riots and escape attempts. I spent 24 hours with other officials in a chapel of a certain prison in the North of England some years ago during the course of a riot. We were waiting for the surrender of prisoners who had barricaded themselves in a part of the chapel which had a gallery. Weapons can be hidden in the chapel more easily than in other parts of the prison. Prison chapels are outside high-security surveillance areas and the present tendency to allow high- and low-risk prisoners to mingle at church services is a definite security risk. Communal services should be held for those of all religious persuasions but the services for Category "A" prisoners should be held separately, meaning at different times from those held for other prisoners. This arrangement means that high-risk inmates could be more efficiently observed by adequate staff. The alternative would be to discontinue religious services which would cause offence.

Basically, adequate security depends on psychological attitudes.

James *et al* (1991) described a scheme whereby two psychiatrists attended an inner London magistrates' court (Clerkenwell) one day per week in order to examine and report on offenders for whom psychiatric reports had been requested by the court. Those appearing in court on days when the psychiatrists were absent were remanded in Brixton prison until the day of their next visit. Reports were made to the court on the same day and direct admission to a psychiatric facility (on the basis of recommendations under the Mental Health Act 1983) was implemented when possible. All necessary reports from the various other relevant agencies were available for the psychiatrists.

This scheme reduced the waiting time for admission to the relevant mental hospital (on the basis of hospital orders) from 50.8 days for those remanded to Brixton prison hospital for psychiatric examination to 8.7 days.

Comment. This scheme is admirable as it reduces the number of remands in prison and as a result reduces *overcrowding*. However, it is only fair to state that harsh criticisms of prison hospitals are not always justified. Furthermore, suicides are not unknown in mental hospitals and conditions in these hospitals are usually but not invariably ideal. The scheme would not be suitable for those remanded to higher courts on serious charges as more prolonged observation would be necessary.

Reports dealing with the services for mentally disordered offenders were published in late 1991. They were based on investigations undertaken jointly by the Home Office and the Department of Health. Recommendations were made to the effect that defendants should not be remanded to the hospitals of penal institutions for psychiatric reports. Obviously those who represent an immediate and serious danger to the public would need to be remanded to adequately secure psychiatric facilities which would, it is hoped, exist in the relevant court area.

Recommendations of the Tumim Inquiry, 1991

1. That the Director General should hold urgently an enquiry into the workings of DOC, in particular as to analysis of information received, internal communications with the Category "A" Unit and otherwise, and communications and responsibilities between Governors, Area Managers and the Directorate of Custody (DOC).

2. The Director General should review the current policy of not classifying remand prisoners as exceptional risk which would require them to be held in a Special Secure Unit, and also review the practice of treating high-risk and standard-risk prisoners the same.

3. That the Director General should produce or cause to be produced contingency plans for duties by staff when a gun or other weapon is found in a prison, and set up a training scheme accordingly.

4. That Category "A" prisoners be not held in HMP Brixton until and unless the security provisions recommended in this report are fully implemented.

5. That the gateway through the perimeter at Brixton into the works yard be secured or blocked so that no further escape may take place through it.

6. That there should be a review of the operation of the Emergency Control Room at Brixton, and arrangements made for regular and frequent training and testing both of equipment and of practice.

7. During normal working hours the Duty Governor should be available throughout the establishment and within reach at all times by UHF radio.

8. That searching and checking baggage at Brixton be re-organized and in particular:

(a) X-ray examinations be made of all parcels and baggage coming into the prison by mail or otherwise.
(b) all visitors and staff be subjected to random searching and examination by metal detector;
(c) all such machinery for searching be regularly tested and the manner of using it checked.

9. That the Area Manager should urgently inquire into the adequacy of the dog provision and of the manner in which they are used.

10. That in so far as Category "A" prisoners are held at Brixton, they are held on the wing and not permitted to attend chapel or leave the wing save under the specific directions of the Governor.

11. That a Standard Performance Test be applied to the CCTV system at Brixton and an Operational Requirement be defined.

12. That procedures between Brixton prison and the police should be regularly tested and checked.

The Psychiatric Rehabilitation of Offenders

General Principles
Following the introduction of modern drug treatments in the 1950s, psychiatric rehabilitation has become an increasingly important and skilled branch of medical work. Certain general principles have become widely accepted.

Almost any psychiatric patient can be rehabilitated if enough skill, effort and resources are put into the endeavour. Relapses, however, are common and a long-term monitoring system is essential with access to further shorter periods of reablement.

The work itself has distinctive features. Like virtually all psychiatric work, it is multi-disciplinary and here the role of the doctor is less dominant. The main burden of day-by-day work falls upon psychiatric nurses, social workers and occupational therapists. Psychologists, too, are important in planning programmes and monitoring progress.

Despite these limitations, the role of the doctor is vital in all aspects, including assessment, planning, treatment and monitoring progress.

Rehabilitation work tends to differ from traditional psychiatric treatment in that it has a wider concept of the treatment process. It includes:

(a)   orthodox medical treatment;
(b)   wide retraining in social and inter-personal skills;
(c)   intensive training in daily living skills including, for example, budgeting, cooking, laundry work, etc.;
(d)   work-orientated training with a view to future employment,
(e)   social work input to help with housing, access to local authority services etc.

The work is difficult but rewarding.
Tumim (Dec. 1992) also reported on Long Lartin Prison, Worcestershire. This high security prison houses 21 Category "A" prisoners. "Hard" drugs such as heroin and alcohol were indulged in even in the presence of prison officers until the later part of 1992. Racial problems also existed there. The authorities have now allegedly restored order. Crisis point was reached when the P.O.A. and management became involved in a dispute and as a result the workshops were closed meaning that inmates were locked in their cells for most of each 24-hour period.

Rehabilitation of Offenders
There is not much evidence of decreasing recidivism in persistent offenders following psychiatric treatment. However, there are some successes and certainly there can be measurable improvements in general personality functioning. Taken together with the natural maturing of the personality that occurs in many as they get older, treatment is worthwhile.

Rehabilitation of offenders takes place in a number of different settings. These include:

(1) Prisons. Loss of freedom is not always a disadvantage. Without the distractions of street life, in theory all the offenders energies can be channelled into the treatment process. Open prisons share a particular advantage here in that living conditions are less oppressive and the advantages of a different life-style are more readily apparent to the offender.

Prison staff, medical and non-medical, often do not have sufficient training and experience in psychiatric work to be really effective in this role. In prisons, too, there is often a conflict in philosophical terms between the concept of punishment and confinement on the one hand and that of treatment on the other.

Changes in the organisation and staffing of prison services are inevitable. From the treatment point of view it would be desirable to organize the supervision of prisoners into smaller groups with more civilizing features, in individual cell accommodation and with closer links with local communities as well as with families.

In many cases, it is possible to avoid imprisonment by means of suspended sentences, probation supervision and other alternatives. Offenders with obvious psychiatric illness should not be placed in ordinary prisons. For young offenders, too, every effort should be made to find an alternative to a custodial sentence.

(2) The Special Hospitals. These are 'hospitals' that offer intense security for highly dangerous offenders with either psychotic illness or psychopathic disorder and yet can offer highly sophisticated psychiatric treatment over a period of years.

Working with carefully selected serious offenders, the results achieved by the special hospitals are commendable. They have developed a sophisticated follow-up and monitoring service in the community.

(3) Grendon Prison. This is a pioneering endeavour where the prison is run as a therapeutic community as far as this is possible. Extensive use is made of group-therapy techniques, enabling offenders to appreciate the effect some of their actions have on fellow inmates. Research shows that major improvements in personality functioning occur but that, unfortunately, there is no reduction in the subsequent rate of re-offending.

(4) Mental Hospitals. Many offenders are treated in neighbourhood psychiatric hospitals. Many are petty offenders but some are more serious offenders, including murderers.

Some are treated under compulsory court orders whilst others are treated on an informal basis. Some detained patients have restriction orders imposed, limiting the scope of the responsible medical officer to organize treatment in the way he would choose. Such orders are understandably imposed by Judges because of fears of further offences, including violence, if the convicted person is discharged too soon. From the point of view of the hospital treatment, this can, however, lead to a frustrating situation for both staff and the patient where further progress in treatment is not possible and indeed, the frustration may lead to a deterioration in the patient's condition.

The rundown of traditional mental hospitals in the U.K. has had an increasing effect in making those hospitals unable or unwilling to accept court patients that they successfully treated a decade ago. This is sometimes perfectly justifiable because of lesser resources in these doomed hospitals and because more secure wards are no longer available within them. It is also true that sometimes staff attitudes can be negative and unco-operative in accepting offenders into hospitals to the frustration of the courts.

(5) Secure Units. Because of the difficulty in having offenders treated in district psychiatric hospitals and units, new secure units are being introduced in each health region in the UK. Special Government finance is available to build and staff them. They are staffed with specially trained forensic psychiatrists, nurses and other therapists. They are designed to cope with those offenders who are too disturbed, too violent or too dangerous for the ordinary open psychiatric ward and yet need psychiatric treatment.

Some are run as locked units while others rely on high staffing with skilled staff for security. They are intended to be highly selective, taking only a small minority of offenders with special needs. They should fill a gap between what is provided in ordinary psychiatric units as opposed to the special hospitals.

(6) Community Treatment. This is widespread, especially for minor offenders and is carried out by the staff of district psychiatric services.

Treatment can be either on an in-patient or an out-patient basis. It is often carried out in close collaboration with probation officers. An added safeguard (that is seldom used in practice) is a Guardianship Order under section 7 of the Mental Health Act. Under such an order there are a number of provisions:

a) a patient can be directed to live at a specified place;
b) he can be required to attend for medical treatment at a specific time and place (including treatment by nurses and paramedics and attendance at Day Care);
c) it gives doctors, other medical workers and social workers guaranteed access to the patient at his place of residence.

If patients do not conform to the terms of a Guardianship Order it is in practice hard to enforce compliance.

A Guardianship Order has to be applied for by the Local Authority Social Services Department. These departments often see guardianship as a frustrating and toothless power that is difficult to implement and are reluctant to apply for such an order.

Most offenders in this category are supervised by Probation Officers themselves without recourse to back up from psychiatric services. The probation service has become increasingly effective in such work.

Community treatment is the ideal outcome for minor offenders, enabling family relationships, employment and other community links to be retained (and indeed developed) whilst other treatment proceeds.

Background characteristics of offenders

Traditionally adverse social circumstances have been considered important in causing delinquency in an individual. Such a view has now been largely abandoned although most would recognize that social circumstances are important in influencing the course of delinquency.

It is difficult to prove an association between poor housing and delinquency or between unemployment and delinquency. Traditionally crime in young people has been linked to such factors as poor parental example, broken homes, parents with criminal records, poor parental supervision, poverty, poor models of socialization, etc. However, research results are not clear-cut.

What is abundantly clear is that most offenders are young and are male. The peak ages for offenders found guilty or cautioned is 15 for males and

14 for females. Males commit five times more offences than females, 10 times more violent offences, 30 times more burglaries and 13 times more offences of criminal damage.

Rehabilitation is therefore particularly important in the case of young male offenders. Despite the lack of a clear-cut causal link, adequate attention should be paid to the social circumstances of offenders.

Assessment

Most of the assessment of the backgrounds of offenders is carried out by probation officers. A minority come to psychiatrists, especially those where psychiatric illness is suspected.

The aims of assessment are:

a)   To identify the disabilities and weaknesses of offenders. Attention is paid to such factors as poor education, poor family background, lack of work skills, poor intelligence, unstable family or marital relationships, persistent offending, etc.

b)   To identify strengths or potential strengths in an individual. Important factors are intelligence, education, motivation, family links, work-record, ambitions etc.

c)   An in-depth evaluation of the psychiatric state and of the personality of the offender.

d)   To try and work out a proposed package of care for the individual with a programme of implementation that would appear to be reasonable to the court.

e)   To outline and enlist the multi-disciplinary care that would be needed.

f)   To build a monitoring element into the proposed treatment in as scientific a manner as possible. This would include regular targets for achievement within a time scale as assessed by a multi-disciplinary team.

Assessments should be as realistic as possible but in such an inexact science as the rehabilitation of offenders, in a number of cases only a trial run will indicate whether rehabilitation is possible.

Treatment and after-care techniques

The first requisite is staff of adequate quality and extensive experience. They need special qualities of motivation and sufficient patience to make a relationship with these difficult people. Professional attitudes should be non-judgmental.

Treatment needs to be widely based and should include:

a) A psycho-therapeutic element including counselling and a re-educative role. The developing relationship with the therapist is in itself a powerful treatment tool.

b) An attempt at social rehabilitation designed to make the offender fit back into society in an acceptable manner. Group techniques are valuable in improving interactions with others. The offender will need to learn new ways of coping with problems and the stress they induce.

c) Work-based re-training is extremely important in raising self-esteem.

d) Physical training can be very helpful in young people who have been following unhealthy life-styles. It can help to improve the self-image and to develop pride in body and personality.

e) Close work with families and spouses is vital in re-integrating the offender in society.

f) Medical treatment including psycho-active drugs and other physical treatments.

The aftercare and follow-up of offenders is essential in reducing the chances of re-offending.

After-care is largely carried out by probation officers with some of the work in selective cases being done by doctors and other health professionals.

It is important that the offender change his whole life-style and that he move out of the delinquent sub-culture.

A range of different types of living accommodation may be of crucial importance. For married men, adequate modern housing may make all the difference to the offenders' adjustment. For the single, divorced or separated man, such options as probation hostels or approved land lady placements can give the socially isolated offender the roots and community support he needs.

Violence

The control and assessment of violence is particularly important in the psychiatric rehabilitation of offenders. Violence may be directed towards others or towards one self – in fact the two are often inversely related. Violence may also be directed at property, at social networks or towards the environment.

In handling violence, treatment is based on three foundations:

a)   psycho-therapeutic treatment;
b)   the type of regime and environment in which the offender is handled;
c)   the use of psychotropic drugs.

Psycho-therapeutic treatment is especially important and may be either individual treatment or by means of group-based treatment where the social consequences of violence can emerge more clearly.

Violent patients may be easier to handle in hospital than in prison because control is exercised in a different way and the tendency to rebel against rules and discipline may be avoided. Undoubtedly many offenders do not fit easily into any structured organization and if security conditions permit, out-patient treatment has advantages. In more dangerous cases the best regime is to allow as much freedom as possible within a secure outer perimeter. In a psychiatric setting drug treatment can be very helpful. Anti-psychotic drugs like the butyrophenones or phenothiazines either by mouth or by injection are most commonly used. Benzodiazepines can be used too but here one must balance the calming effect against the possible dis-inhibiting effects of the drug. The prophylactic mood-regulating properties of lithium treatment have also proved effective, especially in those with an underlying instability of affect.

Violence often has a relationship to the unhealthy use of alcohol or drugs and control of these tendencies may be vital.

Schizophrenics show more violence than the general public especially those with paranoid delusions and treatment of the psychoses is vital. Manic patients are often violent and prophylaxis of the mood swings is the key to control.

Sexual offences
This comprises a relatively small part of the range of violent offences. In some such offences, the sexual element is more important and the prognosis is relatively better – e.g. in voyeurism, indecent exposure and obscene telephone calls. In other cases, the violence is the more important component of the offence and the prognosis is more uncertain.

Such violent offences include rape, many cases of underage sex and some child molestation cases. Many offenders against children are non-criminal in other ways but have difficulty in making adult relationships. This can point the way to effective treatment. Psychological treatment is once again the cornerstone of treatment. The libido-suppresing drug cyproterone acetate is valuable in treating persistent offenders. It is helpful to have a proportion of female staff in treating male sexual offenders.

Continuing treatment and supervision is important as it helps to reduce the relapse rate.

Assessment of dangerousness

This is particularly difficult to achieve and it is a field in which medicine does not shine. In some subgroups the prognosis is easier to determine – e.g. the continuing dangerousness in cases of pathological jealousy.

Doctors are often asked for an opinion about the danger of further violence. An opinion is likely to be considered more valuable where the doctor has special experience in the field and has also had a close contact with the offender over a period of time. He should look for an increase in self-esteem and an improvement in inter-personal relationships in forming his opinion. In sexual cases, attention should be paid to changes in the strength of libido and to changes in the fantasy life of the offender.

In younger offenders and in those with a number of previous offences, the prognosis should be more guarded.

Arsonists

This comprises a very mixed group with wide variation in the personality disturbance accompanying the crime. Short term offenders seldom re-offend but in the case of long term offenders up to 20 per cent re-offend. There is a highly dangerous smaller group of persistent fire-setters.

In general arsonists are difficult to treat medically.

Special categories of offenders

Alcohol abuse

Treatment falls into two phases, an initial detoxification followed by efforts to promote long-term abstinence. The detoxification is the easier part of the treatment. Longer term abstinence can be facilitated in various ways – out-patient supervision, counselling, use of voluntary agencies such as Alcoholics Anonymous, and the use of drugs such as Disulfiram

(Antibuse).

The alcoholic then faces the long-term problem of rehabilitating himself in his social life, in his employment, in his physical health and in the psychological problems that so often remain. It is indeed a long road back to a productive life after stopping drinking but specialists in the field can produce surprisingly good results in many.

Drug Abuse

The treatment is broadly along the same lines as in alcohol abuse but the condition is much more serious. Detoxification takes longer and is much more difficult to control. Sometimes maintenance on a lower dose of drug is the best that can be achieved.

Time out in a residential hostel is very useful and should be accompanied by efforts to change the whole life-style of the offender. Long-term counselling is the basis of treatment. Drugs that act as "blocking" agents (e.g. Naltrexone) can be helpful. The programme of the voluntary body Narcotics Anonymous appeals to some.

Mental Handicap

The emphasis of rehabilitation has to be different because of the low level of intelligence. A greater emphasis is put on socialization, on developing domestic and occupational skills and particularly on pursuing further education. The mentally handicapped can learn but the time taken is much greater than in the ordinary offender. Great patience is needed.

Offences involving violence, arson or sexual misdemeanours need careful assessment because such offences are more often repetitive than in the case of offenders with mental illness.

Because of the lack of maturation and the poor self-control, long-term monitoring, even life-long monitoring may be necessary.

Brain-damaged offenders

This includes such conditions as Huntington's Chorea, brain trauma from various causes and senile and other forms of dementia. The brain damage is irreversible and in some cases progressive. In practical terms brain damage limits the effectiveness of rehabilitation programmes. The crimes are often relatively minor like shop-lifting and sexual exhibitionism but may include violence.

Psychopathic personality

This implies persistent anti-social behaviour dating back to pre-adolescence or early adolescence accompanied by an inability to learn from experience and by lack of feeling for others.

There is no evidence that medical treatment is effective. Despite this, about a quarter of patients in the special hospitals are psychopaths. Treatment suffers from the lack of a clear-cut philosophy with difficulty in defining objectives.

Borderline personality

These patients are characterized by impulsive behaviour, emotional instability, unstable relationships, a poor self-image together with psychotic episodes.

Medication, social therapy and psychotherapy form the basis of treatment. Treatment is difficult but the long-term prognosis is reasonable and certainly better than in schizophrenics.

Inadequate personality

Offenders of this sort are likely to need life-long support and help in managing their affairs. Often many caring agencies, both statutory and voluntary are involved. Sometimes placement in a hostel or group home may be necessary, perhaps combined with day-care.

Psycho-sexual disorders

This subject covers a wide range of conditions ranging from relatively mild offences such as voyeurism to serious crimes where sexuality may be accompanied by violence.

Assessment of general personality as well as of sexual functioning by a doctor experienced in the field is the first step, with treatment likely to be largely psycho-therapeutic. Diminishing the libido chemically with cyproterone is necessary in some more serious cases.

In most of the milder conditions, results of treatment are good but in cases where violence and repetition are involved the prognosis is much poorer.

Psychoses

Characteristically, schizophrenics are quiet and withdrawn people but investigations indicate that statistically they show more violent behaviour than the general population. Many respond well to psychotropic drugs, especially as far as "positive" symptoms like delusional ideas and hallucinatory experiences are concerned. A minority of patients – perhaps 15 per cent – are non-drug responders and their treatment is more difficult. In addition "negative" symptoms such as apathy, withdrawal and self-neglect do not respond well to drugs. They need the methods of traditional psychiatric rehabilitation to improve their level of functioning. Many, for example, are better off not living with close relatives. With appropriate rehabilitation virtually all can be settled in the community.

In the case of affective illness, treatment is usually both easier and more effective than in schizophrenia. However, when restored to normal health, there can often be a problem in coming to terms with the consequences of a crime committed when the mind was disturbed by illness.

Psychoneurosis
Where this is a factor in offending, treatment is largely psycho-therapeutic. Cooke (1992) studied the criminal records of 120 alleged offenders between 13 February 1985 and 17 February 1986. They had been diverted from the usual process of prosecution to a forensic psychiatric clinic where they had psychotherapy. These records were examined (on average) 31 months after the original assessment at the clinic. Only 30 (25 per cent) reoffended and their offences included four cases of shoplifting, 14 of breach of the peace, four were drunk and disorderly and two were sexual offenders. One may conclude that a good case can be made for treatments as 75 per cent did not reoffend.

The Home Secretary's Proposals for the Reorganization of the Probation Service:
The document – "Organizing Supervision and Punishment in the Community" (1990) indicated that the probation service would continue to operate as a local service but that this would take place within a centrally determined framework of objectives and accountability.

Some of the government's proposals would require primary legislation and the government intends to consult further on the detailed issues.

In summary the government has decided that:

1)   The service will remain locally structured and partly funded by local authorities for the time being. It will, however, operate within a framework of national standards for the main areas of probation service work.

2)   A tightly structured resource-planning mechanism will be set up

to ensure that the probation service operates effectively within a centrally determined framework of objectives and tasks.

3) Probation committees will be reformed to enable them to carry out their policy-making and budget management functions more effectively. The respective roles of probation committees and their chief officers will be clearly defined, the size of probation committees will be reduced, the proportion of magistrate members will be reduced and the membership base broadened.

4) New liaison arrangements will be set up between probation services, magistrates and Judges. The government will discuss with the service with the Judges and with magistrates how to enhance the role of probation liaison committed at magistrates' courts and to provide better opportunities for productive contact between the probation service and the judiciary. The government will also consider how to ensure more effective cooperation between the prison and the probation services.

5) Regional collaboration between services will be encouraged to ensure that the full range of community sentences can be available to the courts. In some cases, where this is justified, the government will encourage the amalgamation of smaller services which cannot effectively provide the full range of sentences on their own or the necessary degree of managerial support.

6) HM Inspectorate of Probation will be put on a statutory basis under provisions in the Criminal Justice Bill. It will continue with its work of inspecting the efficiency and effectiveness of probation services, of providing advice on senior appointments and on training. In addition it will take on new duties of inspecting the work of the voluntary and private sectors with the probation service.

7) An amendment to the Criminal Justice Bill will be introduced to give the Secretary of State power to initiate default procedures in respect of any probation committee which seriously or persistently fails to comply with any duty prescribed by a statute or rule. This will provide the Secretary of State with a last-resort power to ensure that the Criminal Justice Bill is effectively implemented. The government will consider further whether a power of direction may also be needed.

The probation service can operate most effectively as a local service organized on a local basis. Delivery of the local service must take place within a centrally determined framework of objectives and accountabilities. The aim of many of the proposals set out in the paper is therefore to strengthen the local structure within the framework of greater accountability to the centre.

The Criminal Justice Bill will significantly increase the importance of the work of the probation service. These changes will combine to ensure that the probation service effectively meets these new challenges. They aim to encourage high standards of practice. clarify accountabilities and responsibilities, improve the effectiveness of management, increase the confidence of the sentencer in the probation service and encourage and strengthen links between the probation service and the local community.

Probation Officers' Role in After-Care from Psychiatric Hospitals

Discharge of patients subject to restriction orders.
Under section 37 of the Mental Health Act 1983, where an offender is convicted of an offence, the court may under certain circumstances, and if the offender is reported to be suffering from one of the forms of mental disorder defined in the Act, by order authorize his/her admission to and detention in a hospital for psychiatric treatment. Where such an order is made by a crown court and it appears that there is a risk of the offender committing further offences if set at large, the court may for the protection of the public make a further order known as a "restriction order", the principal effect of which is that the patient may not be allowed to leave the hospital, be transferred to another hospital or be discharged without the authority of the Home Secretary.

A mentally disordered person who is a danger to the public and who is found not guilty by reason of insanity or is unfit to plead, may with agreement of the jury be detained in hospital with restriction on discharge under the Criminal Procedure Act 1991. A prisoner, having been sentenced to imprisonment may be transferred to a hospital by the Home Secretary during the sentence because he/she is in need of treatment for mental disorder. The restriction order is may be of indefinite duration but may be for a finite period if the court so orders. In the case of a transferred prisoner the restrictions last as long as the sentence of imprisonment which the court imposed (ss. 47 and 49 of Mental Health Act, 1983).

Where a patient subject to special restrictions has in the past committed an offence of violence or where there is apprehension that he/she might have dangerous tendencies, the Home Secretary will ordinarily prefer that his/her discharge from hospital should be subject to conditions – normally of residence at a stated address, supervision by a suitable probation officer or social worker and medical surveillance.

Probation officer's duty
It is part of the duties of a probation officer, if so requested, to undertake the supervision of any person who has been released from an institution and is subject to supervision in England and Wales by virtue of a condition or requirement of a licence. This includes a person discharged from a hospital if he/she might have been remitted to a prison, youth custody or to a community home on the basis of a care order, instead of being discharged.

Procedure prior to discharge
The decision as to discharge rests with the Home Secretary (Home Office C3 Division). Pre-discharge and post-discharge procedures are given in a memorandum issued to supervising officers. The probation officer to be involved in the patient's after-care must be brought into consultation as early as possible. The responsible medical officer will initially approach the chief probation officer for the area concerned who will nominate the after-care officer. As soon as discharge has been agreed in principle, provisional arrangements can be made and the probation officer may be asked to assist in finding lodgings or a place in a hostel and in making arrangements for employment. Generally the bias should be towards making the employer aware both that the patient has been under treatment in a particular hospital and that he/she will be under supervision by a particular person after discharge. The patient should be told that information about him/her is given to an employer.

References
Bluglass, R. (1988) "Mentally Disordered Prisoners: Reports but No Improvements", *Brit. Med. J.* 296: 1757.
Bond, M. (1989) "Referrals to a New Regional Secure Unit – What Happens to Patients Refused Admission?" *Med. Sci. Law*, 29(4): 329-32.
Chiswick, D. (1992) "Reed Report on Mentally Disordered Offenders: They Need Health and Social Services, not Prison", *Brit. Med. J.*, Vol. 305., p. 1448-49.
Coid, J. (1984) "How Many Psychiatric Patients in Prison?", *Brit. J. Psychiatry.* 145: 78-86.
Cooke, D.J. (1992) "Reconviction Following Referral to a Forensic Clinic: The Criminal Justice Outcome of Diversion", *Med. Sci. Law* (1992), vol. 32, no.4, pp. 325-330.
Criminal Statistics, July 1991, Home Office.

Department of Health (1992)*The Health of the Nation*, H.M.S.O., London (Cm 1986). (Committee Chaired by Dr. John Reed.)

Dooley, E. (1990) "Prison Suicides", 1972-87, *Brit. J. Psych.*, 156: 40-56.

Eysenck, S. (1987) "Mentally Disordered Individuals in the Prison System", *Justice of the Peace*, Vol. 151: 265.

Howells, K., Hollin, C.R. (1989) "Clinical Approaches to Violence", Pt. 2, 11. In *Violence in Prisons*, John Wiley & Sons, Chichester, 275.

Inquiry by Her Majesty's Chief Inspector of Prisons into the Escape of Two Category "A" Prisoners from Her Majesty's Prison Brixton on 7 July, 1991, Home Office, Aug. 1991.

James, D.V., Hamilton, L.W. (1991) "The Clerkenwell Scheme: Assessing Efficacy and Cost of a Psychiatric Liaison Service to a Magistrates' Court", *Brit. Med. J.* 303: 282-5.

Prison Disturbances (1991) Report of Inquiry by Rt. Hon. Lord Justice Woolf and His Hon. Judge S. Tumim, London, H.M.S.O. Cm 1456.

Report of Work of Prison Service, 1988-89, H.M.S.O.

Steadman, H. (1985) "Prediction System Level" in *Dangerousness: Probability and Prediction, Psychiatry and Public Policy*. Webster, DC., Ben-Aron, M.H., Hucker, S.J. (eds), Cambridge University Press, 145-59.

CHAPTER XIV

A Need for Education and Training When Coping with Violence: A Nursing Perspective
BY D.A. JONES AND A. LITTLER (1994)

It has been alleged that nurses do not train in forensic psychiatry but rather train in the nursing of patients in secure environments. This is a rather tenuous distinction which apparently does not apply to those who qualify in other disciplines. It is difficult to understand how violent patients (offenders or otherwise), who are seriously disordered mentally, could be efficiently nursed by staff who do not have, at least, a good basic knowledge of the principles of forensic psychiatry. It is also evident that these nurses are constantly with the patients as opposed to psychiatrists who see patients periodically and base their opinions on nurse observations to a not inconsiderable extent. A good case could well be made out for forensic psychiatric charge nurses to countersign psychiatric reports to criminal courts.

Nurses who specialize in forensic psychiatry may be Registered Mental Nurses or have an appropriate Enrolled Nursing Qualification. A good basic knowledge of general medicine and psychiatry is obviously necessary for the potential forensic psychiatric nurses who should be awarded the appropriate diploma on completing the course and passing the examination.

Consequently, I will begin this chapter with reference to training in general psychiatry appropriate to nursing staff. Some of this material has been dealt with in detail in earlier chapters and is unavoidably repeated in modified form in this chapter.

Aims and Objectives of Psychiatric Experience for Psychiatric Student Nurses.

Overall aims initially to the psychiatric experience:
   1. To emphasize the importance of preparing the psychiatric student

nurse in acquiring skills to care for patients as a whole and to identify the patient as an individual who, when in hospital has to be cared for in relation to physiological, psychological, spiritual and sociological needs.

2. To introduce the learner to the causes and symptomatology of mental illness and the concepts of psychiatric nursing, and to apply this to present-day society's views on mental illness and the education of the learner in overcoming any form of social stigma associated with such disorders.

3. To enable the learner to relate mental symptoms that may present secondary to an underlying physiological disorder, and apply this knowledge when they are nursing physically ill patients back in their base hospitals. Also to make the learner aware of the incidence of physiological illness secondary to an underlying psychological problem, and how psychological trauma can precipitate organic changes. Psychosomatic illness is where the organic pathology is secondary to the emotional disturbance.

Aims of the psychiatric experience

The learner should gain a basic understanding of:

a)   The types of mental disorders and their symptomatology.
b)   The importance of attitudes of the nurses in relation to the mentally ill.
c)   To give an introduction into the legal implications of mental illness and a broad outline of the Mental Health Act, 1983.
d)   To outline the role of the nurse within the psychiatric team and the relationship that exists between nursing, medical, paramedical, social and voluntary organizations within the team concept of patient care.

Overall objectives of the experience

The learner should be able to:

1.   Observe and recognize mental symptoms, report these accurately to Senior Nurses and Medical Officers and give appropriate nursing care relating to the patient's mental disorder.
2.   Provide supportive therapy for patients in his/her care, give guidance to patients, talk to patients and listen, assist patients in habit-training and conforming to social conventions expected by society and encourage socialization of patients. The learner

should also relate these skills to the rehabilitative programme of patients in preparation for their discharge into society.

3. Supervise and protect patients, protect their property and safeguard patients' welfare and general interests especially in accordance with the Mental Health Act 1983, and the Health and Safety at Work Act 1974.

4. Make use of terminology used in psychiatry and associate aetiological and symptomological factors with particular forms of mental disorder.

5. Recognize early signs of possible hostility and aggression in patients, assess patients' behaviour and utilize this skill and power of observation in preventing aggressive outbursts and maintaining an environment of tranquillity which will enhance the creation of a therapeutic environment.

Topics of instruction

Admission procedure:

Means of referral.
Meeting the patient.
Accompanying the patient.
Introducing the patient.
Administrative elements:
Nurses notes.
Kardex notes (nursing process).
Physical observations.
Assisting at medical examination.

Fire procedure:

Hospital regulations.
Location of alarms.
Location of fire exits.
Location of fire appliances.

Care of keys and sharp instruments and drug administration:

Suicide:

Preventative measures.

Action on attempt at suicide by cutting, hanging, burning, poisoning, drowning, scalding, starvation.

Care of the detained patient:

The Mental Health Act 1983.
Reporting of absence and relevant documentation.
Seclusion.

Dealing with aggression:

Acceptable and unacceptable outlets.
Channelling aggression.
Impulsive aggression.
Current chemotherapy in psychiatry.

Treatments:

Essential knowledge of essential medications prescribed for mental disorder.
Electroconvulsant therapy (ECT)
    Preparation of patient   )
    Care during ECT   )
    Care following ECT   )   Physical and psychological.

Refusal to eat:

Stimulation of appetite.
Observation at mealtimes.
Care of the mouth.
Anorexia nervosa management.

Self-isolation:

Dangers of self-isolation.
Reaching the withdrawn patient.
Encouraging socialization.
Rehabilitation programmes including benefits of occupational therapy and the industrial training unit.

Self-neglect:

Personal hygiene)
Personal appearance)   Habit training
Degraded habits)
Restoring pride)
Behaviour modification programmes and token economy systems.

After-care of mentally ill:

Community services.
Social services.
Allied voluntary organizations.

These lectures and discussions will be covered in the clinical areas shared equally by the Ward Sisters/Charge Nurses from the particular areas where student nurses are allocated.

Procedure for Admission of Patient

1. A bed and locker are prepared prior to arrival of patient.
2. On notification of arrival of patient at the hospital, a nurse is sent to:
   a) the Reception Officer, if admission has previously been arranged;
   b) the Emergency Assessment Clinic if a potential patient arrives without admission having previously been arranged. Here the nurse remains with the patient whilst he is being seen by the Duty Medical Officer who will decide whether admission to hospital is necessary.
3. The nurse welcomes the patient in a friendly, reassuring manner and escorts him to the ward accompanied by any relatives or friends, and together with all the necessary documents collected from the Reception Officer.
4. On arrival on the ward, Sister/Charge Nurse or Senior Nurse in Charge welcomes the patient.
5. The duty Medical Officer is notified of his arrival.
6. A Kardex sheet is filled in with all necessary information concerning patient and admission entered into patient's folder.
7. The escorting nurse:
   a) introduces fellow patients to him;
   b) explains the geography of the ward to him, e.g. location of bathroom, toilet, etc.'

c)   takes him to his bed asking him to undress and get into bed to await arrival of the doctor who will physically examine him. Alternatively, the patient may wait for doctor in a dressing gown in a ward lounge. Here the nurse assesses the need for washing or bathing the patient, and observes the state of the hair and general condition. Note is made of any abnormalities, marks or bruises, etc. Detailed observation of these will be made and recorded during the doctor's physical examination.

8.   All property of the patient, such as dentures, wedding ring, jewellry, etc., are especially noted and recorded in the Ward Patients' Property Book. Any small bags or cases retained by patient in his locker are examined in his presence and after permission from the patient has been tactfully requested. Any sharp instruments, drugs of any description or anything which could prove harmful or promote injury to patient or to others are removed. Sharp instruments are marked and locked in a safe place on the ward. Drugs are sent to the pharmacy.

9.   Relatives or friends are seen by the Sister/Charge Nurse or acting Charge Sister/Charge Nurse and are asked for any further relevant details concerning the patient. Here the accuracy of name and address of next of kin is checked, telephone numbers are noted to ensure quick notification in the event of any emergency.

10. It is advisable that patients' clothing is marked, especially in the case of elderly patients and this should be explained to relatives. The patient is advised that money and valuables may be placed for safe-keeping in the hospital cashier's department. If relatives remove articles of the patient's property, they must sign to say they have removed them from the hospital. The notice concerning patient's property, absolving the Area Health Authority of responsibility for them, is drawn to the attention of the patient and relatives.

South Glamorgan Health Authority "Search of patients" Policy

1. The Informal Patient who Refuses to be Searched

The consent of the patient to be searched must be sought. If consent is refused, a body search should not take place. Such a search could amount to a charge of assault against the nurse. The property of the informal patient should not normally be searched without consent. All search procedures should be carried out in the presence of another nurse as witness, and in the patient's presence where property is involved. Where difficulties ensue, the nurse must seek the support of a Nursing Officer and a responsible Medical Officer and must not act independently and in isolation. It will be for the Nursing Officer and the Medical Officer to determine what further action to take, e.g. discharge, call police, or compulsory detention. It is essential that written statements are made by nurses concerned.

2. The Formal Patient who Refuses to be Searched
The nurse should initially seek the consent and the co-operation of the formal patient. In the absence of consent, the advice of a Nursing Officer and Medical Officer should be sought before a decision is made whether to proceed with a search, and in certain circumstances, the police should be called in to assist a search to take place.

3. Informal Patients on Written Contracts suspected of being in possession of drugs/alcohol but refusing to be searched
The rules under Section 1 apply here under Section 3, but the signed contracts should include reference to specific items (e.g. alcohol, drugs, sharp instruments and other weapons).

4. Visitors to the ward who might be suspected of carrying articles that might be deemed dangerous
Visitors should not be subjected to body search. Consent must be sought to search bags/containers or any other property brought in.

If the visitor refuses, then access to the ward may be denied. The advice/support of a Senior Nurse/responsible Medical Officer or Hospital Administrator may be sought.

5. Any patient who is in Possession of an Offensive Weapon
An attempt should be made to persuade the patient to relinquish the weapon. If the patient is at all resistive or threatens the staff carrying out the search, no attempt should be made to disarm. Disarming should be left to suitably trained and organized staff and never attempted by those who are untrained.

It may be necessary to contact the police if the situation warrants. Section 118 of the Mental Health Act 1983 requires the Secretary of State to periodically revise a Code of Practice. This Act although not imposing a statutory duty to comply with the Code of Practice does nevertheless provide important guidance for all those working with the mentally ill. Failure to comply with the code could be referred to in cases of litigation against individuals, health authorities or social services. This chapter sets out to examine a key area within the code, namely patients presenting particular management problems.

Although the key responsibilities of the authors rest in post basic nurse education, the contents of this chapter can apply equally to all health care workers. Furthermore, it is felt that all staff are potentially at risk from violence and therefore *all* should respond in a mutually beneficial and positive fashion – that is as a team!

Above-average Job-related Risk?

There is an obvious risk to welfare workers and nurses (women) of violence and threats, placing them on a par with entertainment managers and security (men). They are at least three times more at risk than the "average" person.

Breakwell (1989) points out the scarcity of comprehensive surveys, the restriction relating to the diversity of professional groups studied, and the relatively small geographical areas examined.

The authors themselves have recognized a degree of selectivity amongst nursing staff in reporting physical attacks. For example, there appears to be a greater tolerance towards the elderly than amongst the younger age groups. The overall picture therefore is difficult to quantify.

Tables XXIX and XXX demonstrate the incidence of minor injury and verbal threats as extracted from the Health Services Advisory Committee "Violence to Staff in the Health Services" (1987).

Training

Training for staff in the management of disruptive behaviour must remain one of the overriding principles. It should become an integral part of any induction programme and must be ongoing. There will obviously be a variation in how training is organized but it must always include the key elements – theory and practice. It must be meaningful, realistic and aimed at providing increased confidence in the staff. Wherever possible this training should be multi-disciplinary in nature.

The teaching and learning methods should be varied and imaginative, so the interest is sustained. It is not proposed to describe in depth the content of these training programmes, recognizing there will be a variation in what is included. However, the following areas would need to be addressed:

aetiology of aggressive behaviour
incident levels – national/local
recognition
prevention
diffusion
restraint (breakaway techniques)
legal aspects.

The practical element of the training programme will vary according to time available. It would include elements of Breakaway Techniques and Control and Restraint.   The authors have developed a training programme that combines both of these components. It is reproduced as an indicator of the main areas to be examined. Based on a workshop method of learning, it creates maximum participation from those attending. Although it is planned over three consecutive days the sessions can be organized on a one day per week basis.

Managing Violence and Potential Violence

Day 1

9.15 a.m.	Introductions Objectives of the Course Identifying the Problems
10.15 a.m.	Coffee Break
10.35 a.m.	Causes of Aggressive Behaviour Examination of: a) Internal States b) Influence of the Environment c) Attitudes of Other People. Recognizing the "Warning Signs" Video Presentation
12.30 p.m.	Lunch

1.00 p.m.	Diffusing the Aggressive Situation "What Can We Do?" Practical Options
3.00 p.m.	Coffee Break
3.20 p.m.	Introduction to Day 2 Managing a Physical Outburst/Attack Review of the Day
5.00 p.m.	Dispersal

Day 2

9.15 a.m.	Objectives of the Day Use of Breakaway Techniques Practice of Breakaway Techniques
12.30 p.m.	Lunch
1.00 p.m.	Breakaway Techniques Continued
3.00 p.m.	Coffee Break
5.00 p.m.	Dispersal

Day 3

9.15 a.m.	Feedback on Day 2 Open Forum on "Coping with a Physical Incident"
10.15 a.m.	Coffee Break
10.35 a.m.	Examination of the Legal Issues
12.30 p.m.	Lunch
1.00 p.m.	Improving Communications When Managing "Disturbed" Behaviour

3.00 p.m.   Coffee Break

3.20 p.m.   Evaluation of the Course

5.00 p.m.   Dispersal.

A Case for Care Planning

Having identified those potentially at risk, the authors believe in the case of sound care planning for those patients presenting particular management problems. Good communication is clearly the key to positive management of this group and *all* disciplines need to work to a systematic assessment and care-planning regime.

Most nurses within the U.K. already work to a problem-solving approach when planning nursing care. This philosophy is known as the "Systematic Approach to Nursing Care" (The Nursing Process) and is based on four key areas – namely Assessment, Planning, Implementation and Evaluation. An overriding principle of this philosophy is that it is patient-centred, requiring wherever practicable, patient involvement in the treatment programme.

Darcy (1985) believes that the problem-orientated system of care challenges nursing staff and indeed others to be precise with assessment, and to develop skills through a new approach by seeking solutions to patients' problems.

Recognizing that the planning of the care programme for an individual client involves a variety of disciplines, it would follow that all should be involved in the organizational planning process, i.e. Integrated Care Planning. An adoption of a systematic approach to care planning and its use by all disciplines involved would not only be a positive end in itself but would also more easily facilitate many of the requirements of the Mental Health Act 1983. An example cited here is that of Section 117, where there exists a statutory requirement to plan for aftercare arrangements for clients detained on a Section.

In total, these factors would mediate towards one of the essential, but neglected areas of violence prevention – good communication.

Policies and Procedures

A long-established problem existing with health authorities is the varying commitment to establish policies and procedures for clients presenting management problems. This has certainly been the case when examining the management of potential violence and violence. Action is often retrospective and reactive to a specific serious incident involving staff.

Government guidelines have been criticized in the past as being vague and unspecific. Where commitment is given to policies and procedures they must apply specifically to the area involved. Staff must feel a degree of ownership of any policy or procedure, and feel there exists a consistency in its application.

Those managers responsible for providing such guidelines must be prepared to make amendments in accordance with changes in clinical practice. In addition, there will be a need to frequently evaluate the ways in which policies and procedures are applied.

The authors believe that any set of guidelines should consist of the following components:

1. Main concepts and principles.
2. Agreed response to a psychiatric emergency.
3. A statement on training provisions.
4. The main guidelines dealing with:

    a) preventative measures
    b) recognizing signs of imminent violence
    c) dealing with imminent violence
    d) dealing with the actual violent incident

5. Procedure to be followed after an incident.
6. Calling in the police.
7. The health authority's duty of care to patients and staff (including compensation awards).

The following detailed examples are provided, commencing with an Emergency Response Procedure:

1. Call for assistance by shouting or by using a signalling system.
2. Do not attempt to manage on your own.
3. Initiate the "Psychiatric Emergency" system by:
    a) dialling internally,
    b) stating the words "Psychiatric Emergency",
    c) giving your location.

4. Maintain clear communication with the person (in order to calm the individual), but maintain a safe distance. Face the person at all times.
5. Restraint should only be applied when there are adequate numbers of staff present. Only the minimum amount of force should be used to deal with the incident.

Main guidelines for the management of potentially violent and violent persons

Prevention
Although most people agree with the principle that "prevention is better than cure" is must be stressed that in the case of violence there are many factors working against us. In many situations there might not be a clear indication that something is wrong. The violent action or outburst may well be impulsive (as is the case often with psychiatric patients). There are also situations whereby only a few "warning signs" are recognized. However, it is intended to give a number of possible signs and symptoms as examples of what might be experienced.

Firstly, however, the following must be considered.

It is essential that good relationships are established with potentially violent clients. In an aggressive situation an employee *should try* to act in a calm and rational way, as an aggressive reaction will only induce further and more serious aggression on behalf of the patient.

The first aim should be the prevention of violence.

All those who may be involved should be encouraged to talk and listen.

It must be remembered that the client is an individual with his/her own personality, feelings and beliefs. While these may be impaired by illness the dignity of the patient must always be respected.

Staff should seek to avoid situations where they may become party to deteriorating inter-personal relationships with a patient, and by so doing they may avoid actual physical contact.

New members of staff should be introduced to the client and told immediately about individual characteristics of that person.

When a client is transferred to another ward or hospital, the receiving staff escort and anyone related to the situation should be thoroughly briefed, i.e. given a clear description of the patient's characteristics of behaviour, or temperament, which are in need of special understanding.

Regular opportunities will be afforded for all members of staff in contact with clients to discuss methods and problems with medical and senior nursing staff so that constructive work with patients is continually developed.

There will be a need at times for staff to distinguish between assertiveness and verbal aggression. This can only be done in the light of the situation and knowledge of the individual.

Recognizing the warning signs

Obviously one of the first indications might be that of the person verbally telling someone that he is angry. This might be accompanied by threats.

The following are some other indicators, but it must be noted that these are often peculiar to the individual and the list is not exhaustive.

Verbal	Volume
	Content – e.g. Swearing, Hyper-critical
	Tone – e.g. Threatening, Sarcastic
	Speed of Delivery
Non-Verbal	Change in Mood or Manner
	Clenched Fists
	Bodily Tension Facial Tension
	Agitation – e.g. Finger/Foot Tapping
	Restlessness
	Staring Eyes
	Pacing
	Kicking
	Punching
	Throwing Inanimate Objects
	Slamming Doors
	Making Unnecessary Noise
	Perspiring
	Hyper-Ventilating
	Invasion of Personal Space
	Scowling
	Dilated Pupils
	Crying – tears, sobs
	Deliberate Self-harm/Mutilation
	Withdrawn
	Pushing

It should be understood that in psychiatric illness, those on the receiving end of a client's violence are very often not the intended object, but merely an obstacle in the client's path, or a vehicle for receiving pent-up emotions.

Dealing with imminent and potential violence
Staff who know a client well will generally be able to detect tension in a client in its early stages. This tension may possibly be a portent of potential or imminent violence. If a client who is *unable* to communicate easily becomes restless the more obvious causes should be examined first, for example, full bladder, constipation, pain, toothache, etc.

For the more communicative client:

a) Call for assistance – never approach unobserved by other members of staff.

b) Keep your access to an exit clear – your hands should be in view, and when still, adopt a sideways stance (for easier retreat!) Find a comfortable social distance – remember anger enlarges an individual's personal space. An incursion into this enlarged but sensitive space might be misconstrued as an aggressive gesture.

c) Encourage the person to talk. Ask "open" questions in a confident and interested manner, for example, "What's the problem?" Encourage communication by tactful verbal and non-verbal means (intermittent head nodding). Maintain good eye contact (do not stare). Try to sound confident, even if you don't feel it.

d) If violence seems imminent and until assistance is available make every attempt to avoid physical contact. Attempt discreetly to remove any object that could be used as a weapon. Place a substantial object between yourself and the aggressor. If necessary sound any available alarm.

General guidelines for dealing with a violent outburst (Application of Restraint)
If violence occurs in spite of all efforts to prevent it, then some measures must be taken to contain the incident. Assistance should be sought as soon as possible. This may include calling the police.

While accepting the principle that property is less important than people, consideration must be given as to the extent of damage that should be allowed to take place before it becomes a danger, not only to the person causing the damage but to others.

In some areas, it is a practice to allow patients to act out their aggression. However, where property is being damaged in such a way as to be an actual danger to others, it is advised that immediate, or early intervention, is required.

If a member of staff is attacked, he should try to break away. However, he should endeavour not to put anyone else at risk by so doing. A member of staff should, if possible, avoid grappling with a patient single-handed, and should wait until assistance arrives.

If restraint is necessary, staff should try to move the person to the ground as quickly as possible. Methods of restraining the patients will vary, depending on the nature of the incident. Clothing rather than limbs should be held to restrain physical activity. If limbs are grasped, the following is advised:

a)   pinion the client's arms to his sides, with a "bear hug" from behind;

b)   legs and arms should be grasped near major joints;

c)   weight should be placed on the hips and abdomen by lying across the body;

d)   if there are attempts at biting, the head should be grasped firmly and held still;

e)   if this procedure is followed, the possibility of dislocation or fracture will be reduced, and the least long-term discomfort caused;

f)   if possible, the patient should then be removed to a quieter environment.

When lone members of staff find themselves faced with a violent situation, they should not attempt physical intervention on their own unless it is essential for the patient's safety. Community staff are advised that a withdrawal from a violent or potentially violent situation may be necessary as, by the nature of their work, they may find themselves isolated.

Procedure to be followed after an incident
It is essential that all incidents of violence are reported and recorded adequately. Such material is needed for professional care of the patient and to provide a basis for retrospective analysis of the incident. This may be helpful in his future treatment and management, and in order that any subsequent complaints can be adequately dealt with.

All incidents should be reported on the appropriate documentation.

A full written report will be necessary if the following occurs:

1.   An incident involving physical violence and injury to a client, staff, visitor, relative, or any allegation of such an incident.

2.   Any incident which necessitates the use of physical restraint of a client by members of staff.
3.   Any incident in which isolation for more than a short period forms part of management of the disturbed client.
4.   Any incident causing significant damage to hospital property or to the property of patients or staff.

In making the report the following points should be noted:

1.   When and where the incident occurred.
2.   Names of the people involved.
3.   Brief factual account of the incident.
4.   The action taken
        a)   immediately
        b)   following the incident.
5.   The names of all additional people bearing professional responsibility.
6.   The principal content of the incident, including the main direction of aggression.
7.   Observations on the mental state of the violent client.
8.   Any injury or damage that has occurred.
9.   Any additional comments.
10.   When injury to staff occurs, details should be entered in the designated Accident Reporting Book (as required).

Intervention should be as soon as practically possible, with a show of numbers. It is very often in these circumstances that a few words from a member of staff who has knowledge of the patient and who is seen to be supported by others will be sufficient to stop the incident without any physical restraint being required.

In all instances, and at the earliest opportunity, Senior Medical and Nursing Staff must be consulted regarding treatment.

If a member of staff is attacked he must obviously use the most appropriate means available to defend himself and this, of course, will be a matter of personal judgment. If it is possible for a member of staff to remove himself from the immediate vicinity of his attacker, he should do so, but only if it can be accomplished without putting at risk other patients or staff.

Physical restraint should only be used for the minimum amount of time necessary to control the patient until further action is decided upon, i.e. sedation.

It is recognized that the action suggested for dealing with a violent incident will not cover all eventualities and there is a need for staff to use considerable initiative in this area. In some instances of extreme violence, the degree of force necessary to control the patient becomes a matter of concern for the staff involved, it is only possible to reiterate that the degree of force should be minimum required to control the violence in a manner calculated to calm rather than provoke or intensify further violence.

Note: Staff who have attended the Home-Office-approved course in Control and Restraint will have been trained in an established "three man" containment team. It should be used when verbal methods of persuasion have failed in preventing physical violence.

Calling in the Police
There are some situations when it is recognized that there is a serious risk to the personal safety of both staff and clients.

The decision to call in the police must be left to the most senior person dealing with the crisis in the light of the situation.

Police are seldom called to hospital wards to deal with violent clients. However, in those cases where members of staff have been assaulted or crime has been alleged, police have been called and the matter has been reported and investigated in the same way as any other crime.

It is not possible to offer an assurance that police will attend and assist in every case. Except where a statutory duty exists, the role of police is to act as a back-up force to trained staff, skilled in the handling of violent or potentially violent clients.

Table XXIX
Experience of violent incidents classified by hospital type and location

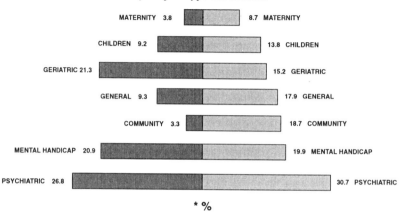

* %

Minor Injury   **Verbal Threat**

*Data expressed as incident rates per cent of each responding occupation in the year preceeding the survey.

Table XXX
Incidence of violent incidents classified by some selected occupational groups

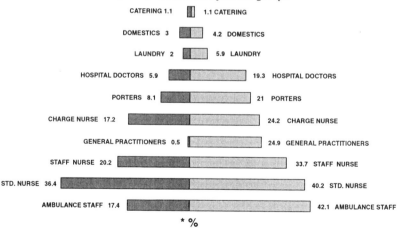

* %

Minor Injury   **Verbal Threat**

*Data expressed as incident rates per cent of each responding occupation in the year preceeding the survey.

References

Breakwell, G.M. (1989) *Facing Physical Violence*, The British Psychological Society & Routledge Ltd., London.

Darcy, P.T. (1985) *Mental Health Nursing Source Book*, Balliere Tindall, London.

Department of Health & Welsh Office, 1990, Code of Practice, Mental Health Act 1983, H.M.S.O.

Department of Health & Welsh Office, Mental Health Act 1983, HMSO.

Jones, D.A. (1989) *Management of the Potentially Violent and Violent Person,* South Glamorgan Health Authority (Whitchurch Hospital), Unpublished.

Littler, A. (1989) *Video: Aggression – An Individual Response,* South Glamorgan Health Authority (Whitchurch Hospital).

Littler, A. (1990) *Preventing Aggression in Waiting Areas and Wards*, South Glamorgan Health Authority (Whitchurch Hospital), Unpublished.

Suggested Further Reading

Brown, R., Bute, S., and Ford, P., 1986, *Social Workers at Risk: The Prevention and Management of Violence*, Macmillan, London.

Hampshire Social Services Department (1985) *The Prevention and management of Violence: Staff Guidelines*, Hampshire Social Services Department, & Southampton University.

Martin, P. (1983) *Care of the Mentally Ill: The Essentials of Nursing*, Macmillan, London.

Owens, R.G. and Ashcroft, J.B., 1985, *Violence: A Guide for the Caring Professions*, Croom Helm, London.

Chapter XV

Dangerous Patients and The Public

One must assume that certain criteria are used by psychiatrists to decide whether a mentally disordered person is or is not a danger to the public. Recent cases have served to highlight yet again, the concern of society in general and the relevant responsible authorities in particular in this context. Psychopathically disordered individuals seem to cause most problems to psychiatrists from the point of view of diagnosis and treatment. The Mental Health Act (1983), defines psychopathic disorder as a persistent disorder or disability of mind (whether or not including significant impairment of intelligence) which results in abnormally aggressive or seriously irresponsible conduct on the part of the person concerned. Furthermore, the individual must be thought treatable. No person is mentally disordered by reason only of promiscuity or other immoral conduct, sexual deviancy or dependence on alcohol or drugs, under s.1(3) of the 1983 Act.

The Home Office indicates that there must be a reasonable hope that the treatment would lead to an improvement of mental condition or of its manifestations or would prevent or lessen anticipated deterioration in either respect. In other words, he or she must be regarded as amenable to treatment, meaning that treatment is likely to alleviate or prevent further personality deterioration. Treatment would reasonably include nursing care and training under medical supervision.

The following investigations indicate the likelihood of repetition of antisocial offences by mentally disordered persons.

Rice et al (1991) studied the recidivism of 136 extrafamilial child molesters who had received phallometric assessment in a maximum security psychiatric institution from 1972 to 1983. The follow-up averaged 6.3 years. Fifty had participated in behavioural treatment to alter inappropriate sexual age preferences. Thirty-one per cent of the subjects were convicted of a new sex offence, 43 per cent committed a violent or sexual offence, and 58 per cent were arrested for some offence or returned to the institution. Subjects convicted of a new sex offence had previously committed more sex offences, had been admitted to correctional institutions more frequently, were more likely to have been diagnosed as personality disordered, were more likely to have never married and had shown more inappropriate sexual preferences in initial phallometric assessment than those who had not. Behavioural treatment did not affect recidivism.

Certain criteria indicate likelihood to repeat serious crime. These are conveniently considered in the context of contra-indications to discharge from hospitals where psychiatric treatment is provided under conditions of adequate security and apply to mentally disordered patients who are a danger to the public.

(i)   Repetition is likely if the patient is prematurely discharged as a result of *pressure* from relatives or perhaps legal representatives. Alternatively, desire by the patient to stay in hospital and/or reluctance of relatives to have him home, would weigh against discharge. Dangerous behaviour may persist after the mental disorder is thought to have been successfully treated.

(ii) Repetition is probable if the patient's *history* indicates that he is prone to indulge in impulsive anti-social behaviour in response to provocation which would not influence the average person. A patient in a special hospital is very likely to represent a permanent danger to the public if aggressive psychopathy coexists with mental impairment.

(iii) The *nature of the crime* which influenced admission to hospital, and a study of previous convictions, provide clues as to the probability of repetition of similar offences in the future. Repetition is virtually certain if victims were specifically chosen, for example, children killed by mentally impaired psychopaths or sexual offences involving members of a particular sex and belonging to a particular age group. These crimes are indicative of habitual *patterns* of serious anti-social behaviour. Unpatterned homicides by schizophrenics and other psychotics who kill strangers, should be regarded as a permanent serious danger to the public. The mentally impaired psychopaths become progressively more callous, weak-willed, frustrated and introspective during long periods in special hospitals and the danger to the public becomes progressively greater with the *passage of time*. Identification and sympathy with the patient militate against objective opinion.

(iv) Cunning psychopaths with criminal propensities tend to behave very well in institutions and may even be trusted to use potential weapons in workshops but they may be very dangerous when free in the community. Violence inside the hospital is obviously ominous, and staff are in constant danger.

(v)   Assessment of *current psychiatric state* is also necessary for prognostic purposes. A mentally impaired person may also suffer from psychopathic disorder, epilepsy or some form of mental illness such as schizophrenia and, in these circumstances, prognosis (including liability to repeat serious crime) is even more uncertain.

(vi)   Sadistic fantasies which are *enjoyed* mean that the patient is still very dangerous. Some people outside institutions have such fantasies, but never commit violence. The violent sex offender obviously has serious sexual problems.

(vii)   A patient should be directly questioned concerning violent tendencies. Paranoid attitudes, morbid jealousy and declared intentions of future violence must be taken seriously. It is also ominous if a patient discusses his or her offence in a dispassionate guilt-free manner.

A history of taking alcohol to excess and/or illicit drug taking is significant. Admission of obtaining satisfaction from inflicting pain on humans and/or animals and inability to learn from experience, indicate poor prognosis.

Warnings are nearly always given by those disposed to violence. Ball (1977), recommended successful mobilization of patients' cognitive resources to help gain insight and avoid future violence.

Adequate supervision and reassessments by psychiatrists, probation officers and social workers are necessary if patients are granted leave of absence from secure hospitals and immediate recall is essential if there is any suspicion that they will again revert to violence against persons.

Patients in special hospitals should be and usually are transferred for varying periods of time, to ordinary mental hospitals as "stepping stones" prior to a decision being made to return them to the community. It would be very important before transfer to assess if such patients with violent histories, would be likely to abscond from hospitals where treatment is provided in the absence of secure facilities. Secure units could also be used as "half-way houses" between special and ordinary mental hospitals although some wards of the latter are locked.

It is necessary to inform relatives, general practitioners, probation and social services and the police when a potentially dangerous patient is discharged or granted leave from a mental hospital, even if he or she refuses this consent. The Home Secretary would automatically be informed in Restriction Order cases under s.41 of the Mental Health Act, 1983.

Howells et al. (1989), indicated that violence is inevitable when an aggressive personality who has a low threshold of anger, is confronted with a dangerous situation which could be a prison riot. They also rightly state that prisons, young offender institutions and psychiatric hospitals breed or produce their own violence which can only be neutralized or attenuated by staff attitudes.

As a general observation, it is a cause for concern that the European Court of Human Rights can overrule the authority of the Home Secretary to have the final decision over a Mental Health Review Tribunal as to the advisability of discharging or granting leave to potentially dangerous patients.

James Lang was first in trouble with the police when he was twelve. A record of sexual offences ended with a three-year sentence for rape. Three weeks after his release from prison he killed a 12-year-old girl, was sent to Broadmoor under s.37 of the Mental Health Act 1983, and a Restriction Order without limit of time under s.41 was added. He was subsequently transferred to another special hospital, namely Park Lane Psychiatric Hospital on Merseyside. This hospital also provides treatment under conditions of maximum security and he spent 14 years there until the psychiatric authorities successfully argued that he was safe for discharge. The then Home Secretary, Mr. Leon Brittan, and his junior minister, Dr. David Mellor, objected to freeing Lang but they were overruled by the European Court of Human Rights. Lang came out of Park Lane, changed his name to Kay, and within a few months, in 1986, tried to strangle two young women. In court it was said Lang had a "terrible record" and to free him was a "tragic mistake". He suffered from "psychopathic disorder and was severely mentally disturbed". He was sentenced to six years' imprisonment at Lancaster Crown Court.

Silver et al. (1991), compared a group of 127 convicted felons with a group of 135 mentally disordered prisoners transferred for hospital treatment. Subjects were followed up from 5 to 17 years after discharge from hospital or release from prison. Subsequent arrests, hospitalizations, employment, and functioning of these large cohorts were studied and compared. The study focused on outcome data at five years after release.

The authors found that, at five years post-release, 65.4 per cent of the prisoner control group, and 73.3 per cent of the mentally disordered prison transfers were rearrested. At 17 years post-release, rearrest rates increased to 75.4 per cent of the prisoner controls, and 78.4 per cent of the prison transfers.

Some psychopaths who are an immediate and serious danger to the public are not admitted to maximum security hospitals such as Broadmoor and Rampton because psychiatrists are apparently free to interpret treatment in the narrowest sense as cure although the above authoritative explanations clearly indicate that it is quite ridiculous to restrict treatment specifically to "cure". Virtually all forms of serious mental disorder are recurrent and no mentally disordered person would ever be detained in an appropriate hospital if "cure" was the only criterion for admission. There are two criteria for admission to a hospital or unit providing secure conditions:

(i)   the individual is judged to be an immediate and serious danger to the public; and

(ii)   he or she is mentally disordered within the meaning of the Mental Health Act 1983, and considered to be treatable. Consequently, a psychiatrist may legally refuse to admit any mentally disordered person by the simple expedient of labelling him or her as "untreatable".

Psychiatry is the only medical discipline for which no reliable objective test exists with the possible exception of intelligence testing for the mentally impaired.

A mentally disordered patient who is dangerous may be admitted to a hospital or unit providing adequate security in the following ways:

(i)   under s.37 of the Mental Health Act 1983, if a Hospital order is issued by the court when an order restricting discharge under s.41 of the same Act would usually be added;

(ii)   under s.3 of the above Act when assessed as too dangerous to retain in an ordinary mental hospital;

(iii) under the Criminal Procedure (Insanity and Unfitness to Plead) Act 1991, when the accused is unfit to plead;

(iv) when found not guilty by reason of insanity on the basis of the *M'Naghten* Rules.

(v)   under s. 47 of the Mental Health Act 1983, when a person is serving a sentence.

Application for admission to a special hospital such as Broadmoor is made to the Special Hospital Service Authority, Charles House, Kensington High Street, London.

Some modern liberal lines of thought to the effect that *involuntary* admissions to mental hospitals must be avoided at all costs would mean that the public would have virtually no protection from dangerous patients, and this type of false reasoning is quite comparable with allegations to the effect that all offenders must be mentally disordered to some extent! Psychiatrists would hopefully be aware that protection of the public must take precedence over civil rights issues when people are a serious danger to the public and suffering from serious mental disorders.

Sturup (1968), described his experience of patients at Herstedvester, which is a hospital in Denmark specializing in the treatment of mentally disordered individuals (including mentally retarded) who have been convicted of serious crimes of aggression.

He gives the following statistics of the granting of parole to patients convicted of crimes like murder, rape and robbery with violence: 9 per cent were paroled less than two years after admission; 34 per cent between two and four years after admission; 57 per cent after spending at least four years in Herstedvester; and 7 per cent remained in the hospital for more than five years from the date of admission. These statistics would indicate a liberal outlook combined with efficient treatment methods in Herstedvester.

Sturup ventures the opinion that young murderers "settle down and become less dangerous with the passage of time". He does not indicate if murderers released from Herstedvester subsequently killed innocent members of the public. He gives statistics concerning mentally disordered patients convicted of sexual offences such as exhibitionism, rape and indecent assaults, which concern an unselected group of "nearly 3,000" individuals studied during a 10-year period and subjected to "long-range" follow-up after release from Herstedvester. They reveal that only 6-9 per cent of first time offenders subsequently committed a similar type of offence, but there is a 40 per cent relapse rate of "three-times" sexual offenders which is reduced to about 2 per cent if castration is carried out. The mentally disordered sex offenders were suffering from retardation and/or psychopathic disorder. He also expressed the opinion that the manner in which a patient is treated after conviction may have an important influence on his attitude towards the public after release from hospital. He believes that the staff should make every effort to ensure that the patient fully understands and accepts that treatment must be carried out under conditions of maximum security. Not all are capable of such comprehension.

Repetition of crimes of aggression may be determined by the situation which an ex-patient meets and the emotional demands which these situations make upon him. Sturup stresses the importance of *accurately estimating the patient's mental resources and provisionally deciding whether they are sufficient to enable him to cope with community life.* The latter assessment is vital before making a final decision as to a patient's suitability for release. Treatment must ensure that an effective "emotional" rapport is established between the patient and the hospital staff. Continuation of such rapport after release, would help prevent perpetration of another serious crime as the ex-patient would (theoretically) have sufficient confidence to seek help if and when he felt tempted to endanger the public.

The following recommendations for the assessment and disposal of mentally disordered offenders are described in general terms. They are based on the report of a team headed by Sir Carl Aarvold, Recorder of London, and published in January 1973 and also on the enquiry led by the then Home Secretary, Lord Butler and published in October 1975. These committees were convened in response to public concern as a result of Graham Young's sentence of life imprisonment for poisoning offences in June 1972, and the ease with which he had access to poisons even in a special hospital. The former report dealt specifically with patients subjected to special restrictions on discharge added to Hospital Orders and has been criticized on the grounds that it inferred that all such restrictions should be indefinite and that in consequence, patients could not be expected to cooperate fully in treatment.

Correct decisions about the treatment, rehabilitation, discharge and continuing care of a potentially dangerous patient can be taken only in the light of accurate assessments of the patient's mental condition, response to treatment and likely future behaviour. In the case of an offender the formal assessment process starts when he is before the court, and evidence about his behaviour is presented together with medical opinion as to his mental condition and appropriate ways of dealing with him. It continues when he is admitted to hospital, and the further observations of medical, nursing and other staff can be added to the accumulation of reports. Eventually, when the patient returns to the community, information from his relatives, social workers and others with whom he is in contact will have an important part to play. This process, a continued prediction and evaluation of the results of certain courses of management, is a normal function of the practice of medicine in general. In psychiatry, where the patient's social performance is such an important indicator of his condition, the responsible doctor has to rely on observation of the patient's behaviour in as many settings as practicable, and though complete certainty in prediction may not be attainable, accuracy depends on the doctor having access to all possible sources of information, both within the hospital and outside it, throughout the course of treatment. There is no doubt of the value, in this respect, of the presence at case conferences of representatives of all the disciplines (medical, nursing and occupational personnel, psychologists, social workers and probation officers) who make their own assessments of his or her progress and future prospects, and it should become accepted practice to hold such conferences. For a mentally disordered offender, prediction will involve assessment of the individual patient's personality, the nature of his mental disorder, his response to therapeutic help, the circumstances, both material and emotional under which the offence took place, the likelihood of those circumstances recurring, the resources available in the social situation to which the patient would go on leaving hospital, his likely reaction to that situation, and the chances of his successful reintegration into the community despite any stresses which may develop.

In many cases of mental illness a clear prediction of the future course of the illness can be made. Many cases of psychopathic disorder mature with the passage of time, given social and psychiatric help. Sufferers from mental impairment retain their intellectual handicap for life but many of the consequences can be ameliorated with suitable training. Predictions in many such cases can be founded with confidence on long experience of psychiatric practice. But there are some cases which do not fall easily within these identifiable categories, or in which, though the nature of the patient's disorder may be clear enough, a particular factor may render successful management extremely difficult, or the prediction of future behaviour uncertain.

There are cases in which there might be risk of mistakes being made, and for them special care in assessment is required. It should be possible to identify early in the course of treatment these exceptional cases. If this was done it would be possible to apply special procedures in these cases, so as to reduce the possibility of error in coming to a conclusion in the context of degree of dangerousness.

There would be two factors present in cases identified as needing special assessment:

(a)   a clearly unfavourable or an unpredictable psychiatric prognosis; and

(b)   an indication that there is a risk of the patient harming other persons.

It is doubtful if either the formal psychiatric diagnosis or the legal description of a past offence would be an adequate criterion for the identification of such cases. Where, for example, a murderous assault is seen to have derived from a mental condition for which the prognosis is clearly favourable, one would not expect the case to fall within the special category unless there was a definite likelihood of relapse. The degree of care called for must be related to the potential risk to society, so that, for example, a persistent personality disorder resulting in kleptomania, but without any indication of more serious dangers, would not require the special assessment procedures. The nature of personality deviance is probably more important than a particular psychiatric label, especially where there is a factor, such as the derivation of pleasure from the commission of an offence, tending towards the repetition of serious anti-social behaviour.

Sadists and other sexual offenders and some arsonists would thus be likely to be among the candidates for the special assessment category, but each case would need to be considered individually to see whether there were elements of special obscurity (and therefore doubt about prediction) or dangerous tendencies which might resist therapeutic measures. A working party of experts in this field would be able to draw up a set of guidelines which would command understanding and acceptance in determining which patients subject to the special restrictions should be identified as needing special care in assessment.

The state of medical knowledge is continually improving and it should not be necessary to identify more than a small minority of patients subject to restrictions as needing extra precautions beyond the normal procedures. It is important that the classification should not be too freely applied. The provision of accepted criteria to assist individual consultants in applying a uniform standard of judgment should help towards this end.

Since the identification of such patients and the application of special procedures to them would be fundamentally a means of obtaining extra assurance in the interests of public safety, responsibility for this usually rests ultimately with the Home Secretary in the case of patients subject to restrictions. One may consider what part the Home Secretary should play in the classification process. The process is essentially a medical assessment which must be undertaken primarily by the consultant psychiatrist who is responsible for the patient's treatment. The consultant should be able to reach a conclusion within three months of the patient's admission to hospital, by which time he should be in possession of copies of past medical reports, police reports, etc., and will have had time to assess the patient and his initial response to treatment, by personal observation and in the light of reports by other professional personnel in the hospital. It is reasonable to assume that when the patient has been in hospital for three months, the responsible medical officer should be prepared to say whether in his opinion the case calls for special care in assessment. It is recognized however, that there might be a very few exceptional cases in which the *nature of the offence* committed might in itself give rise to such a degree of public concern that the Home Secretary would feel bound to look for special care in the assessment of the case, even though there might be no great psychiatric obscurity. The Secretary of State for Social Services, as hospital manager, should also be able to raise the question as to whether a patient at a special hospital should be so classified.

In the case of a patient detained in a secure hospital under the Mental Health Act 1983, the following considerations for the protection of the public may be summarized in the context of deciding on discharge or transfer. The final decision may be based on the following factors:

(i)   the opinion of the consultant in charge of the patient's *treatment* backed up by the conclusions of multi-disciplinary case conferences;
(ii) the supporting opinion of a second consultant;
(iii) the conclusion of an advisory body independent of the treating hospital;
(iv) the opinion of the Secretary of State for Social Services;
(v)   the decision of the Home Secretary – where relevant;
(vi) result of appeal to European Court of Human Rights at Strasbourg which may or may not be made.

Vielma *et al* (1993), studied 83 male patients who had treatment at the Rampton special hospital. They were diagnosed as suffering from psychotic disorders and all were guilty of homicide. Investigations indicated that all these patients had been mentally disordered at the material times of the homicides but *only 25 per cent were receiving treatment after discharge.*

There is increasing concern at the number of people suffering from various forms of mental disorder and who for various reasons are not receiving treatment in the community.

Mr. Jonathan Zito was stabbed to death by Christopher Clunis at Finsbury Park Tube Station, London, on 17th December 1992. Clunis had a history of paranoid schizophrenia and violence. The official enquiry made more than 50 recommendations and directed criticism at psychiatrists, community psychiatric nurses, social services, Clunis' general medical practitioner, the police and the Crown Prosecution Service for failing to bring a conviction after Clunis stabbed a fellow resident in a Southwark hostel for the homeless, some 5 months before Mr. Zito's death.

The criticisms were mainly in the context of the lack of adequate communication between the above agencies and the lack of sense of urgency in the context of alleged failure to appreciate the high degree of danger which Clunis represented.

Recommendations included the following:

As from April 1994 there will be identification of a new *Special Supervision Group* of patients – with their names kept on a national register – who would receive closer supervision and support by specialist teams. They would be selected for specialist support by multi-disciplinary teams if they fulfil two out of four criteria. They would be patients who have been detained more than once; have a history of violent or persistent offending; have failed to respond to treatment; or who are homeless. The inquiry believes there are up to 4,000 such patients nationwide.

Each team should have access to an approved social worker available 24 hours a day, 365 days a year to respond to crises.

A befriender should also be appointed for each patient. The befriender could be a relative or public volunteer. This arrangement could enable a patient's condition to be monitored and the authorities alerted in the event of deterioration.

Community psychiatric nurses should follow patients across health boundaries until responsibility is firmly transferred to another team.

Health workers should also use registers to keep track of discharged psychiatric patients who are potentially dangerous.

Under proposals unveiled by the government in August 1993, patients considered a potential danger to themselves or others are discharged from psychiatric hospitals only under strict conditions and these include the requirements that they live in a specified place, attend centres for medical care, agree to a treatment plan and have a designated minder to supervise treatment.

In January 1994, the Secretary of State for Health tightened guidelines further by making hospitals give detailed assessments of the risk involved in discharging a patient and ensure that proper care and supervision is available outside.

The committee's detailed recommendations for a *supervised discharge order* say that England and Wales should follow Scottish practice so that a patient can be recalled to a hospital during the first six months of an order, and thereafter during each subsequent 12 months. It would be possible to detain the patient, or not. "Only by permitting such power of recall will the patient be likely to comply with the treatment plans," the inquiry team said.

As far as England and Wales are concerned, the government apparently has a plan to make £45,000,000 available to provide 1,000 more beds in secure psychiatric units by 1995-96 and it is also proposed to increase the number of general psychiatric beds by 20 per cent. It is recommended that haven-type accommodations be provided for people who cannot cope with community life after leaving mental hospitals and subject to supervised discharge orders. The management of patients should *not* be determined by the economies of the marketplace. It is also stressed that the training of medical and social workers should be improved especially in the context of how to identify potentially violent individuals and police should also be trained to deal with mentally disordered persons.

The enquiry team also considered it essential that the Department of Health sets up effective *monitoring* of psychiatric services, laying down minimum standards in manpower and facilities which health authorities will be "required" to purchase. Hospitals and units should then have a contractual duty "*to satisfy an external inspectorate or accrediting body* that they have currently achieved published standards of services and facilities". *Community health services should be inspected every three years* so national standards may be maintained and improved on.

The enquiry concluded... " only if the *whole package* is provided will care in the community work effectively".

The above recommendations should become part of the legislature and be issued in the form of binding directions. Failure could mean that the Care in the Community Policy could be discontinued for the mentally disordered.

References

Ball, M. (1977) *Issues of Violence in Family Casework,* Jan. Vol. 58(1), pp.3-12..

Howells, K., Hollin, C.R. (1989) *Clinical Approaches to Violence,* 4, p.77. Pub. John Wiley & Sons; Chichester.

Sturup, G.K. (1968) "Treatment of Sexual Offenders in Herstedvester, Denmark", *Therapists Acta Psychiatrica et Neurologica Scandinavica*, Supplement 204, 44.

Rice, M.E., Quinsey, V.L., Harris, G.T. "Sexual recidivism among child molesters released from a maximum security psychiatric institution", *J. Cons. Clin. Psychol;* 1991 June, 59(3), pp.381-6.

Silver, S.B., Cohen, M.I., Spodak, M.K. "Follow-up after release of mentally disordered offenders and convicted felons n the State of Maryland", *Bull. Am. Acad. Psychiatry Law,* 1991, 17(4), pp.387-400.

Vielma, M., Hages, G.D., Larkin, E.P., Jenner, F.A. (1993) "Mentally Abnormal Homicide – a Review of a special hospital male population" , *Med. Sci. Law.*, Vol 33, No.1, pp.47-54.

Chapter XVI

Main Provisions of the Mental Health Act 1983

I shall first refer to the Mental Health Act 1959, which was a comprehensive Act in line with medical and social advances and covering all types of mental disorder. Mental illness was to a large extent placed on the same basis as physical illness.

Designation of hospitals was removed and any kind of hospital permitted to receive any type of mentally disordered person on an informal basis or under detention. The Act finally terminated the principle of compulsory segregation of the sexes.

There was a shift of emphasis from hospital to community care, and stress on integration and treatment, as opposed to segregation, isolation and custodial care. Hospitals and local authorities were given more important parts to play than under previous Acts and co-operation of the public was considered to be essential so that suitable patients could be accepted in the community.

The single term "mental disorder" included all forms of mental illness and disability and four groups of mentally disordered patients recognised as (i) mentally ill, (ii) severely subnormal, (iii) subnormal, and (iv) psychopathically disordered.

A patient aged 16 years or over could enter hospital on an informal basis even if the nearest relative withheld consent. Informal treatment of the mentally disordered was established as normal practice and compulsory powers of detention used only when other appropriate methods of dealing with the patient failed or could not be used, and where detention was considered necessary in the interest of the patient and/or the protection of other persons. Application for a patient's admission (other than informal) could be made by (i) the nearest relative, (ii) the appropriate social worker of the Local Health Authority normally after consultation with the nearest relative (except in emergencies).

The patient must have been suffering from one or more of the statutory forms of mental disorder, which rendered him/her suitable to be detained in a hospital for treatment.

Compulsory admission to hospital for assessment for a period not exceeding 28 days or emergency admission for three days was made applicable to all forms of mental disorder.

Mentally disordered patients of any age convicted in the courts could be detained in hospital for treatment if the court considered this the most suitable course.

The 1959 Act also enabled the authorities of ordinary and special hospitals to refuse admission to any person considered unsuitable and this decision caused problems which are discussed later in this chapter.

The following conditions were defined in the 1959 Act: see Table XXXI on p. 531;

(i) *Mental disorder* means mental illness, arrested or incomplete development of mind, psychopathic disorder or any other disorder or disability of mind.

(ii) *Severe subnormality* means a state of arrested or incomplete development of mind, which includes subnormality of intelligence and is of such a nature or degree that the patient is incapable of living an independent life and guarding himself against serious exploitation or will be so incapable when of an age to do so.

(iii) *Subnormality* means a state of arrested or incomplete development of mind (not amounting to severe subnormality) which includes subnormality of intelligence and is of a nature and degree which requires or is susceptible to medical treatment or other special care or training of the patient.

(iv) *Psychopathic disorder* means persistent disorder or disability of mind (whether or not accompanied by subnormality of intelligence) which results in abnormally aggressive or seriously irresponsible conduct on the part of the patient, and requires or is susceptible to medical treatment.

(v) No person is *mentally disordered* by reason only of promiscuity or other immoral conduct.

The Mental Health Act 1983, which came into operation on September 30, 1983, retains all the advances of the 1959 Act from the legal, medical and administrative points of view and introduces further amendments.

Part I

The new Act alters the definitions of mental disorders as follows:
For references in the Mental Health Act, 1959, to subnormality or

severe subnormality there shall be substituted references to *mental impairment* or *severe mental impairment*.

Severe mental impairment will henceforth mean a state of arrested or incomplete development of mind which includes severe impairment of intelligence and social functioning and is associated with abnormally aggressive or seriously irresponsible conduct on the part of the person concerned.

Mental impairment will mean a state of arrested or incomplete development of mind (not amounting to severe mental impairment) which includes significant impairment of intelligence and social functioning and is associated with abnormally aggressive or seriously irresponsible conduct on the part of the person concerned.

In this Act *psychopathic disorder* means a persistent disorder or disability of mind (whether or not including significant impairment of intelligence) which results in abnormally aggressive or seriously irresponsible conduct on the part of the person concerned.

No person is mentally disordered by reason only of promiscuity or other immoral conduct, sexual deviancy or dependence on alcohol or drugs: s.1(3) of 1983 Act.

The Royal College of Psychiatrists indicated that the new definition of *mental impairment* would include only a minority of the mentally handicapped resulting in the possible exclusion of the majority from the provision of the 1983 Act. These individuals might also be deprived of protection similar to that provided under Parts 8 and 9 of the 1959 Act and consequently they could be exposed to ill-treatment, misuse of their assets, sexual abuse and other forms of exploitation. Furthermore, increasing numbers of these patients could easily find themselves remanded to already overcrowded prison hospitals.

The definitions of severe mental impairment and mental impairment contain part of the definition of psychopathic disorder in the 1983 Act but the word "persistent" is not used.

The new definition of psychopathic disorder does not include the statement that the individual "requires or is susceptible to medical treatment" but he or she must be thought treatable, meaning that treatment is likely to alleviate or prevent further personality deterioration.

Patients requiring treatment for mental disorder may be admitted to any hospital informally and can remain on an informal basis after ceasing to be liable to be detained.

Part 2

Section 2: Admission for assessment (or for assessment followed by medical treatment) for up to 28 days. Application may be made by the nearest relative or an approved social worker. The application must be supported by two medical recommendations (one complying with s.12). They must agree that (a) the patient is suffering from mental disorder of a nature or degree which warrants the detention of the patient in hospital for assessment (or for assessment followed by medical treatment) for at least a limited period, and (b) that he should be so detained in the interests of his own health or safety or with a view to the protection of other persons.

Section 3: Admission and detention for treatment may be made on the grounds that the patient is suffering from mental illness, severe mental impairment, mental impairment or psychopathic disorder, *whatever the patient's age.*

The application must be made by the nearest relative or an approved social worker, founded upon the written recommendations of two doctors who must indicate the grounds for their opinion and why other methods of dealing with the patients are inappropriate. The grounds which may support an application are:

(a) that the patient is suffering from mental illness, severe mental impairment, psychopathic disorder or mental impairment and his mental disorder is of a nature or degree which makes it appropriate for him to receive medical treatment in hospital;

(b) in the case of psychopathic disorder or mental impairment, such treatment is likely to alleviate or prevent a deterioration of his condition; and

(c) it is necessary for the health or safety of the patient or for the protection of other persons that he should receive such treatment which cannot be provided unless he is detained under this section.

Medical recommendations must each specify that the patient is suffering from the same form of mental disorder whether or not he is described as suffering from another form. Application for admission for assessment under s.2 or treatment under s.3 may be made by the nearest relative or the appropriate social worker who must consult the nearest relative unless this is not reasonably practicable or would involve unreasonable delay. The application cannot be made if the nearest relative notifies his objection. The applicant must have personally seen the patient within 14 days ending with the date of the application which must be addressed to the managers of the particular hospital in which the vacancy is sought and a hospital is under no legal obligation to accept any patient if the latter is considered unsuitable and serious problems have arisen in this context. Patients could not legally be refused admission under summary reception orders of repealed acts, and in this context, Lord Justice Lawton stated that health service unions or nursing staff who obstruct court (hospital) orders for the admission of patients to mental hospital secure units, could be held in *contempt of court*. He made this statement in response to being told by a prison medical officer that admission to such units seemed to depend not on consultant psychiatrists but on the people working under them. (*The Guardian*, 1983).

A social worker also has authority to over-rule medical practitioners by refusing to make an application. The nearest relative (if available) would have the final word.

Section 4: Admission for assessment in emergency

In the case of "urgent necessity" provision is made for the making of an emergency application for admission to hospital but in the first instance this will be only for assessment.

The social worker or nearest relative making the application must state that the case is urgent and that the ordinary procedure for admission for assessment under s.2 would involve unnecessary delay. This statement must be verified in a medical recommendation given, if possible, by a doctor who had known the patient previously. Consequently, only one recommendation is required for this particular section. Within 72 hours after admission to hospital the recommendation ceases to have effect unless a second medical recommendation is received by the manager of the hospital when the patient may then be detained for assessment and/or treatment for 28 days in all, beginning with the day of admission.

The medical recommendations must together comply with s.12(2). *Certain mental hospitals may be designated to receive emergencies under s.4 but there is no legal obligation in this context.*

Section 5: Detention of informal patient already in hospital

(1) Application for treatment under s.3 may be made in respect of a patient detained under s.2.

(2) If it appears to the responsible medical officer or one nominated deputy that a patient already in hospital should be detained, he may report to the managers that he considers that an application should be made under Part 2 of the Act, for assessment or treatment with a view to implementing ss.2 or 3 respectively. The patient may then be detained for 72 hours beginning with the day on which the report was furnished, but if the applications are not completed within that period he must, if he wishes, be allowed to leave. The 72-hour period would include any period during which a nurse's holding power was used.

(3) A registered mental nurse or a registered nurse for mental impairment may detain a mentally disordered patient (receiving in-patient treatment) for up to six hours in the absence of a medical practitioner when it is necessary for the patient's health or safety or for the protection of others. The nurse must inform the hospital managers in writing as soon as possible.

Section 6: Conveyance to hospital

When an application has been duly completed it shall be sufficient authority to enable the applicant, or any person authorized by him, to take the patient to hospital at any time within the following periods:

(a) For assessment or treatment, within 14 days or the last medical recommendation. Sections 2 and 3 referred to in this context.

(b) In the case of an emergency application, admission must take place within 24 hours beginning at the time when the patient was examined by the practitioner giving the medical recommendation which is referred to in s.4 above, or at the time when the application is made, whichever is the earlier.

Section 7: Application for Guardianship

This section allows a patient who has attained the age of 16 years to be placed under the supervision of a guardian. The applicant may be the nearest relative or an approved social worker (who must have seen the patient within the last 14 days) and application is made to the local social services authority. The application must be based upon medical recommendations from two doctors (one approved under s.12) who have examined the patient together or within five days of each other. The patient must be agreed to suffer from one of the four forms of mental disorder and the doctor must agree that it is necessary in the interests of the welfare of the patient that he should be received into the guardianship of an individual or of the local social services authority.

Section 8: (1) *The Authority of the Guardian is limited to deciding: (i) where the patient shall live, (ii) that treatment education or training will be provided and (iii) that he or she may be visited at home by any doctor, approved social worker or other specified person.*

(4) If within the period of 14 days beginning with the day on which a guardianship application has been accepted by the local social services authority the application or any medical recommendation given for the purposes of the application, is found to be in any respect incorrect or defective, the application or recommendation may, within that period and with the consent of that authority, be amended by the person by whom it was signed; and upon such amendment being made the application or recommendation shall have effect and shall be deemed to have had effect as if it had been originally made as so amended.

Section 10: (3) If it appears to the county court, upon application made by an approved social worker, that any person other than a local social services authority having the guardianship of a patient received into guardianship under this Part of this Act has performed his functions negligently or in a manner contrary to the interests of the welfare of the patient, the court may order that the guardianship of the patient be transferred to the local social services authority or to any other person approved for the purpose by that authority.

Section 12: (1) Medical practitioners may examine patients either together or at intervals of not more than *five* days. One medical practitioner at least must be approved by the Secretary of State as specially experienced in diagnosis or treatment of mental disorder. The other should have been previously acquainted with the patient. One medical recommendation may be given by a doctor of the staff of the hospital except in the case of registered nursing homes or private patients.
(2) One of the medical recommendations for admission under ss.2 or

3 shall be given by a practitioner approved by the Secretary of State.

Section 15: Rectification of applications and recommendations

(1) If within the period of 14 days beginning with the day on which a patient has been admitted to a hospital in pursuance of an application for admission for assessment or for treatment, the application or any medical recommendation given for the purpose of the application, is found to be in any respect incorrect or defective, the application or recommendation may, *within that period and with the consent of the managers* of the hospital, be amended by the person by whom it was signed, and upon such amendment being made the application or recommendation shall be deemed to have had effect as if it had been originally made as so amended.

(2) Without prejudice to the provisions of the foregoing subsection, if within the period therein mentioned it appears to the managers of the hospital that one of the two medical recommendations on which an application for the admission of a patient is founded is insufficient to warrant the detention of the patient in pursuance of the application, they may, within that period, give notice in writing to that effect to the applicant; and where any such notice is given in respect of a medical recommendation, that recommendation shall be disregarded, but the application shall be, and shall be deemed always to have been , sufficient if:

(a) a fresh medical recommendation complying with the relevant provisions of this Part of this Act (other than the provisions relating to the time of signature and the interval between examinations) is furnished to the managers within that period; and

(b) that recommendation, and the other recommendation on which the application is founded, together comply with those provisions.

(3) Where the medical recommendations upon which an application for admission is founded, are, taken together, insufficient to warrant the detention of the patient in pursuance of the application, a notice under subs.(2) of this section may be given in respect of those recommendations.

Section 16: (1) *Position of patients subject to detention or guardianship*
If in the case of a patient who is for the time being detained in a hospital in pursuance of an application for admission for treatment, or subject to guardianship in pursuance of a guardianship application, it appears to the

appropriate medical officer that the patient is suffering from a form of mental disorder other than the form or forms specified in the application, he may furnish to the managers of the hospital, or to the guardian, as the case may be, a report to that effect; and where a report is so furnished, the application shall have effect as if that other form of mental disorder were specified in it.

(2) Where a report under sub-s.(1) above in respect of a patient detained in a hospital is to the effect that he is suffering from psychopathic disorder or mental impairment but not from mental illness or severe mental impairment the appropriate medical officer shall include in the report a statement of his opinion whether further medical treatment is likely to alleviate or prevent a deterioration of the patient's condition; and if he states that in his opinion such treatment is not likely to have that effect the authority of the managers to detain the patient shall cease.

(3) Before furnishing a report under sub-s.(1) above the appropriate medical officer shall consult one or more other persons who have been professionally concerned with the patient's treatment.

(4) Where a report is furnished under this section in respect of a patient, the managers or guardian shall cause the patient and the nearest relative to be informed.

(5) In this section "appropriate medical officer" means:

(a)   in the case of a patient who is subject to the guardianship of a person other than a local social services authority, the nominated medical attendant of the patient; and

(b)   in any other case, the responsible medical officer.

Section 17: Leave of absence from hospital
Leave of absence from hospital may be granted to a patient by the responsible medical officer who may make any conditions he considers necessary in the patient's interest or for the protection of others. He may further direct that during leave, the patient should be kept in the custody of an officer on the hospital staff or of any other person authorised by the managers.

Leave may be granted on a specific occasion or for a specific period (which may be extended), or with no time limit stated but a patient may not remain on leave for more than a continuous period of six months, after which the power of recall ceases. A fresh application for hospital care must be made if further control is needed.

Leave may be revoked and the patient recalled to the hospital by notice in writing.

Section 18: (1) *Absence without leave*
If a patient liable to be detained in hospital or under guardianship:

(a) absents himself from the hospital without leave granted under s.17; or
(b) fails to return at the expiration of leave or on being recalled; or
(c) absents himself from any place in which it is a condition of leave that he should reside,

he may be brought back to hospital (or to the place where he is required to reside) by:

(a) any authorised social worker;
(b) any officer on the staff of the hospital;
(c) any constable;
(d) any person authorised in writing by the managers.

(3) Where a patient who is for the time being subject to guardianship under this Part of this Act absents himself without leave of the guardian from the place at which he is required by the guardian to reside, he may, subject to the provisions of this section, be taken into custody and returned to that place by any officer on the staff of a local social services authority, by any constable, or by any person authorised in writing by the guardian or a local social services authority.

(4) A patient shall not be taken into custody under this section after the expiration of the period of 28 days beginning with the first day of his absence without leave; and a patient who has not returned or been taken into custody under this section within the said period shall cease to be liable to be detained or subject to guardianship, as the case may be, at the expiration of that period.

All mentally disordered patients who are absent without leave may be compulsorily returned to the institution concerned within 28 days beginning with the first day of absence. They may not be taken into custody after the expiration of this 28-day period.

Section 19: A patient detained in a hospital may be transferred to another hospital or guardian, or if under guardianship, to another local services authority, to another guardian or to hospital.

Section 20: Duration of authority for detention under s.3 or guardianship
The Mental Health Act (1983), provides that authority for detention under s.3 or guardianship under s.8 will be six months, a further six months, one year and periods of one year at a time. Within the period of two months ending on the day on which a patient would cease to be liable to detention the responsible medical officer must examine the patient and where appropriate, recommend to the hospital management committee or guardianship authority, detention or renewal of guardianship for the specified periods provided the following conditions are satisfied:

(a) the patient is suffering from mental illness, severe mental impairment, psychopathic disorder or mental impairment, and his mental disorder is of a nature or degree which makes it appropriate for him to receive medical treatment in a hospital; and

(b) such treatment is likely to alleviate or prevent a deterioration of his condition or in the case of mental illness or severe mental impairment, that the patient, if discharged is unlikely to be able to care for himself, to obtain the care which he needs or to guard himself against serious exploitation.

(c) it is necessary for the health or safety of the patient or for the protection of other persons that he should receive such treatment and that it cannot be provided unless he continues to be detained.

Before furnishing a report to the managers the responsible medical officer shall consult one or more other persons who have been professionally concerned with the patient's medical treatment.

In regard to renewal of authority for guardianship, the responsible medical officer must be satisfied that:

(a) the patient is suffering from mental illness, severe mental impairment, psychopathic disorder or mental impairment and his mental disorder is of a nature or degree which warrants his reception into guardianship; and

(b) it is necessary in the interests of the welfare of the patient or for the protection of other persons that the patient should remain under guardianship.

The guardian and the patient must be informed that authority has been given for renewal.

Section 22: (1) Where a patient who is liable to be detained by virtue of an application for admission for treatment or is subject to guardianship by virtue of a guardianship application is detained in custody in pursuance of any sentence or order passed or made by a court in the United Kingdom (including an order committing or remanding him in custody), and is so detained for a period exceeding, or for successive periods exceeding in the aggregate, six months, the application shall cease to have effect at the expiration of that period.

In the case of an individual who received treatment in hospital on the basis of an order under s.37 (*without restriction on discharge*) which was made before imprisonment, this order would presumably cease to have effect after six months imprisonment whether the individual were on remand and awaiting trial or serving a sentence.

Section 23: Powers of discharge

In addition to discharge by a tribunal, the following persons and authorities have power of discharge:

For assessment under s.2 or treatment under s.3:

The responsible medical officer.

The managers of the hospital.

The nearest relative unless discharge prevented under s.25.

Patients in a mental nursing home under ss.2 and 3 may be discharged by:

The registration authority.

The nearest relative unless discharge prevented under s.25.

The Secretary of State.

The responsible health authority (if patient maintained under contract).

Patients under guardianship may be discharged by:

The responsible medical officer.

The responsible local social services authority.

The nearest relative but s.10(3) may apply if the guardian is considered to be unsatisfactory.

Section 25: Discharge by nearest relative may be restricted

This power is extended to all mentally disordered patients detained in pursuance of an application for treatment under s.3. The conditions are as follows: Seventy-two hours' notice must be given in writing to the managers. If within this period, the responsible medical officer reports that in his opinion the patient would be likely to act in a manner dangerous to others or himself, discharge will not be allowed and the nearest relative will not have the right to order discharge again during a period of six months beginning with the date of the medical officer's report. Within the period of 28 days after being informed of refusal of discharge, the nearest relative may apply to a mental health review tribunal.

Section 26: The nearest relative is ascertained as if that person who would otherwise be the nearest relative were dead if he or she is under 18 years of age and not the husband, wife, father or mother of the patient or is a person in respect of whom the order under s.38 of Sexual Offences Act (1956) has been made and not rescinded or is not ordinarily resident in the UK. The adopted child is treated as a natural child, half-blood as whole blood and illegitimate as legitimate child of the mother.

Section 27: The Local Authority is deemed to be the nearest relative under s.10 of the Children and Young Persons Act (1969) or s.3 of the Child Care Act (1980).

Section 29: If the patient has no nearest relative or if the nearest relative unreasonably objects to making application for treatment or guardianship or exercising power of discharge contrary to the welfare of the patient or to the interest of the public, the county court may transfer the function of the nearest relative to the proper person to exercise those functions. The relative against whom the order is made may appeal against it.

Part 3

Patients concerned in criminal proceedings or under sentence
Remands to hospital

Section 35: A Crown Court or a magistrates' court may remand an accused person to a hospital specified by the court for a *report* on his mental condition. The person must be awaiting disposal of his case before a Crown Court for an offence punishable with imprisonment or convicted by a magistrates' court of an offence punishable on summary conviction with imprisonment.

The court must be satisfied on the written or oral evidence of *one* registered medical practitioner that there is reason to suspect that the person is suffering from one of the forms of mental disorder and that it would be impracticable to obtain a medical report on bail. The practitioner should be responsible for eventually making the report and indicate that arrangements for admission to hospital within seven days have been made. The order lasts for twenty-eight days initially, renewable at twenty-eight day intervals for up to twelve weeks by application to the court. The patient need not be present. The court may terminate the remand at any time. The Act authorises that an independent report may be obtained if it is needed at the request and expense of the accused.

Section 36: A Crown Court may remand a person awaiting trial to a hospital for *treatment.* The person must not be awaiting trial for an offence the sentence for which is fixed by law, e.g., murder. The person must be suffering from mental illness or severe mental impairment of a nature or degree which makes it appropriate for him to be detained for treatment. This section is not applicable to psychopathic disorder and mental impairment. Written or oral evidence of two registered medical practitioners is necessary and the practitioner who will be in charge of the patient's treatment must supply evidence to the effect that arrangements have been made for admission to hospital within seven days. The accused would be detained in a prison hospital pending admission to the psychiatric hospital.

The order for 28 days initially may be renewed at 28 day intervals for up to 12 weeks. It may be terminated at any time. An independent examination may be obtained at the request and expense of the accused.

Section 37: A hospital order may be made by a Crown or magistrates' court if satisfied that:

(a)   on the written or oral evidence of two registered medical practitioners (at least one of whom must be approved under s.12 of the Act), the offender is suffering from mental illness, severe mental impairment, mental impairment or psychopathic disorder and that either:

(i)   the mental disorder from which the offender is suffering is of a nature or degree which makes it appropriate for him to be detained in a hospital for medical treatment and in the case of psychopathic disorder or mental impairment, that such treatment is likely to alleviate or prevent a deterioration of his condition; or

(ii) in the case of an offender who has attained the age of 16 years, the mental disorder is of a nature or degree which warrants his reception into guardianship under this Act; and

(b) the court is of the opinion, having regard to all the circumstances including the nature of the offence and the character and antecedents of the offender, and to the other available methods of dealing with him, that the most suitable method of disposing of the case is by means of an order under this section.

A hospital order for admission of an offender to a hospital shall not be made unless the court is satisfied on the written or oral evidence of the registered medical practitioner who would be in charge of his treatment or of some other person representing the managers of the hospital that arrangements have been made for his admission to that hospital in the event of such an order being made by the court, and for his admission to it within the period of 28 days beginning with the date of the making of such an order; and the court may, pending his admission within that period, give such directions as it thinks fit for his conveyance to and detention in a place of safety which is invariably the hospital wing of a local prison.

A hospital order can be made in respect of mentally disordered persons of any age.

The order is for six months unless renewed for a further six months (then annually). A magistrates' court may make a hospital order without recording a conviction.

An order placing an offender under the guardianship of a local social services authority or of any other person (in this Act referred to as "a guardianship order") shall not be made under this section unless the court is satisfied that that authority or person is willing to receive the offender into guardianship.

A hospital or guardianship order shall not be made unless the offender is described by each of the practitioners whose evidence is taken into account under that subsection as suffering from the same one of those forms of mental disorder, whether or not he is also described by either of them as suffering from another of them.

If in the case of a person of or over the age of 14 years who is convicted by a magistrates' court of an offence punishable on summary conviction with imprisonment and the conditions for making a hospital order are satisfied and it appears to the court, having regard to the nature of the offence, the antecedents of the offender and the risk of his committing further offences if set at large, that if a hospital order is made a restriction order should also be made, the court may, instead of making a hospital order or dealing with him in any other manner, commit him in custody to the Crown Court to be dealt with in respect of the offence.

Section 38: Where a person is convicted before the Crown Court of an offence punishable with imprisonment (other than an offence the sentence for which is fixed by law) or is convicted by a magistrates' court of an offence punishable on summary conviction with imprisonment and the court before or by which he is convicted is satisfied, on the written or oral evidence of two registered medical practitioners:

(a) that the offender is suffering from mental illness, psychopathic disorder, severe mental impairment or mental impairment; and

(b) that there is reason to suppose that the mental disorder from which the offender is suffering is such that it may be appropriate for a hospital order to be made in his case, the court may make an *interim hospital order*, authorising his admission and detention in a specified hospital. One of the doctors supplying evidence should be the one who would be in charge of the person's treatment in hospital, and he must indicate to the court that arrangements have been made for admission within 28 days.

The two doctors must agree that the accused is suffering from one of the forms of mental disorder.

The order has a limit of 12 weeks initially, renewable at 28-day intervals for up to six months (without the necessity of the patient being present). There is no right of access to a tribunal.

In the case of an offender who is subject to an *interim hospital order* the court may make a *hospital order* without his being brought before the court.

A court has the right to decide not to issue a hospital order even if the necessary criteria are fulfilled.

Regional health authorities will be required to give information to courts, on request, about what hospital places are available for mentally disordered offenders.

Section 41: (1) *Restriction Orders*

Where a hospital order is made by a Crown Court, a restriction order with or without limit of time may be added on the basis of the following considerations:

(i) the nature of the offence.
(ii) The previous convictions of the offender.
(iii) The risk of his committing further offences if free in the community.
(iv) Restriction on discharge is necessary for the protection of the public from serious harm.

(2) Oral evidence is required from at least one of the doctors supplying the medical recommendations and he must be recognised under s.12(2).

(3) The provisions of Part II of the Act relating to duration, renewal and expiration of authority for detention shall not apply. The nearest relative will have no direct access to a tribunal and the provisions of s.66 will not apply.

The Secretary of State has authority to grant leave, recall transfer or to order conditional or absolute discharge.

(4) A hospital order may continue in force under the relevant provisions where a restriction order ceases to have effect.

(5) While a person is subject to a restriction order the responsible medical officer shall at such intervals (not exceeding one year) as the Secretary of State may direct examine and report to the Secretary of State on that person. (See ss.70 and 71 for the rules governing applications by restricted patients to tribunals and ss.73 and 74 for rules governing their discharge).

A magistrates' court cannot make a restriction order.

Section 46: The Secretary of State may by warrant direct that any person who is required to be kept in custody during Her Majesty's pleasure shall be detained in such hospital (not being a mental nursing home) as may be specified in the warrant.

A direction under this section in respect of any person shall have the same effect as a hospital order together with a restriction order, made without limitation of time.

Section 47: Removal of prisoners to hospital

Where the Secretary of State is satisfied by reports of at least two medical practitioners in the case of a person serving a sentence of imprisonment:

(a)   that he is suffering from mental illness, mental impairment, severe mental impairment or psychopathic disorder and

(b)   the nature or degree of the mental disorder is such as to make it appropriate for him to be detained in hospital for medical treatment, and, in the case of psychopathic disorder or mental impairment, that such treatment is likely to alleviate or prevent a deterioration of his condition and that the patient is described in each of those reports as suffering from the same form of disorder, whether or not he is also described in either of them as suffering from another form, the Secretary will issue a *transfer direction* for the removal of the person from prison to a mental hospital where a vacancy has been provided by an area health authority of the DHSS. A transfer direction will not be issued unless a vacancy is available in a hospital (not being a mental nursing home).

The authorities of an ordinary or special hospital may agree in principle to accept a patient on the basis of s.47 but a specific date for admission may not be given. The authority for the transfer direction lapses if the patient is not transferred to the hospital *within 14 days of issue* and in these circumstances fresh applications to the Home Office would be necessary and the patient would continue to serve his sentence in a prison hospital.

Section 48: Removal to hospital of other prisoners

If in the case of a person to whom this section applies the Secretary of State is satisfied by the like reports as are required for the purpose of the last foregoing section that that person is suffering from *mental illness or severe mental impairment* of a nature or degree which warrants the detention of the patient in a hospital for *urgent* medical treatment, the Secretary of State shall have the like power of giving a *transfer direction* in respect of him under the section as if he were serving a sentence of imprisonment.

This section applies to:

(i)   persons detained in a prison or remand centre, not being persons serving a sentence of imprisonment;

(ii)   persons remanded in custody by a magistrates' court;

(iii) persons detained under the Immigration Act 1971;

(iv) civil prisoners committed by a court to prison for a limited term (including persons committed to prison in pursuance of writ of attachment) not being persons falling to be dealt with under s.47 of this Act.

It may be noted that no intervals are specified during which medical practitioners must examine a patient for the purpose of ss.37, 47 and 48 of the Act. The recommendations under these sections are not legal documents.

Section 49: The Secretary of State may add a direction restricting discharge in respect of a patient removed to hospital on the basis of ss.47 or 48 of the Act.

While a person is subject to a restriction direction the responsible medical officer shall at such intervals (not exceeding one year) as the Secretary of State may direct examine and report to the secretary of State on that person.

The Mental Health Act 1983 enables the period of restriction to expire at the EDR (earliest date of release) rather than at the end of the period of sentence. This is equivalent to granting the patient the full one-third remission of sentence. The Act also indicates that restriction orders apply to offender patients only for the protection of the public from serious harm. In practice restriction orders are almost invariably applied when offenders are committed to special hospitals on the basis of ss.37, 47 and 48 of the Act. However, restriction orders are frequently imposed when offenders who may not represent a serious danger to the public are sent to ordinary mental hospitals on the basis of ss.47 or 48. This procedure is considered justified on the grounds that the offender is still under the jurisdiction of the Home Office until sentence has expired.

The following additional provisions of the Mental Health Act 1983 are described and reference is also made to certain important provisions some of which were included in earlier sections of this chapter.

Part 4:

Section 57: Treatments of special concern may be given only with the patient's consent (independently attested) *and* the written agreement of a doctor appointed by the Mental Health Act Commission and written consent of two other persons appointed by the Secretary of State (not being registered medical practitioners). The doctor appointed by the Commission must also consult the above mentioned two other persons who have been professionally concerned with the patient's treatment and one shall be a nurse and the other neither a nurse nor a doctor. Surgery for destroying functioning brain tissue and the implantation of hormones with the object of modifying sexual urge would be included in this section which also applies to informal patients.

Section 58: Treatments which may be given with the patient's consent *or* written agreement of an independent doctor appointed by the Commission who must consult two people from other professions who have been concerned with the patient's treatment before giving consent. One of these two people shall be a nurse and the other neither a nurse nor a doctor. Electroconvulsant therapy and drug treatment prolonged beyond three months would be relevant here.

Medications may be given without consent and at the discretion of the doctor in charge of the patient's treatment and without a second opinion but not for more than three months. After which the opinion must be sought of an independent doctor who must consult two other persons as described above. This section relates exclusively to *detained* patients. A patient may withdraw consent before treatment is completed.

The doctor referred to above as appointed by the Commission is distinct from the responsible medical officer in charge of the patient's treatment.

Section 62: Allows treatment to be given without the patient's consent in order to save life or prevent permanent or serious deterioration in a patient's condition. Minimum treatment necessary to prevent violence or danger to himself or others is also permissible. However, any treatments given must not be irreversible or hazardous. In this respect electroconvulsant treatment could be permitted but not psychosurgery.

Sexual deviation, alcohol and/or drug dependence *per se* are excluded from the definition of mental disorder in general and psychopathic disorder in particular.

Restriction orders may be applied only "for protection of the public from serious harm". Responsible medical officers must send yearly reports on these patients to the Secretary of State.

Convicted persons may be sent to hospital by courts on the basis of interim hospital orders for up to six months for the purpose of assessing the appropriateness of a full hospital order.

Remands to hospitals for medical reports, assessments and treatments are also recommended.

The Act indicates also that informal psychiatric patients in hospitals will be able to make a declaration which allows their names to be included on the electoral register.

The definitions of mental impairment and severe mental impairment stress significant and severe impairment not only of intellectual but also of social functioning.

Psychopathically disordered and mentally impaired patients may only be detained in hospital if they are thought treatable, meaning that treatment is considered likely to alleviate or prevent deterioration. The Mental Health Act 1960, relating to Scotland, specifies that a patient may not be detained in hospital unless the mental disorder requires or is susceptible to medical treatment and all forms of mental disorder are included in this context. Mentally ill patients and those suffering from severe mental impairment may continue to be detained in hospitals in England and Wales on and after September 30, 1983, even if a definite statement cannot be made to the effect that treatment is likely to alleviate or prevent mental and/or physical deterioration.

Mental welfare officers were replaced by approved social workers from October 20, 1984.

There is a legal obligation on hospital managers to do what they can to ensure that detained patients understand their legal status and their rights and also to give written information to the patient's nearest relative if possible. Furthermore, hospital managers must not discharge a detained patient without first informing the nearest relative unless the patient or the relative requested that this information be withheld. The patient would obviously not be discharged if considered a danger to the nearest relative.

The district health authority and the local social services department will have the responsibility of providing after-care services for any person who has been detained under ss.3 or 37 of the Act and this responsibility will continue until the two authorities are satisfied that the person concerned is no longer in need of such services. These after-care services are arranged in co-operation with relevant voluntary agencies.

A new legal framework for taking decisions about medical treatment for mentally incapacitated patients has been proposed by the Law Commission, the official law reform body for England and Wales. The proposals would plug a gap in the law under which nobody, not even a court, can consent to treatment for adult patients unable to decide for themselves. At present a court can declare only that doctors giving or discontinuing treatment would not be committing a crime or a civil assault.

The framework would cover unconscious patients and those who are demented or too mentally handicapped or mentally ill to take a particular decision about treatment. It would allow substitute decisions to be taken "at the lowest appropriate level and with the least possible procedural formality." (1993).

Mental Health Review Tribunals

Part 5

Section 65: A mental health review tribunal has been appointed for each of the 15 regional hospital areas in England and Wales.

Each Tribunal consists of the following members appointed by the Lord Chancellor:

(a) persons with legal experience, one of whom must be appointed as chairman;

(b) medical practitioners, appointed after consultation with the Secretary of State;

(c) persons appointed, also after consultation with the Secretary of State, who have experience of administration, knowledge of social services or other qualifications or experience considered suitable.

Other members constituting the tribunal for the hearing of applications shall be appointed by the chairman. Of these:

(a) one or more must be appointed from legal members;

(b) one or more must be appointed from medical members; and

(c) one or more from category (c) but not legal or medical members.

Jurisdiction may be exercised by any three or more members of a tribunal. The Mental Health Act 1983 doubled the frequency of access to mental health review tribunals and consequently detained patients who number about 5,000 including those on conditional discharge from hospital will in future have these increased rights of appeal.

Section 66: Applications may be made to Tribunals by a *patient* where:

(a) a patient is admitted to a hospital in pursuance of an application for admission for assessment, within 14 days beginning with the day of admission;

(b) a patient is admitted to a hospital in pursuance of an application for admission for treatment, within six months beginning with the day of admission;

(c) a patient is received into guardianship in pursuance of a guardianship application, within six months beginning with the day on which the application is accepted;

(d) a report is furnished under s.16 in respect of a patient within 28 days beginning with the day on which the applicant has been informed that the report has been furnished;

(e) a patient is transferred from guardianship to a hospital in pursuance of regulations made under s.19, within six months beginning with the day on which the patient is transferred; and

(f) a report is furnished under s.20 above in respect of a patient and the patient is not discharged, within the period for which authority for detention or guardianship is renewed by virtue of the report.

Applications may be made to tribunals by the *nearest relative* in the following instances:

(i) as in (d) above;

(ii) where a report is furnished under s.25 in respect of a patient who is detained in pursuance of an application for admission for treatment, within 28 days beginning with the day on which the applicant is informed that the report has been furnished; and

(iii) where an order is made under s.29 above in respect of a patient who is or subsequently becomes liable to be detained or subject to guardianship under Part II of this Act, within 12 months beginning with the date of the order and within any subsequent 12 month period during which the order continues in force.

Section 67: (1) The Secretary of State may, if he thinks fit, at any time refer to a mental health review tribunal the case of any patient who is liable to be detained or subject to guardianship under Part II of this Act.

Section 68: (1) Where a patient who is admitted to a hospital in pursuance of an application for admission for treatment or a patient who is transferred from guardianship to hospital does not exercise his right to apply to a mental health review tribunal, the managers of the hospital shall at the expiration of the period for making such an application refer the patient's case to a tribunal unless an application has then been made on his behalf by the nearest relative under ss.66 or 67(1).

(2) If the authority for the detention of a patient in a hospital is renewed under s.20 and a period of three years (or, if the patient has not attained the age of 16 years, one year) has elapsed since his case was last considered by a mental health review tribunal, whether on his own application or otherwise, the managers of the hospital shall refer his case to such a tribunal.

Applications and references concerning Part III patients concerned in criminal proceedings or under sentence

Section 69: (1) Application to a mental health review tribunal may also be made:

(a) in respect of a patient admitted to a hospital in pursuance of a hospital order, (without restriction on discharge) by the nearest relative of the patient in the period between the expiration of six months and the expiration of 12 months beginning with the date of the order and in any subsequent period of 12 months; and

(b) in respect of a patient placed under guardianship by a guardianship order:

(i) by the patient, within the period of six months beginning with the date of the order; or

(ii) by the nearest relative of the patient, within the period of 12 months beginning with the date of the order and in any subsequent period of 12 months.

(2) Where a person detained in a hospital is treated as subject to a

hospital order or transfer direction and the orders restricting discharge cease to have effect, that person may make an application to a mental health review tribunal in the period of six months beginning with the date on which the restriction order ceased to have effect.

Section 70: A patient who is a restricted patient within the meaning of s.79 and is detained in a hospital may apply to a mental health review tribunal:

(a)   in the period between the expiration of six months and the expiration of 12 months beginning with the date of the relevant hospital order or transfer direction; and

(b)   in any subsequent period of 12 months.

Section 71: (1) The Secretary of State may at any time refer the case of a restricted patient to a mental health review tribunal.

(2) The Secretary of State shall refer to a mental health review tribunal the case of any restricted patient detained in a hospital whose case has not been considered by such a tribunal, whether on his own application or otherwise, within the last three years.

(5) Where a person who is treated as subject to a hospital order and a restriction order by virtue of an order under s.5(1) of the Criminal Procedure (Insanity) Act 1964 does not exercise his right to apply to a mental health review tribunal in the period of six months beginning with the date of that order, the Secretary of State shall at the expiration of that period refer his case to a tribunal.

Discharge of patients by mental health review tribunals

Section 72: (1) Where application is made to a mental health review tribunal by or in respect of a patient who is liable to be detained under this Act, the tribunal may in any case direct that the patient be discharged, and:

(a)   the tribunal shall direct the discharge of a patient liable to be detained under s.2 above if they are satisfied:

(i)   that he is not then suffering from mental disorder or from mental disorder of a nature or degree which warrants his *detention in a hospital for assessment* (or for assessment followed by medical treatment) for at least a limited period; or

(ii) that his detention as aforesaid is not justified in the interests of his own health or safety or with a view to the protection of other persons;

(b) the tribunal shall direct the discharge of a patient liable to be detained otherwise than under s.2 above if they are satisfied:

(i) that he is not then suffering from mental illness, psychopathic disorder, severe mental impairment or mental impairment or from any of those forms of disorder of a nature or degree which makes it appropriate for him to be liable to be detained in a hospital for medical treatment; or

(ii) that it is not necessary for the health or safety of the patient or for the protection of other persons that he should receive such treatment; or

(iii) in the case of successful application on the basis of s.25, that the patient, if released, would not be likely to act in a manner dangerous to other persons or to himself.

(2) In the case of psychopathically disordered and mentally impaired patients, a tribunal shall have regard to the likelihood of medical treatment alleviating or preventing a deterioration of the patient's condition in deciding on discharge, and in the case of a patient suffering from mental illness or severe mental impairment, to the likelihood of the patient if discharged, being able to care for himself, to obtain the care he needs or to guard himself against serious exploitation.

(3) A tribunal may recommend leave of absence with a view to eventual discharge.

(4) After hearing an application, the tribunal may direct that a patient be discharged from guardianship and *shall* so direct if satisfied:

(a) that he is not then suffering from mental illness, psychopathic disorder, mental impairment or severe mental impairment; or

(b) that it is not necessary in the interests of the welfare of the patient or for the protection of other persons, that the patient should continue under guardianship.

(5) If a tribunal does not direct a patient's discharge, it may reclassify the patient by substituting for the form of mental disorder from which the

patient was stated to be suffering in the application for his admission to hospital or reception into guardianship, such other forms of mental disorder as the tribunal think appropriate.

Section 73: (1) A tribunal shall direct the absolute discharge of a patient subject to a restriction order if satisfied:

(a)   as to the matters mentioned in para.(b)(i) or (ii) of s.72(1) above; and
(b)   that it is not appropriate for the patient to remain liable to be recalled to hospital for further treatment.

(2) Where in the case of any such patient as is mentioned in sub-s.(1) above the tribunal are satisfied as to the matters referred to in para.(a) of that sub-s. but not as to the matter referred to in para.(b) of that sub-s. the tribunal shall direct the conditional discharge of the patient.

(3) Where a patient is absolutely discharged under this section he shall thereupon cease to be liable to be detained by virtue of the relevant hospital order under s.37 and the restriction order under s.41 shall cease to have effect accordingly.

(4) Where a patient is conditionally discharged under this section:

(a)   he may be recalled by the Secretary of State;
(b)   the patient shall comply with such conditions (if any) as may be imposed at the time of discharge by the tribunal or at any subsequent time by the Secretary of State.

(6) Where a restriction order in respect of a patient ceases to have effect after he has been conditionally discharged under this section the patient shall, unless previously recalled, be deemed to be absolutely discharged on the date when the order ceases to have effect and shall cease to be liable to be detained by virtue of the relevant hospital order.

(7) A tribunal may defer a direction for the conditional discharge of a patient until such arrangements as appear to the tribunal to be necessary for that purpose have been made to their satisfaction.

Section 74: (1) Where a patient subject to a direction restricting discharge under s.49, applies to a mental health review tribunal, the Secretary of State must be notified by the tribunal if the patient is entitled to be absolutely or conditionally discharged under s.73, and if not discharged that he should continue to be detained in hospital.

Table XXXI

A few comparisons between the old and new Acts

1959 Act	1983 Act
Section 25 authorized detention for 28 days for observation	*Section 2* substitutes "assessment" for observation. Detention for 28 days on the recommendations of two doctors to be changed so that the maximum time between examinations will be reduced from seven to five days. Patients detained under s.2 will be able to apply to a mental health review tribunal within the first 14 days of detention.
Section 26 Psychopathically disordered and mentally impaired persons could only be detained for treatment if under the age of 21 years and could not be detained after the age of 25 years unless discharge restricted under s.48.	*Section 3* Age limits to be removed and treatability test to be imposed for psychopathically disordered and mentally impaired patients. Duration of authority to detain reduced from one year to six months in first instance and renewable for a year at a time. More opportunities therefore to apply to mental health review tribunals. Medical officer must confirm that treatment cannot be provided unless patient detained.
Section 29 authorized admission within 3 days of the signing of the medical recommendation.	*Section 4* indicates that the patient must be admitted to hospital within 24 hours of the signing of the medical recommendation or the making of the application, whichever is the earlier. Right to make emergency application restricted to patient's nearest relative or approved social worker and this condition also applies to ss.2 and 3 applications.
Section 30(2) gave power in an emergency to prevent informal patients leaving hospital for up to three days but only on the authority of a doctor.	*Section 5* indicates that power of detention to be exercised by any doctor on the staff of hospital who is nominated by the doctor in charge of the patient's treatment. Registered mental nurse or registered nurse for mental impairment will be able to invoke a holding power until the arrival of a doctor, for up to six hours.

Table XXXII

Numerical Comparison of Some Section Changes

	1959 Act	1983 Act
Admissions for assessment	Section 25	Section 2
Admission for treatment	Section 26	Section 3
Admission for assessment in cases of emergency	Section 29	Section 4
Detention of patient already in hospital	Section 30	Section 5
Time limits in context of application for admission	Section 31	Section 6
Application for guardianship	Section 33	Section 7
Effect of guardianship application	Section 34	Section 8
Regulations for guardianship	Section 35	Section 9
Medical Recommendations		
(Approval by Secretary of State)	Section 28	Section 12
Rectification of applications and recommendations	Section 32	Section 15
Reclassification of patients	Section 38	Section 16
Leave of absence from hospital	Section 39	Section 17
Return and readmission of patients absent without leave	Section 40	Section 18
Regulations as to transfer of patients	Section 41	Section 19
Duration of authority for detention or guardianship	Section 43	Section 20
Authority to discharge patients	Section 47	Section 23
Restrictions on discharge by nearest relative	Section 48	Section 25
Remand to hospital for report on mental condition		
of accused	-	Section 35
Remand of accused person to hospital for treatment	-	Section 36
Hospital and guardianship orders	Section 60	Section 37
Interim hospital orders	-	Section 38
Restriction orders	Section 65	Section 41
Transfer to hospital of sentenced prisoners	Section 72	Section 47
Removal to hospital of other prisoners	Section 73	Section 48
Restriction on discharge of prisoners removed to hospital	Section 74	Section 49
Correspondence of patients	Section 36	Section 134
Protection for staff	Section 141	Section 139

Differences between Mental Health Legislation in England/Wales and Scotland

The Mental Health Act 1983 is applicable to England and Wales and the Mental Health (Scotland) Act 1984 is now in force. Changes which have been effected in both Acts bring them more into line with each other than formerly but significant differences remain.

Definition of mental disorder

Section 1 of the 1983 Act for England and Wales contains a much more detailed definition of mental disorder than does section 1(2) of the 1984 (Scotland) Act which defines mental disorder simply as "mental illness or mental handicap however caused or manifested".

The grounds for compulsory admission to hospital are set out in s.17(1) of the 1984 Act and the conditions for reception into guardianship in ss.36 to 42 of the same Act. Taken together the various definitions and the grounds for compulsory admission to hospital or reception into guardianship, show some basic similarities in both Acts. One exception which persists is that the 1983 Act for England and Wales provides that a person suffering from psychopathic disorder may be admitted to and detained in hospital for treatment if such treatment is likely to alleviate or prevent a deterioration of his or her condition whereas the 1984 Act for Scotland does not define psychopathic disorder and continues to *exclude* a persistent disorder of the mind which is manifested *only* by abnormally aggressive or seriously irresponsible conduct, as a condition which on its own, would justify detention.

Admission procedure and renewal of detention

The major differences between the two Acts reflects the different court systems in England and Wales on the one hand and Scotland on the other. The Scottish Sheriff is a Judge who has no exact counterpart in England and Wales and there are no Mental Health Review Tribunals in Scotland. Furthermore, applications for admission must be approved by the Sheriff under s.21(1) and medical recommendations may be scrutinized by him under s.21(2) in the event of objections to applications for detention.

Under the Scotland Act, all compulsory admissions are initiated on the basis of *emergency* admission under s.24 when the patient may not be detained for more than 72 hours unless s.26 is implemented when detention for a further 28 days is authorized and the patient may when necessary, be detained under s.30(1) for two further periods each of six months and subsequently for periods each of 12 months.

There is in Scotland no equivalent to the provision in s.2 of the 1983 Act for England and Wales, for *initial* admission for 28 days for assessment. In Scotland, renewal of authority for detention is effected by the responsible medical officer furnishing the appropriate report under s.30(3) to the managers of the hospital and the Mental Welfare Commission, within two months before authority for detention is due to expire.

Offender patients

The Secretary of State for Scotland is responsible for both home and health affairs and he exercises a similar discretion in relation to patients under restriction orders to that which in England and Wales is exercised by the Secretary of State.

The criminal justice functions concerned with mentally disordered offenders carried out in England by the Home Office, and the health functions which rest with the DHSS, are more closely integrated in Scotland through the Scottish Home and Health Department. It should be noted, in passing, that provisions relating to the remand and trial of mentally disordered offenders in Scotland were removed from the 1984 Act to the Criminal Procedure (Scotland) Act 1975.

A difference in practice rather than legislation concerns medical recommendations to courts. In England and Wales it is normal practice for one of the medical recommendations to be given by a member of the prison medical service and the other by a NHS psychiatrist, whereas in Scotland the usual practice is that both recommendations are given by the NHS consultants, one of whom will be on the staff of the receiving hospital. It is thought that this direct involvement of hospital psychiatrists, including those at the state hospital, facilitates the work of the courts and the transfer of patients between the state hospital and other hospitals and, where appropriate between prisons and hospitals.

Mental Welfare Commission

The Mental Health Act Commission in England and Wales does not have quite so extensive a range of functions and powers as the Mental Welfare Commission for Scotland. For example, it does not have power to discharge patients, nor will its proceedings in inquiries have court privilege in contrast to the Commission for Scotland.

Some Differences Between the Mental Health (Northern Ireland) Order 1986 and The Mental Health Act 1983

Section 3 of the Northern Ireland Act indicates that Mental Disorder includes mental illness and arrested or incomplete development of mind. Reference is not made to mental impairment, severe mental impairment or psychopathic disorder. This somewhat simpler legislation facilitates executive action and makes the work of the judiciary and psychiatrists less complicated, especially in the context of court proceedings where conflicting opinions tend to surround attempts to define the psychopath. This may disappoint some psychiatrists. Compulsory admission is initially on a *temporary* basis.

Section 4 is the equivalent of s.2 of the Mental Health Act 1983. The application is made by the nearest relative or approved social worker. The applicant must have seen the patient within 14 days immediately prior to the admission date. In Northern Ireland only one recommendation is required for admission under this Section. The patient must be admitted within two days beginning with the date of the medical examination, which forms the basis of the medical recommendation, and must (on admission) be examined by the resident medical officer on the staff of the receiving hospital or a medical officer appointed by the commission for that purpose, and a written report sent to the responsible board. If this report is in agreement with the recommendation, the patient may be detained for not more than seven days (beginning with the day of admission) unless s.12 is implemented. Section 4 means admission for *assessment*.*

Section 12 is the equivalent of s.3 of the Mental Health Act 1983. When during the period for which the patient is detained for assessment he is examined by the resident medical officer or a medical practitioner appointed by the commission for that purpose and a report is made on the prescribed form to the responsible board, recommending detention under s.12, he may be detained for six months beginning with the day of admission. If within one month ending with the last day of detainment, the patient is examined by one of the above mentioned medical officers, who sends a report to the responsible board recommending a further period of detention, the patient may be detained for a further period of six months and subsequently for periods of six months, twelve months and twelve months on the basis of the same procedures.

Section 44 is equivalent to s.37 of the Mental Health Act 1983. The relevant Health and Social Services Board designates the hospital to which the patient is to be admitted. This is a considerable advantage in comparison with England and Wales where a hospital order under s.37 cannot be made unless the authority of a particular hospital is willing to receive the patient. This decision could be influenced by the attitudes of nursing staff, NUPE and COHSE.

Orders restricting discharge are made under s.47 of the Northern Ireland Act. Section 110 of this Act makes provision for "special accommodation"

---

* There is no equivalent in the Northern Ireland Act, to emergency admission under Section 4 of the Mental Health Act 1983.

for mentally disordered persons who require treatment under conditions of special security because of their dangerous, violent or criminal propensities.

Section 190 of the 1931 Mental Treatment Act for the *Republic of Ireland*, deals with voluntary admissions and ss.162 and 184 deal with compulsory detention. Section 207 deals with the transfer of dangerous patients who also suffer from serious mental disorder, from local authority psychiatric hospitals or direct from criminal courts, to the Central Mental Hospital, Dundrum, Dublin. The latter is the Republic's only secure psychiatric hospital. Future legislation will make it more difficult to detain patients involuntarily which will require certification by 2 doctors. Review bodies are also introduced. This Act refers to unsoundness of mind, mental illness, addiction to drugs or intoxicants (including alcohol), and perverted conduct but psychopathic disorder and mental handicap are not specifically defined. However, s.184 para.4, allows for *compulsory* detention of drug addicts or alcoholics who require at least 6 months for recovery.

References

Mental Health Act 1959 7 & 8 Eliz. 2 Ch. 72 (Pub. HMSO).

NAMII Guide to the Mental Health Act 1959, by Aphra L. Hargrove, NAMII, London.

"Consent to psychiatric treatment: practical implications of Mental Health (Amendment) Bill (1982)", *Brit. Med. J.*, 284, 1613-16.

"Mental Health (Amendment) Bill", (1982) *Brit. Med. J.*, 284, 1053.

"Psychiatry in Practice" (1982) 1, 3, 46-51, *Medical News Group.*

Gunn, J. (1981) "Reform of Mental Health Legislation", *Brit. Med. J.*, 283, 1487-88.

Mental Health Act (Northern Ireland) 1961, Reprinted from *Northern Ireland Legal Quarterly,* 16, No.3, September 1965.

Mental Health (Scotland) Act 1960; *Some differences from Mental Health Act 1959;* Scottish Home and Health Department; (personal communication, May, 1982).

Mental Health (amendment) Act 1982 DHSS Health Circular.

Summary of Mental Health Act 1983 Royal College of Psychiatrists.

"Judge attacks power of mental hospital workers", *The Guardian,* 1983, June 10.

New Law proposed for Treating Mentally Incapacitated People, Law Commission, (1993).

Addendum
Criminal Justice and Public Order Act
1994

The Criminal Justice and Public Order Act deals with: young offenders, bail, court procedure, DNA, prevention of terrorism, obscenity, pornography and videos, prison services, public order, sexual offences and other miscellaneous matters.

Young Offenders

Section 1: Provides a new sentence, the secure training order, for persistent offenders aged 12-14.

Section 7: Allows the Secretary of State to contract out the design, building and management of secure training centres.

Section 16: Extends the category of serious offences for which children and young people may receive extended periods of detention.

Section 17: Doubles the maximum sentence of detention for 15-17 year olds in a young offenders institution.

Section 19: Allows the independent sector as well as local authorities to provide secure accommodation for juveniles.

Section 20: Gives courts the power to remand 12-14 year olds to local authority secure accommodation.

Section 24: Gives police the power, in exceptional circumstances, to detain 12-14 year olds in police stations.

Bail

Section 25: Ensures that an individual charged with murder, manslaughter or rape and previously convicted of one of those offences is remanded in custody without the prospect of bail.

Section 26: Removes the right to bail for an individual charged with an offence allegedly committed while on bail.

Section 27: Allows conditions to be attached to the grant of police bail.

Section 28: Allows the police to deny bail for an individual charged with an imprisonable offence in order to prevent offending on bail.

Section 29: Provides a power of arrest for breach of bail.

Section 30: Allows a court to reconsider a decision to grant bail when new information comes to light.

Court Procedure

Section 32: Removes the current requirement for a Judge to warn the jury over uncorroborated evidence in sexual offence or accomplice cases.

Sections 34-38: Allows a court to draw inferences from a suspect's failure to answer police questions or refusal to give evidence in court.

Section 40: Disqualifies people on bail from serving on juries.

Sections 41-42: Clarifies the arrangements for determining whether a disabled person should serve on a jury and that an individual may be excused jury service on religious grounds.

Section 44: Replaces all forms of committal hearings with an administrative procedure for transferring cases from the magistrates' court to the Crown Court.

Section 48: Provides sentence discounts for those pleading guilty at an early stage in the court process.

Section 49: Allows for a juvenile charged with a serious offence who is unlawfully at large to be identified.

Section 51: Creates a new offence of intimidating a witness, juror or person assisting in the investigation of an offence.

Police Powers to Take Samples

Section 55: Allows the police to take non-intimate body samples for DNA analysis from anyone charged with or convicted of a recordable offence.

Section 59: Extends police powers of search on arrest to allow a person's mouth to be examined for hidden substances.

Section 60: Allows a senior police officer to approve stop and search operations for offensive weapons for a limited time and in a limited area where there are reasonable grounds for believing that serious violence may take place in that area.

Public Order

Sections 61-62: Extends new powers to the police to direct trespassers to leave land and to remove vehicles if they fail to comply with such directions.

Sections 63-67: Gives the police new powers to prevent and stop raves.

Sections 68-71: Provides new sanctions against aggravated and mass trespass.

Sections 72-74: Provides greater protection against squatters for owners and occupiers of property.

Sections 75-76: Gives new criminal sanctions against squatters who fail to leave premises within 24 hours after an interim possession order has been served or who return as trespassers within a year.

Sections 77-80: Gives local authorities new powers against illegal campers and removes the current duty of local authorities to provide gypsy caravan sites.

Prevention of Terrorism

Section 81: Provides new police powers against terrorists to stop and search vehicles and their occupants, and to stop pedestrians to search anything they are carrying.

Section 82: Creates two new offences of possessing items intended for terrorist purposes and possessing information likely to be of use to terrorists in planning or carrying out acts of violence.

Section 83: Provides greater powers for the investigation of terrorist organizations' financial resources.

Obscenity, Pornography and Videos

Section 84: Clarifies the law to ensure that possession of child pornography simulated by computer graphics is an offence.

Sections 86, 87 & 91: Increases the maximum penalty for possession of an indecent photograph of a child to include a term of imprisonment, and make the enforcement of current laws against pornography more effective.

Section 88: Increases penalties under the Video Recordings Act 1984 for supplying unclassified videos (ie, ones which have not been submitted to the British Board of Film Classification (BBFC) or have been refused a classification by the BBFC) to a maximum of two years' imprisonment and an unlimited fine.

Section 89: Restricts the circumstances in which videos are exempt from the requirement to be classified by the BBFC.

Section 90: Sets down in statute the criteria to be followed by the BBFC in deciding on the classification of videos, and allows the Home Secretary to institute a procedure for the BBFC to review classification decisions made before the new criteria come into force.

Section 92: Increases the maximum penalty for making an obscene or malicious telephone call.

Prison Services

Sections 93-101: Amends and improves current provision for the contracting out in England and Wales of prison services and prisoner escort functions, including a provision allowing for maritime penal establishments.

Sections 102-117: Provides for the first time prisons and prisoner escorts to be contracted out in Scotland.

Sections 118-125: Provides for the contracting out in Northern Ireland of prisoner escort functions.

Section 126-128: Enables organizations representing prison officers (and other prison staff who have the powers of a constable) to be trade unions, without the right to call industrial action; extends to the staff concerned the same range of employment rights as other Crown employees and provides for the introduction of new pay machinery.

Cross-Border Policing

Sections 136-141: Provides various measures to improve the efficiency of cross-border policing within the UK.

Sexual Offences

Section 142: Defines rape to include 'male rape' and the rape of a man of his wife.

Section 143: Defines the circumstances in which buggery is an offence.

Section 144: Revises the penalties for buggery and indecency between men.

Section 145: Lowers the homosexual age of consent to 18.

Sections 146-147: Decriminalizes homosexual activity in the armed forces and merchant navy.

Section 148: Defines the term 'homosexual acts' under Scottish law to include acts of 'shameless indecency'.

Miscellaneous Measures

Section 149: Establishes the Parole Board as a non-departmental public body.

Section 150: Revises the arrangements for the recall of prisoners released on licence.

Section 151: Introduces powers to test prisoners for drugs.

Section 152: Gives civilian staff powers to search prisoners.

Section 154: Makes a new offence of causing intentional harassment, alarm or distress.

Section 155: Makes the publication or distribution of written material intended or likely to stir up racial hatred (an offence under s. 19 of the Public Order Act 1986) an arrestable offence under the Police and Criminal Evidence Act 1984.

Section 156: Makes it an offence to use female germ cells derived from an embryo or foetus for fertility treatment.

Section 157: Increases maximum financial penalties for various drugs offences.

Sections 158-159: Improves extradition procedures.

Section 161: Makes it an offence to procure the disclosure of computer-held personal information.

Section 162: Ensures that the Computer Misuse Act 1990 does not prevent police officers from gaining access to computer material (in order to investigate, eg, computer pornography offences).

Section 163: Clarifies local authority powers to provide closed-circuit television.

Section 166: Makes it an offence to sell tickets for designated football matches without authorization.

Section 167: Makes it an offence for taxis and mini-cabs to tout for business.

Section 169: Gives a statutory power to the Home Secretary to make grants and spend money for crime prevention.

Safeguards

- the new powers will be checked by similar safeguards which cover fingerprinting;

- a person from whom a non-intimate sample is taken without consent must be told the reason beforehand and the reason must be recorded as soon as possible;

- the database will carry records relating only to convicted offenders and unsolved crimes. Information on people who are acquitted or where no criminal proceedings are pursued may not be retained; and

- samples taken simply for the purposes of elimination (ie, from non-suspects) may not be used in speculative searches against the database. However the samples themselves may be retained if they have been processed in a batch with one taken from a person who is then convicted of a recordable offence. This is to ensure complete and accurate records, for quality control purposes and in allegations of a miscarriage of justice.

Existing Law

- under the Police and Criminal Evidence Act 1984 samples may not be taken from a suspect unless authorized by a police superintendent or above. The officer must have reasonable grounds for believing that the sample is capable of confirming or disproving the suspect's involvement in a serious arrestable offence.

- if this is so, a non-intimate sample may be taken *without consent*. An intimate sample may only be taken if the suspect gives his written consent.

Young Offenders

The Secure Training Order (STO)

The Act provides a new custodial sentence for persistent juvenile offenders. Previously, courts could not impose custodial sentences on

12-14 year olds who had repeatedly committed crimes such as burglary, joy-riding and theft, regardless of how many crimes they had committed.

Youth courts will be able to sentence a 12-14 year old to a Secure Training Order if they:

- have been convicted of at least three imprisonable offences; and
- have committed an offence while subject to a supervision order or have previously failed to comply with such an order.

The court will need to be satisfied that the offence is so serious that a custodial sentence is justified, or, in the case of a violent or sexual offence, that the public needed to be protected from serious harm.

The Secure Training Order will last for between six months and two years. The first half of the order will be spent at a Secure Training Centre and the second half will be spent under close supervision in the community. Supervision will be carried out by a probation officer, a social worker or a person designated by the Home Secretary.

Secure Training Centres (STCs)

The regime at the STC will aim to:

- provide a high standard of care and discipline in secure conditions;
- provide a flexible training and education plan specifically tailored to individual needs;
- provide education for at least 25 hours a week; and
- tackle the offending behaviour of the young person.

It is intended that each of the five STCs will offer 40 places.

The centres will be provided under the terms of the Government's private finance initiative. Organizations which can meet the high standards required and give value for money will be selected to finance, design, build or refurbish, maintain and operate the new centres following a process of competitive tendering.

The centres will also be subject to inspections by the Social Services Inspectorate and the Office for Standards in Education (OFSTED).

Other custodial sentences

Section 53 of the Children and Young Persons Act 1933 gives Crown Courts powers to order long periods of detention for 10-17 year olds convicted of certain grave crimes.

The Criminal Justice and Public Order Act extends that power. It will now apply to:

-   10-13 year olds convicted of any offence for which an adult can be jailed for 14 years or more (including rape, arson, domestic burglary and robbery). Previously they could only be given long terms of detention if they had been convicted of murder or manslaughter; and

-   any 10-15 year old convicted of indecent assault on a woman. Previously, only 16 and 17 year olds could be detained for this offence.

The Act doubles the maximum length of the sentence of detention in a Young Offender Institution for 15-17 year olds from one to two years.

The Act allows courts to remand 12-14 year olds to secure accommodation, extending the power for such remands for 15 and 16 year olds. It also allows police to arrest a young person who breaks a condition of his remand to local authority accommodation and extends to 12-14 year olds the police's current power to detain 15 and 16 year olds.

The Act allows courts to lift the ban on the media identifying 10-17 year old defendants of witnesses in youth court proceedings. Where a juvenile has been charged with a serious offence and is unlawfully at large, the court can lift the identification restriction so that the young offender can be caught, returned to custody or brought before a court.

The Act allows the court to bind over parents to ensure that their children comply with a community sentence given to them.

Bail

One in ten people given bail commit offences.

50,000 offences are committed each year by people on bail.

The new measures will:

- exclude bail for those charged with murder, attempted murder, manslaughter, rape or attempted rape, who have a previous conviction for any of those offences and, in the case of manslaughter, where the previous conviction carried a custodial sentence;

- remove the presumption in favour of bail for those charged with indictable-only or triable either-way* offences allegedly committed on bail;

- give police powers to attach conditions to police bail after charge;

- give police the power of arrest without warrant for breach of police bail;

- give police the power to detain a person after charge to prevent further offending;

- give courts a power to revoke bail, on application by the prosecution, if relevant new information comes to light or if there is a relevant change in circumstances; and

- prevent someone on bail in criminal proceedings from serving on a crown court jury.

* "Indictable-only" cases can only be tried at Crown court. "Triable either-way" cases can be tried at a Crown or a magistrates' court.)

Background

The Bail Act 1976 establishes a presumption in favour of bail. But bail can be refused to prevent the defendant absconding, committing offences, or obstructing the course of justice.

Before the Criminal Justice and Public Order Act, police were not able to attach conditions to bail or arrest a defendant for not attending a police station when bailed to do so.

Court Procedure

Right of Silence

The Act will allow courts to take account of defendant's refusal to answer police questions or to give information during his trial.

The Act sets out the circumstances in which inferences could be drawn:

- if a suspect has failed to tell the police something which he later uses in his defence;

- if a defendant does not give evidence on his own behalf at trial;

- if a suspect fails to account for incriminating objects, substances or marks found on or about his person or in the place where he was arrested;

- if a defendant fails to account for his presence at a particular place at the time of his arrest.

In the last two circumstances, the arresting or investigating officer must have a *reasonable* belief that the suspect's presence at the time of arrest, or the suspicious marks found, may be attributable to his participation in an offence.

There are a number of safeguards surrounding these provisions:

- defendants will still be able to exercise their right of silence;

- the presumption of innocence will remain;

- the prosecution will still have to prove its case against a defendant beyond reasonable doubt;

- the court will not be able to convict someone just because they have remained silent;

- the police will have to warn, under caution, a suspect they are questioning or charging about the possible consequences of remaining silent; and

- any significant silence which occurs *outside* a police station will be put to the suspect at the start of any formal interview at a police station.

The proposed new caution published in August 1994 is:

"You do not have to say anything. But if you do not mention now something which you later use in your defence, the court may decide that your failure to mention it now strengthens the case against you. A record will be made of anything you say and it may be given in evidence if your are brought to trial."

Imputations on character

The Act removes an anomaly which allowed the accused to attack, with impunity, the character of a victim who has died.

Under the Criminal Evidence Act 1898, an accused person may be cross-examined in court on his previous misconduct. If he attacks the character of the prosecutor or of any prosecution witness, including the victim, but if the victim of the crime has died then the accused may attack his character with impunity. The Act means that if he does this he may be questioned on his own previous misconduct.

Corroboration

The Act removes a potentially offensive warning in rape cases which can discourage reporting of sexual offences.

At present, the trial Judge must warn the jury that it is dangerous to convict the accused solely on the basis of the unsupported evidence of a complainant in a case involving a sexual offence, or of an accomplice.

Also, under the Sexual Offences Act 1956, a person cannot be convicted of a procuration offence solely on the basis of the unsupported evidence of a single witness.

The Act abolishes these restrictions. It gives the courts more flexibility to treat each case on its merits.

Juries

The Act:

- disqualifies a person who is on police or court bail in criminal proceedings from serving as a juror;

- gives a Judge discretion to allow them to separate after being directed and before they deliver their verdict;

- makes it clear that if a potential juror is physically disabled and his capacity to serve on the jury is in doubt, the Judge should allow him to serve unless he believes that the disability would prevent him acting effectively as a juror; (this does not affect existing arrangements where a disabled person may apply for and be granted excusal if there is good reason why he should not serve); and

- adds certain groups to the list of people who may be excused jury service as of right because they are practising members of some religious societies or orders with beliefs which are incompatible with jury service.

Child evidence

The Criminal Justice Act 1988 provides for a video of a child's evidence in certain cases to be shown in court, and to replace the examination of the child by the prosecution. This prevents the prosecution asking a child witness about issues which are mentioned but not fully explored in the video.

The Act allows the prosecution to examine the child on matters already covered in the video, if they were not dealt with "adequately" there.

The Childrens and Young Persons Act 1933 required courts to examine a child to satisfy itself that he understood the nature of an oath before he could give evidence. The Criminal Justice Act 1988 abolished this requirement, but was interpreted in some quarters as creating a sophisticated and inappropriate competence test for children.

The Act puts matters beyond doubt. It requires Judges to admit the evidence of a child unless the child is incapable of giving intelligible testimony.

Witness intimidation

The Act:

- creates a new offence of intimidating a witness, juror or someone assisting the police where the intention is to interfere with the course of justice or to take revenge;

- sets the maximum penalty at five years' imprisonment or an unlimited fine; and

- will make it easier to prosecute than existing offences such as perverting the course of justice because if the prosecution can show that the defendant knew the victim was a witness, juror or someone assisting the police, it will be for the *defence* to prove that the behaviour was not intended to pervert the course of justice or to exact revenge.

Curfew orders

The Act allows trials of electronically monitored curfew orders.

Pre-sentence reports

The Act gives greater discretion to courts in dispensing with pre-sentence reports where they are satisfied they can sentence an offender without one.

In the 1991 Criminal Justice Act, courts did not have to call for such a report for offences which can only be dealt with by Crown Courts. The new Act extends that power to those cases which can be dealt with by magistrates or those offences which can be dealt with by either magistrates or at Crown Court. However, a court can only dispense with a report in the case of juvenile offenders if it has considered the latest pre-sentence report on the offender.

Guilty pleas

The Act requires all courts to take account of the timing and circumstances of a guilty plea by a defendant when passing sentence. This follows a recommendation of the Royal Commission on Criminal Justice.

Transfer for trial

A new system of "transfer for trial" will replace the committal proceedings by which magistrates send cases to the Crown Court for trial. This follows a recommendation by the Royal Commission on Criminal Justice that committals should be abolished.

The transfer procedures which already exist for cases of serious and complex fraud and for cases involving children's evidence will remain.

The new system will:

- allow cases to be transferred to the Crown Court administratively. This will apply in all indictable-only cases and in cases triable either-way once a decision on mode of trial has been reached in the magistrates' court;

- still allow a procedure under which the defence could argue that there was no case to answer in advance of trial at Crown Court, as recommended by the Royal Commission;

- enable the defence to apply to magistrates to dismiss the charges on the papers before them. Oral arguments could be admitted at the court's discretion; and

- ensure that no witnesses are called to give evidence in these transfer proceedings. This will mean that there will be no question of vulnerable witnesses, including victims, being required to give evidence twice.

DNA

The proposals widen police powers to allow them to take non-intimate body samples in all recordable offences. Recordable offences are all offences triable on indictment and some others. There are around 500,000 prosecutions a year.

Effects of new powers:

- the new system places DNA profiling on the same basis as fingerprinting and takes account of the fact that serious sexual offenders will often have previous convictions for lesser offences;

- the new measures enable the police to take non-intimate samples without consent from all persons charged with recordable offences and retain them on a database if they are committed;

- the definition of a non-intimate sample is adjusted to include saliva and a swab taken from the mouth. Dental impressions are classified as intimate samples;

- an intimate sample now refers to blood, semen, urine, pubic hair, or a swab taken from a body orifice. Non-intimate sample refers to hair, a sample taken from under a nail, a swab taken from a person's body (other than an orifice), or a footprint or a similar impression of any part of a person's body (other than a part of his hand);

-   so that a DNA database can be used as a major investigative tool, fingerprints and samples will be searched against existing records relating to convicted offenders or unsolved crimes;

-   the requirement for a suspect to consent in writing before an intimate sample can be taken will remain;

-   the police will be able to take an intimate sample with consent from someone who is not in police detention if two non-intimate samples previously taken have proved insufficient;

-   the collection of non-pubic hair will be clarified so it will be permissible to obtain hair samples by plucking as well as cutting, in order to secure the tissue necessary for DNA profiling; and

-   police powers of search upon arrest will be extended to permit the search of a suspect's mouth. This is intended to target suspected drug dealers who may be concealing small packages of drugs in their mouths.

Prevention of Terrorism

The Act provides a power for police officers to stop and search for articles which may be used for terrorist purposes.

The provisions are:

-   a senior officer (at least Assistant Chief Constable or equivalent) may authorize the use of the stop and search powers at any place within the force area, or in any specified location for up to 28 days;

-   within the specified area, a uniformed officer will be able to stop and search vehicles and their occupants for articles of a kind which might be used in connection with terrorism. The power also covers articles carried by pedestrians; and

- a person who is stopped under this power will have the right to a written statement confirming the fact.

The Act creates offences of failing to stop when required to do so by a constable, and of wilfully obstructing a constable in the exercise of those powers.

- this is a summary offence. The maximum penalties on conviction are six months' imprisonment, a £5,000 fine, or both.

Offences against public security

The Act creates a new offence of possession of articles intended for terrorist purposes.

This is similar to the existing offence in section 30 of the Northern Ireland (Emergency Provisions) Act 1991.

The Act will mean that:

- it will be an offence for a person to have in his possession any article in circumstances which give rise to reasonable suspicion that it is to be used in connection with acts of terrorism;

- a person charged with this offence will have a defence against it if he can prove that he did not possess the article for such a purpose;

- a new offence of collecting information for terrorist purposes wil be introduced. A similar, but more wide-ranging power is found in s. 31 of the 1991 Act; and

- it will be an offence for a person to collect, record, or to have in his possession, any information which is of such a nature as is likely to be useful to terrorists in carrying out any act of violence. Both acts are triable summarily or on indictment and carry a maximum penalty of 10 years' imprisonment or a fine, or both.

Obscenity, Pornography and Videos

Pornography

The Act:

- increases the maximum sentence for possession of indecent photographs of children to up to six months and/or a £5,000 fine. Previously the maximum sentence was just a £5,000 fine;

- gives police the power to arrest without warrant people suspected of obscenity and certain child pornography offences;

- gives police greater powers to search and seize obscene material and child pornography; and

- strengthen the powers of trading standards officers under the Video Recordings Act 1984 by allowing them to act outside their area to trace and seize prohibited material and bring prosecutions in one court against those trading in such material.

The Act also takes measures on computer-related pornography, including:

- closing a potential legal loophole by extending the law to cover simulated child pornography manufactured and stored on computer;

- making possession of such an image an offence punishable by up to six months in prison and/or a £5,000 fine;

- extending the definition of "publication" under the Obscene Publications Act 1959 to cover the transmission from one computer to another, for example from a computer bulletin board or by a computer network; and

- making it clear that a computer system's owner cannot invoke the Computer Misuse Act (which prevents unauthorized access to computer system) by putting a notice on a bulletin board - denying the police access to the board, otherwise accessible to the public.

Videos

The Act increases the penalties for those who supply videos illegally. The maximum penalty for supplying or possession for supply an unclassified video will be two years' imprisonment and/or an unlimited fine and for the supply of a classified video to an under-age person the maximum penalty will be six months' imprisonment and/or a £5,000 fine.

The Act also lays down, for the first time, criteria which the British Board of Film Classification (BBFC), must take into account when deciding whether a particular video is suitable for classification and, if so, the category.

THe BBFC will be required to look specifically at the harm which may be caused by the way in which a video deals with:

-    criminal behaviour;
-    illegal drugs;
-    violent behaviour or incidents;
-    horrific behaviour or incidents; or
-    human sexual activity.

The Board will continue to consider bad taste, bad language, offensiveness to minority groups or any other matters which may be relevant.

The Act provides the Home Secretary with the power to lay an Order which would establish a system for reviewing works which were classified before the introduction of the new statutory criteria. The BBFC may alter a classification decision on a particular work in the light of the new criteria. There will be a right of appeal to the Video Appeals Committee against such a decision.

Previously under the Video Recordings Act, video works which are designed to inform, educate or instruct, or which are concerned with sport, religion, music or which are video games, were generally exempt from the need for classification. The new Act adds to the previous list of subjects which cannot be depicted to any significant extent in an exempted work:

- techniques likely to be useful in the commission of criminal offences; and
- the commission of criminal offences themselves in a way likely to encourage imitation.

The Act also extends the definition of "video recording" under the Video Recordings Act 1984 to include any device capable of storing data electronically, such as computer chips and cartridges. This is to ensure that the appropriate legislation keeps pace with technological advances.

Prison Services

Industrial relations

In November 1993, the Home Secretary obtained an injunction to prevent the Prison Officers' Association (POA) calling industrial action which would have caused serious disruption to the criminal justice system as a whole.

The court accepted that prison officers have the power of a constable and consequently the POA was not in law a trade union and did not enjoy the legal immunities of a union under current legislation. It was thus unlawful for the POA to induce prison officers to breach their employment contracts.

The Act places industrial relations in the Prison Service on a sound footing by:

- applying to prison officers the same employment rights as other Crown employees;

- giving bodies representing them the same status and immunities of trade unions;

- maintaining the position that it is unlawful to induce prison officers to take industrial action; and

- enabling the making of regulations governing procedure for pay and pay-related conditions.

Contracting out

The Act clarifies and extends the arrangements for the contracting out of prisons and prisoner escorts in England and Wales, building on the provisions introduced in the Criminal Justice Act 1991.

The measures will allow improvements in the efficiency of the Prisoner Escort Service and to facilitate private sector involvement in the prison system. The Act allows:

-       contractors to be tasked to carry out *all* escorting duties;

-       contractors to look after prisoners overnight where they have been sent to prison by a court but where it is too late to secure their admission that day (currently only the police can hold prisoners in these circumstances);

-       arrangments to be made so that staff at directly managed and contracted out prisons can provide assistance to each other if required in an emergency (in the same way that directly managed prisons currently provide support to other directly managed prisons);

-       separate functions within a directly managed prison to be contracted out;

-       the private sector to bid for contracts to design, construct, manage and finance new prisons; and

-       floating structures to be used as prisons if required.

Mandatory drug testing

The Act confers new powers upon prison officers allowing them to require prisoners to produce a urine sample for purposes of testing for the presence of a controlled drug in their bodies. Amendments to prison rules will make misuse of drugs within prison a specific disciplinary offence.

The measures are designed to bring to the attention of the authorities those who misuse drugs and will:

- send a clear message to all prisoners that if they misuse drugs they will now run an increased chance of being detected and punished;

- allow those identified to be offered assessment, help and counselling; and

- provide valuable management information on the scale, nature and trends of drug misuse within prisons.

Public Order

The measures strengthen the law on aggravated trespass on land and provide the police with new powers to prevent or stop raves.

Trespass

At present the police can remove trespassers residing on land under s. 39 of the Public Order Act 1986:

- where the trespassers have refused a request by the occupier to leave the land; and either

- they have been abusive, insulting or threatening to the occupier, his family or his agent; *or* they have damaged property on the land; or

- they have brought 12 or more vehicles onto the land.

It is an offence to disobey the direction to leave or to return to the land as a trespassers within three months. The maximum penalty is three months' imprisonment and/or a fine of £2,500.

Section 39 is made more effective by the new Act by:

- extending it to cover all trespassers on the land - whether or not they entered as trespassers. (This will provide protection against those who may have been welcome initially but outstay that welcome);

-          including damage to the land itself;

-          extending the application of s. 39 to byways, green lanes and other minor highways;

-          clarifying the way it applies to common land;

-          reducing the number of vehicles from 12 to six; and

-          providing the police with powers to remove vehicles.

Aggravated trespass

The measures provide protection for occupiers of private land and their guests whose lawful activities might be disrupted by trespassers. The most obvious examples are hunting and shooting.

The Act will:

-          give the police the power to direct trespassers to leave land if they believe that the trespassers will seek to disrupt or to prevent a lawful activity. It will be a criminal offence to ignore a direction; and

-          create an offence of intentionally disrupting a lawful activity, or seeking to intimidate someone so as to deter him from engaging in that activity.

This will enable the police to prevent disruption and to take action against those who have been responsible for any disruption which has occurred.

This offence carries a maximum penalty of three months' imprisonment and/or a £2,500 fine.

Mass trespass

The measures will prevent public assemblies of trespassers.

The Act will:

- enable the chief officer of police to ask the local authority for an order banning trespassory assemblies on land in a given area for a given period.

This can be done if he believes that it is necessary to prevent serious disruption to the life of the community or to prevent significant damage to land, buildings or monuments of scientific, historic, architectural or archaeological importance. Such orders will require the consent of the Home Secretary.

Breaching, or seeking to breach, an order will be a criminal offence; and the Act will:

- provide the police with powers to stop, within a five mile radius, persons or vehicles they reasonably believe intend to defy an order and direct them not to proceed in the direction of the assembly. It will be an offence to fail to obey the direction.

The maximum penalty for organizing a prohibited assembly is three months' imprisonment and/or £2,500 fine.

Raves

Mass open-air raves are a relatively new phenomenon. They are a public rather than a private menace as they affect large numbers of people who are kept awake, sometimes for nights on end, by incessant music.

The measures give the police powers:

- to direct people to leave land if two or more are preparing for a gathering, or if 10 or more are waiting for or attending a gathering and the police believe that they will be joined by others to play loud music during the night such as to cause serious distress to the local residents. It will be a criminal offence not to comply;

- to seize vehicles or sound equipment in the possession of those who refuse a direction to leave; and

- to stop persons they believe will attempt to go to a rave site within a radius of five miles of the site and direct them not to proceed. It will be an offence to fail to obey the direction.

The failure to obey a direction to leave land carries a maximum penalty of three months' imprisonment and/or a £2,500 fine.

Squatters

The Criminal Law Act 1977 already provides protection to people who find their homes invaded by squatters but there are many instances where squatters will not be caught under the terms of the Act and where the existing civil procedure for having them removed may prove to be a slow and expensive process for the property owner.

The Act provides greater protection to property owners by:

- enabling them to apply for a new interim possession order; and

- making it an arrestable offence for squatters who, in failing to leave the property within 24 hours or in returning as trespassers within 12 months, do not comply with the order;

The Act provides a safeguard against abuse of the procedure by unscrupulous landlords by:

- allowing occupants, having complied with the order to leave, to seek a full hearing at which the court can, if satisfied, order the reinstatement and the payment of damages; and

- making it an offence to provide a false or misleading statement in connection with proceedings relating to an interim possession order.

Ticket touting

The Act makes it an offence to sell tickets for and on the day of a football match without the authority of the home club or the match organizers.

The offence applies in a public place or a place to which the public have access or, in the course of a trade or business, in any other place.

The maximum penalty is a £5,000 fine.

Sexual Offences

Definition of rape

The Act extends the definition of rape to include buggery without consent of a man or a woman.

As a consequence:

- the maximum penalty for buggery without consent of a man aged 16 or over is increased from 10 years to life imprisonment, as this act is now classed as rape;

- more victims, both male and female, will be protected from cross-examination of their sexual history which the law already provides for victims of rape.

The Act also:

- confirms a court judgment that a man who had intercourse with his wife without her consent is guilty of rape;

- lowers the age at which men may lawfully perform consenting homosexual acts in private from 21 to 18. If either party is under 18, both will continue to be liable to prosecution, regardless of consent;

- makes buggery of a woman in private lawful where both parties consent and are over 18. Previously all anal intercourse between men and women was unlawful; and

- extends the protection from publicity to the victims of conspiracies or incitement to commit sexual offences from the time an allegation is made. Previously such protection was only for victims of the actual acts.

Miscellaneous Measures

The Act covers the following miscellaneous provisions:

Intentional harassment:

A new offence of intentionally causing harassment, alarm or distress through threatening, abusive or insulting words, behaviour or displays is created, carrying a maximum penalty of six months' imprisonment and/or a £5,000 fine.

Material likely to stir up racial hatred:

The publication or distribution of written material intended or likely to stir up racial hatred is made an arrestable offence.

Use of foetal eggs:

It will be an offence for female germ cells (including foetal eggs) to be used in fertility treatment. The offence will carry a maximum penalty of 10 years' imprisonment and/or an unlimited fine.

Taxi touting:

A new offence of touting for hire car services in a public place comes into force attracting a maximum fine of £2,500.

Extradition:

Countries with extradition arrangements under the European Convention on Extradition are now required to submit 'information' rather than 'evidence' sufficent to justify any request for the issue of a warrant of arrest or any request for a provisional arrest.

There are amendments to the Backing of Warrants (Republic of Ireland) Act 1965 covering extradition between the United Kingdom and Irish Republic. A United Kingdom court will be empowered to endorse the execution in the United Kingdom of an arrest warrant issued in the Irish Republic in respect of a person believed to be travelling to the UK.

The period of validity of a provisional arrest warrant issued by a UK magistrate will be increased from five to seven days. The length of time for which a person arrested under such a warrant may be held pending the receipt of an Irish warrant is extended from three days to seven.

Crime prevention:

A measure which clarifies the powers of local authorities to set up, operate and maintain closed circuit television systems for crime prevention purposes.

The Home Secretary will have the power to make grants for crime prevention purposes.

Serious fraud:

Assistance may be given to overseas authorities with their enquiries into suspected offences involving serious or complex fraud.

Copyright enforcement:

Trading standards officers will be empowered to enforce copyright offences under the Copyright, Design and Patents Act 1988.

Security costs at party conferences:

A measure will give the Home Secretary statutory authority to reimburse the main political parties for the costs of security measures incurred at party conferences.

Index